Highway
Engineering

Highway Engineering

Laurence I. Hewes
Late Chief, Western Headquarters
U. S. Bureau of Public Roads

Clarkson H. Oglesby
Professor of Civil Engineering
Stanford University

JOHN WILEY & SONS, INC., NEW YORK
CHAPMAN & HALL, LIMITED, LONDON

To

THOMAS H. MacDONALD

Foreword

The publication in 1941 and 1942 of *American Highway Practice*, in two volumes, by Dr. L. I. Hewes, provided a record of development and an informed interpretation of highway engineering design and construction. The content had the penetrating quality that recognized and selected values which could result only from "living the experience."

Doctor Hewes came to the U. S. Bureau of Public Roads in 1911 with an academic teaching experience. His early work was in research and experimental road construction, but in 1920 he became Chief of the Western Headquarters of the Bureau, a new position which, under his leadership, assumed important administrative responsibility, but also provided excellent opportunities to develop his abilities for successful authorship of works of great merit related to his professional field. The depth and breadth of his engineering experience were augmented by an almost equally rare ability to convey clearly and concisely to others the great store of his theoretical and practical knowledge. *American Highway Practice* itself is a standard text and reference work, and is a fitting monument to a man whose achievements have added much to the prestige of the Bureau of Public Roads and of the highway engineering profession generally.

Doctor Hewes accepted fully the dynamic quality of highway engineering, and immediately after *American Highway Practice* was completed began the preparation of a textbook of highway engineering. Partially because of the magnitude of the undertaking, and partially to endow the content and form with the critical perception of an educator actively engaged in teaching the subject, Doctor Hewes obtained the collaboration of Professor C. H. Oglesby of the department of civil engineering of Stanford University, and the new work had been well advanced at the time of Doctor Hewes' death.

In Professor Oglesby, Doctor Hewes found an engineer particularly qualified for the work in hand, and one who was thoroughly in accord with the objectives of the book. Professor Oglesby brought to this task a broad experience in highway engineering practice, including nine years of work in the Arizona Highway Department. For the last eleven years he has taught highway and construction engineering at Stanford University, and has participated in the preparation of a number of excellent reports and papers in the highway field. After Doctor Hewes' death, Professor Oglesby assumed the task of completing the book, and has contributed generously from his own experience. It is largely through his devotion to the task that it now appears in print.

The completed work is a lucid, authoritative, and thorough exposition of the best modern highway practice. The publication of *Highway Engineering*, by Hewes and Oglesby, may be regarded as an event of equal importance to that of *American Highway Practice*.

THOMAS H. MacDONALD

Preface

This book is designed primarily as a text for junior and senior college courses in highway engineering. A second objective is to offer a starting point for advanced courses and individual study for those having a special interest in the highway field. A third aim is to offer a summary of important new developments in highway technology as an aid to practicing highway engineers.

Highway engineering is a troublesome subject for the college student. He is confronted with a new and often ambiguous terminology and with seeming wide variations in design and construction practices. In this book, every effort has been made to minimize this confusion by an orderly approach. Wherever possible, the governing principles underlying each topic are developed first; then current practice is explained in terms of these principles. Finally research findings that point up the shortcomings of present-day knowledge and methods are outlined in order to indicate the probable changes to come.

Taken in its entirety, this book fits a three semester-unit course in highway engineering. However, it has been arranged to be suitable for the somewhat shorter course offered in many schools. Much of the more advanced or detailed subject matter has been set in smaller type, and can be omitted without the continuity of the presentation being destroyed.

To the greatest extent possible, this text has been directed to the college junior, as the first course in highways in many schools is given in that year. It has been necessary, however, to presuppose some knowledge of dynamics, fluid mechanics, and engineering economy to develop certain basic principles properly. The alternative of omitting these subjects from the book was not acceptable, as it would greatly reduce the value to more advanced students and practicing engineers.

Certain features of this book are aimed particularly at the needs of the advanced student and practicing engineer. Present-day knowledge in almost every phase of highway engineering is being rapidly expanded by intensive research and study. As a result, many commonly accepted practices are being modified or seriously questioned. The presentation on each subject includes a brief discussion of pertinent research findings and the nature and direction of studies not yet completed. In each case, the most authoritative references have been listed as an aid in further study.

Textbooks such as this one must cover both engineering design and construction practices, and a decision must be made regarding the apportionment of the limited space between the two. As compared with other books in the field, this one places much greater emphasis on engineering design and the principles that underly it and much less on construction practices. It has been reasoned that the student has considerable familiarity with highways through his daily use of them and that highway construction can be seen at first hand by persons interested in it. On the other hand, the student must rely almost solely on his instructor and his textbook to learn about modern design practices and to gain a critical evaluation of them.

Particular subjects of increasing importance in highway engineering have been given added emphasis in this book. Chapter 4, Highway Economy, presents detailed data on highway-user costs and develops techniques for justifying or comparing highway improvements in terms of savings to users in time and in operating and accident costs. Chapter 5, Highway Finance, reviews past and present highway financing practices of the various levels of government and traces their effects on highway development. It also gives the background for such controversial issues as added financing for highways, toll roads, truck taxes, and the place of Federal aid in highway financing plans. Chapter 7, Rights of Way, treats the problems encountered in taking property for highway purposes and in compensating property owners for loss of access, light, air, and view. Although right of way is more a legal than an engineering matter, it is of primary concern to highway engineers because of the tremendous sums of money spent for it. Chapter 9, Highway Drainage, emphasizes the value of engineering analysis as contrasted with rule-of-thumb methods in drainage design. It also offers the application of research findings to problems in hydrology and culvert flow. Chapter 11, Traffic Engineering, introduces such important subjects as pavement markings, traffic markers, signs, traffic signals, arterial routes, one-way streets, illumination, motor-vehicle accidents, and parking. The chapters on soils, bases, and pavements devote particular attention to design techniques and to the effects of research findings on them.

The untimely death of Dr. Hewes on March 2, 1950, cut off his active participation in the final preparation of this work. His writing of portions of the first 11 chapters and critical review of other sections is gratefully acknowledged. His contribution in planning this book and in setting its tone, although less tangible, had an even greater influence on the finished work. As a tribute to Dr. Hewes, Mr. Thomas H. MacDonald, Commissioner of Public Roads, arranged for a careful word-by-word review and detailed criticism of the manuscript by specialists of the U. S. Bureau of Public Roads. Thirty-one members of the Washington staff of the Bureau participated in this endeavor, which has made the finished work far better and much more authoritative. Particular appreciation is expressed to Mr. MacDonald and to Mr. R. E. Royall, chief of the Research Reports Branch, who coordinated the entire activity and went far out of his way to be gracious and helpful.

A set of 124 problems has been grouped together at the back of the book. To the greatest extent possible they are based on real situations and actual data. It is not anticipated that instructors will assign all or even a large fraction of the total. However, with this number to choose from, examples should be available on most topics selected for special emphasis. Most of the problems are for Chapters 4, 8, 9, 12, 17, and 18 since the basic principles and design techniques presented in them may be illustrated to good advantage with carefully selected problem assignments. Problems for the remaining chapters fall largely into two classes: (1) those that require investigation and reporting of local situations as contrasted with the national viewpoint presented in the textbook, and (2) those that force the student to apply to a particular situation the principles or ideas developed in the textbook, by class discussion, or by supplementary reading. This group of problems may well be regarded as a listing of suggested topics for advanced study. Certainly there is little time for them in the required three semester-hour course offered at many colleges.

Special thanks are hereby expressed to Professor Eugene L. Grant, executive head of civil engineering, Stanford University, for a detailed review and criticism of the chapter on highway economy and even more for his continual encouragement during the years the manuscript was in preparation. Professors Ray K. Linsley and John K. Vennard of Stanford offered very helpful suggestions for the chapter on highway drainage. Professor Ralph A. Moyer of the University of California read the chapters on highway subgrade structure and constructing the roadway and proposed a number of improvements. Robert C. Phelps, a graduate student and instructor at Stanford, made a marked contribution by reading and criticizing the manuscript from the student point of view. Credit also is given Professors Lloyd F. Rader and Bruce M. Davidson of the University of Wisconsin. They had prepared a set of problems for the textbook for the use of their students, and graciously made it available to the author. Problems taken from their set or adapted from it have been marked with an asterisk. Finally, wholehearted appreciation is due the host of practicing engineers who through their writings or by personal contacts with the authors contributed greatly to this book.

CLARKSON H. OGLESBY

Stanford University, California
March, 1956

Contents

1 ———————————— Introduction

THE IMPORTANCE OF HIGHWAY TRANSPORTATION

In the United States today there are more than 3 million miles of roads and streets, over which (by 1954) some 55 million motor vehicles travel more than 500 billion miles annually. This motor-transport operation in all its phases costs more than $40 billion per year and utilizes about 9 million persons, or 1 in 7 of those gainfully employed in the country. It consumes 20% of the nation's steel production, 80% of its rubber, and vast amounts of many other products. In the year 1952 some 41 billion gallons of motor fuels were burned. There is one motor vehicle for every 3 persons, enough to transport the entire population simultaneously.

The degree to which our economy depends on highway transportation is not generally recognized. Almost four-fifths of the total expenditure for transporting persons is absorbed by the purchase and operation of private automobiles and about three-fourths of all passenger-miles are ridden in them.[1] On the average day, three-fourths of all the automobiles are used in connection with making a living or with shopping; in one week, 92% are employed for such purposes. In almost all communities, motor buses or trolley coaches operating over the roads and streets have replaced or supplemented the streetcar as a mass-transportation carrier. The motor truck has a dominant place as a carrier of goods. The 9 million trucks, which represent about one in six of the vehicles on the road, require over 5 million drivers. They haul 75% of the nation's tonnage and account for 11% of the total ton-miles.[2]

[1] Of each dollar spent for transporting persons, 79 cents goes to automobile purchase and operation; 13 cents for local mass transit by streetcar, bus, and ferry; and 7 cents for intercity transport by railroad, airline, bus, and water.

[2] Railroads, pipelines, and water carriers, respectively, handle 14, 6, and 5% of the tonnage and 49, 9, and 31% of the ton-miles. (Source Automobile Manufacturer's Association)

1

Until about 30 years ago transportation of persons and goods was largely by rail, water, or horse-drawn vehicle, and urban populations were concentrated in limited areas. With the increasing freedom of movement offered by the motor vehicle, the stage was set for the veritable "explosion" of our cities which is now well under way. Residential areas and in some cases industry and business also are moving to suburban locations. The years ahead may well see our urban areas assume an entirely new form.

Highway transportation has also brought great changes in rural areas. Practically all farm products are moved initially by motor vehicle. Many, such as milk, perishable food, and livestock for which quick delivery is important, travel all the way to market in that manner. With the school bus, the consolidated school has replaced the one-room schoolhouse. Medical attention and like services are almost as close at hand in the country as in town. There are increased opportunities for recreation, social contacts, and education. In fact, the rural mode of living has become much like that of town and city.

Motor transportation has shown extremely rapid growth in the years since World War II. A record 8 million motor vehicles were manufactured in 1950, and production totaled 6.8 million units in 1951 and 5.5 million in 1952, in spite of restrictions resulting from the war in Korea. The net average annual gain in vehicles on the road from 1945 to 1953 has been about 3 million. Vehicle-miles of travel have shown a like increase; on rural roads there has been an average gain of about 10% each year from 1948 through 1952. Such a rise, if continued, would result in a doubling of travel each 10 years. There have been even greater increases in trucking with the year 1952 showing a 116% rise in rural ton-miles over 1946. Thus the indications are strong that highway transportation will assume even greater importance in the years ahead.

Highway transportation, unlike rail transport, is not under unified control or management. Motor vehicles are privately owned and operated. With the exception of certain licensed carriers, the individual driver has free selection of time, route, and speed of travel subject only to regulations imposed for the safety and welfare of others. In turn, through motor-fuel taxes, the motor-vehicle operator furnishes most highway financing. Government as one of its primary functions [3] provides and operates the roadbed over which motor ve-

---

[3] Early Saxon law imposed upon all lands an obligation to perform three necessary duties: to repair roads and bridges, to maintain castles and garrisons, and to aid in repelling invasion.

hicles travel and has established highway agencies to plan, construct, and maintain the roads, to license motor vehicles and drivers, and to police their operation.   Of the motor-transport dollar, roughly 10 cents is spent for the roads and streets on which vehicles move.   During the years 1929 to 1953, some $66 billion has been thus invested. Current expenditures are about $5 billion annually, and many signs indicate a sizable increase in the years ahead.

The function of the highway engineer is to plan, design, construct, maintain, and operate this highway and street system.   It is a difficult task.   Satisfactory solutions are yet to be found for many current problems, and many new problems will arise in the future.   Highway engineering is both a large and a challenging field for the civil engineer.[4]

HISTORY OF HIGHWAY DEVELOPMENT

Early roads

Traces of early roads have been found which antedate recorded history.   The first hard surfaces appeared in Mesopotamia soon after discovery of the wheel about 3500 B.C.   On the island of Crete in the Mediterranean Sea was found a stone-surfaced road constructed before 1500 B.C.   The direction in the Bible (Isaiah 40:3–5) "make straight in the desert a high road" refers to a road constructed soon after 539 B.C. between Babylon and Egypt.   In the Western Hemisphere evidence exists of extensive road systems constructed by the Mayan, Aztec, and Incan people of Central and South America.   The Romans bound their empire together with an extensive system of roads radiating in many directions from Rome.[5]

With the fall of the Roman Empire, road building became a lost

[4] *Highways in Our National Life* (a symposium), Princeton University Press (1950), offers an excellent general discussion of the importance and influence of highways.   For a more specific and factual discussion of the importance of highway transportation see two works by Wilfred Owen, *Highway Transportation,* Brooking Institution (1949), and *Automobile Transportation in Defense or War,* Defense Transport Administration (1951).

[5] The Appian Way, constructed southward about 312 B.C. illustrates the elaborate procedures that the Romans employed.   First a trench was excavated to such a depth that the finished surface would be at ground level.   The pavement was placed in three courses: a layer of small broken stones, a layer of small stones mixed with mortar and firmly tamped into place, and a wearing course of massive stone blocks, set and bedded in mortar.   Many such roads are still in existence after almost 2000 years.

art. It was not until the 18th century that Tresaguet (1716–96) in France developed improved construction methods that at a later time, under Napoleon, made possible a great system of French roads. Highway development in England followed soon after that in France. MacAdam (1756–1836) in particular made use of crushed stone as a road-surfacing material in a manner that is still widely used with some modification. Both in France and in England the problem was chiefly to produce a road surface usable under all conditions of weather.

Early American roads

Few roads were constructed during the early history of the United States. Most early settlements were located along bays or rivers, and transportation was largely by water. Inland settlements were connected with the nearest wharf, but the connecting road usually was just a clearing through the forest. Before the Revolutionary War travel was mainly on foot or horseback, and roads were merely trails cleared to greater width. Development was extremely slow for a time after the war's end in 1783. For example, poor roads were the real cause of the Whisky Rebellion in western Pennsylvania in 1794. The farmers of this area objected to a tax on the whisky that they were making from grain. One historian has recorded that "a pack horse could carry only four bushels of grain over the mountains but in the form of whisky he could carry the product of twenty-four bushels." Construction of the Philadelphia-Lancaster Turnpike resulted from this incident. It was a toll road 62 miles long, surfaced to a width of 24 ft with hand-broken stone and gravel.

Between 1795 and 1830 numerous other turnpikes, particularly in the northeastern states, were built by companies organized to gain profits through toll collections. Few of them were financially successful. During this period many stagecoach lines and freight-hauling companies were organized.

The "Old National Pike" or "Cumberland Road" from Cumberland, Md., to Wheeling on the Ohio River and on to St. Louis was one of the few roads financed by the Federal government. It was originally toll-free. The Cumberland-Wheeling section was authorized by Congress in 1806, and was completed 10 years later. It was 20 ft in width, and consisted of a 12-in. bottom and a 6-in. top course of hand-broken stone. Some 20 more years elapsed before the road was completed to St. Louis. During this same period, canals were constructed, particularly along the Atlantic Seaboard; but they offered little competition to turnpike development, since the terrain of most of the country was unsuited to canal construction.[6]

The railroad era

The extension of turnpikes in the United States was abruptly halted by the development of the railroads. In 1830 Peter Cooper constructed America's first steam locomotive, the *Tom Thumb,* which at once demonstrated its superiority over horse-drawn vehicles. Rapid growth of the railroad for transportation over long distances followed. Cross-country turnpike construction practically ceased, and many already completed fell into disuse. Rural roads served mainly as feeders for the railroads, and improvements were made largely by local authorities and were to low standards. However, the improvement of city streets progressed at a somewhat faster pace. Regarding highway development before 1900, the Bureau of Public Roads has stated that: [7]

At the end of the century, approximately 300 years after first settlement, the United States could claim little distinction because of the character of its roads. As in most parts of the world, the roads were largely plain earth surfaces that were almost impassable in wet weather. Neither the Federal nor state governments had undertaken to provide funds on a scale that would permit general road improvement. Those seeking knowledge on road-building methods and administration turned to the countries of Europe for information.

The first two decades of the 20th century saw the improvement of the motor vehicle from a "rich man's toy" to a fairly dependable method for transporting persons and goods. There were strong demands for rural road improvement, largely for roads a few miles in length connecting outlying farms with towns and railroad stations. This development has been aptly described as "getting the farmer out of the mud." Great improvements also were made in city streets.

In this period it was recognized that road improvement was a matter of Federal and state concern rather than of purely local interest to be dealt with by county and city governing bodies. Organizations were established and small amounts of money appropriated by Congress and the state governments to deal with road problems.

[6] See the issues of *American Highways,* the quarterly magazine of the American Association of State Highway Officials, for a series of historical sketches on early roads. The entire series has been published by the association in two volumes titled *Public Roads of the Past* and *Historic American Highways.*

[7] *Highway Practice in the United States,* Public Roads Administration (1949).

Modern highway development

The period since 1920 might well be called the "automobile age," for during this period highway transportation has assumed a dominant role on the American scene. Figure 1 presents this growth in graphical form. The first 15 years saw primary attention focused on the completion of a network of good rural roads linking all parts of the

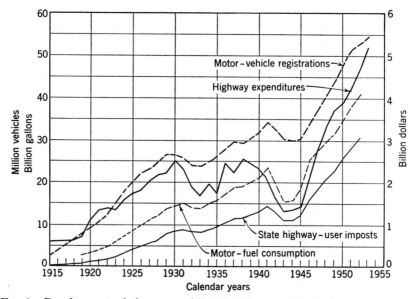

Fig. 1. Development of the automobile age (Courtesy U. S. Bureau of Public Roads)

country, and by 1935 cross-country travel by automobile in almost any direction was practicable. Since then, increasing attention has been focused on urban areas which have been struck with tremendous impact by the shift from mass transportation to the private automobile. Extreme congestion exists in the central areas of many cities and towns, parking space is often insufficient, and decentralization of many cities is occurring rapidly. As yet, this urban problem is largely unsolved.

Technological advance has been great during the age of modern highways. Knowledge has been extended in the fields of soils and other highway materials so that designs are now more economical and more reliable. Developments in machinery have revolutionized construction methods. The highway engineer has become conscious that a highway can be attractive as well as useful and has learned much about roadside improvement and erosion control. Entirely new sciences are developing in the fields of highway planning, geometric design, and traffic control. In every branch of highway engineering the foundation has been laid for tremendous gains in the years ahead.

Highway Systems, Organizations, and Associations

HIGHWAY SYSTEMS

Introduction

There are in the United States about 3 million miles of rural high-ways, or about 1 mile to each square mile of area. Over the country, distribution varies with population and development; it ranges from 0.2 mile per square mile for Nevada and 0.3 for Wyoming to 3.5 and 3.3 miles for New Jersey and Rhode Island, respectively. This mileage developed slowly from colonial days and has grown about 25% since the turn of the century. Before 1890 this vast rural road mileage as a whole had never been classified. Its establishment and upkeep in general were a local government responsibility. Counties and towns took care of the roads, and their condition generally was poor. There were a few exceptions: in 1891 New Jersey initiated state aid to counties, and by 1900 six other states had followed suit.

In 1893 Massachusetts considered 1500 miles of its 18,000 total as of leading importance. In 1907 New York's legislature adopted an official map of highways which the state would help finance. Maryland in 1908 chose a state system of 1200 miles. In 1910, California adopted a state system of 3082 miles. Similar action occurred in other states. In Iowa in 1914 a great state system of 15,000 miles set a new mark. State highways thus continued to expand for more than 2 decades.

The Federal-aid system

Beginning in 1912, Congress made several appropriations to aid in the construction of post roads.[1] It soon developed, however, that construction confined to post roads resulted in scattered improvements without any assurance of continuity or an ultimate system of im-

---

[1] Roads over which the mail was carried.

proved highways. To remedy this situation, the Federal-Aid Highway
Act of 1921 required the states to make an initial selection of 7% or
less of their total mileage as a system of primary and interstate highways. Selections were subject to the approval of the Secretary of
Agriculture operating through the Office of Public Roads of that Department.[2] Federal aid was to be restricted to these roads. After the
1921 act, the main trunk roads of the nation, totaling 180,000 miles
in length, were quickly selected. This primary Federal-aid system,
often referred to as the "7% system," now totals 231,000 miles, including about 15,000 miles within cities, and has had important improvement over about 85% of its length. It overlies, or is included in, the
larger system of state highways. Under the Federal-Aid Act, when
a state has provided for improvement of 90% of its Federal-aid primary system, the mileage by Federal law may be increased by another
1%. Thus, the present total Federal-aid primary mileage is about
7.7% of all our rural mileage. These roads form a dominant part of
our rural highway system. Table 1 shows the approximate Federal-
aid and other road and street mileages by states.

The Federal-aid secondary system

Congress established the Federal-aid secondary system in 1944 to
supplement the Federal-aid primary system. Its mileage consists of
important county highways (57%) and secondary state highways
(43%), and in 1953 totaled 440,000. Selection of the routes is the
joint responsibility of local authorities, the state highway departments,
and the Bureau of Public Roads. The mileage of the combined systems of Federal-aided highways totals 671,000. It carries about 85%
of our rural traffic.[3]

Urban Federal-aid routes

Urban streets and alleys total some 320,000 miles. Travel on them
amounts to about one-half the nation's total. In earlier years, construction and maintenance of streets and alleys were considered to
be of local concern. Federal, state, and county spending was devoted
almost exclusively to rural highways. As traffic in urban areas has
increased, more and more attention has been focused on the problems
created; and Federal, state, and sometimes county funds are now used

[2] Now the Bureau of Public Roads of the Department of Commerce.
[3] All vehicle movements outside cities with populations over 5000 persons are
classed as rural traffic.

TABLE 1. MILEAGE OF ALL ROADS AND STREETS UNDER STATE AND LOCAL
CONTROL *

AASHO Survey of All Member Departments as of August 1953

State	Federal-Aid Systems †		State Systems,† excluding Federal-Aid Systems			County Roads, excluding Federal-Aid Systems	Township and Other Local Roads, excluding Federal-Aid Systems	Local City Streets, excluding Federal-Aid Systems	Total
	Primary	Secondary	Primary	Secondary	Other Mileage				
Alabama	5,106	11,249	389	......	.....	44,214	......	3,500	64,458
Arizona	2,520	2,867	75	......	.....	14,716	......	1,556	21,734
Arkansas	3,441	13,061	.....	......	319	48,860	......	4,315	69,996
California	7,013	9,506	3,446	......	285	61,752	......	19,187	101,189
Colorado	4,050	3,705	.....	......	4,727	56,846	......	3,918	73,246
Connecticut	1,089	1,096	.....	......	995		7,686	4,021	14,887
Delaware	517	1,267	.....	......	2,194			516	4,494
District of Columbia	148	59	.....	......	.....			958	1,165
Florida	3,854	10,409	168	300	.....	27,628	......	11,235	53,594
Georgia	7,298	12,271	1,243	......	.....	70,148	23	5,139	96,122
Hawaii	538	579	.....	......	.....	1,007	......	‡	2,124
Idaho	3,210	3,655	246	......	.....	16,445	9,263	1,332	34,151
Illinois	9,944	7,428	2,518	......	1,180	11,796	73,319	17,440	123,625
Indiana	4,800	15,575	207	......	.....	65,069	......	10,584	96,235
Iowa	9,720	32,424	30	......	.....	60,419	......	9,153	111,746
Kansas	8,170	21,283	11	......	.....	43,489	53,818	6,736	133,507
Kentucky	3,531	8,157	4,192	......	.....	42,404	......	3,104	61,388
Louisiana	2,654	5,607	.....	......	6,863	25,525	......	4,790	45,439
Maine	1,627	2,259	445	6,791	.....		9,933	754	21,809
Maryland	1,865	5,498	529	......	.....	9,333	......	2,233	19,458
Massachusetts	2,074	2,170	91	......	141		13,570	6,223	24,269
Michigan	5,901	17,563	260	......	.....	70,780	......	12,252	106,756
Minnesota	7,379	14,680	70	......	849	32,694	54,539	8,800	119,011
Mississippi	4,563	8,613	.....	......	209	48,297	......	3,402	65,084
Missouri	8,336	11,395	196	138	.....	79,166	......	‡	99,231
Montana	5,865	3,291	.....	......	25	60,105	......	1,538	70,824
Nebraska	5,271	10,109	342	......	33	61,114	23,210	5,014	105,093
Nevada	2,197	2,109	.....	1,909	.....	19,399	......	464	26,078
New Hampshire	1,172	1,319	156	1,411	21	104	8,748	726	13,657
New Jersey	1,503	1,921	254	......	452	4,793	19,769	‡	28,692
New Mexico	4,073	4,320	2,933	......	.....	46,101	3,946	1,424	62,797
New York	10,544	19,349	455	......	.....	3,812	54,220	15,100	103,480
North Carolina	6,745	13,898	865	45,956	.....		......	5,290	72,754
North Dakota	3,238	10,595	321	......	.....	11,672	88,500	1,662	115,988
Ohio	7,535	12,280	4,086	......	.....	24,257	40,525	13,620	102,303
Oklahoma	7,124	10,691	584	......	.....	74,504	......	6,888	99,791
Oregon	3,922	4,756	42	230	.....	29,343	......	4,010	42,303
Pennsylvania	7,829	10,879	1,833	20,675	.....	748	44,787	13,930	100,681
Puerto Rico	560	924	14	39	1,501		764	460	4,262
Rhode Island	460	336	211	......	64		1,767	1,216	4,054
South Carolina	4,437	10,615	132	8,529	119	25,652	......	2,500	51,984
South Dakota	4,202	11,993	181	......	.....	10,605	65,048	2,015	94,044
Tennessee	5,153	9,332	.....	......	376	49,554	687	4,378	69,480
Texas	15,986	23,293	762	9,307	.....	149,255	......	24,662	223,265
Utah	2,247	2,940	1,001	......	.....	15,490	......	2,958	24,636
Vermont	1,250	1,784	2	......	4	1,579	8,548	521	13,688
Virginia	5,106	16,736	95	27,608	.....	774	......	2,289	52,608
Washington	3,396	6,829	84	300	16	34,038	......	6,141	50,804
West Virginia	2,409	10,991	55	18,241	.....		1,913	2,424	36,033
Wisconsin	6,016	13,967	8	......	.....	10,229	58,171	7,084	95,475
Wyoming	3,408	1,983	32	7	33	14,115	......	875	20,453
Total	230,996	439,616	28,564	141,441	20,406	1,477,831	642,754	268,337	3,249,945

* Differences between the mileage shown in this table and other published data are largely the result of differences in the classification of designated routes not yet constructed and in the effective dates of the reports. For most states, projected mileage is not included in this table. Also, due to state statutes, local roads may be state, county, or township.
  † Includes urban sections.
  ‡ Data not available, usually included in local road category.

to improve major routes inside the limits of our cities. Federal participation began when Congress in 1944 authorized special funds to aid in constructing urban highways. Accordingly a system of *urban Federal-aid routes* that extend the Federal-aid primary routes into the cities is now being established.

State highway systems

In each state a system of roads has been designated by the respective state legislature as a state highway system. These routes in the main are those of primary interest to the state as a whole, as contrasted with roads primarily serving local needs.[4] These state systems incorporate the primary Federal-aid system, some routes from the Federal-aid secondary system, and usually some other mileage as well. The combined length of the 48 state highway systems is 600,000 miles, including about 36,000 miles of extensions into cities.

County and local roads

In the 2800 counties of the United States there are 2¼ million miles of rural roads not in the state highway system.[5] These are commonly classified as local rural roads. Not all of them are administered at the county level, for there are some 15,000 rural towns and townships that have their own distinct and separate road systems.

Although these local rural road systems constitute about 80% of the nation's rural road mileage, the vehicle-miles accumulated on them are only about 20% of the rural total. Only 10% of the mileage serves more than 100 vehicles per day. Its function is largely that of land service; development is often of a low order. Land-use studies by the highway planning surveys have revealed that many counties have mileage in excess of that needed for proper land service and that much money is wasted in maintaining these roads.

City streets

As noted, some important city streets have been incorporated into the Federal-aid or state highway systems. There remains something

[4] In some instances, state highway systems have been enlarged to include local roads because members of state legislatures hoped to shift the financial responsibility for them to the state highway departments. There is now a trend, largely attributable to the findings of the highway planning surveys, to transfer this responsibility back to local agencies.

[5] A relatively small portion of this mileage is in the Federal-aid secondary system.

over 250,000 miles of streets and alleys in 16,000 urban communities. Some serve primarily as arteries for local traffic, and others mainly provide access to property.

The interstate system of highways

The interstate system is a selected 40,000 miles of the most-used primary Federal-aid highway routes. It connects and extends into most of the larger cities, serving 209 of the 237 cities having populations of 50,000 or more inhabitants (see Fig. 1). Joint selection was authorized by the Federal-Aid Highway Act of 1944 and was approved by the several state highway departments and the Commissioner of Public Roads and finally adopted [6] in August 1947. Included are about 6000 miles of extensions into urban areas and a reserve of 2200 miles for city circumferential urban routes. Although it constitutes only 1.1% of all road mileage it is estimated to carry about 20% of all motor-vehicle traffic. This interstate system is to be progressively improved at the highest standard appropriate for the terrain traversed and the traffic to be served. The average daily traffic on the entire rural mileage is estimated at about 2900 vehicles, but a considerable rural mileage necessarily will be of a four-lane divided type to serve traffic that exceeds an average of 3000 vehicles per day. Less frequently it will be a six-lane type. Rights of way will be wide (in places from 288 to 300 ft) to permit roadside improvement and to set back all service or "parasite" activities such as motor courts, hot-dog stands, and filling stations. On many sections limited or controlled access will be established.

Strategic net highways

After the First World War a network of highways for military purposes known as the "strategic network" (SN) was selected by cooperation of the state highway departments and the U. S. Bureau of Public Roads with the War Department. This strategic network was restudied and revised during World War II and now totals 78,000 miles. It overlies all the interstate system and part of the Federal-aid system. Essentially, it is a system of interstate routes selected to serve strategic areas and objectives.

[6] The interstate system is an outgrowth of studies of nationwide routes begun in 1939 by the Public Roads Administration under a directive from Congress. The work was continued by a committee appointed by the President in April 1941. This committee, composed in part of outstanding highway engineers and assisted by a staff from the Public Roads Administration, completed its work in January 1944. Its report, *Interregional Highways,* House Document 379, 78th Congress, 2d session, is an outstanding accomplishment, and is highly recommended for supplementary reading.

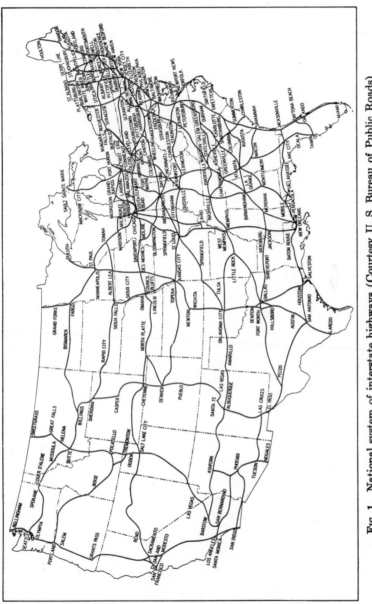

Fig. 1. National system of interstate highways (Courtesy U. S. Bureau of Public Roads)

United States highway routes

Overlapping mostly the Federal-aid highways and state highways, there also are the so-called United States highway routes. These U. S. routes total about 186,000 miles, designated across the country east and west by even route numbers and north and south by odd numbers, beginning, respectively, on the north and east and progressing southward to Route 90 and westward to Route 101. Unfortunately this sequence in several instances has been upset. These numbered routes are for operating convenience, especially for interstate traffic. They were set up in 1927 by a joint board designated by the Secretary of Agriculture at the request of the American Association of State Highway Officials. Approval by each state highway department concerned in any given route was required. The routes are marked with a characteristic shield marker and shown correspondingly on most commercial highway maps. On quite a number of routes there are alternative sections designated by a prefix digit. Thus, U. S. 312 designates the third alternative route section on east-west U. S. Route 12.

HIGHWAY ORGANIZATIONS

Bureau of Public Roads

The Bureau of Public Roads is the agency designated by Congress to administer the road program of the Federal government.[7] Before 1912 its functions were mainly the gathering of available knowledge and teaching others how to build roads. The Post Office Appropriations Act of 1912, which set apart $500,000 to be expended for post roads, launched the organization on its career of responsibility for road building. Since the Federal-Aid Highway Act of 1916, Public Roads has been the agency of the Federal government charged with primary responsibility for roads and for distributing Federal funds to the various states. The bulk of Federal-aid funds is expended by the state highway departments subject to approval by the Bureau of Public Roads. This is in direct contrast to the procedures of such agencies as the Bureau of Reclamation and the Civil Works Division of the Army Engineers, which execute the projects themselves.

[7] Created in 1893 as the Office of Road Inquiry of the Department of Agriculture, this office, under several names, operated on a very limited scale until 1916, when its functions were greatly broadened by the Federal-Aid Highway Act. In 1918 it became the Bureau of Public Roads of the Department of Agriculture. Under a Federal reorganization effective July 1, 1939, it was transferred to the Federal Works Agency and became the Public Roads Administration. In 1949, under a reorganization of the Executive Branch of the government, it was transferred to the Department of Commerce and again named the Bureau of Public Roads. In this book it will be referred to by either of the latter two names, depending on the date of reference.

Functions of the Bureau are as follows:

1. To allocate Federal-aid funds to the various states in accordance with laws enacted by Congress.

2. To supervise the manner in which allocated funds are spent. This involves, among other things, the approval of plans and specifications and inspection of construction for all Federal-aid projects.

3. To conduct research in the highway field. The Bureau of Public Roads has its own research staff which conducts investigations in all phases of highway engineering. In addition, it sponsors research work in several universities throughout the country.

4. To gather and disseminate information. Publication of the magazine *Public Roads* and of numerous technical bulletins illustrates this function.

5. To design and construct highways in national parks and national forests.

Since World War II the Bureau has undertaken the added tasks of training foreign engineers in American highway procedures and practices. This has involved offering short courses, conducting tours over the country, and at times arranging assignments with state highway departments. The Bureau has also provided advisory staffs of American engineers to a number of foreign governments.

State highway departments

The public highways of the country are under the full control of the 48 state governments. Administrative authority has in turn been delegated partly to the state highway departments and partly to subdivisions of the state like the counties and cities.

Organization of state highway departments began in 1891 when New Jersey passed legislation providing funds to aid the several counties in improving their highways. In 1893 Massachusetts authorized the construction of state highways. New York, Pennsylvania, Connecticut, and other northeastern states quickly followed by establishing state highway departments and state highway systems. By 1910, more than half the states had set up state highway departments with varying degrees of authority and financing; by 1916, 33 states had such organizations. The Federal-Aid Highway Act of 1916 made participation in Federal aid conditional on a state's having a highway agency, and immediately thereafter the remaining states created departments.

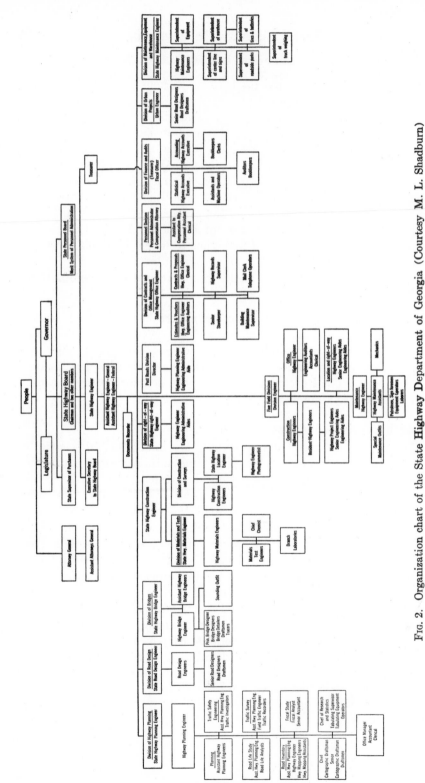

Fig. 2. Organization chart of the State Highway Department of Georgia (Courtesy M. L. Shadburn)

16

By 1946 the several state highway departments had been granted jurisdiction over all primary road systems and in many cases over "state secondary systems." Several state highway departments now also have been given legal control of all, or virtually all, rural roads. North Carolina, Virginia, West Virginia, and Delaware are examples. Some state highway departments now also have certain authority over extensions of main rural routes into cities. In all, as mentioned, there are 36,000 miles of such urban extensions of state primary highways. Also, under the Federal-Aid Highway Acts, the state highway departments alone are permitted to expend Federal-aid funds, so that they must administer both Federal aid and Federal-aid secondary programs.

State highway departments differ greatly in size. Mileages administered range from less than 1000 to more than 60,000; annual expenditures from $7 million to $300 million, and number of employees from less than 200 to more than 16,000. Organizations also vary. Typically they are headed either by a director or by a commission of three to seven members (with a chief engineer). A director's responsibility is clear and centralized, but frequently he has and needs an advisory board. Under the commission form of organization, responsibility may be divided, and, if its members represent respective state subdivisions, there is a tendency to distort the annual state highway budget to satisfy local demands. Commissioners appointed at large by the governor and with staggered terms therefore are preferable. The chief engineer under a commission usually (but not always) is appointed by the commission, and his position is relatively secure and permanent. Governors usually appoint directors (sometimes superintendents), who obviously are subject to political changes. Figures 2 and 3 show the organization charts of the Georgia and Michigan state highway departments.

The completed establishment and strengthening of state highway departments throughout the country was a most important result of the Federal highway legislation. For more than 100 years of our national existence, county, town, and other local officials had been in charge of our highways, and the results in general were feeble.

Local road administration

The most heavily traveled roads of the country are administered by 48 state highway departments. In marked contrast, some 35,000 county, town and township, urban, and special agencies administer local roads and streets. Sizes and organizations of these agencies differ

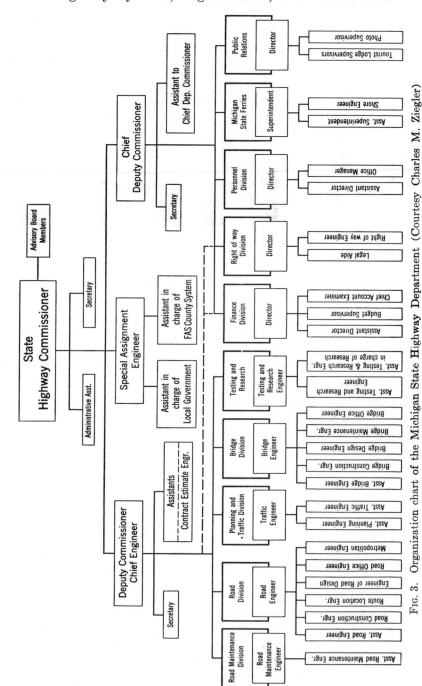

Fig. 3. Organization chart of the Michigan State Highway Department (Courtesy Charles M. Ziegler)

widely. Many of them have good engineering and administrative supervision, but many do not. This lack always was wasteful, but with modern motor traffic it becomes critical.

Although the county and local road situation in general is not good, important measures are under way for its improvement. Among them are the classification of county roads by state law with state aid restricted to the more heavily traveled routes, the establishment of a Federal-aid secondary system, the inventory of all local roads by the highway planning surveys, and the extension of state supervision to local roads. Other improvements include the widespread adoption of civil service in place of the once prevalent spoils system, and the consolidation of many road administrations into a single unit under a qualified engineer to replace several distinct organizations, each operating independently under an elected official.

HIGHWAY ASSOCIATIONS

American Association of State Highway Officials (AASHO)

The American Association of State Highway Officials, established in 1914, is an association of state, territorial, and District of Columbia highway departments and the Bureau of Public Roads. Officials of these agencies govern its operations. Engineering activities are carried on through standing committees on standards, which, among other duties, prepare specifications, manuals, and standards representative of the best current practice.

Publications of the AASHO include, among others, *Highway Materials,* part I, *Specifications,* and part II, *Tests; Standard Specifications for Highway Bridges; Manual of Highway Construction Practices and Methods;* and a group of "policy" pamphlets on important highway subjects. All these works are authoritative, as they are prepared and approved by representatives of the various state and Federal highway agencies. Frequent reference will be made to them in this book.

The Association also publishes a quarterly magazine *American Highways,* which reports on current highway subjects and summarizes important legislation, papers, and speeches pertaining to the highway field.

Highway Research Board

The Highway Research Board is organized under the auspices of the division of engineering and industrial research of the National Research Council, which, in turn, is a part of the National Academy of Sciences. Membership consists of some 40 educational, technical, and industrial associations of national scope. The Board provides a forum for the discussion and publication of the results obtained by individual research workers, organizes committees of experts to plan and suggest research work and to study and correlate the results, publishes and otherwise disseminates information, and carries on fact-finding investigations.

Publications of the Highway Research Board include the *Proceedings* of its annual meetings and numerous reports and bulletins on special subjects. These publications are, without question, the most fruitful single source of advanced knowledge of highway problems.

American Road Builders Association

This association is a nonprofit, noncommercial organization whose membership includes highway officials and engineers, equipment manufacturers and distributors, materials producers, and contractors. The association has a number of committees active in all branches of the highway field.

Before World War II the Association published an annual *Convention Proceedings*. Since the war it has released many technical bulletins, most of which have been prepared by technical committees. References to some of these bulletins will be found in this book.

Other highway associations

Numerous trade associations interested in promoting the use of their products are active in the highway field. Typical of this group are the Asphalt Institute, the Portland Cement Association, and the Wire Reinforcement Institute. Each of these organizations publishes magazines and technical bulletins and releases other data concerning its product. Many have field engineers located strategically over the country. Much reliable and useful information can be gained from these sources.

There are also associations whose concern is highway transportation. Representative of these are the automobile clubs, the National Highway Users Conference, and the American Trucking Association. Most of these also publish magazines or bulletins.

University and college activities

Most engineering colleges have specialists in highway engineering on their teaching staffs. Some schools not only offer instruction for college students but also provide extension courses and in-service training in the highway field. In addition, the universities conduct many research projects on highway problems, often with the cooperation and financial support of highway agencies or other interested sponsors.

3 ──────────── Highway Planning

HIGHWAY PLANNING SURVEYS

Introduction

Beginning about 1930 when the initial improvement of main rural roads had established definite flows of motor traffic, it became increasingly apparent that future growth of the country's highway transportation system should be on a scientific rather than a haphazard basis. City streets were in relative distress, and many rural highways were overloaded. The practice of using all Federal-aid and the bulk of state highway funds for the improvement of main rural highways needed modification. And yet what were the next most important groups of roads or streets? Should their improvement supersede the demand for reconstruction of much of the main system which was rapidly becoming inadequate for increased traffic?

From the data at hand such questions were unanswerable. So, beginning in 1935, the so-called "highway planning surveys" were undertaken. The Federal-Aid Act of 1934 authorized expenditure not to exceed 1½% of Federal-aid funds apportioned to each state for the making of surveys, plans, and engineering investigations of projects for future construction. By 1940 the state highway departments were enthusiastically engaged in surveys to determine the status of the rural systems and the service they rendered. They were also assembling facts to estimate the cost of owning and maintaining a comprehensive road system necessary in a long-range highway-improvement program.

The highway planning surveys generally were of uniform pattern. A summary of the major subjects covered would include the following:

1. An inventory of all rural roads.
2. An estimate of the volume and character of traffic on rural highways.

3. A review of the highway-financing practice of the state and its subdivisions.

4. An estimate of the number of motor vehicles owned by residents of the various subdivisions of each state, and of the use of the roads and streets by these residents.

5. Road-life studies based on past records of construction and reconstruction, from which service lives of existing and future roads can be estimated.

In recent years, origin and destination surveys for many metropolitan areas and numerous other special studies have been conducted by the planning survey organizations.

Road inventory

The first road inventories were made by personal observers who recorded width, type, and condition of roads and structures and located farms, dwellings, schools, churches, and other cultural features which were potential sources of traffic. The presence of sharp curves, steep grades, and restrictions of visibility were noted as traffic hazards. The data were summarized in tables and plotted on straight-line diagrams and served as a basis for general highway maps. Special study maps showed school-bus routes, important truck and commercial bus routes, and traffic volumes. The original road inventory cost somewhat less than $1 per mile. When the data from the several states were assembled there was, for the first time, a firm record of the country's highway mileage and its condition and distribution. Highway maps for most of the country are to a scale of 1 in. equals 1 mile.[1]

Most state highway planning agencies have kept these original inventories up to date for the roads on the state highway system, so that correct data regarding widths, types, conditions, and horizontal and vertical alinements are always at hand. Many have expanded their records to include traffic volumes and speeds, accident experience, and maintenance costs. From all this, an intelligent appraisal of the needs of the entire system and priorities for improvement can be established.[2]

Many of the road inventory data can be presented to good advantage in graphical form. This technique is illustrated by Fig. 1, which shows a road inventory sheet developed by the Connecticut State Highway Department.

[1] These maps can be had from the several state highway departments and are available generally at both full and half scales.

[2] For more on this subject see the chapter on highway economy.

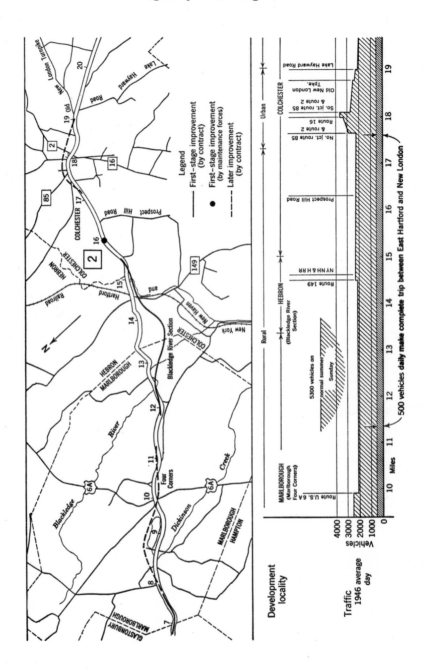

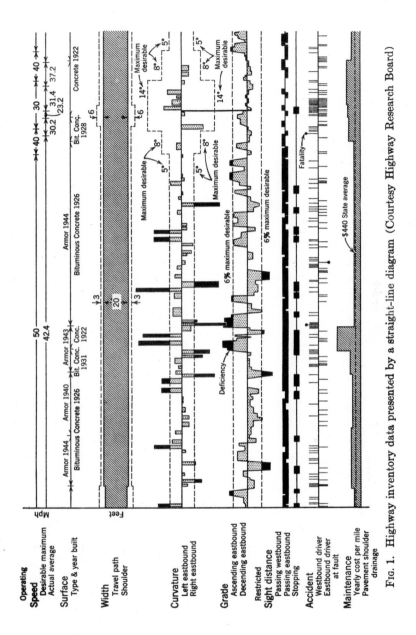

Fig. 1. Highway inventory data presented by a straight-line diagram (Courtesy Highway Research Board)

Rural traffic surveys [3]

In the beginning, rural traffic information was obtained by manual methods, sometimes by maintenance personnel. Today numerous photoelectric and other types of machines at key locations count traffic continuously on an hourly basis. These continuous-count stations provide information concerning the distribution of traffic by hours of the day, days of the week, months of the year, and the trend from year to year. Many such stations have been operated without interruption and at the same locations for a number of years, some since 1937. Thus there is available a firm record of traffic trends. To determine traffic flows on individual roads, records of 24- to 48-hr duration are taken at "coverage" stations. Longer records at a smaller number of "control" stations provide the basis for expanding the "coverage" counts into an estimate of average daily traffic. Portable recording devices, often actuated by pneumatic detectors laid across the roadway, are commonly employed for these shorter counts. There are more than 1000 continuous-count and more than 100,000 control and coverage-count stations operated in the United States each year. The composition of the traffic by type of vehicle is obtained by manual operations as needed.

Another phase of the traffic survey is the *loadometer study*. In the original planning surveys (1936–40), more than 3000 stations were operated and over 2.5 million trucks were weighed. Information was obtained regarding type of vehicle; rated capacity; gross weight; payload; axle load; width, height, and length of vehicle; commodity hauled; and origin and destination of trip. Such information is valuable for road-design and traffic-regulation purposes. It is also the foundation for all studies pertaining to the assignment of highway costs to heavy vehicles.[4]

Each year since 1942 weight stations have been occupied for 8 hr at more than 500 locations to determine trends in truck weights and numbers. In most states the highway. departments and Bureau of Public Roads are now making more extensive loadometer surveys during all hours of the day and at least during three seasons. On

[3] For a review and annotated bibliography of traffic-survey methods, see Origin-Destination Surveys and Traffic Volume Studies, *Highway Research Board Bibliography 11* (1951).

[4] Engineers of the U. S. Bureau of Public Roads have developed an electronic device that measures axle weights, spacings, and speeds of vehicles in motion. See O. K. Normann and R. C. Hopkins, in *Public Roads*, April 1952, pp. 1–17, or in *Highway Research Board Bulletin 50* (1952).

certain selected pieces of road, the weight data are combined with careful review of the roadway and pavement design and condition. From these studies should come increased knowledge of the causes of pavement failure and improvements in design and construction methods. In addition, further information will be gained on the troublesome problem of truck damage to highways and of the allocation of highway costs to trucks.[5]

Urban origin and destination studies

One of the important findings from the rural traffic surveys concerned the change in traffic volumes as highways approached cities or

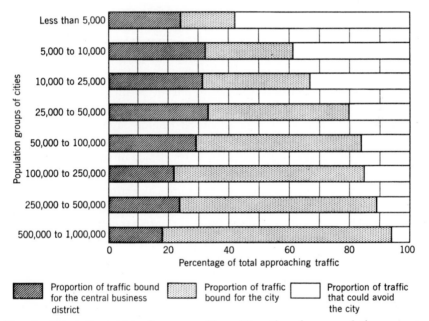

FIG. 2. Proportions of traffic approaching cities of various population groups which are bound beyond the city, to the city, and to the central business district (Courtesy U. S. Bureau of Public Roads)

towns. Accurate data concerning vehicular origins and destinations were collected by roadside interviews at *"cordon stations"* at the outskirts of highly settled areas. Important knowledge gained in this manner is illustrated in Fig. 2. It shows, for example, that about 95%

[5] For a report on trends in traffic volumes, vehicle types, and vehicle weights, see **T. B. Dimmick** in *Public Roads,* February 1953, pp. 111–124, and December 1953, pp. 235–247.

of traffic approaching cities of one-half million population or more is destined into the city and not beyond, and that almost 20% is destined to the central business area. Such information demolishes the hope that traffic congestion of large cities can be relieved by bypasses outside the city limits. On the other hand, the data recorded in Fig. 2 also prove that major highways should skirt small towns. Up to 58% of the traffic may bypass cities of population under 5000. This percentage is even higher if such places are near larger cities.

Data collected outside urban limits threw only partial light on traffic ebb and flow within the urban areas, and to measure these conditions the urban area origin and destination surveys were undertaken. The first approach was to take traffic-volume counts on the city streets. Soon it was obvious that favorable street capacity or condition rather than preferred routing was governing city traffic flows. Consequently, traffic counts did not give a conclusive index of the traffic volume that would use an improved, more direct facility, and so the origin-destination type of survey resulted.

The most accurate type of origin-destination survey is based largely on personal interviews of the "doorbell-ringing" type made at every tenth or every twentieth domicile, depending on the size of the city. Such personal interviews determine the methods of transportation and the destinations of each member of the family on the previous day. The interviews are supplemented by counts at cordon stations and by facts about bus, truck, and taxi movement gained from company records. All interview data are punched onto tabulating cards which can be sorted and counted at great speed in automatic machines. By segregating the cards in different ways, any desired combination of facts from the interview data can be quickly found, as, for example, the number of vehicles traveling from one specific zone of the city to another during a given time interval. *Check counts* of movement within the cities are made at *control* points, such as well-known bridges or other landmarks, or along screen lines which intercept all arteries of travel. It has been found that 90% or more of the traffic passing control points in 16 hr was accounted for by the expanded interview data. The small difference is explained in part by omissions from the interview data like unimportant short trips and trips by drivers from outside the area who were not intercepted at the external cordon stations. Figure 3 shows the screen-line check for the St. Paul–Minneapolis survey, with close agreement between ground-count and interview data.

From origin-destination survey data a number of important facts have developed. Some of these are illustrated by Fig. 4. Notice that, for this typical artery, city-bound vehicles from outside constitute but a small part of the total volume. Most of it comes from within the city's boundaries. Note also that much of this flow is destined beyond the central business district but passes directly through it for

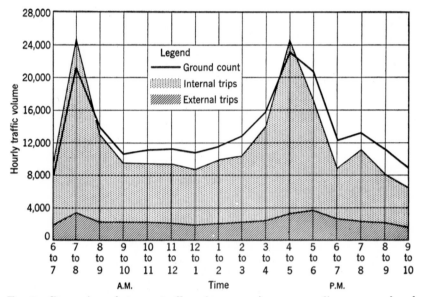

FIG. 3. Comparisons between traffic volumes passing a screen line as reproduced from interviews and as recorded by actual ground count, St. Paul–Minneapolis traffic survey, 1950 (Courtesy U. S. Bureau of Public Roads)

want of another route. This suggests that some relief from the congestion of downtown areas can be gained by removing these vehicles to an inner-belt freeway or other artery that skirts the business district.

A number of graphical methods for presenting origin-destination survey and other traffic-flow data have been developed. Figure 5 shows a *traffic-flow* diagram which records by width of line the number of vehicles traveling the traffic arteries of a city. Figure 6 is a *desire-line* diagram based on origin-destination data. This shows traffic flow between various subdivisions of the city, assuming a straight-line path between areas. Such a diagram is extremely useful in freeway and arterial street planning.

The home-interview type of traffic origin and destination survey has been made in more than 90 metropolitan areas. The costs of such studies vary with the population. One interview for each 10 dwellings should suffice for cities of population 100,000 to 300,000. The cost for the field work, coding and punching tabulating cards, and their

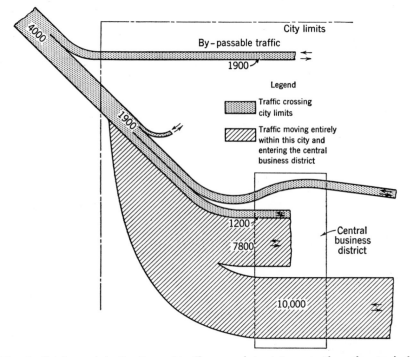

Fig. 4. Origins and destinations of traffic on an interstate route through a typical city of 50,000 to 100,000 population (Courtesy U. S. Bureau of Public Roads)

processing will thus run about 30 cents total per inhabitant and for the larger cities, where one dwelling sample for each 20 will suffice, as low as 15 cents. These figures are based on 1949 costs. The time required for the field work varies considerably but is usually several months. Then at least 6 months more are required to process the data.

In most origin and destination surveys, the location of a particular origin or destination is stated in terms of the zone and subzone in which it lies. An alternative method records such a location by giving its rectangular coordinates on a grid system covering the area under survey. With the data in this form, it is possible, among other things, to draw contours of constant traffic which resemble the contour lines of a topographic map.[6]

An alternative origin-destination study technique is to distribute a postcard questionnaire to motorists passing a cordon line. Replies, however, are reported not to exceed 25%, and there is no way of checking results. Ohio and West Virginia have had better results in smaller cities by mailing the card questionnaire to city vehicle owners and requesting a log of the next day's travel. By good publicity they got 50 to 60% returns which could be checked with screen-line counts. Another procedure is to conduct internal roadside interviews which develop the origin and destination of traffic crossing the boundaries of certain zones of the entire area. But for large metropolitan areas there has not been developed any technique superior to the home interview.[7]

Studies of highway financing

Long-range plans to achieve and maintain suitable highway facilities can avail little unless accompanied by long-range financial plans to carry the improvement programs to completion. Before such financial plans can be made it is necessary to have the following types of information from all affected governmental subdivisions:

1. The types, rates, and revenues produced by taxation imposed specifically for highways, and by taxes for other purposes.

2. Income received from other sources, such as commercial enterprises and borrowings.

3. The purposes and amounts of spending, with special emphasis upon those for highway purposes.

4. The amount, nature, purpose, terms, and interest rates of outstanding debt.

An early activity of the highway planning surveys of the several states was to collect such financial facts. In many instances, they came from published reports of governmental units or agencies. Where published reports were not available, the data came from original

---

[6] See *Traffic Survey of the Sacramento Area* by California Division of Highways and the U. S. Public Roads Administration (1947–48). A summary of this report by K. A. MacLachlan appears in *Proceedings Highway Research Board*, pp. 349–364 (1949).

[7] For more information on planning and conducting origin and destination surveys see Origin and Destination Surveys, Methods and Costs, *Highway Research Board Bulletin 76* (1953).

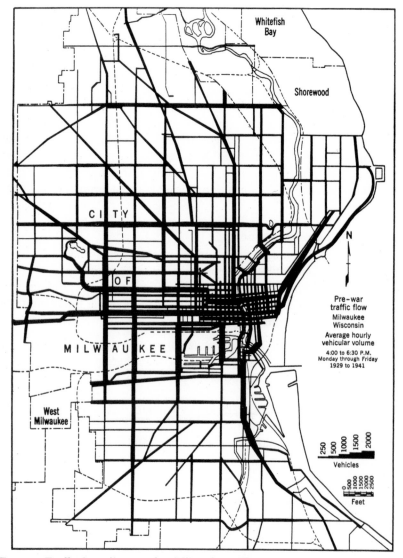

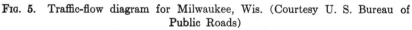

FIG. 5. Traffic-flow diagram for Milwaukee, Wis. (Courtesy U. S. Bureau of
Public Roads)

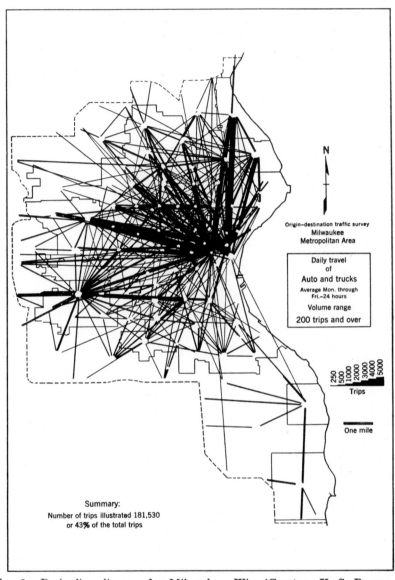

FIG. 6.   Desire-line diagram for Milwaukee, Wis. (Courtesy U. S. Bureau of
Public Roads)

financial records of the agencies involved. Analysis of these records revealed, among other things, the relative magnitude of special taxes on motor-vehicle users by the several levels of government, the support provided highways by road users and other taxpayers residing in each taxing jurisdiction, and the dispositions of the funds so raised. Comparisons were possible also between highway financing and financing for other governmental activities. These broad one-time fiscal studies have been followed with a continuing annual reporting of highway-finance operations at all levels of government. Thus, sound information on highway-financing problems is now readily available.[8]

Studies of motor-vehicle ownership and use

Two studies regarding vehicle ownership and travel over the various road and street systems were undertaken in many states in the period 1936–40. One survey involved motor-vehicle allocation. Questionnaires were sent to a relatively large percentage of motor-vehicle owners in order to determine the precise place of residence of the owner (i.e., city, incorporated town, or rural); the make, year, model, body type, weight, etc. of the vehicle; the total miles traveled in the preceding 12 months in the state of residence; and the fuel consumed. Another study was of road use. It involved personal interviews with a small percentage of vehicle owners. Data sought included the information collected in the allocation study plus more detail regarding the road system that was used, classification of places where the vehicle was driven, and the purposes of the travel.

Beginning in 1951 new studies of vehicle ownership and use were undertaken, as the earlier data were no longer considered reliable. Many state highway departments now have them completed. Data include the same types gathered for the earlier surveys, plus information regarding the number of persons holding driver's licenses and how employed persons traveled to and from work. The home-interview technique was employed, but the sample base was households rather than registration lists. Travel data covered only trips ending on the most recent weekday. Interviews were generally in four cycles to reflect seasonal variations.

---

[8] This program, which involves in many instances the collection of data from original records, is geared closely to the joint collection, by the state highway departments and the Bureau of Public Roads, of annual statistics on state highway taxation and finance, motor-vehicle registrations, motor-fuel consumption, and highway mileage.

Ownership and use statistics, coupled with those on finance and traffic flow, provide a firm base for determining the importance of the various highway systems and the individual roads in the systems. They also offer means for measuring the equity of present taxation schedules and the benefits motorists gain from road improvement.

Road-life studies

Road-life studies are concerned with finding the life expectancy of the various elements that make up a highway. To date particular attention has been devoted to the more common surface types. Data have been developed regarding their average service lives, average ages, retirement rates, construction costs, salvage values at retirement, maintenance costs, functional obsolescence, and structural deterioration.[9]

Special planning studies

Special planning studies pointed toward specific objectives and too numerous to detail here have been made by the Bureau of Public Roads, the state highway departments, and other organizations. Such publications as the *Proceedings* of the Highway Research Board devote many pages to reports on subjects related to planning. In addition, many special bulletins are published. To illustrate: a typical study is titled "Time and Gasoline Consumption in Motor Truck Operation as Affected by the Weight and Power of Vehicles and the Rise and Fall in Highways." [10]

USES OF PLANNING DATA [11]

The statewide highway planning surveys were undertaken to obtain control information, to determine what should be done to provide facilities for modern traffic, and to find how funds for long-range programs could be provided. The "planning surveys" are permanent divisions of the state highway departments. These agencies and the Bureau of Public Roads now use planning data from day to day in programming their work and in determining design requirements.

[9] See p. 61 for a more complete discussion and for references.

[10] *Highway Research Board Research Report 9-A* (1950).

[11] See Bibliography on Uses of Highway Planning Survey Data, *Highway Research Board Bibliography 4* (1948), for a listing of some 400 papers and articles on the uses of planning survey data. Also see *A Bibliography of Highway Planning Reports* published by the U. S. Bureau of Public Roads (1950).

Much information from state highway planning surveys has been studied, assembled, and published in the form of tables by the Bureau of Public Roads. *Highway Statistics,* published annually, shows state mileages, revenues, costs, gasoline consumption, motor-vehicle registrations, etc. There also are monthly bulletins showing traffic-volume trends, and in the magazine *Public Roads* appears an analysis of trends, truck weights, ton-mileages, etc.

INFLUENCE OF HIGHWAY PLANNING SURVEYS

The influence of the highway planning surveys already has been tremendous. Highway development is being placed on a scientific rather than a haphazard basis, and almost constant reference is made to facts developed by the planning surveys and allied studies. In subsequent paragraphs, two examples of the influence of highway planning data on transportation planning are discussed.

Freeways, expressways, and parkways

A *freeway* is a divided arterial highway for through traffic. Access is "fully controlled" by the administering highway agency, which means that admission or departure from the through lanes takes place only at points designated by the highway agency rather than at points selected by abutting property owners. Generally there are grade separations at intersections. An *expressway* corresponds to a freeway except that control of access may be only partial rather than full. A *parkway* is an arterial highway for noncommercial traffic, with full or partial control of access, and usually located within a park or a ribbon of parklike development.[12] Development of the design principles of these facilities has followed logically from the findings of the highway planning agencies.

Freeways will accommodate many times more vehicles per lane than the usual urban highways and will permit much greater speeds. Control of access will insure freedom from the encroachments of business and like activity, and thus assure permanence as a free-flowing artery. Accident opportunity will be markedly reduced. Every present indication is that the freeways and like arteries now finished and

---

[12] These definitions are based on approved policy of the American Association of State Highway Officials adopted June 25, 1949. The action was taken by the AASHO to remove the misunderstanding and confusion in the use of these and other terms.

to be completed will do much to speed up motor-vehicle travel and to relieve street congestion in urban areas.[13]

The typical freeway is of multilane design (usually four or six) with a center dividing strip separating traffic in opposite directions. The width and design of this center strip varies from a narrow multiple striped zone or elevated curb to a landscaped area 30 ft or more in

Fig. 7. A section of rural freeway in Connecticut

width. Wide shoulders are provided in more recent designs as a refuge for disabled vehicles. Usually no provision is made for pedestrians except for occasional elevated or depressed crossings. Often high fences are erected to prevent their entering the facility at all. Vehicles normally leave a freeway by "peeling off" to the right from the slow-moving, right-hand lane. Entry is accomplished by blending into the same slow-moving lane (see Fig. 7). On freeways, cross traffic at grade is eliminated by *grade-separation structures*. At junctions with other important highways, grade-separation structures become *interchanges*, designed to permit turning movements without conflict. In Fig. 7, the interchange is of conventional cloverleaf design, modified in one quadrant.

[13] More detailed discussions of control of access, highway capacity, and highway safety appear in Chapters 7, 8, and 11, respectively.

The urban transportation problem

Data accumulated by the planning surveys and particularly from origin and destination studies have done much to clarify the urban transportation problem which, with the great increase in motor transportation, has become acute. On an average, over 90% of the traffic that approaches our larger cities is destined to them. In terms of vehicle-miles, about half of our vast highway transport is within urban areas. Excepting intercity traffic there is, in proportion to the size of our cities, a typical "traffic radius" that measures the limit of motor movements to and from the heart of the city. Around the largest cities, its length is about 35 miles.[14]

While the motor vehicle has enabled cities to expand outwardly, thus improving residential conditions, it has caused traffic congestion to increase alarmingly in the hearts of the business districts. In some instances, cities are threatened with a complete jam. Much of the congestion and impedance is due to the rectangular street pattern that involves interrupting cross traffic. Much also can be attributed to a lack of convenient and available parking space. Fundamentally, however, individual transportation by motor vehicles in the heart of urban areas is extravagant in its use of the limited and expensive ground space. Ten times as many persons can be moved over a given street in mass-transportation vehicles as in private autos. In addition, the mass-transportation vehicle moves on after discharging its passengers whereas the private car must be parked while its driver and riders transact their business.

The facts developed about the downtown congestion problem indicate the need for a new approach. Primary attention must be focused upon the movement of *people* rather than the movement of *vehicles*. Mass-transportation facilities must be improved, so that fewer automobiles will come into the downtown area. In addition, freeway plans must include not only radial lines feeding into the downtown area, but also belt lines circling the downtown area. In this way, vehicles destined beyond the congested section will be diverted from the streets. Off-street parking must be provided, partly to make up the present deficiency and partly to release street space now used for storing vehicles to the more productive purpose of carrying moving

---

[14] In fact, almost all trips by motor vehicles (85%) are short and begin in or end in a city or town. There is only a minor movement of vehicles beyond 100 miles, and "transcontinental" traffic is relatively negligible. There are exceptions to this rule in some of the less densely populated western states. There the longer trips account for more than half the state's total rural vehicle mileage.

vehicles. Capacity of streets must be further increased by one-way and off-center operation. This multiple approach offers the only reasonable solution.[15]

STATEWIDE PLANNING REPORTS

During the decade 1930–40 expenditures for highways failed to keep pace with road use as measured by either the number of motor vehicles or the miles driven. Then during World War II the roads were subject to intense use by large numbers of heavy vehicles. In addition, maintenance operations were curtailed. By 1945 the condition of many roads had become unusually bad and in places actually hazardous to traffic. When gasoline rationing was lifted there was an immediate increase in motor traffic and a corresponding demand that something be done to better the highways. In California organized pressure on the legislature resulted in the appointment in 1945 of a legislative "joint fact-finding committee on highways, streets and bridges." [16] The committee secured excellent technical assistance and the cooperation of the state and Federal government specialists and held hearings throughout the state. Its three-part report [17] in 1946, based largely on the accumulated facts of the highway planning surveys during the decade 1935–45, was precedent-making. It presented data for all the roads in a large state that has a continued high record of motor-vehicle use. It recommended, as one item, that state, county, and metropolitan highways be reclassified. It estimated the state's current and long-range needs and the corresponding costs for a ten-year program beginning in 1950. Not all the conclusions of the interim committee have been enacted into law, but the California Act of 1947 reflected their influence.[18] This law revised and increased motor-vehicle taxes to provide added funds for state and county roads and for major city streets. An important feature related to county highways. They were classed as primary and secondary with the use of some funds restricted to primary roads. Provision also was made for a more equitable division of statewide user revenues among the counties. A most sig-

---

[15] An excellent discussion of urban highway planning by Joseph Barnett and 16 others appears in *Transactions American Society of Civil Engineers*, pp. 637–700 (1947). See also *Highway Research Board Bulletin 86* (1954).

[16] See California Senate Concurrent Resolution 27, June 16, 1945.

[17] A Study for the California Legislature—*Engineering Facts and a Future Program, A Proposed System of Highway Financing,* and *An Analysis of Taxation for Highway Purposes in California* (1946).

[18] Collier-Burns Act of 1947.

nificant section of the Act (2111) provided that "The moneys payable to the counties . . . shall be apportioned as follows: (a) First each county shall be paid five thousand dollars during each of the months of January, April, July, and October which amounts shall be used exclusively for engineering costs and administrative expenses in respect to county roads. . . ." Thus funds to put California's local roads on a sound engineering basis are now available.

By 1953, this California report of 1946 had been followed by similar reports in over half of the other states. The organization of the investigating and reporting agency varied somewhat from state to state, but the fact-finding action was a scientific one based on accumulated data from ten years of statewide highway-planning and economic studies. All surveys were made by experienced highway engineers and economists, and were filed with the state legislatures. They show the several classes of roads in the states; their traffic, present and future; and their long-term costs over the years. Invariably they reflect the needs of (a) greatly increased revenue and (b) better-organized local road administration and engineering.[19] Most important of all, they set the pattern for sound, long-range development of an integrated highway system.

---

[19] As examples, in Illinois the counties were classified with respect to highway administration, and there were recommendations for state civil service and increased pay for highway engineers. In Kansas there was recommended a yearly increase of $32,872,000 for highways for 25 years. The legislature then raised the gas tax from 3 to 5 cents. In Michigan's report was a recommended annual expenditure of $179,141,000 for 12 years of which 41% should go to cities. In the Washington report was an excellent county-road financing section. A 15-year program for all road systems was estimated at $76,360,000 annually.

4 ——————————— Highway Economy

INTRODUCTION

Highways are constructed because they provide benefits to society as a whole or as individuals. Good transportation facilities raise the level of the entire economy by providing for ready transportation of goods; [1] they are of assistance in problems of national defense; they make easier the provision of community services like police and fire protection, medical care, schooling, and delivery of the mails; they open added opportunities for recreation and travel. Highways benefit the landowner because ready access makes his property more valuable. They benefit the motor-vehicle user through reduced cost of vehicle operation, savings in time, reduction in accidents, and increased comfort and ease of driving. On the other hand, road improvements take money that might be used for other productive purposes by individuals or by government. They can be justified only if the benefits exceed the costs entailed in providing them, including some allowance for return on the money invested.

The *total* cost of motor transportation is the essential consideration in long-term planning for highways. In 1952 some $40 billion was spent to operate some 52 million motor vehicles. It is the effect of highway improvement on this total operating bill that must be observed. There is definite justification for highway improvement until it no longer decreases this total cost of motor transportation.

Over a century ago, highway economy was under discussion. W. M. Gillespie, professor of civil engineering at Union College, in his *Manual of the Principles and Practice of Road Making*, stated that "A minimum of expense is, of course, highly desirable; but the road which is

---

[1] The cost per ton-mile for transporting goods in primitive countries where humans or small animals carry loads on their backs exceeds a dollar per ton-mile even when computed at the usual depressed wage scale. This is probably 20 to 50 times the cost of truck transportation in the United States.

41

truly the cheapest is not the one which has cost the least money, but the one which makes the most profitable returns in proportion to the amount expended upon it." For many years attention was focused largely on the relative economy of various road surfacings, and later on the costs of motor-vehicle operation. Only after the advent of the statewide planning surveys with the masses of data developed by them has attention to many other factors of the subject been possible.

The following paragraphs summarize present knowledge and indicate the direction of research and study in highway economics.[2]

COST OF MOTOR-VEHICLE OPERATION [3]

There is no single easy answer to the question: What does it cost to operate a motor vehicle? However, a reasonable answer is prerequisite to economical highway design. Much is already known about motor-vehicle costs, and yet much is still to be determined by experiment and study. At present, intensive research is under way on many phases of the problem.

Some operating expenses increase more or less directly with miles driven; in other words, their cost per vehicle-mile is relatively constant. In this classification fall such items as fuel, tires, oil, maintenance and repairs, and that portion of depreciation attributable to wearing out. Other costs vary mainly with time and are constant for a given period such as one year; or, stated in costs per vehicle-mile, they vary inversely with the number of miles driven annually. Included here are drivers' license and registration fees, garage rent, insurance, and obsolescence, which is the portion of depreciation that results from inadequacy or being out of date. Some costs are dependent wholly or in part on speed. The most important of these is the value of the travel time of operator and rider; charges for these vary inversely with speed. However, certain operating costs like fuel and oil consumption and tire wear increase as driving speed increases.

Of the costs mentioned above, those that vary with mileage or speed are often affected by roadway improvement. These are of particular

---

[2] For a basic discussion of highway transportation economics see Richard M. Zettel in *Public Roads,* August 1952, pp. 37–49.

[3] This discussion is based largely on data contained in *A Committee Report on Road User Benefit Analysis for Highway Improvement,* November 1951, prepared by the committee on planning and design policies of the AASHO. This excellent work presents the most authoritative information that is currently available. On subsequent pages it will be referred to as the report of the AASHO committee.

concern in highway economy studies, for justification of highway improvement depends largely on savings in operating costs to offset the expenditures required. However, care must be exercised to consider only those costs or savings that are relevant to a particular comparison. Stated differently, only *increment* costs or savings should be included in economy studies.

Motor-fuel costs

Motor fuel consumed per mile traveled varies, for a particular vehicle, with the running speed [4] attained, the degree of congestion of the road, the road surface, the grade or slope of the road, road curvature and superelevation, and the number and duration of stops. Between vehicles, it varies with weight and size, the efficiency and adjustment of the engine, and the skill of the operator. Figure 1 gives estimated fuel consumption in gallons per mile for passenger cars operating on tangent two-lane rural highways. Values cover restricted, normal, and free operation [5] and the usual range of running speeds. For operation on tangent, divided rural highways the values are quite similar. Fuel use from Fig. 1 was applied at 28 cents per gallon to find the fuel costs of Table 1.

Tests have shown that gasoline consumption actually is determined by attempted speed rather than by running speed. The explanation is that the extra fuel consumed in accelerating to the attempted speed at every opportunity offsets the fuel economy of the lower running speed. In Fig. 2 the curve shown by a dashed line gives the miles per gallon (average) to be expected if the road is free of other traffic so that constant-velocity operation at the speed selected by the driver is possible. From this same curve is read the miles per gallon actually attained for a given *attempted* speed. Figure 2 also shows the approximate running speeds to be expected under varying road and congestion conditions. The dotted lines illustrate the use of the chart: for an attempted speed of 50 mph, gasoline mileage is 14.6 miles per gallon; for this attempted speed on a normal two-lane highway or a divided highway on which speed is restricted by large numbers of vehicles, actual running speed will be about 43 mph.

The actual gasoline used on a mile of road equals the product of the number of vehicles times the average consumption of individual vehicles. This average consumption is slightly higher than that for a car traveling at average speed

[4] Running speed is the distance traveled divided by the running time, which is the time the vehicle is in motion.

[5] Vehicle operation is classed as "restricted" when the ratio between the 30th highest hour volume and practical capacity exceeds 1.25. Operation is "normal" if this ratio lies between 0.75 and 1.25, and is "free" if the ratio is less than 0.75. Further discussion of traffic volumes and capacities appears in Chapter 8.

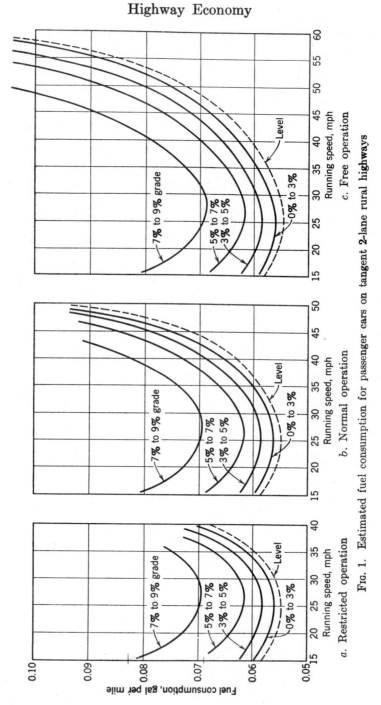

Fig. 1. Estimated fuel consumption for passenger cars on tangent 2-lane rural highways

TABLE 1. OPERATING COSTS FOR PASSENGER CARS IN RURAL AREAS

Tangent Roadway, 0–3% Grades

Class of Highway	Surface	Type of Operation	Running Speed	Operating Costs, Cents per Vehicle-Mile					
				Fuel	Tires	Oil	Maint. and Repairs	Depreciation	Total
Divided	Pavement in good condition	Free	40	1.75	0.28	0.12	0.80	1.00	3.95
			44	1.83	0.34	0.14	0.80	1.00	4.11
			48	1.93	0.41	0.16	0.80	1.00	4.30
			52	2.05	0.47	0.19	0.80	1.00	4.51
			56	2.20	0.54	0.25	0.80	1.00	4.79
			60	2.39	0.56	0.35	0.80	1.00	5.10
		Normal	32	1.62	0.23	0.10	0.80	1.00	3.75
			36	1.67	0.27	0.11	0.80	1.00	3.85
			40	1.75	0.32	0.12	0.80	1.00	3.99
			44	1.85	0.38	0.14	0.80	1.00	4.17
			48	1.99	0.45	0.16	0.80	1.00	4.40
			52	2.20	0.53	0.19	0.80	1.00	4.72
			56	2.55	0.60	0.25	0.80	1.00	5.20
		Restricted	28	1.58	0.24	0.10	0.80	1.00	3.72
			32	1.62	0.28	0.10	0.80	1.00	3.80
			36	1.70	0.33	0.11	0.80	1.00	3.94
			40	1.82	0.39	0.12	0.80	1.00	4.13
			44	2.01	0.47	0.14	0.80	1.00	4.42
Two-lane	Pavement in good condition	Free	32	1.62	0.21	0.10	0.80	1.00	3.73
			36	1.67	0.26	0.10	0.80	1.00	3.83
			40	1.75	0.32	0.12	0.80	1.00	3.99
			44	1.85	0.40	0.14	0.80	1.00	4.19
			48	1.99	0.50	0.16	0.80	1.00	4.45
			52	2.20	0.63	0.19	0.80	1.00	4.82
			56	2.55	0.75	0.25	0.80	1.00	5.35
			60	3.19	0.84	0.35	0.80	1.00	6.18
		Normal	28	1.58	0.19	0.10	0.80	1.00	3.67
			32	1.62	0.23	0.10	0.80	1.00	3.75
			36	1.70	0.29	0.11	0.80	1.00	3.90
			40	1.82	0.36	0.12	0.80	1.00	4.10
			44	2.01	0.45	0.14	0.80	1.00	4.40
			48	2.37	0.56	0.16	0.80	1.00	4.89
		Restricted	20	1.60	0.18	0.09	0.80	1.00	3.67
			24	1.58	0.21	0.09	0.80	1.00	3.68
			28	1.59	0.24	0.10	0.80	1.00	3.73
			32	1.64	0.29	0.10	0.80	1.00	3.83
			36	1.75	0.36	0.11	0.80	1.00	4.02
			40	1.99	0.45	0.12	0.80	1.00	4.36
	Loose surface in good condition		20	1.81	0.44	0.12	1.20	1.00	4.57
			24	1.78	0.50	0.12	1.20	1.00	4.60
			28	1.78	0.57	0.13	1.20	1.00	4.68
			32	1.84	0.65	0.14	1.20	1.00	4.83
			36	1.93	0.75	0.15	1.20	1.00	5.03
			40	2.09	0.87	0.17	1.20	1.00	5.33
			44	2.35	1.01	0.19	1.20	1.00	5.75
	Unsurfaced		16	2.36	0.53	0.17	1.60	1.00	5.66
			20	2.24	0.61	0.18	1.60	1.00	5.63
			24	2.20	0.71	0.18	1.60	1.00	5.69
			28	2.20	0.82	0.19	1.60	1.00	5.81
			32	2.29	0.96	0.20	1.60	1.00	6.05
			36	2.44	1.07	0.21	1.60	1.00	6.32

because more gasoline per mile is consumed at higher speeds.[6] By making use
of speed-distribution curves (see Fig. 5, page 147) this correction can be made.
However, the costs developed in this chapter do not include this refinement.

Grades also affect fuel consumption. Different studies have reached
different conclusions, but all showed greater fuel use on upgrades and
smaller consumption on downgrades than for operation on level roads.
The AASHO committee applied percentage corrections to the values

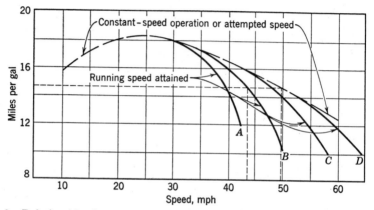

Fig. 2. Relationships between attempted speed, running speed, and gasoline consumption for an assumed average passenger car operating on a rural, level, paved
highway

Curve *A*. Restricted 2-lane highway
Curve *B*. Normal 2-lane or restricted divided highway
Curve *C*. Free 2-lane or normal divided highway
Curve *D*. Free divided highway

found for level roads to obtain the values shown in Fig. 1. Surface
type has marked effect on fuel consumption. For smooth paved surfaces, regardless of type, there appears to be little difference. Compared with smooth pavements, loose surfaces such as untreated gravel
lower performance by about 2 miles per gallon; for unsurfaced roads
this difference is in the range of 5 miles per gallon. These are average
values and were used by the committee in computing Table 1.

Curvature has little effect on fuel consumption, providing the road
is properly superelevated. Where proper superelevation is lacking,
side friction is called upon to keep the vehicle in its curved path, and

[6] This greater gasoline consumption is caused largely by increased air resistance.
At 25 mph one-third of the tractive effort is consumed by air resistance; at 55
mph air resistance accounts for 70% of the total.

fuel consumption increases. After considering the results of several studies, the committee adopted the rule that "the percent excess of fuel required on curves is considered directly proportional and numerically equal to the (side) friction factor developed" (see Table 2).

TABLE 2. FUEL USE AND TIRE WEAR ON CURVES WITH INSUFFICIENT
SUPERELEVATION COMPARED WITH TANGENT OPERATION

Coefficient of Side Friction	Fuel Use as % of That on Tangent Roadways	Tire Wear as % of That on Tangent Roadways
0	100	100
0.05	105	160
0.10	110	220
0.15	115	300
0.20	120	390

Oil consumption

The influence of roadway design upon oil consumption is difficult to isolate. Data have been accumulated to prove that oil consumption increases with speed and that progressively more oil is used as the roadway changes from pavement to loose gravel to unsurfaced. Test results, as adjusted to recognize the difference between new test vehicles and the average vehicle, and converted to money using a price of 30 cents per quart, are given in Table 1. No data have been gathered on other possible variables like the use of filters and frequency of oil change.

Tire costs

Test results show that tire wear is influenced by type of surface, speed, grade, curvature, and type of operation, whether free, normal, or restricted. Tire care also is important. Attention to inflation, tire rotation, wheel balance, overload control, and other careful maintenance practices employed in testing operations prevent damage which often occurs under normal conditions. Figure 3 shows estimated average tire-life mileages for operation on level, straight highways.[7]

[7] In converting test results to average tire life, it was first assumed that tires would normally be replaced when 85% of the tread was gone, the wear permitted on the test tires being considered as 100%. Then the rate of wear for ordinary vehicle operation was assumed as 125% of that found on the test vehicles, in recognition of the fact that the average driver does not use all possible measures to prolong tire life. Finally, the rate of wear was increased another 20% to recognize that "average wear" is greater than that on a vehicle traveling at

Highway Economy

Variables recognized are running speed and type of surface. Notice that tire wear increases sharply with increasing speed; for example, the wear on pavement at 53 mph is three times that at 33 mph. Mileages from Fig. 3 applied to a set of four tires costing $100 total were employed to obtain the tire costs given in Table 1 for "normal" operation on two-lane highways. These figures were decreased by 10% to obtain the costs for "free" operation and increased by 25% for "restricted" operation.

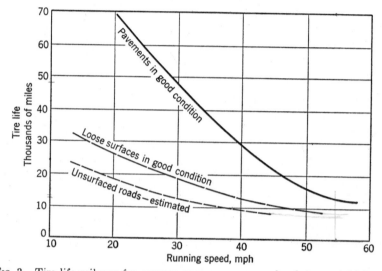

Fɪɢ. 3.   Tire-life mileage for average passenger cars on level, tangent highways

Grades influence tire wear. Little research has been conducted, but it is logical that increased driving and braking forces will increase wear. On the basis of limited test data, the AASHO committee assumed that, compared with operation on relatively level pavements, wear would be increased 15% in the 3 to 5% grade range, 50% in the 5 to 7% range, and 100% in the 7 to 9% range.

Driving around curves that are not properly superelevated increases tire wear and tire costs. Wear is related to the coefficient of side friction that must be developed to keep the vehicle traveling in a circular path.[8] Table 2 relates tire wear on curves with insufficient superelevation to that on tangent roadway.

average speed, because of the excessive wear on the tires of vehicles traveling at high speeds.

[8] See p. 183 for method for computing coefficient of side friction.

Vehicle repair and maintenance

Costs of vehicle repair and maintenance decreased almost continuously until 1939. Studies made at that time placed them at 0.6 cent per vehicle-mile on concrete pavements and 0.9 on gravel roads, both in rural areas. No figures were available for operation on unsurfaced roads. No data have been developed since that time. However, costs of both labor and parts have increased; the change assumed by the committee was one-third of the 1939 figures. For operation on pavement, then, the repair and maintenance cost was set at 0.8 cent per vehicle-mile; on loose surfaces it rose to 1.20 cents. Cost of operation on unsurfaced roads was arbitrarily set at 1.60 cents per vehicle-mile. No variation for different operating conditions was recognized.[9]

Depreciation

Depreciation has been defined as "the inevitable march to the junk heap." One part of depreciation is attributable to wearing out and might be assigned as a mileage cost, at so much a mile. The remainder which is attributable to obsolescence or being inadequate or out of date might be assigned to age at so much a year. In any event, such assignments are arbitrary. They are complicated by the variation in annual mileage driven, which for passenger cars ranges from 100,000 or more to almost none. The committee in assigning depreciation allocated one-half to mileage and one-half to time.[10] Further, it assumed that the average vehicle runs 100,000 miles at 10,000 miles per year; thus its life is 10 years. First cost was set at $2000; salvage value is neglected. From this, the depreciation assigned per mile of driving becomes 1.00 cent.

In making economy studies for road improvement, only the mileage portion of depreciation is charged against each alternative. The time portion may be omitted from the calculation, as it is the same for all conditions. If cost studies are for alternative routes of equal length, mileage charges also will be the same for each alternative and will not affect the results at all. They will be a factor, however, when designs requiring different travel distances are being compared.

[9] See, however, the section on Costs of Stops.

[10] For trucks, all depreciation is often charged to mileage. It is argued that annual truck mileage is high and that the vehicles usually will be completely worn out before major improvements in design or marked changes in first cost occur. Strictly speaking, this assumption would be true only if the resale value of a new and unused truck would remain constant for the full assumed life.

Table 1 presents a summary of the increment costs of passenger-vehicle operation on rural roads of 0 to 3% grade, as developed by the AASHO committee. Figure 4 presents like data in graphical form for two-lane rural paved roads, including those for 3 to 7% grades.

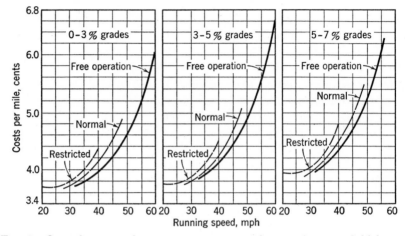

Fɪɢ. 4. Operating costs for passenger cars on 2-lane tangent rural highways. Value of time not included

Time saving

Road improvement almost always results in reduced travel time. For trucks, buses, and other commercial vehicles, reduced travel time in turn often means savings in wages of drivers and helpers. In some cases hourly ownership costs of the vehicles also may be a factor. These same conditions apply for passenger vehicles used for business purposes by salesmen and others. There is general agreement that these savings should be included in computing the benefits of road improvements. The most serious difficulty is assigning the proper money value to them.

The greater part of private passenger-car use also is devoted to necessity travel like trips for business, to work, and for family services.[11] Without question, drivers and passengers would pay something if time devoted to these purposes could be made available for business, pleasure, or rest. However, there is no direct economic

[11] Traffic surveys in 15 cities found that 56% of all passenger automobile trips were for work or business purposes, 28% for personal or family services, and 16% for social-recreational uses. From *Traffic Engineering Handbook,* 2d edition, p. 44 (1950).

measure of its worth. Some economists would not consider this time saving as a tangible benefit at all, but would class it as an intangible which argues in favor of highway improvement. Others have attempted to measure its value in terms of the costs of driving extra distances in order to save time. The AASHO committee adopted

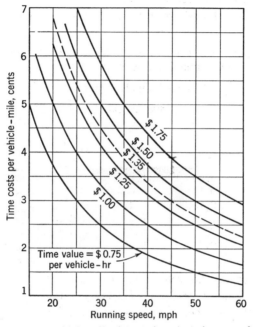

Fig. 5. Time costs per vehicle-mile for various running speeds and costs per vehicle-hour

$1.35 per vehicle-hour as representing the current opinion for "a logical and practical value" for all passenger vehicles. This represents 75 cents per person per hour because the typical passenger car has 1.8 persons in it. Engineers, when making highway economy studies, must remember that the value for time savings is not exact; in fact, it is an approximation based only on informed opinion.

Time savings per vehicle-mile for speeds up to 60 mph and for vehicle-hour savings between $0.75 and $1.75 per hour are shown in Fig. 5.

Stopping costs

It costs money to stop and start an automobile. The costs of fuel, wear on tires and brakes, and other operating items like oil consumption and repair and maintenance are higher for stopping and starting than for normal operation. Based on data available to it, the committee has established *additional* operating costs per stop for various approach speeds. These are given in Table 3. Then, too, cost con-

TABLE 3. ADDITIONAL COST OF A PASSENGER-CAR STOP OVER THAT OF CONTINUED OPERATION AT A GIVEN SPEED

Time Value Not Included

Additional Cost per Stop, Cents

Approach Speed, Mph	Fuel	Tires and Brakes	Other Operating Costs	Total Operating Costs
10	0.05	0.02	0.04	0.11
20	0.12	0.06	0.09	0.27
30	0.18	0.13	0.16	0.47
40	0.24	0.26	0.25	0.75
50	0.39	0.48	0.44	1.31
60	0.48	0.64	0.56	1.68

tinues to mount as the vehicle stands waiting for a traffic light to change or for some other cause of delay to dissipate. This cost was set at 0.006 cent per second of waiting. Total costs per stop (exclusive of time costs) for various approach speeds and for delays up to 1 min are shown in Fig. 6.

Stopping takes additional time compared with operation at constant speed. The vehicle must be decelerated to a stop and then accelerated to its original speed again. In addition, there is usually a standing interval between stopping and starting. Time losses for stopping and regaining speed as measured by the Oregon Highway Department were adopted by the AASHO committee.[12] These were:

Approach speed, mph	10	20	30	40	50	60
Time losses per stop, sec	0.5	2	5	9	15	21

[12] See The Effect of Surface Type, Alignment and Traffic Congestion on Vehicular Fuel Consumption, *Oregon State Highway Department Technical Bulletin 17*, p. 173 (1944).

The money equivalent of stopping and starting time losses for several assumptions of the worth of vehicle time appear in Fig. 7. Similar values for time losses for standing vehicles appear as Fig. 8.

To find the total cost of a single vehicle stop, the sum of the ordinates of Figs. 6, 7, and 8 must be taken. For example, assume that a vehicle approaching an intersection at 50 mph is stopped by a traffic light. It stands 30 sec and then resumes full speed again. The time value of a vehicle-hour is taken as $1.35. Then the cost of the stop, over and above that of driving straight through the intersection at 50 mph equals 1.5 cents (Fig. 6) plus 0.6 cent (Fig. 7) plus 1.1 cents (Fig. 8), a total of 3.2 cents.

Driver comfort and convenience

Origin and destination surveys have shown that many drivers choose routes along freeways and expressways in preference to those along conventional highways or streets, even though over-all distances are much longer and travel times greater on the former. Also, many drivers are willing to use toll roads, even though they can reach their destinations in fewer miles and with little time difference on a free but congested route. Thus, there is substantial evidence that drivers place a money value on the comfort and convenience provided by modern highway facilities.

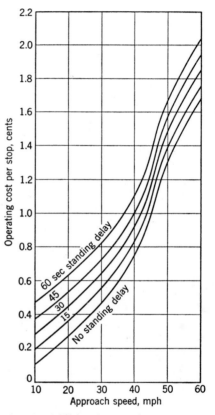

FIG. 6. Additional operating costs per stop for passenger cars. Time costs not included

Highway economists agree that improved comfort and convenience is an economic benefit. However, they do not agree on how it should be treated in economy studies. One approach is to state degrees of discomfort and inconvenience in monetary terms. These charges are then counted as another cost of vehicle operation. The other viewpoint is that improved comfort and convenience is an intangible benefit favoring highway improvement, and that, as such, it cannot be stated in dollars and cents.

The AASHO committee adopted the first approach. For restricted operation, operating costs were increased by 1.0 cent per vehicle-mile

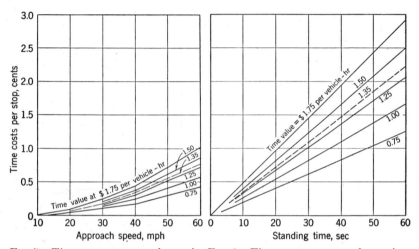

FIG. 7. Time costs per stop for various approach speeds and costs per vehicle-hour

FIG. 8. Time costs per stop for various standing delay times and costs per vehicle-hour

to allow for discomfort and inconvenience. For normal operation, the charge was 0.5 cent per vehicle-mile. For loose, unpaved surfaces, the figure was 0.75 cent per vehicle-mile. No cost assignment was made against free operation. In discussing the assigned values, the report stated that "positive identification of values for assignment to various degrees of comfort and convenience is not possible. Rather than omit the factor altogether, assumed comfort and convenience values are included."

Values for discomfort and inconvenience were purposely omitted from the listing of operating costs shown in Table 1. As indicated above, there is debate as to whether or not they should be included at all. Furthermore, comfort and convenience are far less finite and measurable than the other vehicle operating costs, and for this reason should be kept entirely separate.

Cost of truck and bus operation

Trucks constitute a growing percentage of the vehicles using our roads, and, consequently, the cost of truck operation is assuming increasing importance in economy studies for highways. The AASHO committee after examining all available data adopted the ratios of Table 4 to express truck and bus costs in terms of passenger-car costs.

TABLE 4. RATIO OF OPERATING COSTS OF TRUCKS TO OPERATING COSTS OF PASSENGER CARS

Type of Vehicle	Approximate % of Total on Main Highways	Ratio to Operating Costs of Passenger Cars
Single-unit trucks	70	2 to 4
Truck combinations	29	4 to 6
Buses	1	2 to 4
U.S.A. composite	100	2.5 to 4.5

The committee indicated a range of values rather than fixed ratios because size and weight characteristics vary widely between sections of the country.[13]

It was found in Arizona in 1947 that for "pickup" and "panel" trucks the mileage costs were 3.9 cents per vehicle-mile. Adding $2 per hour for time costs while the vehicle was in operation at 30 mph gave a total of 10.6 cents per vehicle-mile. For light trucks, mileage costs were 8.8 cents, and time costs at 30 mph were 6.7 cents, a total of 15.5 cents per vehicle-mile. Records of a fleet of "heavy" trucks of 40,000 lb gross weight gave mileage costs (including 100% of depreciation) of 20.5 cents per mile. Adding time costs of 7.3 cents per vehicle-mile (at 30 mph) gave a total of 27.8 cents per vehicle-mile.

Extensive cooperative tests on the costs of truck operation were begun in 1948 by the Bureau of Public Roads, the AASHO, the Highway Research Board, the American Trucking Association, and other organizations. Test vehicles ranged in weight from 20,000 to 139,500 lb. Test locations were the Pennsylvania Turnpike, 148.7 miles between the Carlisle and New Stanton interchanges designed to high standards, and U. S. Highways 11 and 30 from Carlisle to Greensburg, 149.8 miles of various types. Findings of these tests are partially reported in Time and Gasoline Consumption in Motor Truck Operation as Affected by the Weight and Power of Vehicles and the Rise and Fall in Highways, *Highway Research Report 9-A* (1950). This report does not give complete costs like those presented in Table 1 for passenger cars. Two findings, however, are particularly significant. First, it was proved that gasoline consumption is definitely related to the gross weight of the vehicle and

[13] The California Division of Highways uses 10 cents per minute ($6 per hour) for operating costs and 5 cents per minute ($3 per hour) for the value of time.

travel time to the weight-power ratio. Second, it was established that gasoline consumption and travel time vary in a definite manner with the *rate* of rise and fall, regardless of the length of section or the number and steepness of individual grades. This finding makes it possible to apply the results to entire sections of highway without considering individual grades separately. The results, presented in a number of tables and charts, can be applied to gasoline-powered commercial vehicles in any part of the country.

Motor-vehicle costs in urban areas

The AASHO committee suggested that, in the interim until more exact data were available, vehicle-operating costs in urban areas be based on their findings for rural areas, modified where necessary. For major streets and expressways where traffic flow is reasonably continuous the same cost data will apply directly. On major streets where traffic flow is not continuous but has only a moderate amount of interruption, the costs given should be increased by 10 to 30%. With stop-and-go operation, special field investigation is required to determine conditions and values to use.

Summary of motor-vehicle operating costs

To find the operating costs on a particular road or street, traffic counts and vehicle speeds must be determined by field observation on the existing facility. Future traffic volumes and speeds on both existing and new facilities must be estimated. Lengths, grades, and other physical characteristics will be taken from preliminary or construction plans. Then, using data from the figures and tables, money values may be obtained.

Results of such cost studies are far from exact. Some of the figures represent approximations. Others, like the assignment of depreciation between wearing out and obsolescence and the value of time saving, have been set arbitrarily. However, savings in motor-vehicle operating costs are tangible and real. If highway planning and design are to be placed on a scientific basis, these benefits must be considered in justifying highway expenditures.

ACCIDENT COSTS [14]

The tremendous toll of motor-vehicle accidents not only causes much suffering and misery but in addition is a waste of our resources. For 1952, the National Safety Council set this loss at $3.6 billion

[14] Further discussion of highway accidents and the efforts now under way to decrease them appear in Chapter 11.

which was roughly three-fourths of the expenditure in that year for constructing, maintaining, and operating our entire highway system. This sum includes loss of services for that year and later years because of death and disablement, medical expenses, property damage, and the overhead costs of insurance.

One method proposed by the National Safety Council for computing accident costs involves multiplying the number of traffic deaths by a round sum which represents the cost of 1 death, 35 personal injuries, and 225 property-damage accidents—the average ratio of occurrence for these types. The sum used before 1941 was $45,000, by 1946 it had increased to $65,000, and in 1952 it had become $95,000. A second method is suggested where the number of deaths is less than 10 or the ratio of deaths to injuries varies from those stated above. Losses from deaths alone are set as follows:

	Cost per Person	
Age	Male	Female
0–14	$18,000	$12,000
15–55	32,000	20,000
56 and older	6,700	5,400
Average for all ages and both sexes	$21,800	

Personal injuries are counted at $950 each and property-damage accidents, excluding those costing less than $25, at $180 each. Either method must be used with caution.

Benefits resulting from accident reduction when a substandard facility is replaced with one of modern design are difficult to evaluate. Usually the saving is large, but this is not always so. There are instances where, probably because of excessive speeds and driver inattention on the new road, modern facilities have records as poor as their predecessors. Only with much more knowledge about the driver and his characteristics and with careful, uniform, and complete reporting of accidents will precise evaluation and assignment of accident costs become possible.

The evidence is conclusive, however, that accidents are greatly reduced when traffic is transferred from heavily traveled highways and streets of conventional design to properly designed freeways. For example, the fatality rate on the Merritt Parkway in Connecticut was about 40% of that on the parallel Boston Post Road. On the Arroyo

Seco Parkway between Los Angeles and Pasadena, Calif., it was only 24% of that for all rural roads in California.[15]

Actual savings through improved design may be illustrated by an example. In 1949, an 8.8-mile section of the four-lane, undivided Bayshore Highway approaching San Francisco from the south was replaced by a six-lane freeway of advanced design. During a one-year period on the old highway there were 13 fatalities; on the freeway there was none. Total reported accidents were 10 times greater on the old than the new. If we use the first method cited above for computing accident costs and the 1952 cost per fatal accident, annual savings from construction of the freeway were 13 × $95,000 or $1,230,-000. This is $140,000 per mile, or about 12% of the total cost per mile of the completed facility including rights of way.

SECONDARY BENEFITS OF HIGHWAY IMPROVEMENT

Reduced vehicle operating costs resulting from highway improvement are sometimes called *primary* benefits. Other gains from this source, accruing either to individuals or to the public in general, might then be classed as *secondary* benefits. A listing of secondary benefits would include the following, among others:

1. Increased land values. For example, farmland increases in value when good roads make it more accessible to markets. Again, land in areas penetrated by freeways and expressways is often put to higher use, as when farmland becomes residential or industrial property.

2. Increased business activity. To illustrate, it has been found repeatedly that business improves when bypasses take through traffic from city streets.

3. Decreased commodity costs brought by cheaper transportation.

4. Increased value of natural resources. For example, new roads through forest areas may make timber accessible so that it can be logged and marketed, where before it was valueless.

5. Development of recreational values such as sightseeing, camping, hunting, fishing, and sports.

6. Improvements in or lowered costs of public services. These would include better police and fire protection, readily accessible medical care, and consolidation of schools.

7. Improved mobility of defense forces.

[15] See also Table 2, p. 289.

As yet, highway economists have given only limited attention to secondary benefits. Few attempts have been made to evaluate them in money terms or to include them in economy studies. It is to be expected, however, that the subject will be given increasing attention in the future.

When proposed highway improvements are not justifiable on primary benefits alone and secondary benefits are employed to justify the improvements, considerable caution must be exercised in making the monetary evaluation. For example, highways, as such, may not cause an over-all increase in land values or business activity. The improved situation along new roads may be offset or more than offset by depressed land values or reduced business activity at other locations. Only when the improvement brings an over-all economic gain can it properly be included in an economy study. Again, care must be taken to avoid "double counting," which is counting the same benefit in two or more different forms. To illustrate, it is quite probable that lowered vehicle operating costs on an improved road will result in lower prices of goods hauled over the road to retail outlets in the area. Either the reduced operating costs or lowered prices can be taken as a fair measure of the economic gain, but if both are included the same benefit has been counted twice.

COSTS OF HIGHWAYS

Annual cost computations

The total first cost for improving a section of highway includes engineering and design expenditures, the outlay for acquiring rights of way, and the costs of constructing roadway, structures, and pavements. For the purposes of economy studies, these first costs are assigned as annual charges over assumed useful lives. To them are added annual expenditures for maintenance to find the total annual cost. Assumptions for first costs and annual maintenance charges for a section of road are developed from cost data available in the records of most highway agencies. The useful lives of the various elements that make up a highway have been and continue to be the subject of intensive research. Selection of interest rates for converting first costs into annual charges is a source of continuing disagreement.

The first cost of a capital improvement is converted into annual costs by the formula

$$R = P\left[\frac{i(1 + i)^n}{(1 + i)^n - 1}\right] \tag{1}$$

where i = the interest rate per interest period.

n = the number of interest periods.

P = a present sum of money, in this case the first cost of any particular element of road improvement.

R = the end of period payment in a uniform series continuing for the coming n periods, the entire series equivalent to P at interest rate i.

For assigned values of i and n, the conversion factor $\dfrac{i(1 + i)^n}{(1 + i)^n - 1}$ is constant. It is called the *capital recovery factor (CRF)*. Capital recovery factors appropriate for the solution of highway engineering problems are given in Table 5.

TABLE 5. CAPITAL RECOVERY FACTORS (CRF) FOR VARIOUS LIVES AND INTEREST RATES

Life, Years				Interest Rate				
	0%	2%	3%	4%	5%	6%	8%	10%
5	0.20000	0.21216	0.21835	0.22463	0.23097	0.23740	0.25046	0.26380
10	0.10000	0.11133	0.11723	0.12329	0.12950	0.13587	0.14903	0.16275
15	0.06667	0.07783	0.08377	0.08994	0.09634	0.10296	0.11683	0.13147
20	0.05000	0.06116	0.06722	0.07358	0.08024	0.08718	0.10185	0.11746
25	0.04000	0.05122	0.05743	0.06401	0.07095	0.07823	0.09368	0.11017
30	0.03333	0.04465	0.05102	0.05783	0.06505	0.07265	0.08883	0.10608
35	0.02857	0.04000	0.04654	0.05358	0.06107	0.06897	0.08580	0.10369
40	0.02500	0.03656	0.04326	0.05052	0.05828	0.06646	0.08386	0.10226
50	0.02000	0.03182	0.03887	0.04655	0.05478	0.06344	0.08174	0.10086
60	0.01667	0.02877	0.03613	0.04420	0.05283	0.06188	0.08080	0.10033
80	0.01250	0.02516	0.03311	0.04181	0.05103	0.06057	0.08017	0.10005
100	0.01000	0.02320	0.03165	0.04081	0.05038	0.06018	0.08004	0.10001

The total annual cost of a particular capital improvement is the sum of the annual costs for all new elements, computed by the method indicated above. It is incorrect to include any charge for earlier investments in an existing road, however. These are referred to as *sunk costs* because none of them can be recovered by any present or future action. Of course the cost of resurfacing an existing road to make it serviceable is an appropriate charge against that alternative. Likewise, if money can be realized by selling some element of the existing road such as the right of way, the effect is to reduce the cost of the new road, and appropriate credit should be taken for it.

In some engineering economy problems, an allowance is made for salvage value at some future date. The deduction from annual costs to recognize salvage value is found by multiplying the salvage value by the *sinking-fund deposit factor,* which is the difference between the capital recovery factor and the interest rate. Salvage values are seldom considered in highway economy studies.

There is an approximate method for computing annual costs without using interest tables. This method understates the true annual cost, the understatement increasing with interest rate or assumed life. Because the lives used for highway economy studies are comparatively long, the approximate method is usually not suited to highway problems.[16]

Road-life studies

Road-life studies were begun about 1935 in several states and to date have been mainly devoted to determining the useful lives of the various highway surfaces. To set up tables of life expectancy for all kinds of highways in various environments will be a long and difficult program. There are many variables such as soil, climate, topography, and traffic volume that will affect the life of essentially the same type of highway in different places. In flat country the alinement may remain unchanged for many years. On the other hand, a paved mountain road originally built on cheap crooked alinement often becomes obsolete for the increased volume and speed of traffic and is relocated before the life of the pavement is reached. Also, the art of highway building changes so that the date of construction will influence the probable life of a new highway of given type. For practical purposes, however, there are increasing amounts of data on the useful life of the various elements of a highway. A typical life expectancy or *survivor* curve [17] is shown in Fig. 9. This graph illustrates the method employed to determine, for each surface type, the average life of the mileage built in a particular year. The solid-line curve is plotted from data on actual pavement retirements. The dotted-line curve is one of a family of 18 survivor curves and was

[16] For a more detailed presentation of the techniques for economy studies. refer to E. L. Grant, *Principles of Engineering Economy,* 3d edition, Ronald Press (1950); H. G. Thuesen, *Engineering Economy,* Prentice-Hall (1950); or B. M. Woods and E. P. DeGarmo, *Introduction to Engineering Economy,* The Macmillan Co. (1953).

[17] Similar curves are used by life insurance companies for estimating the expected lives of policy holders so that premiums can be set. They are likewise employed in industry, for example, by the Bell Telephone System.

selected because it afforded the best fit. A pavement is classed as
retired when it is resurfaced or reconstructed or the road is abandoned
or reverts to a lower type. The average life is determined by dividing the area under the type curve by 100.

The Bureau of Public Roads has made continuous studies of road
life. Basic data (1948) cover 249,000 miles and the period Jan. 1,

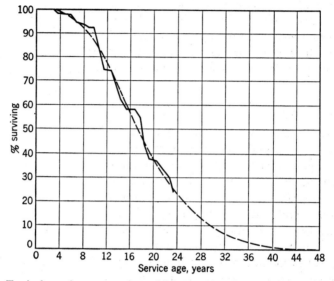

Fɪɢ. 9. Typical survivor curve for a highway pavement. Bituminous concrete,
sheet asphalt, or rock asphalt on gravel or stone base. Year of construction 1923;
retirements to January 1, 1947; type of survivor curve *L2*; estimated average
life, 18.5 years

1900, to Jan. 1, 1946, for eight types of surfaces. The later practice
is to group surfaces into three types: low, intermediate, and high.
From analysis of data from 16 states 64% of the surfaced mileage
existing in 1946 will be worn out by 1956. Of the low-type group (soil
surface and gravel) only 6% will remain in service; of the intermediate types (bituminous-surface treated and mixed bituminous)
26%; and of the high types (bituminous penetration, bituminous concrete, Portland-cement concrete, and brick or block) 56%. These
percentages indicate the magnitude of the pavement-replacement
problem with which the state highway departments are faced. Probable lives of these road types [18] range as follows: low 10 to 15 years,
intermediate 14 to 22, high 23 to 26.

[18] See Life Characteristics of Highway Surfaces by Fred B. Farrell and Henry

Rights of way, grading, and major structures of modern highways should be subject to very little depreciation or obsolescence, so that the assumption of long lives for them appears warranted. However, pavements need major repairs or replacement at intervals, and shorter lives appear in order for them. In a report to Congress in 1939, by the Public Roads Administration,[19] the life for rights of way was set at 100 years, for grading and structures at 40 years, and for pavements at 30 years. The AASHO committee in its study reduced pavement life to conform to the findings outlined in the preceding paragraph, but retained the other lives employed in the earlier study.

After the assumptions regarding the lives of the various elements of the roadway have been made, the annual capital recovery charge for each element is computed separately, and their sum is the annual cost of the total.[20]

Theoretically the best highway management would require a "set of books" that annually would disclose the financial or economic position of any route in any part or subdivision of a state system or systems. The annual depreciation and expected life would be of record as well as other items of cost such as maintenance and operation. With such data at hand, planning and budgeting for pavement and like replacements could be done for several years in advance. Earnings (user revenue) for the accrued vehicle-miles would also appear.

Interest as a cost

Engineers are in disagreement regarding the interest rate to be used for highway economy studies. Three different viewpoints are advocated: [21]

1. Interest should not be charged at all, except where road improvements are actually financed by borrowing. In these situations, the rate should be the cost of borrowed money.

R. Paterick in *Proceedings Highway Research Board*, pp. 40–52 (1948). A previous article by Robley Winfrey and Farrell was published in the 1940 *Proceedings* and in *Public Roads*, March 1941, pp. 1–24.

[19] *Toll Roads and Free Roads*, House Document 272, 76th Congress, 1st Session.

[20] Some engineers compute annual cost by using the weighted life of all elements of the highway. This procedure is correct only if interest tables are employed in computing the weighted life. If a simple weighted life is made the basis of computation, the resulting annual cost will be lower than is correct.

[21] It is beyond the scope of this book to offer in detail the arguments favoring each viewpoint. To present them only briefly would be unwise.

2. Interest should be charged at the current rate at which a particular highway agency could borrow money. The charge is included even though road improvements are financed from current income.

3. Interest should be charged at a rate representing the *minimum attractive return*. This would be somewhat higher than the cost of borrowed money. The rate would be set for each agency after representative projects which promise the best use of (usually) limited highway funds were analyzed. In any event, the rate of return would be high enough to discourage investments that do not appear attractive in the light of future uncertainties.

The decision regarding interest rates has a tremendous influence on the results of economy studies. Assume, for example, that interest rates of 0, 3, and 6%, respectively, are appropriate for the three viewpoints and that the proposal under study has a first cost of $1000 and an estimated life of 30 years. Then the annual return needed to recover the $1000 in 30 years, using interest at 0%, will be $33.33; at 3%, $51.02; and, at 6%, $72.65 (see Table 5).

The second of the three viewpoints outlined above was adopted by the AASHO committee. Several interest rates, generally around 2 to 3%, were used in their illustrative examples.[22] The third point of view comes closer to that found in private enterprise. The minimum attractive rate of return would be high enough to include a charge for the use of the invested funds and a safety factor to reflect the risk involved in even the best estimates. The actual rate might be set at a somewhat higher level where funds are limited and there are many opportunities for investment.[23]

The inclusion of interest as a cost decreases the importance of the probable life adopted for the economy study. To illustrate: at 0% interest the annual cost doubles if the assumed life is reduced from 100 to 50 years. At 3%, however, the annual cost increases by only 22% with this change in assumption; and at 6% the increase is but 6%.

One of the reasons for the argument about interest rates is the very natural tendency to confuse economy studies with budgetary and fiscal problems. The purpose of economy studies is to predetermine which of the many possible uses of highway funds are best. Budgetary and fiscal activities relate to the actual allocation of funds and to accounting for them when spent.

[22] Federal agencies operating in the field of river-basin development generally use an interest rate of 2½% in computing costs for benefit-cost ratio studies.

[23] This is presented more fully in Grant, *Principles of Engineering Economy*, 3d edition, pp. 505–508.

PROCEDURES FOR ECONOMY STUDIES

An economy study must first answer the question: "Why do it at all?" In other words, does the proposed improvement represent an attractive investment when compared with other possible uses of available funds? Where there is only one plan for a particular improvement, a favorable answer clearly indicates that the project is desirable. However, where there are alternative methods for improvement, a second question is in order. It is "Why do it this way?" or "Which of the proposals is the best?" This is answered by finding whether or not the *increment* of investment between cheaper and more expensive plans also appears attractive. By successively eliminating those proposals that fail either the first or the second of these tests, the best of the lot may be found.

Textbooks in engineering economy usually present three alternative procedures for making economy studies. These are an annual cost comparison, a comparison of the present worth of all present and future expenditures, and a determination of the interest rate at which the alternatives are equally attractive. Many engineers in the public works field favor another: the benefit-cost ratio, often called the benefit ratio. For most situations the results of any of the four, properly interpreted, lead to sound economic decisions.

The succeeding paragraphs present brief discussions of three of these methods. One example problem is also included.

Annual-cost method

As already indicated, the annual cost of an element of capital improvement is found by multiplying its first cost by the appropriate capital recovery factor (given in Table 5). The amount so found, if charged at the end of each year for the assumed life span, will exactly repay the initial investment—with interest. The total annual cost of a particular improvement is the sum of all the annual costs of capital recovery plus annual maintenance and user costs. Annual costs are computed for the existing facility and for each of the proposals for improvement. Other things being equal, that alternative which has the smallest total annual cost is the best choice. A typical solution by the annual cost method appears on page 69.

Except for the depression and World War II years, the number of vehicles on most roads has increased steadily, and predictions are that the trend will continue. If an analysis indicates that traffic on a proposed project will increase with time, this increase should be recognized in the economy study. An approximate method is to compute annual user costs on the basis of the average annual traffic. Generally this assumption results in an overstatement of annual user costs. However, an exact value for uniform annual user costs may be gained by using an *equivalent annual traffic volume* and computing annual user costs based on it. The formula is

$$\text{Equivalent annual traffic volume} = a + b + \frac{b}{i} - \frac{nb}{i}(CRF - i) \quad (2)$$

where a = the present annual traffic volume.

b = the annual numerical traffic increase.

CRF = capital recovery factor for n years at interest rate i.

Results of solutions by the annual-cost method are markedly affected by interest rate. Low interest rates favor those alternatives that combine large capital investments with low maintenance or user costs whereas high interest rates favor reverse combinations.

One use of economy studies is to establish priorities among projects. For this purpose the adopted interest rate should be near that earned by the most badly needed improvements, for then it will be more clearly indicative of the proper choice.

Rate-of-return method

The rate-of-return method involves finding the interest rate at which two alternative solutions to an economy problem have equal annual costs. The first step is to find the rate of return on each proposed investment as compared with the solution that requires the least capital outlay, which often is the status quo. Those plans that fail to show the minimum attractive return on the total proposed investment are discarded as they fail the test "Why do it at all?" Next the rate of return is computed on the *increase* in investment between proposals having successively higher first costs. Any proposal that fails to show the minimum attractive return as compared with the next lower is eliminated from the series before the rate of return on the next increment is computed. This is to answer "Why do it this way?" The alternative of highest first cost that offers more than the minimum attractive return on both total and increment investments is the best from an economy standpoint. A typical rate-of-return solution is included in the example on page 70.

In economy studies for highways, there is definite advantage to the rate-of-return method. The total cost of badly needed road improvements almost always greatly exceeds the funds available. If the rates of return for all proposed projects are known, a firm basis for priority of improvement can be established. From these same results the attractive rate of return for a highway system can be found for use in comparing alternative solutions to particular highway problems. Finally, a rate-of-return solution completely avoids all disagreement over interest rates.

Some engineers object to the rate-of-return method because answers can be found only by trial-and-error solution whereas by other methods the answers can be worked out directly. Admittedly, trial-and-error methods take more time. However, most of the effort required for economy studies goes to collecting data and making estimates on traffic and costs; little goes to compound interest calculations. Thus the extra time is still but a small fraction of the total and is amply justified if the results are in more usable form.

Benefit-cost ratio method

The benefit-cost method, currently favored by many highway engineers and others in the public works field, expresses the comparative worth of projects by the ratio of annual benefits to annual costs.[24] The benefit-cost ratio is expressed by the equation

$$\text{Benefit-cost ratio} = \frac{\text{annual benefits from improvement}}{\text{annual costs of improvement}} = \frac{R - R_1}{H_1 - H} \quad (3)$$

where R = the total annual road-user cost for the basic condition or existing road, or for that alternative of lower first cost.

R_1 = the total annual road-user cost for a proposed improvement, or for that alternative of higher first cost.

H = the total annual highway cost for the basic condition or existing road, or for that alternative of lower first cost.

H_1 = the total annual highway cost for a proposed improvement, or for that alternative of higher first cost.

[24] In the Flood Control Act of June 1936 Congress specified that benefits from proposed flood-control projects to whomsoever they accrue should be in excess of estimated costs. This resulted in Federal agencies dealing with river-basin

The procedure for a benefit-cost economy study, like that for a "rate-of-return" solution, involves two sets of computations. First the benefit-cost ratios between each alternative and the basic condition are found, and those plans that fail to reach the minimum attractive ratio are discarded. Then the benefit-cost ratio for each increment of added investment is computed, each plan being proved against the preceding acceptable plan. The alternative of greatest first cost that reaches the prescribed benefit-cost ratio on both total and increment investment is the most acceptable on the basis of the assumed interest rate. A typical benefit-cost solution appears in the example.

The minimum attractive benefit-cost ratio can be set by analyzing a selected group of badly needed projects. It is probable that in many states numerous highway projects showing benefit-cost ratios of 3, 4, or 5 to 1 can be found.

The choice of interest rate seriously affects the results of benefit-cost solutions. As a rule, interest charges appear only in the highway-cost portion of the equation; thus an increase in the interest rate increases only the denominator and results in a less favorable benefit-cost ratio. For example, assume that the entire annual cost difference between two alternatives is based on a capital investment of 30-year life. Then, if the benefit-cost ratio at 0% interest is 4.0, at 3% it will be 2.6, and at 6% only 1.8. This means that benefit-cost ratios computed at different interest rates are not comparable. To state completely the results of a benefit-cost solution, both the ratio itself and the interest rate must be given.

The benefit-cost ratio as given by equation 3 does not fit some highway problems. For example, the purpose of many drainage and resurfacing projects is to reduce maintenance costs. User costs (or benefits) are affected very little if at all. In these cases, the benefit-cost ratio is the annual reduction in maintenance cost divided by the annual cost of the improvement. In such instances, the annual cost or rate-of-return methods may be more convenient.

development projects making benefit-cost studies for all such projects. However, there are no such legislative stipulations that require benefit-cost studies for highways. Benefit-cost studies were used by the Oregon State Highway Department in 1937. [See *Oregon State Highway Department Technical Bulletins 7 and 10* by C. B. McCullough and John Beakey (and Paul Van Scoy), 1937–38, titled, respectively, The Economics of Highway Planning and An Analysis of the Highway Tax Structure in Oregon.]

A SAMPLE HIGHWAY ECONOMY STUDY

Problem statement

A particular section of road follows a circuitous route between two junction points. Its surface is in bad condition and must be renewed. Since a small additional expenditure for grading and structure widening will bring the road to fairly high standards, this cost is also included in the basic improvement, here called alternative A. There are two other likely proposals both of which call for abandonment of the present road and for construction along new alinement. Alternative B is shorter than the present road by 1.65 miles but requires a sizable expenditure for rights of way, grading, structures, and surfacing. Alternative C is shorter than alternative B by 0.55 mile. It also calls for new rights of way and construction. Grading and structure costs are much higher as the terrain is rougher and a river is crossed at a very unfavorable site. Estimated lives and costs including engineering are as follows:

Element	Estimated Useful Life, Years	Cost Alternative A	Alternative B	Alternative C
Right of way	60	$ 0	$ 12,000	$ 11,000
Grading	40	48,000	227,000	390,000
Structures	40	30,000	235,000	468,000
Surface	20	55,000	142,000	127,000

The present average annual daily traffic as determined by counts is 800 passenger cars and 110 commercial vehicles. This volume is assumed to remain constant for the study period. Free operation at 45 mph average speed is expected since the traffic volume is relatively low. The small volume of traffic with origins or destinations along the road is ignored. Costs introduced by grades, curvature, or stops are assumed equal for all plans. Time costs per vehicle-hour are set at $1.35. Accident hazard is considered equal on all locations. Increment maintenance costs are estimated as $1000 per mile per year for all alternatives.

Solution by annual-cost method. Interest at 4%

		A		B		C	
		First Cost	Annual Cost	First Cost	Annual Cost	First Cost	Annual Cost
Rights of way	CRF (n = 60) = 0.04420	$ 0	$ 0	$ 12,000	$ 500	$ 11,000	$ 500
Grading	CRF (n = 40) = 0.05052	48,000	2,400	227,000	11,500	390,000	19,700
Structures	CRF (n = 40) = 0.05052	30,000	1,500	235,000	11,900	468,000	23,600
Surface	CRF (n = 20) = 0.07358	55,000	4,000	142,000	10,400	127,000	9,300
Total annual cost of capital recovery			$7,900		$34,300		$53,100

Annual Road-User Costs:

Passenger cars

Operating cost per vehicle-mile (see Table 1, p. 45)	$0.0425
Time costs per vehicle-mile at $1.35 per vehicle-hour (see Fig. 5, p. 51)	0.0300
Total user costs per vehicle-mile	$0.0725

Commercial vehicles (somewhat lighter than U. S. composite average)

Operating costs per vehicle-mile (see Table 4, p. 55) 0.0425 × 3.0	$0.1275
Time costs per vehicle-mile (at $2.50 per vehicle-hour)	0.0556
Total user costs per vehicle-mile	$0.1831

Total road-user costs per mile of road per year

Passenger cars = $0.0725/mi × 800 cars/day × 365 days/yr	$21,170
Commercial vehicles = $0.1831 × 110 cars/day × 365 days/yr	7,350
Total	$28,520

Summary of Annual Costs:

	Alternate					
	A		B		C	
Cost Item	Length	Annual Cost	Length	Annual Cost	Length	Annual Cost
Capital recovery		$ 7,900		$ 34,300		$ 53,100
Maintenance costs $1,000/mi	10.05	10,000	8.40	8,400	7.85	7,900
Road-user costs $28,520/mi	10.05	286,600	8.40	239,600	7.85	223,900
Total annual cost		$304,500		$282,300		$284,900

Alternative *B* appears to be the best solution because it has the lowest total annual cost. However, this finding is based on the assumption that 4% is an attractive return. At some lower interest rate alternative *C* with its higher capital investment might have been the most attractive. At some higher interest rate alternative *A* would have appeared to be the best.

Solution by rate of return on investment

(a) Comparing alternatives *A* and *B*.

At 8% Interest

Alternative *A*, total annual cost [25] = 48,000 × 0.08386 + 30,000 × 0.08386 + 55,000 × 0.10185 + 10,000 + 286,600 = $308,700

Alternative *B*, total annual cost = 12,000 × 0.08080 + 227,000 × 0.08386 + 235,000 × 0.08386 + 142,000 × 0.10185 + 8400 + 239,600 = **$302,200**

At 10% Interest

Alternative *A*, total annual cost = 48,000 × 0.10226 + 30,000 × 0.10226 + 55,000 × 0.11746 + 10,000 + 286,600 = **$311;000**

Alternative *B*, total annual cost = 12,000 × 0.10033 + 227,000 × 0.10226 + 235,000 × 0.10226 + 142,000 × 0.11746 + 8400 + 239,600 = **$313,100**

The rate of return lies between 8 and 10%. At 8% interest alternative *A* costs *more* annually than alternative *B* by $6500, but at 10% interest their relative positions are reversed, and alternative *B* costs more by $2100. The rate of return is found by straight-line interpolation either by graphical means or by calculation as follows: [26]

$$i = 0.08 + 0.02 \times \frac{6500}{6500 + 2100} = 0.095 \text{ or } 9.5\%$$

Alternative *B*, then, is better than alternative *A* if the minimum attractive return is 9.6% or less.

(b) Comparing alternatives *A* and *C*. By a solution identical in method to that just demonstrated, the interest rate at which alternatives *A* and *C* are identical is 6.8%. Alternative *C*, then, is better than the basic condition if the minimum attractive return is 6.8% or less.

(c) Comparing alternatives *B* and *C*. By the same method, the interest rate at which alternatives *B* and *C* are identical is 3.0%. Only if the minimum attractive return is 3.0% or less is alternative *C* better than alternative *B*. Assuming that the 4% used in the earlier part of this example represents the minimum attractive return, alternative *B* is the best.

Solution by benefit-cost method

Annual benefits and costs for computing benefit-cost ratios are found exactly as indicated in the solution by the annual-cost method. To complete the solution, these results are substituted in formula 3, page 67. Benefits are the differences in road-user costs; costs will be all outlays of the highway agency. From the summary in the solution by the annual-cost method:

R = annual road-user costs for alternative *A*　　= $286,600
R_1 = annual road-user costs for alternative *B*　　= $239,600
H = highway cost for alternative *A* = $ 7,900 + $10,000 = $ 17,900
H_1 = highway cost for alternative *B* = $34,300 + $ 8,400 = $ 42,700

$$\text{Benefit-cost ratio } (B \text{ vs. } A) = \frac{286,600 - 239,600}{42,700 - 17,900} = 1.9$$

In like manner:

$$\text{Benefit-cost ratio } (C \text{ vs. } A) = \frac{286,600 - 223,900}{61,000 - 17,900} = 1.5$$

[25] These computations are made in exactly the same manner as those shown for the annual-cost method, except for changed capital recovery factors.

[26] Interpolation does not give an exact solution. The error introduced is small, however, and well within the limits of accuracy of the basic data.

This shows that, if 4% is the minimum attractive return, either of the two alternatives represents improvement over the basic condition.

$$\text{Benefit-cost ratio } (C \text{ vs. } B) = \frac{239,600 - 223,900}{61,000 - 42,700} = 0.9$$

This proves that (at 4% interest) the added expenditure for alternative C compared to alternative B is not justified, for the benefits are less than the costs. However, if the interest rate had been set at 2%, the benefit-cost ratio would have been 1.2 and the added expenditure would have seemed proper. Here, then, is proof of the earlier statement that *both* benefit-cost ratio and interest rate must be stated to provide a complete solution.

✳ SUFFICIENCY RATINGS FOR HIGHWAYS [27]

Sufficiency ratings are used by some highway agencies to establish priorities for road improvement. Each segment of the particular highway system is rated on the basis of its efficiency, safety, and service. Results are weighted to recognize traffic volume. Roads in perfect condition have a sufficiency rating of 100%; deficiencies of any kind cause the rating to drop. A tabulation of all projects in the order of ascending sufficiency ratings will form a priority schedule for road improvement. Such a list gives highway administrators a basis for allocating funds. It also provides an effective basis for resisting the demands by pressure groups that their favored projects be completed first.

At present there is no uniform method for presenting highway needs to Federal and state legislative bodies. It has been proposed that sufficiency ratings be used for this purpose. Each highway administration would establish a minimum tolerable sufficiency rating for its system and estimate the cost of bringing all roads at least to that level. This would establish a statement of highway needs in terms understandable to legislative bodies and the public.

Highway economists recognize that sufficiency ratings are not economy studies based on cost comparisons. Instead, the sufficiency rating measures the quality of a road by an arbitrary assignment of weights to certain of its characteristics (see below). A change in selection or weighting of these characteristics will, of course, affect the final sufficiency rating so that ratings normally are not comparable between agencies. Even so, as a start toward economy studies, sufficiency

[27] For further information see particularly *Highway Research Board Bulletin 53* (1952).

ratings have real merit because they compel a periodic and orderly appraisal of a highway plant.

The sufficiency rating was first developed by the joint efforts of the Arizona Highway Department and the U. S. Bureau of Public Roads. By September 1952 a total of 29 state highway departments had adopted the scheme. Each of them has developed its own factors for measuring sufficiency.

Roadway characteristics considered in the Arizona plan, and the weights assigned to each are as follows:

	No. of Points
Condition	
Structural adequacy	17
Anticipated remaining life	13
Maintenance economy	5
Condition total	35
Safety	
Roadway width—or marginal friction	8
Surface width—or medial friction	7
Sight distance, or intersectional friction	10
Consistency	5
Safety total	30
Service (expressed in terms of dispatch and ease of driving)	
Alinement (dispatch)	12
Passing opportunity (dispatch)	8
Surface width (ease)	5
Sway in cross section (ease)	5
Roughness of texture (ease)	5
Service total	35

Rules have been set for evaluating each of these factors to assure uniformity in rating various roads. Final results are weighted, a set of special graphs being used to give priority to roads carrying large volumes of traffic.

HIGHWAY SOLVENCY [28]

With information from the statewide planning surveys it is now possible to determine annually in each state the total vehicle-miles

[28] See particularly *Oregon Highway Department Technical Bulletins 7* and *10.*

of motor traffic. When the corresponding state total user revenue is divided by this total state motor-vehicle mileage, there results the average state operating revenue per vehicle-mile. This figure is useful for finding the user revenue produced by any given route or routes for which the total annual traffic is known.[29] Earnings in the several states in 1948 were between 5 and 7 mills, and, with the Federal excise tax of $1\frac{1}{2}$ cents per gallon of gasoline and other Federal excise taxes included, between 8 and 10 mills.

A "solvent" highway, as the term is used, has a favorable relation between its earning power (operating revenue) and its total annual cost. This is sometimes expressed as a "solvency quotient" which is the ratio of annual user revenue to total annual cost. For example, the 8.9-mile Arroyo Seco Parkway in Southern California cost about $800,000 per mile for a six-lane design. Its average daily traffic in 1948 was about 75,000 vehicles. If we apply the 1948 national average earnings of 6 mills per vehicle-mile, this highway was earning about $164,000 annually. This was 20.5% of the initial cost which, on the basis of a 40-year life for the facility, indicates that the road is paying for itself and, in addition, is earning 20% on the investment. The solvency quotient, using interest at 4%, would be greater than 4. However, at this same revenue rate per vehicle-mile, a mile of highway carrying 100 vehicles would have an earning power of only $220, or about $\frac{7}{10}$ of 1% of a $30,000 first cost. In this case, the solvency quotient is only 0.15. These results serve to illustrate the concept of solvency. Exact computations would include annual maintenance costs also.

Many secondary routes are not carrying enough traffic to earn their annual costs through user taxes. In other words, their solvency quotient is less than unity. However, their "errand value" is high and, in addition, they feed traffic into major arteries and thus increase their earning power. This in turn suggests the importance of the solvency of entire highway networks as well as that of individual roads.

[29] H. E. Hilts of the Bureau of Public Roads stated the concept in 1940 as follows: "By dividing the total taxes collected on a motor vehicle while consuming 1 gallon of gasoline by the total distance traveled, the total tax burden on a motor vehicle per mile is obtained. This amounts to 0.582 cent." (See Planning the Interregional Highway System, by H. E. Hilts, *Public Roads,* June 1941, p. 90. McCullough in 1937 used a gross ton-mile unit revenue and a nineway classification of traffic. The resulting net revenues per vehicle-mile varied from 2.7 mills for foreign passenger cars to 24 mills for school buses and trucks with trailers. (See Tables XXVI and XXVIII, *Oregon Highway Department Technical Bulletin 7.*)

5 ——————————— Highway Finance

INTRODUCTION

The highways and streets on which motor vehicles travel are provided by government as one of its primary functions. Just as with other government services, the funds to pay for them are raised through taxes levied by the various legislative bodies; expenditures are made by appropriate highway agencies. To date the total investment in the United States amounts to some $35 billion. Converted to the price level of the end of 1950, this would be about $60 billion.

As already indicated, approximately 10 cents of the motor-vehicle dollar goes to roads. However, there is much evidence that this percentage should be increased. To bring roads that are now obsolete up to reasonably adequate standards for today's traffic would require about $41 billion, and, if traffic increases as indicated, this sum will increase by $14 billion in 10 years. Since the $1.4 billion spent annually for construction just about keeps pace with these new demands, the present $41 billion of obsoleteness will remain.[1] There are other measures to show that highway expenditures are too small. *Real* expenditures for roads were but slightly greater in 1950 than in 1930, the peak year prior to World War II. Total highway expenditures during the earlier year were $2.5 billion and in the later year $4.3 billion, an increase of about 70%. However, because of increases in construction costs, $1.70 was required in 1950 to purchase the same highway work [2] that $1.00 would have purchased in 1930. During

[1] These data are from Wilfred Owen, *Automotive Transportation*, Brookings Institution (1949). An estimate made in December 1951 by the AASHO placed the immediate needs of the Federal-aid systems alone at $32 billion.

[2] This comparison is based on the Bureau of Public Roads Price Index. At stated intervals the cost of constructing a hypothetical mile of highway is computed by applying average current prices to fixed quantities of excavation, surfacing, and structural materials. The index is found by dividing the cost of constructing the hypothetical mile in any particular year by the cost of building

this same time interval, the annual vehicle-miles of travel more than doubled. From this it follows that the 1930 highway expenditure per vehicle-mile of travel was more than double that of 1950. From 1950 to 1953, annual highway expenditures increased about one-third, but the combination of vehicle miles of travel and inflation grew a like amount, so that the 1950 picture was relatively unchanged in 1953.

The Joint Committee on the Economic Report, 81st Congress, Second Session (January 1950), gathered other data of like import. For example, in 1936 construction expenditures amounted to 1.8 mills per gross ton-mile of vehicle travel; in 1948 the figure was 0.86 mill. Another illustration: for each dollar spent for new motor vehicles in the period 1929–36, 62 cents was spent for highways. The comparable figure for 1946–48 was 27 cents for highways for each dollar spent on new vehicles.

In recent years few entirely new roads have been added to the major highway systems. Rather, expenditures are almost entirely for modernizing or rehabilitating the existing mileage. However, these improvements are being made at a rate that is much too slow. For example, the primary Federal-aid system contains 231,000 miles of the most important rural and urban roads. Expenditures on this system were about 50% of what were needed. Again, in early 1953 less than 25% of the interstate system was adequate for present traffic. If we use the 1950 rate of spending as a measure, 67 years will elapse before its completion.

Thus the evidence seems conclusive that road improvement is not keeping pace with the growth of motor transportation. Unless highway expenditures are greatly accelerated, the time may soon come when vehicle travel will be seriously affected. Without question, the problem of adequate financing is at present the most serious one facing highway engineers.

The remainder of this chapter discusses the responsibility of various beneficiaries for highway financing, the sources and distribution of highway funds, and current proposals for accelerating highway improvement.[3]

it during the base period 1925–29. Actually, this cost index does not reflect the full change in highway costs for it neglects the added outlay per mile introduced by higher design standards. For further data regarding this and other cost indices see the construction cost issue of the *Engineering News-Record* which is published annually.

[3] For an extensive bibliography covering all phases of highway financing see *Selected Bibliography on Highway Finance,* Department of Commerce, Bureau of Public Roads (1951).

RESPONSIBILITY FOR HIGHWAY FINANCING

Distribution of cost among government, road users, and others [4]

Public roads serve multiple functions. They make it possible for government to render various essential services, supply the avenues of intercommunity mobility, facilitate the movement of persons and goods within each neighborhood, and give access to land and dwellings. However, different classes of roads are devoted more to some of these functions than to others. At one extreme would be a rural freeway on the interstate system. Its most important functions are to provide essential government services and intercommunity mobility.[5] At the other extreme is the cul-de-sac (dead-end street) of the modern residential subdivision or a road ending at a farm gate. In both instances, the sole purpose is to give access to land and dwellings. Although the main functions of most roads and streets cannot be so clearly distinguished, it seems possible to arrive at a logical method for classifying roads on the basis of their more important or predominant functions.[6] The division of administrative responsibility for roads between state highway departments and various agencies of local government represents a limited application of this scheme.

Many economists support the theory that financial responsibility for roads should be assigned among the beneficiaries on the basis of services received. The first step in implementing this theory is to classify each road segment on the basis of its functions. Then, like roads would be grouped into systems and the responsibility for them given to appropriate governmental agencies, and they would assess proper charges against the various beneficiaries. Following this line of reasoning, financial responsibility might reasonably be distributed as follows:

1. Responsibility of the Federal government would be limited to payment for activities designed to serve broad national objectives.

---

[4] The discussion presented here is extremely brief and .has been greatly simplified. For a detailed discussion see Charles L. Dearing, *American Highway Policy,* Brookings Institution (1941), and G. P. St. Clair, Suggested Approaches to the Problem of Highway Taxation, *Proceedings Highway Research Board,* pp. 1–6 (1947).

[5] However, evidence is accumulating that freeways cause marked increases in land values in the areas that they traverse.

[6] Two proposals have been advanced: the *theory of relative use* and the *theory of predominant use.* For more on this subject, see the references at the beginning of this section.

Road needs for national defense would clearly be one of these. Without question, the Federal government would supply a sizable portion of the financing for the interstate system and continue to participate in the Federal-aid primary system. Continued appropriations for certain roads now in the Federal-aid secondary system probably would be questioned, while proposed Federal aid for local roads would be ruled out. Those who suggest such limits on Federal participation often argue that Federal appropriations should be from general taxes and that user taxes should be collected only by the states.

2. Highway-user responsibility would be limited to providing avenues of interneighborhood mobility. These would include, as a minimum, all principal state highways, other rural roads connecting towns, and major city streets.

3. Local governments would assume responsibility for roads and streets within each neighborhood [7] and for access to land and dwellings. The former would be financed largely by general taxes and the latter by direct assessments against the property served. Only where there was marked use of a road by interneighborhood traffic would user taxes be devoted to its improvement.

There are many who for one reason or another disagree with the theory outlined above. However, it provides a valuable frame of reference from which to judge the present methods for raising and distributing highway funds.

Distribution of highway costs between passenger cars and trucks [8]

Taxes on buses and trucks are a subject of bitter dispute. The trucking interests maintain that they are now paying more than their

[7] There is no firm basis and little precedent for defining a neighborhood. In the cited paper by G. P. St. Clair it was suggested that a neighborhood be defined as an area producing a given number of access units per day, an access unit, in turn, being defined as a trip origin or destination. This procedure would have the effect of producing neighborhood areas of very small size in the congested parts of cities and areas of relatively large size in outlying districts and open country. An example was worked out, using data from the report titled Transportation Study, Baltimore Area, Maryland State Roads Commission, 1945–46. It was shown that, if 5000 access units per day were taken as the standard of neighborhood area, the size of such areas would vary from 0.02 square mile in the downtown section to more than 5 square miles in the outlying suburban zones.

[8] For a recent summary of the problem, see *A Factual Discussion of Motor-Truck Operation, Regulation, and Taxation,* U. S. Bureau of Public Roads (1951), particularly pp. 56–74 and 89–112. For a detailed report of the road-user and property taxes now levied against typical vehicles of all sizes and weights, see F. M. Cope and R. W. Meadows in *Public Roads,* April 1953, pp. 127–153.

share of highway costs. They cite, among other sources, the "East-man Report" [9] to support their claims. On the other hand, some legis-lators and highway officials attribute much highway damage and congestion to large or overweight trucks and urge both increased truck taxes and prohibition on further size increases. The American Asso-ciation of Railroads strongly advocates that truck taxes be increased "to remove the subsidy which truckers now enjoy." They contend that trucks are subsidized because they do not pay their just share of the costs of the highways over which they travel and also because railroads must pay taxes on the roadbeds over which they operate while the truckers operate over publicly owned highways which are tax-exempt.[10] Many motorists, alarmed by the increasing ·congestion of our roads and streets, advocate measures to reduce the number and size of trucks now on the highways. As would be expected, proponents of both sides are continuously pressing the state legislatures for changes in present tax rates. They often turn to engineers or econ-omists for advice and assistance.

Four basic theories of truck taxation are under discussion in the United States. These are the "increment-cost theory," the "ton-mile theory," the "unit-vehicle operating-cost theory," and the "theory of differential benefits." These are described briefly in the paragraphs that follow.

Increment-cost theory. The increment-cost theory (sometimes called the differential-cost theory) assumes that highways are constructed for the joint use of passenger vehicles and trucks. It seeks to distribute equitably the cost of a basic road suitable for passenger cars among all classes of users, but to assign to heavier vehicles all costs for which they are solely responsible.[11] Taxes would be computed as follows:

[9] Federal Coordinator of Transportation, *Public Aids to Transportation,* vol. IV (1940).

[10] See particularly *Transportation in America,* Association of American Rail-roads (1947); and C. B. Breed, Clifford Older, and W. S. Downs, *A Study of Highway Costs and Motor Vehicle Payments in the United States,* submitted to the Association of American Railroads (1939).

[11] The selection of the name "increment-cost theory" is unfortunate since the principle of *increment* or *added costs* is followed only partially. For a true increment-cost study, it would be assumed that the passenger car was the basic vehicle to which all costs of the basic road system would be assigned. Trucks would be held responsible for all costs occasioned solely by their presence. The cost assignments obtained by this method would represent the level at which each heavier weight group was barely paying its way free of outright subsidy. The portion of joint costs to be allocated to trucks would be a matter for separate determination.

1. Joint costs would be distributed among the various weight classes on some reasonable basis. For example, it has been suggested [12] that highway administrative expense and right-of-way costs be distributed to the various weight groups in proportion to the number of vehicles in each group. Costs of traffic control and of the portions of construction and maintenance expense that are unaffected by vehicle weight would be allocated on a basis of vehicle-miles. On the other hand, some engineers have proposed distributing all joint costs on the basis of ton-miles.

2. Weight costs like the expense of greater pavement and base thicknesses, stronger structures, and additional maintenance would be assigned among the heavier vehicles, on a cumulative basis. Thus all motor vehicles would share in the lowest or basic increment applicable to passenger cars and other vehicles of similar loading characteristics. All vehicles except the basic or passenger-car group would share in the second assignment of incremental responsibility (representing the added costs needed to provide for the second weight group in the ascending scale). This process would continue until the final or topmost assignment of incremental costs would be borne singly by the highest-weight group of vehicles.

It has been clearly established that heavier vehicles have caused extensive damage to existing highways and that designs for new roads are more costly because of them. However, firm data are lacking. For example it is not yet known how many (frequent) and just how heavy are the truck loads that cause the destructive "pumping" of cement-concrete pavement slabs or what it costs to prevent its occurrence. Partial answers to this particular question have come from Road Test MD-1 in Maryland.[13] A like test for bituminous surfaces in Idaho will provide further data. These two instances are but the beginning. In all areas of highway design and operation are unknowns which must be evaluated before a precise assignment of costs can be made.

The ton-mile theory. The ton-mile theory of truck taxation makes no attempt to relate vehicle size and weight to the cost of the highway over which the vehicle travels. Rather it assumes that taxes graduated to reflect the combination of gross weight and distance give a fair charge for the use of the highway. Thus, the charge against a truck and load weighing 20 tons and traveling one mile would be ten times that levied against a 2-ton passenger car traveling the same distance. Studies have been made in a number of states, notably California, Illinois, New York, Ohio, and Washington, in which the gross-ton-mile theory has been wholly or in large part the basis for the recommended allocation of motor-vehicle taxes. The enactment of such recommendations into the law has been only partially successful as there has been much opposition to the gross-ton-mile theory from those whose interests are affected.

In revising an existing tax structure (whether on the gross-ton-mile-basis or any other), it is first necessary to take account of the usual registration fees and motor-fuel tax. Then an additional impost, sometimes called a third-structure tax, may be needed to make the actual tax payments approximate

[12] See *A Factual Discussion of Motortruck Operation, Regulation, and Taxation,* pp. 93–97.

[13] See p. 554 for a description of this test and for references.

the intended tax. Since a large increase in the registration fees of heavy vehicles would tend to discriminate in favor of high-mileage vehicles as against those having a low annual mileage, the effort is generally to devise a third tax that will vary with the mileage traveled. Such a variation may be accomplished by means of a ton-mile tax. This weight-distance tax, as such, should not be confused with the gross-ton-mile theory. It may be imposed as a means of equalizing the tax burden even though something very different from the gross-ton-mile theory was used in the tax-allocation procedure. The basic objective is to supplement the registration fees and gasoline tax to make the tax burden of heavy and high-mileage vehicles approximate the recommended magnitudes.

A ton-mile tax in one form or another has been enacted in several states and is under consideration in others. For example, the 1951 New York legislature enacted a ton-mile tax which is now in force after approval by the state Supreme Court. On the other hand, several states, including Kentucky and Oklahoma, have tried the ton-mile tax and later abandoned it. The principal argument for repeal was that it could not be administered fairly since determination of the tax depended solely on the accuracy and honesty of the taxpayer's records. In any event it is probable that the ton-mile tax will be the subject of repeated legislative strife in the years ahead.[14]

The unit-vehicle-operating-cost theory. The unit-vehicle-operating-cost theory proposes a tax based on operating costs. Like the ton-mile theory, it is a charge for use of the highway, and does not consider highway costs. It has been established that vehicle operating costs increase with the weight of the vehicle but that the cost per ton-mile of pay load decreases. It follows that, if the tax on passenger cars were fixed at some designated level, truck taxes set by the operating-cost theory would be lower than if the ton-mile theory were used.

Theory of differential benefits. The theory of differential benefits has been proposed but is as yet relatively untried. It suggests that the service that highways render can be measured in terms of the savings resulting from road improvement. By analysis of the current improvement program, savings to each class of users would be computed, such items being considered as reduction in distance, improved surfacing, reduction in rise and fall, improved grade and alinement, and reduced impedance. Taxes would be set in proportion to these benefits.

SOURCES OF HIGHWAY FUNDS

Early highway financing

Before about 1890, public roads and streets were financed almost entirely by local property taxes.[15] The record of nationwide annual

---

[14] For a discussion largely in favor of the ton-mile tax see *Highway Safety— Motor Truck Regulation*, Council of State Governments (1950). For arguments against it see *The Ton-Mile Tax and Related Third-Structure Taxes*, National Highway Users Conference (1950).

[15] An exception was a Federal appropriation for the Cumberland Road in 1806. In the decades that followed, President Madison's belief that Federal spending

expenditures, however, is fragmentary. Apparently in 1914 about a quarter billion dollars was expended on all rural roads, which then totaled 2,446,000 miles. By 1921 annual expenditures exceeded $1 billion. In the northeastern states the road tax unit was the town, elsewhere the county. Commonly, the tax rate was low. In New England it was fixed at town meetings; elsewhere, county boards of assessors usually set the rates. Often taxpayers "worked out" their tax on the road. When money was borrowed by a town or county bond issue, a vote of the people, frequently a two-thirds majority vote, was required. Administration generally was lax and technique poor.

Later, the financing of state aid to county highways or of state highways was by the state legislatures. They often initiated bond issues, and popular vote authorized them. The taxes for state highways largely fell on the cities where there were high concentrations of property values. Thus, in 1915 Boston paid an estimated 40% of the Massachusetts state highway bill and New York City 60% of the New York total. There was, however, a corresponding city use of rural highways as city-owned motor vehicles became more numerous.

The early state or state-aid highways did not extend into the cities, and city streets were paved and maintained wholly by city property taxes. For many years after modern rural highways began to develop, city streets were presumed to be adequate. They thus at first were denied any Federal aid whatever.

Hauling over county roads was exclusively by horse-drawn vehicles with limited loads. Grades, mud, and sand were severe handicaps. Early bond issues for county road improvement naturally were used largely for macadam and gravel surfaces; some of the money was wasted.[16]

Up until 1914, 1230 counties had voted or issued about $287 million of county and district highway bonds.[17] Forty-one per cent of the counties had bond issues.

for internal improvements was unconstitutional prevailed and Federal aid for roads ceased. Not until 1912 did the Federal government again participate to any extent in financing road improvements.

[16] Investigations by the Office of Public Roads revealed that county taxpayers often were burdened unnecessarily with taxes for long-term sinking-fund bonds. It advocated a shorter-term serial type by which service charges annually were reduced by beginning retirement of the bonds as soon as the new roads were built. This serial type highway bond with the longest-term portion usually not exceeding 20 to 30 years has become prevalent.

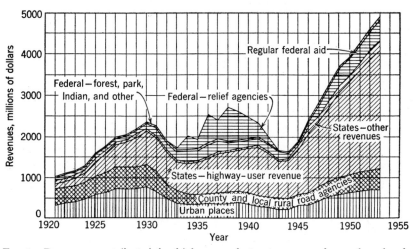

FIG. 1. Revenues contributed for highway and street purposes by various levels of government, 1921–1953

Current sources of highway funds

Figure 1 shows by sources the annual highway revenues since 1921. It clearly reflects the road-building surge of the 1920's, the limitation in highway improvement during depression and World War II years, and the increased spending for highways since the close of the war. This latter activity is not so spectacular as the graph of dollar values might indicate since it does not recognize the continuing decrease in purchasing power since World War II. A brief discussion of each major source is given in the paragraphs that follow.

Federal aid for highways. The advantages of state aid for improving rural highways had become clear by 1910, and the movement in some form had spread to many states. There naturally arose the question of how the Federal government similarly might aid this movement for better rural roads, especially along mail routes. Several bills were introduced in Congress, and in 1912 one became law which appropriated $500,000 to be used on post roads in states whose governors accepted the act. The principal stipulation was that the state (or its subdivision) should match the Federal dollars two for one. The re-

17 See Highway Bonds by L. I. Hewes and James W. Glover, *U. S. Department of Agriculture Bulletin 136* (1915, revised 1917); also Economic Surveys of County Highway Improvement, *U. S. Department of Agriculture Bulletin 393* (1916), by J. E. Pennybacker and M. O. Eldridge.

sponse was not enthusiastic. Nine projects in as many states finally were begun, but before all of them were finished in 1916 the first Federal-aid road law was passed. It carried $5 million for the first year with an increase of $5 million each year for 5 years—$75 million in all. This "Federal-aid" money was to be matched on an equal basis by the states or their subdivisions and was allocated to the several states on a basis of relative (a) population, (b) area, (c) miles of post roads—each of these items to have equal weight. The first appropriation was greatly increased in 1919 by an emergency appropriation of $200 million, largely as a re-employment measure for veterans of World War I.

TABLE 1. ANNUAL FEDERAL-AID APPROPRIATIONS, 1946–1957, IN MILLIONS OF DOLLARS

High-way Act of	Appropriations for Year Ending June 30	Federal-aid System				Total
		Pri-mary	Sec-ondary	Urban	Inter-state	
1944	1946, 1947, 1948	225.0	150.0	125.0	0	500.0
	1949	None—Used funds remaining from 1944 act				
1948	1950, 1951	202.5	135.0	112.5	0	450.0
1950	1952, 1953	225.0	150.0	125.0	0	500.0
1952	1954, 1955	247.5	165.0	137.5	25.0	575.0
1954	1956, 1957	315.0	210.0	175.0	175.0	875.0

In 1921, Congress passed the fundamental Federal Highway Act which amended the old law and which as later supplemented and further amended is still the organic Federal law. Under this act (through 1954) approximately $10 billion Federal aid to the states has been authorized. Table 1 shows annual Federal-aid appropriations since World War II.

Each Federal-aid act includes money for forest, park, Indian reservation, Inter-American, and other special road systems administered by the Bureau of Public Roads. Authorizations in the 1954 Federal-aid Highway Act for the years ending June 30, 1956, and June 30, 1957, totaled approximately $90 million annually.

Federal funds for the primary Federal-aid system are distributed among the several states as they were in the 1916 act. The money is divided into thirds; these are distributed in proportion to relative population, area, and miles of rural post roads. The allocated amount is available only if matched by an equal sum of state funds, except in the so-called public-land states where 5% or more of the land area is owned by the Federal government.[18] For them there is a sliding-scale matching ratio that permits the Federal percentage to increase above 50 by one-half the percentage of federally controlled land. Nevada has the most favorable ratio; for there the Federal government controls (1953) 67.4% of the area. In this state 83.7% of the cost of a Federal-aid project can be paid from Federal funds so that the state must contribute only 16.3% of the total.

Federal-aid secondary funds, which have been available since 1938, are distributed among the states on a basis like that for primary Federal aid, except that rural population replaces total population in the formula. Federal funds for urban extensions of Federal-aid highways, available since 1946, are distributed in proportion to urban population.[19] Federal funds for the interstate system have been available since 1953. Half of these are distributed among the states on a basis of population and the remainder by the formula for the primary Federal-aid system. The matching ratio is 60% Federal, 40% state.

Before World War II, Federal-aid funds could be used only for construction or reconstruction. However, the 1944 act, recognizing the high cost of rights of way, permits Federal participation in this item up to one-third of the Federal contribution to an individual project. Federal aid cannot be used for maintenance. Rather, the act requires that the states assume the maintenance of all projects built with Federal-aid funds.

During the depression years 1933 to 1942, and particularly from 1934 to 1940, Federal expenditures for roads to stimulate employment were large, totaling over $4.3 billion. The maximum occurred in 1938 and totaled $832 million (see Fig. 1). About 94% of the total was spent by the Works Progress Administration (WPA) and other relief agencies and the remainder by the Public Works Administration (PWA). For the most part, WPA expenditures were for short-lived improvements. PWA grants went largely to long-term capital investments, including $29,250,000 for the Pennsylvania Turnpike.

Federal taxes on motor transport. The United States Government collects excise taxes from vehicle manufacturers and road users. By December 1952 they had amounted to a grand total of $15 billion. In the year 1952 they were about $2 billion, or more than 3 times the total Federal-aid appropriation for the same period. About 40% of the total was from excise taxes on gasoline and lubricating oils, and the remainder from those on vehicles, tires and

[18] Nevada, Utah, Arizona, Wyoming, New Mexico, Idaho, Oregon, California, Montana, Colorado, South Dakota, Washington, and Oklahoma.

[19] In the years 1937–43, $190 million for grade-separation projects were made available to the states. Matching funds were not required.

tubes, and accessories. In succeeding years Federal income from these sources will be greater as the result of tax increases in the Revenue Act of 1951.[20]

Federal excise taxes on motor vehicles and motor fuels are strongly opposed by highway-user and supplier organizations; but, as of 1953, their protests were of no avail. Debate also centers on the "linkage theory" which equates excise-tax collections to Federal-aid appropriations. In December 1952 the AASHO, by resolution, urged Congress to increase Federal-aid appropriations to an amount not less than the Federal tax on gasoline. On the other hand, in June 1953 a spokesman of the United States Chamber of Commerce opposed the linkage theory before a congressional committee.

The state gasoline tax and other road-user taxes. The Federal-Aid Act of 1916 required that Federal funds be matched with state funds. Many states issued bonds, usually based on property taxes, to finance their shares. In the succeeding years the total bonded indebtedness for state highways increased, and at the end of 1951 the amount owed was $2.5 billion. The 1919 session of the Oregon legislature, however, decided to tax gasoline for highway construction. A 1½-cent-per-gallon state tax became effective in February of that year. It was an epoch-making law which proved so successful that similar laws forthwith were adopted by other states. By 1926 all the states had a highway motor-fuel tax from which the total net revenue was $188 million—more than twice enough to match all the Federal aid then available.[21]

In the succeeding years there have been many changes in the state tax rates on gasoline, mostly increases; but no state has abandoned this popular method for raising highway revenue. The tax per gallon varies from state to state, in 1952 it ranged from 3 to 7 cents. The weighted average based on gallons sold (for 1951) was 4.74 cents. There have been careful studies to determine the effect of increased gas taxes on the consumption of gasoline. The latest of these concluded: "It is reasonably clear that, at present price, wage, and employment levels, the demand for gasoline is so inflexible that no price or tax increases within reasonable contemplation will increase the total

[20] Major increases in motor-vehicle excise taxes were as follows: On motor vehicles 7 to 10% of the manufacturers' price; on trucks, trailers, buses, parts, and accessories 5 to 8%; on gasoline 1½ to 2 cents per gallon; and on Diesel fuel for highway purposes 0 to 2 cents per gallon.

[21] While the gas tax was independently inaugurated by Oregon, it is of record that the English Road Board was financed in 1919 by a three-pence-per-gallon excise or customs duty tax on petrol manufactured or imported.

price to the consumer to a point where it will measurably affect the demand for highway gasoline." [22]

Motor-vehicle license fees began in New York about 1900. Progressively they developed separate fee schedules for trucks, buses, trailer combinations, etc. In most states such fees as well as license taxes for motor carriers now are applied almost exclusively to highway construction and upkeep. These fees and the "gas tax" now are the largest part of the taxes known as "road-user taxes."

Many states charge fees for drivers' licenses. Often this income goes to operate the state highway patrol. At times, a mileage fee in addition to a license fee and fuel tax has been assessed against trucks. Also, some states assess licensed carriers a fixed percentage of their gross revenues. In California, this tax is 3%, but it is offset in part by a reduction in license fees.

In 1930 the total state-collected user revenue was $810 million, and in 1951 about $2.86 billion, so that such revenues considerably more than tripled. Road-user taxes now provide well over 90% of all state-collected highway funds (see Fig. 1). However, the collection of this vast amount still does not impose hardship on the motor-vehicle owner. In the entire country the average weekly road-service bill (1951) was.about $1.06 per vehicle.

Compared with some other tax sources, such as those on income or retail sales, the revenue from user taxes is relatively inflexible. It increases with vehicle numbers and use but will not change with the value of the dollar. In periods of inflation the income it produces remains relatively constant while the purchasing power of that income decreases.

Property taxes for roads. Property taxes have always provided a major share of the revenues raised by local governmental units. In earlier times, when roads were a local concern, practically all financing came from them.[23] Some of the funds so gained were used directly for construction or maintenance; others went to pay interest and principal on bonds for roads already constructed. Beginning about 1930 at the start of the depression, both county and city collections for road purposes fell off sharply (see Fig. 1). Since that time many local governmental agencies have been successful in gaining state-

[22] See E. M. Cope and L. L. Liston, Effect of Tax Increases on Gasoline Consumption, *Public Roads,* March 1949, pp. 138–144.

[23] Local governmental agencies imposed most of these taxes. State property taxes for roads were less than 5% of the total in 1921 and decreased thereafter.

collected user taxes to meet some of their road needs. In fact, the $1.12 billion of local rural and urban funds collected in 1952 are just about 85% of those gathered in 1930. They amount to only 50% of the 1930 total when a correction is made for change in purchasing power of the dollar.

Bond issues for highways. As mentioned earlier, borrowing to finance road improvement was common practice in the early years of highway improvement. As a rule, the issues consisted of general obligation bonds to be repaid from property taxes. After the boom period of the 1920's, bond financing was less common, largely because of the depression and World War II. Since World War II, however, the urgent need for highway funds has resulted in many proposals for bond issues, generally to be paid from user tax funds or from tolls. In 1951 alone, 20 states assumed obligations exceeding $500 million for highways, bridges, and toll roads.

Many city streets, particularly in residential areas, have been paved under the provisions of street-improvement acts. Each owner pays the cost of paving the street in front of his property plus a prorated share of the costs of improving adjacent intersections. At times the city also may provide some aid. The sale of bonds guaranteed by liens against the property provides funds for these improvements.[24]

EXPENDITURE OF HIGHWAY FUNDS

Federal funds

Federal appropriations for highways are earmarked for specific purposes. Federal-aid funds can be spent only for the planning, design, construction, or reconstruction of Federal-aid highways.[25] Actual expenditure of the funds, including selection of the individual projects and their design and construction, is under the direction of officials of the state highway departments, but is subject to review by the U. S. Bureau of Public Roads. However, the states must allocate to each chosen project an amount equal to the Federal contribution,[26] which in effect permits Federal officials to exert some degree of control over these funds as well. This combination of state and Federal authority has been beneficial in many ways. On the one hand, it

---

[24] For recent trends in highway bond financing, see H. C. Duzan, W. R. McCallum, and T. R. Todd in *Proceedings Highway Research Board*, pp. 1–25 (1952).

[25] Except for a small percentage for operation of the Bureau of Public Roads.

[26] Subject to the exceptions mentioned on p. 85.

has left control and operation of the highway system in state hands. On the other, it has provided guidance to the state highway departments. For example, knowledge of worth-while developments made in one state is spread by Bureau engineers to other states with similar problems. Again, it has aided in introducing uniformity in highway practices over the nation. Probably the most important single result of Federal review of expenditures has been an impetus toward the creation of integrated state highway systems of limited mileage. There are many instances where support of the Bureau of Public Roads has aided state highway officials in resisting demands for the dissipation or unwise use of funds.

State highway expenditures

In all but four states the state highway system consists of a limited mileage of the more heavily traveled roads and streets.[27] Support for this system has always come mainly from highway-user taxes and Federal aid. Expenditures in 1951 totaled $2.6 billion, of which 68% was used as capital outlay for construction or reconstruction, 22% for maintenance, 5% for administration, 3% for highway police, and 2% for interest on indebtedness. Annual expenditures of user taxes on state highways between 1925 and 1951 are shown in Fig. 2.

Expenditures for local rural roads

Local rural-road agencies have two principal sources of support: taxes on property within their jurisdictions and a share of highway-user revenues. Before about 1920 almost all funds came from local property taxes. Since that time local road agencies have been gaining increasing support from highway-user funds (see Fig. 2). Of the $1.0 billion spent in 1951 for local rural roads, only 46% was from local sources; the remainder came largely from state-collected user taxes.[28] Expenditures on local rural roads were divided as follows: 35% for construction or ·reconstruction, 57% for maintenance, 5%

[27] In Delaware, North Carolina, West Virginia, and all but three counties of Virginia the state highway department administers and finances local rural roads.

[28] The percentage of state support for local rural roads varies widely among states. For example, in Ohio in 1950 income from local property taxes was only 26% of that contributed by the state government, while in nearby New York income from local sources was more than double the state's contribution. In a given state, the relative percentages will vary from county to county, depending on the road tax assessed by each county unit and the procedure for allocating state funds.

for administration, and 3% for interest. The shift in emphasis from construction to maintenance, as compared with state highways, is to be expected when the relative mileages, degrees of improvement, and traffic volumes are considered.

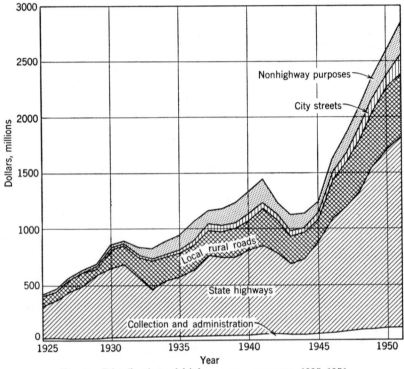

Fig. 2.　Distribution of highway-user revenue, 1925–1951

Expenditures for city streets

Funds for city street work (excluding state highways within the cities) come mainly from local sources, particularly the property tax. In 1951, approximately three-fourths of the $860 million total was from this source. Most of the remainder was from state sources, particularly highway-user taxes.[29] Before 1931 state aid for city streets was very limited in amount. Since that time it has increased

[29] The ratio of state support to local support for city streets also varies widely among states but is lower than that for local rural roads. In 1949 there were 10 states in which no state funds went to local streets and 17 in which the amount totaled $100,000 or less.

almost continuously (see Fig. 2). In 1951, 45% of the total expenditure was for construction and reconstruction, 43% for maintenance, 7% for administration, and 5% for interest.

Trends in highway financing

In 1921 about 70% of all highway revenues were contributed by local rural and urban governmental units, 20% by the states, and 10% by the Federal government. By 1941 local agencies had shifted over half of their earlier burden to the state governments. From 1941 to 1953 the percentage contributions remained fairly constant (see Fig. 3). In 1953 local governmental units supplied 24% of all highway revenues, state governments 64%, and the Federal government

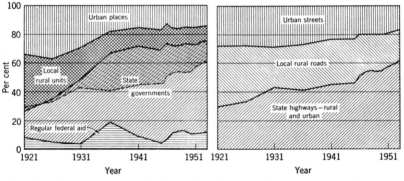

Fig. 3. Percentage contributions to total highway revenues by the various levels of government, 1921–1953

Fig. 4. Percentage expenditures on major road and street systems, 1921–1953 (Direct Federal expenditure of about 1% not shown)

12%. During 30 years, then, the major responsibility for road financing has been shifted from property owners, who pay almost all local road taxes, to highway users.[30] The change in state responsibility for local road and street financing is also shown by Fig. 3. The dotted line across the chart marks the approximate division of total income between state highways (lower portion) and local roads and streets (upper portion). The height of the shaded portion above that

[30] From 1921 to 1930, annual contributions of local agencies, in dollars, increased considerably, but highway-user revenues increased at a much faster rate (see Fig. 1, p. 83). From 1931 to 1940, however, the depression and its aftermath caused collections by local agencies to fall off sharply, while highway-user taxes remained fairly constant. Since World War II, dollar income from both sources has increased markedly and at about the same rate.

line is the approximate percentage of total highway income collected by the state governments but transferred to local road and street · agencies.[31]

The percentages of total highway revenues expended on state highways, local rural roads, and urban streets from 1921 to 1953 appear in Fig. 4. It will be noted that an increasing percentage has been going to the state highway systems. Of the $5.4 billion spent in 1953, 61% was for state highways, 21% for local rural roads, 17% for urban streets, and 1% for direct Federal expenditures.

One measure of the equity in the distribution of funds to road systems is the number of vehicle-miles traveled over each. Of the rural roads, the primary Federal-aid system which includes 7.5% of the mileage carries 60% of the total rural traffic, and the Federal-aid secondary system, including some state highways and some local rural roads of major importance, accommodates another 25%. These two systems, then, carry 85% of the total rural traffic although they constitute only 21% of the total rural mileage.[32] The remaining 2,400,000 miles of local rural roads carry only 15% of the total rural traffic which, in turn, is about 8% of the total for urban and rural areas combined. Yet, in 1953, 21% of the total highway income was expended on them.[33] The disclosure of these and like facts has caused public officials and legislators to question the wisdom of supporting local rural roads with user tax funds, at least to the extent now practiced in some states. For example, a part of a sweeping overhaul of Michigan's highway laws by the 1951 legislature emphasized the principle of local support for local roads and streets. It limits expenditure of state funds on local county roads to 25% of each county's share of state funds. This in effect limits state participation in local rural roads to about 50% of the previous outlay for such roads.

[31] In 1950, 14 states devoted more than 35% of their highway-user tax income to local roads and streets. Six of these used 50% or more for this purpose. Only 9 states gave less than 10% of these revenues to local roads and streets; and, in 4 of these 9, all, or virtually all, rural roads are under state control. All states made some highway-user tax funds available for local rural roads or for county roads under state control, and 32 states provided money for city streets other than state highways.

[32] In the comparison that follows, these systems are assumed to be the equivalent of the state highway systems, although that is not precisely the case.

[33] Like results were found in studies in two particular states. In Michigan road expenditures per vehicle-mile of travel on state trunk lines were 7 mills, on county local roads 29.6 mills. In Oregon the comparsion was 9.1 mills against 42.5 mills.

The results of pilot studies of local rural-road systems indicate that sometimes expenditures may be greater than are warranted. For example, it has been estimated that 600,000 miles of such roads could be abandoned without seriously impairing access to the property now served. Also there is evidence that often the standard of development is too high. To illustrate: Expenditures to provide more than an all-weather surface (without pavement) on roads leading solely to farm gates probably cannot be justified economically.

About half of the total vehicle-miles are generated in urban areas, but only recently have their problems received serious attention. For example, urban Federal aid was first authorized for 1946. Also urban highways and streets have not been supported in proportion to the vehicle-miles traveled on them. In 1951 less than 30% of the total highway income was spent on urban highways and streets. It is now generally recognized, however, that relief from congestion on main urban traffic arteries is one of the most critical highway needs, and larger expenditures of state funds on them seem assured. On the other hand, there appears to be little tendency to increase state support of local street programs. Here again the 1951 Michigan law indicates the trend. It requires that 40% or more of all state highway funds, after deductions for operation and maintenance, be spent on state trunk lines within the limits of incorporated places. On the other hand, it limits expenditures on local streets to 30% of each city's share of state funds.

Diversion of highway-user taxes to nonhighway purposes. Figure 2 (p. 90) indicates that sizable amounts from highway-user funds have been diverted to nonhighway purposes. The estimate of diversions for 1951, made by the U. S. Bureau of Public Roads, is $274 million, or almost 10% of the total amount collected. This does not include excise taxes of the Federal government, which in that year exceeded the Federal contribution to roads by more than a billion dollars.

There are definite differences of opinion regarding what is and what is not diversion. For example, some state governments collect an "in-lieu" tax on each vehicle along with the license fee. This tax is in lieu of the personal property tax on the vehicle and in many cases was instituted to guarantee collection of the personal property tax. It then might be argued that the governmental units that had previously received the personal property tax are entitled to some or all of the "in-lieu" tax and that assigning it to them cannot be classed as a diversion.

Among some highway-user groups and highway engineers there is a strong feeling that diversion of highway-user taxes to purposes other than road financing is improper. They contend that the highway user, in paying these taxes, is contributing his due share to the support of the highway system and that the diversion of a portion of these taxes spoils that measure. On the other side, the argument is that highway-user taxes have no special significance; they merely represent another source of income to the general fund. Roads, like other government functions, would be financed by appropriations from this fund.

By 1952, 24 states prohibited diversion of highway-user funds by constitutional amendment. Also, Federal legislation to discourage added diversion of highway-user funds has been in effect since 1934. In that year the Hayden-Cartwright Act reduced by one-third the Federal-aid allotment to any state that, after that time, increased its percentage diversion of highway-user funds.

METHODS FOR ACCELERATING HIGHWAY IMPROVEMENT

Financing by borrowing

The inadequacy of our highway system, particularly of the major traffic arteries, has been emphasized in the early pages of this chapter. Many highway administrators are convinced that the revenues that can be raised by pay-as-you-go financing will not meet the crisis. They urge that money be borrowed to complete the roads quickly. Principal arguments favoring this view are that (1) the need is immediate whereas pay-as-you-go financing, even with substantial increases in taxes, means slow progress, and (2) based on past history, pay-as-you-go funds will be dispersed over the entire road and street system and not concentrated on the principal arteries where the situation is most critical. Arguments against financing by borrowing are that (1) bond financing has not always been satisfactory and (2) paying interest is wasteful.[34]

Most of the present plans for accelerated financing involve bond issues to be repaid from future road-user taxes. As an example, $80 million will be borrowed to complete the Edsel Ford and John C. Lodge expressways in Detroit, Mich. State, county, and city each will pledge a portion of their future allocations of highway-user taxes to repay the loan.[35]

Another method for accelerating improvement of high-volume arteries is to borrow against their future earnings. The statewide

[34] To illustrate, consider a program for borrowing $100 million for road construction at the start of each year for 10 years, the loan to be repaid in 20 years by equal annual payments covering principal and interest. The cost of borrowing is 2%. For these conditions, the annual end-of-year payments will be $56 million. This is 12% more annually than for a pay-as-you-go program of $50 million per year for 20 years. On the other hand, the early completion of the roads will make possible large savings to road users.

[35] The state will pay 50% and Wayne County and the city of Detroit 25% each.

highway planning surveys now determine annually the yearly traffic on principal rural highways and their urban extensions. From this base could be determined the motor-fuel taxes assessed against vehicles as they travel these roads. There are probably many instances where limited mileages of urgently needed expressways would clearly develop sufficient revenue to pay for their rapid improvement by credit financing. In these cases, enabling legislation against these revenues seems reasonable and sound. Difficulties in accomplishing such financing would include opposition from local agencies who, under present laws, are allocated some of these earnings.[36]

Toll roads [37]

Many early American highways were built with private funds as toll roads. However, private investment had little part in the rapid improvement of our highway system which began with the coming of the automobile. Not until 1940, with the opening of the Pennsylvania Turnpike, did financing based on tolls reappear to contest the free-road concept.[38] It is probable, however, that some 5000 to 6000 miles of these freeway-type facilities may be in operation in the United States within the next few years.[39]

Practically all the potential toll-road mileage falls along the rural sections of the interstate system which constitutes only 1% of the total road mileage. Much of the mileage carries too little traffic for toll financing. Even so, those roads which now or later might be self-liquidating as toll facilities are the trunk lines of the present free-

[36] For more on this proposal, see L. I. Hewes, *Engineering News-Record,* April 13, 1950, p. 42.

[37] For a detailed and carefully documented study on toll roads see Owen and Dearing, *Toll Roads and the Problem of Highway Modernization,* the Brookings Institution (1951).

[38] This statement does not apply to toll bridges. During this period many such structures were constructed, some by agencies created by state and local governments and others by private interests operating under franchise. For the most part these ventures enjoyed a complete monopoly as the motorist often had no alternative to the toll facility.

[39] *American Highways,* October 1953, pp. 10–11, lists and briefly describes toll roads in operation, under construction, authorized, or projected in some 26 states. For a detailed description of the financing, design, and construction of the New Jersey Turnpike, see *Civil Engineering,* January 1952, pp. 26–93. This facility has proved highly successful. Traffic for 1952 was estimated in 1949 at 7.6 million vehicles but actually reached 18 million. Revenues for the year were 127% above the 1949 estimate. A detailed description of the New York Thruway appears in *Civil Engineering,* November 1953, pp. 33–50.

road system. Thus the resurgence of the toll principle of highway financing challenges the very basis on which the American highway system was developed. This in turn raises many policy and administrative problems which deserve serious consideration.

In common parlance, every highway on which tolls are collected is a toll road. Many would be excluded from a stricter classification which comprised only those financed solely by revenue bonds repaid from tolls. For example, the original Pennsylvania Turnpike would not then be considered a toll road. Of its $71,500,000 total cost, $29,250,000 was from a free grant of the Public Works Administration. Likewise, the easterly and westerly extensions need not be self-supporting, since the revenues of the entire turnpike are pledged to pay for the newer sections. Again, the 37-mile Merritt Parkway in Connecticut is not a complete toll road as 10-cent tolls are collected only at the termini. Intermediate traffic at 17 points moves free of tolls. Collections go to pay for the connecting Wilbur Cross Parkway to the north rather than to debt service.[40] The Westchester County parkways in New York were originally built to be public freeways, but authorization to impose tolls was given by the legislature.[41] Another illustration is the Denver-Boulder Turnpike. By legislative action, state user tax revenues are pledged to make up 30% of the principle and interest due each year, plus 30% of a reasonable sinking-fund reserve to repay authorized bonds. Loans for the New Hampshire Turnpike and New York Thruway were guaranteed by the general faith and credit of the states, and were not solely dependent on tolls.

In an exhaustive report to Congress by the U. S. Public Roads Administration [42] in 1939 it was shown that none of the six cross-country toll roads then proposed would prove financially sound at a composite toll rate of 1.5 cents per vehicle-mile. Collections were estimated to fall far short of the annual costs. However, sections between Philadelphia and New Haven appeared financially sound, with the ratio of estimated revenue to combined debt service, maintenance, and operating costs for the year 1960 exceeding 100%. Other sections

[40] The $15 million loan to help finance its construction was secured by the state motor-vehicle fund as a whole.

[41] Before tolls could be imposed it was necessary to rebate Federal-aid funds used in construction since the Federal-Aid Highway Act of 1921 (Sec. 9) provides that "all highways constructed or reconstructed under the provisions of this act shall be free from tolls of all kinds."

[42] *Toll Roads and Free Roads*, House Document 272, 76th Congress, 1st Session.

between Richmond, Va., and Portland, Me., also had high solvency. These sections include the recent Maine, New Hampshire, Connecticut, and New Jersey toll roads. In spite of the fact that traffic volumes have far outstripped those estimated by this report, the conclusion that a network of cross-country toll roads would be financially unsuccessful still appears to be sound.

Unquestionably the demand for toll roads stems largely from the urgent need for limited-access express highways. These cannot be provided soon from "user revenues," unless some means is found for added or accelerated financing. However, motorists appear willing to pay tolls of a cent per mile or more in order to use them.[43] Thus the big advantage of toll roads is that, where feasible, they can be provided quickly. There are two other stated advantages. The first is that, because the projects must be self-liquidating, only those roads that are economically justified will be constructed, and all possible economies will be effected in design, construction, and operation.[44] The second argument is that toll roads will divert part of the traffic from the generally parallel free routes and in part relieve their present congestion.[45]

Many highway engineers are opposed to toll roads. Their principal arguments may be summarized as follows:

1. Toll roads do not offer a nationwide solution to the urgent need for freeways. Only a few highly solvent routes are suitable for toll financing, and generally these are heavily traveled rural connections between large cities. If the toll road is widely accepted as a solution to our highway ills, progress in improving our highway system as a whole will be retarded.

2. It is difficult to fit toll roads into an over-all highway system. For economical toll collection, access and egress must be limited to a few points where traffic volumes are large. This means that, with few exceptions, toll roads can effectively serve only long-haul traffic. Other provision must be made for short-haul vehicles. On a free

[43] A toll of one cent per mile on passenger cars is the equivalent of a gasoline tax of about 15 cents per gallon. The average charge on the New Jersey Turnpike of 1.5 cents per mile equals a gasoline tax of about 22 cents per gallon. On the northern 7 miles, the charge of 30 cents per passenger car is equivalent to a gasoline tax of about 65 cents per gallon.

[44] This argument is not valid when the bonds are underwritten by pledging user taxes or other public revenues to make up possible toll-road deficits.

[45] For a presentation favoring toll roads, see *Civil Engineering*, August 1951, pp. 21–28.

road built to equal standards, access and egress points can be spaced at more frequent intervals and many vehicles on short trips can use the facility. This argument applies with particular force to roads approaching or within metropolitan areas where a predominant portion of the traffic is making short trips.

3. The first cost of toll roads is higher than that of free roads. Interchanges for free roads are simpler as traffic does not have to pass through toll stations. Also, crossings at grade might be permissible on free roads where traffic volumes are low and site conditions favorable; on toll roads grade separations are required at all crossings. Where initial traffic volumes are low, the free road can be built in stages with some refinements postponed; many like features of the toll road must be completed before the facility is opened to traffic.

4. Financing costs are greater for toll roads than for other roads constructed with borrowed money. Current interest rates on revenue band issues guaranteed by the earnings of a single project are almost double those on borrowings guaranteed by road-user taxes or the general faith and credit of the state.[46]

5. Toll collection is costly. On the Pennsylvania Turnpike, collection costs in 1950 were 3.4% of the total collections. On the Maine Turnpike, where traffic is seasonal and volumes are low, collection costs in 1951 were almost 10.5% of the total income.[47]

6. Toll roads are uneconomical. They do not attract as much traffic as similar free roads. This results partially because many highway users will travel the existing road rather than pay tolls, and partially because access to and egress from the toll road is often inconvenient to vehicles making short trips. In addition, there are cases where construction of a new free road will permit abandonment of the old one. Both toll road and old free road must be kept in service.

[46] In September 1951 the interest rate on general faith and credit bonds was 2% or less while that on toll-road bonds was about 3½%. This difference represents an increase of 28% in the annual cost of retiring 40-year annuity bonds.

[47] Among the proposals aimed at reducing the cost of toll collection on the New York Thruway is selling special license plates to repeating users driving passenger cars. Occasional users would pass through toll stations, as would all trucks. (See *Civil Engineering,* November 1953, p. 38.) License plates are now sold on the Merritt and Wilbur Cross parkways in Connecticut. Renting concessions along the road offers another means for partially offsetting operating costs.

6 —————————— Highway Surveys and Plans

INTRODUCTION

Highway location by engineering principles is comparatively recent in the United States. The 2½ million miles of rural highways that had accumulated by 1890 were in positions fixed largely by considerations of law, population, and industry. Many roads had become established by the successive development of trails. In the vast Mississippi valley area, road positions were determined mostly by section and township lines. With few exceptions no highways had scientific or engineering locations.[1] With the beginning of state aid and state highway construction in the 1890–1900 decade came better road location. Since that time the development of the motor vehicle has made increasing demands for locations permitting faster, safer, and cheaper operation. Today the location engineer must do far more than determine a route that with reasonable economy meets certain minimum requirements regarding curvature and grade. His location must blend curvature, grade, and other roadway elements to produce an easy-riding, free-flowing traffic artery that has high capacity and meets exacting safety standards. In settled areas, he further must recognize and evaluate its impact on existent industrial, business, and residential values and on future developments and redevelopments.

In the older, more densely settled eastern states, rural highway location for many years has involved the improvement or replacement of

[1] Among the exceptions was the old National Pike from Cumberland, Md., to Ohio and later to St. Louis. For this the Act of Congress in 1806 authorized the employment of a surveyor at $3 per day, with assistants. Another exception was the North-Western Turnpike from Winchester, Va., to Parkersburg for which the original act of the Assembly of Virginia named an impossible mountainous route. Later Claude Crozet was employed as locator; his location, on which original construction was completed in 1848, is today largely used by U. S. Route 50.

existing roads. In a measure this also has been the situation in the midwestern and southern states. But in the sparsely settled portions of the far western and Pacific states, the problem even in the recent past often has been to find the most favorable new route between widely spaced terminals. At present, however, few new routes are needed, and location work consists mainly of relocation and realinement of sections of the existing road system.

In the past, particularly in the older states, the usual relocation was largely an adjustment of alinement and grade line to eliminate excessive curvature and grade. Only minor departures were made from established rights of way. If the reconstruction involved widening the road, property bordering on one or both sides was taken. However, this concept is no longer applied to the location of major arteries, and the common practice today is to adopt new locations that, insofar as possible, avoid built-up areas of high property value. Wide rights of way and controlled access on these routes make later addition of lanes easy and protect the facility from encroachment by developments on adjacent property.

Before the field survey for any highway location is begun, tentative decisions regarding design speed, roadway cross sections, and maximum grade must be made.[2] These, to be sound, must rest on estimates of the amount, character, and hourly distribution of traffic, coupled with knowledge of the area to be traversed and the available funds. Then, as the location survey progresses, choices between possible routes and decisions regarding design alternatives must be made. These should look toward the cheapest over-all cost, considering capital investment, maintenance expense, and savings to the road user.

The remainder of this chapter deals with some of the problems of highway location in rural and urban areas and the surveys required to solve them. It also treats briefly the subject of highway plans and specifications.

HIGHWAY LOCATION AND SURVEYS IN RURAL AREAS

Reconnaissance

Intensive reconnaissance by the most competent talent is a necessary and fundamental first step toward highway location in new country. This is also true where complete abandonment and replacement of an existing road are planned. The first step should be de-

---

[2] See Chapter 8 for a detailed discussion of these subjects.

liberate study of all available maps, and particularly of topographic maps of the U. S. Geological Survey and other agencies. On such maps, the most promising general routes may be laid out for more careful inspection on the ground. Reconnaissance in the field often is accomplished by crude but rapid survey methods, using a compass for measuring angles and pacing or stadia to determine distances. Where the road must climb or fall at the maximum permissible rate, its tentative positions on the ground may be fixed through the use of an Abney level or clinometer.[3]

Terminals of the road and intermediate points through which it must pass form the primary controls for the survey. A unique bridge site or single mountain pass may become a primary control if no alternative exists. Likewise, for scenic highways, the positions of timbered areas, waterfalls, lakes, and other attractions may be primary controls. Small settlements which would be ignored in locating principal highways may be primary controls for secondary roads. Drainage systems, mountain passes, or low points in ridges often form secondary controls. Cost factors such as favorable or unfavorable soil conditions, the numbers and sizes of structures, and the amount of excavation and embankment required for satisfactory alinement and grade, likewise can be classified as secondary controls.

In mountainous country with well-defined summit ranges, there is usually a suitable pass with possible approaches following along the drainage on both sides. The least expensive and frequently the straightest line may lie just above high water in the streams. Often, however, the rise of the valley or canyon may exceed the maximum permissible grade. Then, if the stream grade is to be followed, extra roadway length must be gained on adjacent mountain spurs or in side canyons. At times a more favorable location lies on the hillside at some height above the stream.

On occasion, the route must climb from stream level or from a stream crossing to an adjoining pass or summit, and the road must be long enough to provide for the required gain in elevation at the maximum permissible rate of climb (see Fig. 1). Excessive use of switchbacks for such development is objectionable and should be avoided. Long stretches in one direction before reversal are preferable. Failure to adopt the correct point of departure from the bottom of the canyon generally results in unnecessary switchbacks. Reconnaissance in these

[3] Slack of ½ to 1% below the ruling grade usually must be allowed to recognize that the final located line is almost always straighter and shorter than is irdicated by reconnaissance.

situations is better run from the summit downward. During reconnaissance, particular notice should be taken of suitable places for switchbacks or turns.

In snow areas, locations should, if possible, be confined to slopes exposed to the sun in order to avoid icing of the roadway and to ease snow-removal problems. Likewise, the spotting of areas where drifts

FIG. 1. Highway leaving Rock Creek Canyon on Red Lodge–Cook City approach to Yellowstone National Park

form, snowslides occur, and the snow melts late is extremely important and may require separate snow surveys in winter or early spring.

Another typical problem in mountain location compares these alternatives: (1) to run to the head of a valley on fairly easy grades and good alinement and then with free use of the maximum grade make a quick climb to the summit by a relatively crooked and steep line on the hill or mountainside, or (2) to depart sooner from the level valley and climb to the summit on less grade and with moderate curvature. There is, in general, increasing preference for the mountainside location with its more uniform grade and probable shorter distance. In such situations, the relative difficulty of serving intermediate points should carry strong weight.

Country that includes spurs, foothills, and generally haphazard terrain will present a serious problem for reconnaissance and subsequent location. Such country will less frequently present snow trouble.

Airplane flights offer a useful method for conducting highway reconnaissance. Examination of possible routes from the air gives a comprehensive picture that cannot be gained from the ground. Often some alternatives can be discarded without subsequent ground examination. At times, secondary controls can be established. Likewise, obstacles which may offer difficulty can be noted and avoided in subsequent steps of the location. Flights after ground reconnaissance is complete are of great advantage in clearly relating the proposed road to details of the surrounding country. Observation of snow conditions on the ground at times is extremely difficult and time-consuming but can be made quickly and easily from the air.

After reconnaissance is complete, it may be summarized in a *reconnaissance report*, which presents for review the findings regarding each proposed route. It must present such important items as the total length of line, the elevation of main and intermediate summits, all adverse grades, stream crossings, sections requiring ruling grades, nature of construction involved (whether light or heavy) right-of-way circumstances, soil conditions, and all unusual or troublesome situations. It should also include an approximate estimate of cost, broken down for individual sections. In fact, there are so many items that the engineer may well use a check list developed for similar country on previous work. A general vicinity map or an outline of the route on an available map such as a Geological Survey quadrangle sheet is a necessity, as are sketch maps and profiles drawn to appropriate scales. Notes that will enable the locator to identify all control points and line directions must be included. Photographs showing views of the general terrain, of unusual or difficult sections to be traversed, and of major bridge sites are an important adjunct to the report.

From the above, it becomes clear that good reconnaissance requires sound understanding of the basic problems of highway design, construction, and maintenance. For location in rough country, a working knowledge of geology is an added need. It follows that good reconnaissance can be accomplished only by skilled and experienced engineers.

Aerial photographs in reconnaissance

Aerial photographs or maps made from them have proved invaluable tools for the highway locator, not only in new country but in settled areas as well.[4] Photographs covering much of the United States are now available from either governmental agencies or private aerial survey companies. If suitable aerial photographs or maps are not to be had, contracts for making them can be made with any one of several firms.

Vertical aerial photographs taken with the camera pointed straight downward are the most useful. The country to be covered is photographed in parallel runs carefully spaced so that the photographs overlap about 30%. Enough runs are made to include all alternative routes. Succeeding vertical photographs in each run are overlapped about 55 to 65% in order that the center (principal point) of one photograph will be included in both adjacent photographs. The scale of photographs is governed by the height from which they are taken. A common practice places the plane about 5000 ft above the ground, which for most cameras results in a scale of about 500 ft to 1 in. Then a typical 9-in.-by-9-in. picture covers a square about three-fourths of a mile on a side. Precision equipment and flying methods are usual.

The scales of aerial photographs taken solely for highway purposes are set by the use to which they will be put. For reconnaissance of areas, 2000 ft on the ground to 1 in. on the photograph is appropriate. For reconnaissance of alternate routes a possible scale is 500 ft to 1 in. Where the photographs or maps made from them are to replace preliminary location on the ground, a larger scale such as 100 or 200 ft to 1 in. is required. Finally, if final location surveys and plans are based on photographs, a scale like 50 ft to 1 in. or even larger may be called for.[5]

Much of value to the locator can be gained from the study of *mosaics*, formed by matching the centers of individual photographs into a composite view of the area. In flat country, at least the general route can be selected almost entirely from mosaics. This technique is particularly helpful in timberland or swampland or in other

---

[4] Photogrammetry, the science of map making from photographs, has developed rapidly during the last decades. Only brief mention of its application to highway problems can be made in this book. For added information see the *Manual of Photogrammetry*, 2d edition, published by the American Society of Photogrammetry, the textbooks on the subject, and the periodical, *Photogrammetric Engineering.*

[5] For further detail see Wm. T. Pryor in *Photogrammetric Engineering*, December 1946; C. D. Hooper, *Proceeding Highway Research Board*, pp. 373–377 (1950); and a Symposium in *Photogrammetric Engineering*, March 1951, pp. 111–180.

areas where reconnaissance on the ground is difficult. Questions of rights of way and property damage may be studied without the notice to individual property owners which inevitably occurs with ground surveys. Drainage problems may be appraised and drainage areas outlined. Thus, with mosaics, reconnaissance in flat country is much simplified and improved. Then too, mosaics are particularly helpful in discussing routes with highway administrative boards.

As aready mentioned, adjacent vertical photographs are taken from different airplane positions, but the photographs overlap 55 to 65%. When the area common to a pair of matched photographs is viewed through a stereoscope, the topography is seen in relief. If a location lies through rolling or rough country, study with a stereoscope will eliminate much leg work on reconnaissance. With precision-type stereoscopic instruments, tentative locations can be laid out in considerable detail on stereoscopic pairs of photographs.

Excellent topographic maps can be made from aerial photographs, and these often are available to the highway locator. For map making, the aerial photographs must be supplemented by "ground control" which consists of a limited number of elevations and distances determined by conventional ground-survey methods. Numerous precision devices for converting the photographs into maps are in current use. Among them are the Brock stereometer, the Zeiss stereoplanigraph, the Wild autograph, the Kelsh stereoscopic plotter, and the Bausch and Lomb Multiplex. With these instruments, maps of excellent accuracy can be made.

The U. S. Geological Survey has adopted aerial photographs as the basic source of data for its quadrangle maps. Except for the essential orientation of the photographs, ground surveys are employed only for checking purposes and for filling in those details that cannot be gained from the photographs. Scale of the finished maps is usually 1:62,500 or about 1 mile to 1 in. In highly developed industrial, agricultural, and urban areas the scale is 1:24,000 or about 2000 ft to 1 in. In preparing the final maps by photogrammetric methods, initial compilation is on "manuscript" maps made to a much larger scale. These are available to highway agencies by arrangement with the Geological Survey. Their value in location work is unquestioned.[6]

[6] For added information see pp. 1–8 of The Appraisal of Terrain Conditions for Highway Engineering Purposes, *Highway Research Board Bulletin 13* (1948).

Rural location surveys

✗ **The preliminary location survey.** After reconnaissance, it is usual first to run a *preliminary* location survey and to follow this with a *final* location survey. Both these are commonly made by transit and chaining methods. In "tight" country, a tentative line fixed more exactly than by reconnaissance may be roughed in by hand-level or transit-stadia methods before the preliminary survey is begun. The preliminary survey forms the skeleton upon which to hang accurate topography; this in turn serves as a basis for fixing the actual highway location.

The base line of the preliminary survey, commonly called the *P* line, should be run as near the expected final line as possible. It need not include run-in curves; rather, short courses avoiding deflection angles greater than about 30 degrees may be used to approximate the longer turns. The locations of natural features and culture which might influence the road's position are then related to this line. Elevations taken with an engineer's level at 100-ft stations and at "breaks" in the ground provide data for the profile, and also serve as a starting point for contour mapping or cross sections covering strips of land on each side of the *P* line. The width covered varies with topography and land use, but usually ranges between 100 and 800 ft. All transit points and bench marks of the preliminary survey must be permanently referenced.

Engineers disagree regarding the standard of accuracy for the preliminary survey. Speed can be gained by using rough chaining or stadia methods to measure distances. However, this practice limits the usefulness of the preliminary line for checking the accuracy of the final location. On the other hand, if both lines are run accurately (preferably to about 1 in 5000), and an occasional common point or tie between them is taken, an excellent check can be made. Comparative bearings are gained merely by turning an angle or two, and an over-all check results from a simple computation of latitudes and departures for both lines.

If the "projection method" of location is used, the next step is to plot plan and profile of the preliminary line. On these drawings the semifinal location line (*L* line) and tentative grade are laid out. In general, the *L* line will follow the *P* line quite closely, although in some places it may depart a considerable distance if study indicates that improvement can be made. Seldom will the best location result if the final line is merely the preliminary line modified by the introduction of curves between its tangents. In rough country, where the preliminary survey includes data for a large-scale contour map, careful study and even a rough computation of the earthwork quantities for alternate solutions may precede fixing the located line.

Some engineers do not make use of maps and profiles of the preliminary line when planning the located line. Instead, they revise the preliminary line directly on the ground. This method, termed "direct location," is not recommended.

The location line on the chosen route preferably should have a corresponding new set of notes and new stationing. The better practice is to base this restationing on the actual length of the curves rather than on the lengths of a series of chords. All field books should be complete and neatly kept. Proper titles and careful indices improve their usefulness.

✳ **The final location survey.** Final location is essentially the staking out on the ground of the center line of the projected road. It offers opportunity for minor corrections like small shifts of the line, adjustments in grade, and positioning of structures, channels, and other drainage facilities. It is usual to make a new profile and accurate cross sections from which excavation and embankment quantities can be calculated with good accuracy. Preferably during final location, but of necessity before construction, sufficient points of curvature and tangency must be carefully referenced to permit easy relocation of the line during all phases of construction. Likewise, bench marks must be set at relatively close intervals and in positions free from disturbance by construction activities.

Directions of all property lines, distances to property corners, and the locations of buildings, fences, and other improvements must be established accurately. On these will hinge the future property acquisitions and settlements made by the right-of-way agents. The making of topographic maps or other special surveys at bridge and structure sites probably will fall to the location party. In the past, location parties also made soil surveys and foundation explorations for structures, but today these functions are usually performed by specially trained and equipped crews.[7]

Often the location party is called upon to bound stream basins and to gather other information from which probable stream flows can be predicted. Where good topographic maps such as the U. S. Geological Survey quadrangle sheets are available, the large areas can be traced

---

[7] See p. 362 for further discussion.

on them, and only the small areas adjacent to the road must be surveyed. If the large areas must also be mapped in the field by conventional surveying methods, the task becomes much more time-consuming. Surveying techniques of limited accuracy, such as compass and pacing, are appropriate for drainage boundary surveys, as the drainage-area data so obtained are finally combined with approximate information on rainfall and runoff to determine the amount of water to be handled by a given bridge or channel. Stereoscopic examination of aerial photographs offers an easy method for bounding drainage basins. Then the areas can be measured on the assembled mosaic.

The highway locator must be sure that all information required for preparation of complete construction plans and specifications has been gathered, for its accumulation at a later time on a piecemeal basis is expensive.

Aerial surveys for rural highway location

As mentioned, large-scale aerial photographs and maps from them can be obtained. From them almost complete preliminary and final locations and even construction plans and cost estimates can be prepared. The need for conventional ground surveying can be reduced to supplying ground control, filling in missing detail, and making soil surveys and like studies. Today, then, each highway agency has two location techniques at its disposal and can use one or both. The practice is far from uniform. Some rely entirely on conventional surveying methods. Others procure copies of photographs or mosaics already prepared for other purposes and use them for reconnaissance purposes. At the other extreme, some agencies contract with aerial survey companies for large-scale maps of the areas to be traversed and do comparatively little location survey work themselves. The trend is toward wider use of aerial-survey methods. This is being hastened by the increasing use of aerial maps by other agencies like planning commissions and governmental administrative and tax bodies.

The location surveys for the Pennsylvania Turnpike extensions are excellent examples of the use of aerial mapping for highway location.[8] The total length was about 208 miles, one section running east from Carlisle to Philadelphia and the other west from near Pittsburgh to the Ohio state line. All preliminary line and grade studies, interchange and grade-separation layouts, and quantity and cost estimates were based on topographic maps produced by photogrammetric meth-

[8] See Frank J. Williams, *Civil Engineering*, December 1950, pp. 23–25.

ods.   The aerial contractor took photographs from a height greater than one mile.   From these were made inked linen topographic drawings to a scale of 1 in. equals 200 ft, and with contours at 5-ft intervals.

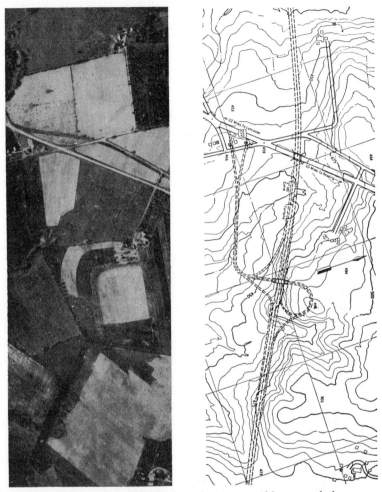

FIG. 2.   A vertical aerial photograph and a topographic map of the same area prepared from matched aerial photographs by precise stereo-plotting equipment (Courtesy Aero Service Corp.)

The width covered was about one mile, which afforded inspection of a belt of country in which to find advantageous alinement with good stream and road crossings and interchange sites.   Mapping costs on the easterly extension of 140 miles were less than $1 per acre; on the western end, which was only 68 miles long and in rougher country, they were about $1.29 per acre. Time required to produce the finished maps was, respectively, 145 and 70 calendar days. A typical section of photograph and topographic map with the location outlined on it appears as Fig. 2.

Bridge locations

Since the purpose of bridges as well as highways is to convey traffic, bridge location and positioning should be subordinate to general alinement and grade. There have been many instances where sharp turns at the approaches and generally tortuous alinement have resulted because the most favorable bridge site was the sole criterion for the location. Sometimes favorable alinement has been sacrificed merely to provide a cheap right-angle crossing of a small stream or wash. Today the general policy is to determine the proper highway location and require the bridge engineer to furnish structures for it. This of course results in more expensive crossings, for skew bridges cost more than right-angle ones, and the introduction of horizontal and vertical curvature into large bridges creates serious design and construction problems. However, the end result is a better roadway.

If traffic would be nearly equally served at several sites, cost will determine the location of the bridge. Foundation conditions for piers and abutments will seriously affect costs, but will not always be determinative. Obviously the cost of approaches is important, and the combined cost of the bridge and its full approaches must be determined before the crossing site is selected. The location engineer must recognize these basic considerations and place his line accordingly.

When the approximate location is fixed, there must be a complete and extensive report and special survey for the site. Printed standard forms for reports are recommended to insure coverage of every possible item. These reports must be supplemented by sketches and additional notes on standard-sized sheets and by full-scale maps and profiles. The bridge-survey report should include accurate data on the channel or waterway for all stages of water, the foundation conditions, and the stream character. Data on adjacent structures on the stream, particularly their waterway openings, is especially important.

Excellent discussions of *bridge-location details* and bridge-survey reports have been presented by C. B. McCullough to the Public Roads Administration,[9] and abridged statements from these bulletins are pertinent.

[9] See Bridge Locations, *U. S. Department of Agriculture Bulletin 1486* (1927),

For small structures, the location of the bridge or culvert itself is generally of secondary importance to the general alinement; in other words, it hardly ever pays to shift alinement to any marked extent, as the accruing advantage is generally not worth the expense. In certain instances, however, waterway conditions even for minor structures may be improved greatly through a slight modification in location. As an illustration, consider Fig. 3. The submitted or original alinement involves (1) a skew-culvert crossing which is in itself undesirable from a standpoint of first cost because of the increased length of

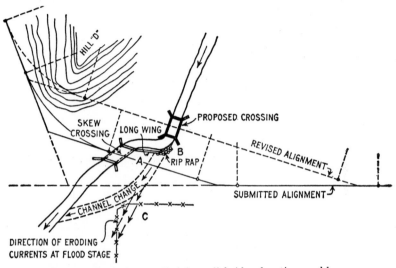

FIG. 3. Typical example of small bridge location problem

barrel, and (2) the construction of a long wing at A to eliminate the tendency of the stream to wash the fill during flood periods. This wing is another element of added first cost. The stream encroaches so near the shoulder of the road at B that it is quite possible that even the length of wing shown may not always prove adequate during a succession of future flood periods. This tendency to cut behind and under wing walls is the source of a great deal of serious trouble in the maintenance of small bridge structures whose location has not been made with attention to this detail. Unless this wing at A (Fig. 3) is lengthened even more than shown, riprap or some other form of bank protection may be necessary at B. This protection is an element not only of added first cost, but of added maintenance also. The channel change (shown dotted) might be a way out of the difficulty, but adds first cost and may not be cheaper than the skewed culvert and long wing. Moreover, the channel change affects the natural watercourse, and the builder at once be-

and Highway Bridge Surveys, *Technical Bulletin 55* of the same agency (1928). Also see R. B. Yule, The Bridge as a Problem in Highway Location, *Roads and Streets*, July 1938.

comes liable for any property damage resulting from overflow and erosion which may take place at C.

All the above undesirable features may be eliminated by the revised aline-ment shown, without added curvature. This method seems logical but for the fact that the new alinement throws into the hill at D, thus involving more cutting and perhaps a more restricted sight distance around the curve. These considerations must be balanced against the undesirable waterway features above enumerated. The solution will obviously depend upon the exact con-ditions disclosed by careful surveys and estimates along both lines. The prob-lem illustrates what may be encountered in the location of minor waterway structures.

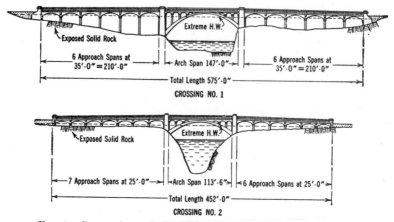

Fig. 4. Comparison of alternative locations for a large bridge

For more important construction, location for the bridge structure itself becomes increasingly important and tends more and more to outweigh consid-erations of cost for the approach alinement. The following factors should be considered:

A bridge structure should take advantage of any narrow neck or point of constriction in the waterway. The two locations shown in Fig. 4 illustrate the difference in cost that may thus accrue. Crossing 2 is downstream from crossing 1 and involves considerably less material, owing to the fact that advantage was taken of a steep rock gorge of comparatively narrow width. Both crossings are over exposed rock, but the natural banks at crossing 2 lend themselves to a shorter channel span, the channel being deeper as well as narrower, thus affording greater waterway area for equivalent horizontal span. The overflow banks at the site of crossing 2 are also higher with reference to floodwater elevation, so that a shorter approach structure is permissible. The yardage of concrete for crossing 1 is 1405 cu yd or 2.44 cu yd per lineal foot, whereas for crossing 2, farther downstream, the total yardage is only 969 cu yd or 2.14 cu yd per lineal foot. The total cost of crossing 2 is, therefore, seen to be about 69% of that of crossing 1, and the cost per lineal foot 88% of that for crossing 1.

The introduction of a skew angle involves increase of first cost. Skewed steel superstructure is generally slightly more expensive, owing to the cost of fabrication. The weight may also be greater, especially if the floor beams are parallel to the piers. The piers and abutments will be increased in length, and

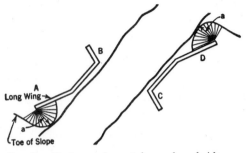

FIG. 5. Abutment layout for a skew bridge

the wing walls on abutments will be longer on two corners. If wing walls A and D in Fig. 5 are not sufficiently long to keep the slope out of the stream, the toe will be eroded.

HIGHWAY LOCATION AND SURVEYS IN URBAN AREAS [10]

General problems

The central business district of the typical American city contains large stores and offices and often the cultural and civic centers. Adjacent to it along the railroad lines or waterways is the industrial district. These merge into secondary business areas which in turn change into neighborhoods of mixed land uses and rundown buildings often referred to as "blighted areas." Beyond these are the newer residential developments which often extend far beyond the city limits in the form of widely scattered subdivisions bounded by farmlands. Vehicular travel in this typical city is heaviest along radial routes to and from the business and industrial areas. Volumes increase with proximity to the central areas. In some cases movements may be substantial in other directions also. (Refer to Figs. 4 and 6, pp. 30 and 33.) Generally this travel is over ordinary city streets on which front business and commercial developments. Through the years, as the number of cars has increased, this through traffic combined with vehicles having local destinations has caused increasing congestion.

[10] The report, *Interregional Highways*, House Document 379, 78th Congress, 2d Session (1944), offers an excellent discussion of this subject on pp. 53–74.

Today, most major city streets are jammed at peak periods, and many are badly crowded for several hours per day.

In the past, widening major arteries to relieve congestion has been tried at great expense but with little success. This procedure failed because it attempted to use a single facility as both business street and traffic artery. Where possible, modern practice separates these two functions, and through traffic is removed from the streets to free-flowing, high-capacity freeways or expressways. Today, then, new arteries in urban areas are generally located clear of the existing streets, although they usually follow parallel courses.

Most American cities have had similar patterns of growth. The original settlement was clustered around a railroad station or docking area. As the community expanded, its growth followed the main roads which usually were surfaced and offered safe passage in all weather. This pattern of growth was accelerated as the automobile developed into the major mode of transportation and thereby increased practical travel distances and gave greater freedom of movement to the individual. Today the developed portions of the average large city resemble a rimless wheel, with a central area forming the hub, and the fingerlike developments along the highways making the spokes. Figure 6 traces the growth pattern of Baltimore, Md., which is typical. Very often favorable locations for new highways can be found between these outstretched spokes or fingers. Right-of-way costs may be lower and the number and complexity of grade-separation and interchange structures reduced. In other instances, the best locations may fall along railroad lines, valleys, or water-courses,[11] where the normal subdivision pattern has been broken and cross streets are widely spaced.

Freeway and expressway locations should be related to the master plan for city development, for these arteries will exert marked influence on all aspects of a city's growth. For example, many master plans call for self-contained "neighborhood areas" about one-half mile to a mile on a side. Each of these has its own grammar school, parks, and playgrounds. Often a neighborhood shopping center is included. Streets within the area are strictly for land service, and major traffic arteries are confined to the borders. Only in exceptional cases should freeways cut through these units. Other problems develop when freeways traverse built-up sections of a city and block

[11] The Henry Hudson Parkway in New York City was built directly *above* the tracks of the New York Central Railroad.

a majority of the cross streets.   The usual access routes to stores, schools, playgrounds, and parks and the established plan for fire and police protection and for mass-transit operation may be disrupted.

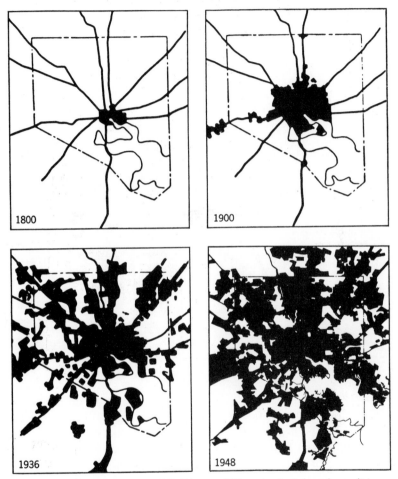

Fig. 6.   Growth pattern of Baltimore, Md., a typical American city

Close cooperation between the agency constructing the freeway and local officials is imperative if the effect of these disruptions is to be minimized.

The controlled-access feature of the modern urban artery in itself has a beneficial effect on city growth for it prevents the fingerlike development along the main roads that was so common in the past.

By the proper combination of major radial and circumferential routes, growth can be made to conform to a logical, reasonable pattern.

Locations for freeways need not pass directly through the central business area of a large city; in fact, for them to do so is often prohibitively expensive. If the routes pass close by, vehicles destined for the central area can traverse the short remaining distance on the

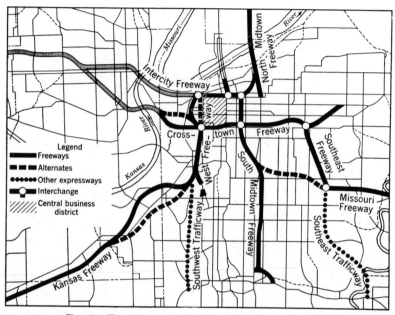

FIG. 7. Freeway layout for downtown Kansas City

streets. Favorable freeway routes often can be found in the blighted districts close to the areas of high property values. Where several new facilities into the heart of a city are planned, it may be advantageous to locate them so that collectively they partially or entirely encircle the business district. Then vehicles whose destinations lie on the far side of the enclosed area can circle the business district on these free-flowing arteries. This serves the dual purposes of accommodating motorists and of relieving the downtown streets of through traffic (see Fig. 7).

The locations for off- and on-ramps connecting freeways with downtown city streets often present serious difficulties. To provide both off and on connections to every street usually is out of the question. One reason is the extreme cost. Another and more compelling argument is that such close spacing of connections impairs the free-flowing and accident-free characteristics of the freeway.[12]   Often the best solution is to change the flow on the adjacent city streets to one-way and to provide connections to appropriate pairs of them.   Where large volumes must be carried by single ramps, good practice calls for an added lane on the freeway solely for these vehicles.

The ideal right-of-way width for a depressed urban freeway is a full city block. This provides amply for all future needs and for on- and off-ramps. Grade separation for cross streets can be provided without disrupting established development in adjoining blocks. Re-arrangement of underground utilities that are cut by freeway excavation is usually less troublesome at mid-block than near intersections. Space remains for developing parks and recreational areas. Then, too, the existing streets along the boundaries serve local traffic and provide full access to fronting property. Unfortunately, rights of way this wide often cannot be taken, either because funds are not available or because there is objection to the removal of so much property from the tax rolls. In some cases, rights of way for freeways or expressways have been gained by widening the alleys which bisect main blocks or by taking a half block including one street and one alley. Alley frontage is of much lower value than street frontage, which makes the over-all cost of such rights of way less.

In many instances, freeways have been placed on structures above ground level. This design largely eliminates interference with normal street traffic and requires little rearrangement of underground utilities. On the other hand, the structures are extremely expensive, and pro-visions for access and egress are both expensive and troublesome. Often the savings in right-of-way costs are largely offset by settle-ments with owners of adjacent property who claim damage to the value of their properties.

Many authorities consider that elevated highways form a barrier much like that created in earlier days by railroad tracks. They assert that on one side normal development will take place but that property on the "other side of the tracks" will decrease in value. They also declare that elevated roads are out of place except in industrial areas or in locations where it is desired to separate one kind of land use

[12] The clear distance preceding each connection should be great enough that drivers can be alerted and given time for appropriate action. Spacings as great as several ordinary city blocks are required where the design speed of the free-way is high.

definitely from another. Experience with elevated highways is not yet sufficient to prove or disprove these contentions.

The location of arterial highways bypassing small communities presents quite a different problem. Here it is often desirable to swing entirely clear of the community rather than to pass between a segment of the residential area and the business district. Rights of way for the close-in route will be more expensive. If the bypass is to be developed as a freeway, more grade separations will be required to accommodate local movements, which means greater first cost. Where limited funds make crossings at grade necessary, traffic on both bypass and local street will be delayed and inconvenienced. Often local business interests will oppose the complete bypassing of their community. Yet much evidence is accumulating to show that business is not hurt and often is improved by this arrangement.

Surveys for urban highways

In general, the sequence of reconnaissance, preliminary location, and final location is followed for urban as well as rural highway surveys. On urban projects, however, procedures are much less uniform and fixed. For example, there may be prior surveys and maps made for property location, street improvement, or other purposes that will furnish most of the information normally gathered by reconnaissance. In many instances these data may be complete and accurate enough that no preliminary survey is required. Thus the finished location can be developed almost entirely from the results of earlier surveys.

Paired aerial photographs or mosaics often are the primary reconnaissance tool for urban location. Examination will suggest alinement that avoids highly developed areas of high right-of-way costs. Often preliminary studies for grade-separation structures and interchanges can also be made from them. Thus, with little field work, the most desirable locations can be selected for further examination on the ground.

Just as in rural areas, location surveys will consist of staking and referencing the center line, taking profiles and cross sections, and determining the locations of all culture and property monuments. Considerable time will be taken in locating surface and underground utilities so that construction plans can include provision for their rearrangement or relocation. Through built-up areas, surveys on new rights of way will be complicated by the many obstructions. Often it will be impossible to run a continuous center line until the right of way is cleared for construction, and all earlier work must be done by using offset lines and improvising in other ways. Then, too, seldom is an urban survey made in a location free from conflict with motor vehicles on the existing streets, which occasions many delays and is at times actually dangerous to the personnel involved. Many of these problems can be minimized by employing large-scale vertical aerial photographs and maps made from the photographs by photogrammetric methods.

HIGHWAY PLANS AND SPECIFICATIONS

Highway plans

Plans and specifications are, in effect, the instructions under which highways are built. Where the work is done by a contractor, they are an integral part of the contract between contractor and highway agency. In general, the plans contain the engineering drawings of the project whereas the specifications present the written instructions.

After the final location for a given project has been completed, including the field soils investigation, the data are forwarded to the design office. There a complete scheme for the road is worked out by specialists in the fields of geometric design, drainage, structures, soils, and pavements. All the dimensional features and many other details of each final design are recorded on a series of drawings commonly referred to as plans. Figure 8 shows one sheet of plans for a typical two-lane rural highway. In this case, the upper half of the sheet is devoted to a "plan" view showing horizontal alinement, right-of-way takings, arrangements for handling drainage, and many other features. The lower half is the "profile" on which are plotted elevations of the original ground surface along the roadway center line and the vertical alinement or "grade line" for the road. The vertical scale of the profile usually is exaggerated 5 to 10 times. Sometimes profiles and other details of drainage channels or connecting roads also are placed here. Many agencies list the estimated earthwork quantities for each 100-ft station or other interval along the bottom of each sheet as they are often needed by contractors or field engineers. Other sheets of the plans show roadway cross sections fitting every situation in the entire project. Figure 14, page 163, is typical. Also included will be sheets of drawings for all structures and roadway appurtenances.

Nearly all highway agencies use standard-size drawings about 36 in. wide and 22 in. high. Some reduce the final plans during the blueprinting process to make for easier handling in the field. Some states

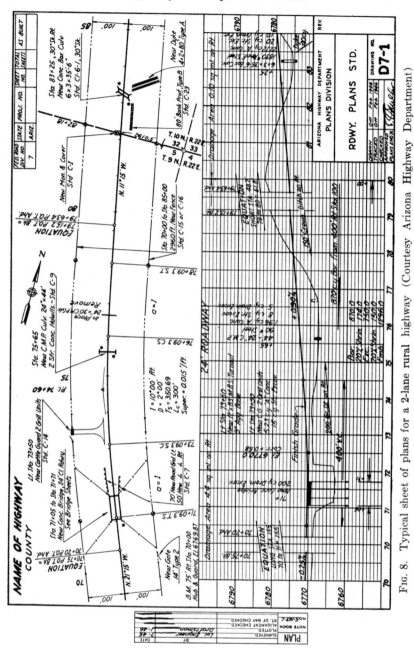

FIG. 8. Typical sheet of plans for a 2-lane rural highway (Courtesy Arizona Highway Department)

have reduced the number of drawings to be supplied for each project by providing "standard drawings" for certain elements that appear repeatedly. Engineers, contractors, and other interested parties are supplied with them or permitted to purchase them. A partial list of subjects covered by the standard drawings would include pipe culverts, concrete box culverts, guard rails and parapets, curbs and gutters and curb returns, sidewalks, drainage inlet and outlet structures of numerous types, manholes, riprap and other devices used for bank protection, fences, and right-of-way and other permanent survey markers.

Highway specifications

Carelessly or loosely worded specifications can result in the use of improper materials and in poor workmanship. On the other hand, specifications that are too exacting result in higher costs. Where work is done by a contractor, the specifications, as part of the contract, become legal documents. Often they come under the scrutiny of the courts. It follows that specification writing is a difficult and exacting task which requires a knowledge of the law of contracts as well as of highway practices. Detailed treatment is beyond the scope of this book, and the reader is referred to the standard textbooks in specifications and contracts.

Specifications contain the written instructions for constructing highway projects and outline carefully and in detail the procedures and methods to be followed for each operation. Often they are divided into two parts: standard specifications and special provisions. The standard specifications apply to every project constructed by the agency and treat subjects that occur repeatedly in the agency's work. The special provisions cover subjects peculiar to the project in question and include additions or modifications to the standard specifications. The special provisions issued by some highway agencies include copies of all the documents required for securing competitive bids and for the contract. This is helpful to both contractor and construction engineer.

It is common practice to incorporate many items into the specifications by reference. For example, standard specifications rarely duplicate the details of specifications or test procedures for highway materials. Instead, a statement is included that the material shall conform to the requirements set out in the appropriate standard of the American Association of State Highway Officials or the American Society for Testing Materials.

Supervision of construction

About 95% of all highway construction funds are expended on projects done by contract. Competitive bids are taken, and the work is awarded (usually) to the lowest responsible bidder. This contractor agrees to execute the work in accordance with the plans and specifications; in return he will be paid at the prices stipulated in his bid. Most highway contracts are on a *unit-price* basis as distinguished from *lump-sum* bids common in building work.

The highway agency is represented during construction by a resident engineer and his staff of surveyors and inspectors. Their responsibility includes inspection of the contractor's work, measuring and computing the quantities for which the contractor will be paid, and usually the surveying and layout work.

7 —————————————— Rights of Way

INTRODUCTION

During the earlier decades of highway development, most rural roads were constructed along section lines or other dedicated ways. The little added rights of way were usually secured cheaply; often property owners were eager to supply land in return for the benefits to be gained from road improvement. In cities, rights of way were available along dedicated streets. Today, however, conditions are far different. Modern highways often require wide rights of way on new locations. Sometimes entire residential or business properties of high value are swallowed up. Access to the new road often is denied the owners of abutting lands, so that they no longer reap immediate and large gains through increased land values. In addition, the feeling is widespread that property owners are entitled to the largest settlements that they can collect. For these reasons, rights of way now are one of the major costs of most highway improvements. To illustrate, the California Division of Highways spent $31 million for rights of way in the fiscal year 1951–52, as contrasted with $82 million for construction. On many urban freeways, expenditures for property or for damages equaled or exceeded those for construction.

With the exception of appraisal work, right-of-way problems are more a legal than an engineering matter. In each state, procedures for acquiring property by purchase or by condemnation are prescribed by law. Court rulings on disputed cases establish the bounds of proper payment for property taken for road improvement or damaged by it. Where a dispute arises that is not covered by an existing court ruling, action to establish precedent may be necessary. On occasion, a higher court will reverse an earlier decision, and this changes the basis for future settlements on the point in question. Sometimes rulings with seemingly contradictory findings appear in the same

123

jurisdiction, which introduces added confusion. Then too, rulings often differ among the individual states, making it hazardous to predict settlements in one jurisdiction on the basis of those in another.[1] It should be clear, therefore, that engineers must seek competent legal advice when dealing with the legislative and judicial phases of right-of-way work.

Almost without exception, the courts have held that highway authorities have the vested power to locate or relocate highways [2] and to determine the standards of improvement, including right-of-way widths.[3] This means, in effect, that highway improvements cannot be blocked by suits questioning engineering design. Authority generally comes through the "police power" which permits the state to legislate to protect the public health, safety, and morals.

Right-of-way acquisition in settled areas is a time-consuming operation. There are instances along urban freeways where 40 separate property settlements were made in each block. In such cases, right-of-way acquisition should begin several years before the time scheduled for construction.

Highway engineers, even though short of knowledge of the legal side of the right-of-way problem, should understand the procedures and rules under which property is obtained. Further, they should know something of the legal factors that so often control property costs and damage settlements. The paragraphs that follow offer a brief introduction to these subjects.[4]

[1] This idea is illustrated by the term "weight of authority," which appears frequently in legal literature. Weight of authority says, in effect, that more of the courts have decided one way than the other on a particular point.

[2] In some states the routes, but not exact locations, are set by the legislature.

[3] In states having "control-of-access" laws, this would include the power to declare a given road a freeway or expressway if such powers have been granted the agency by the legislature.

[4] Excellent references have been published by the U. S. Bureau of Public Roads and the Highway Research Board. See particularly David R. Levin, *Public Land Acquisition for Highway Purposes* (1943), *Legal Aspects of Controlling Highway Access* (1945), and *Public Control of Highway Access and Roadside Development* (revised 1947), published by the Public Roads Administration; *Bulletins 4* (1946), *10* (1948), *18* (1949), *30* (1951), *38* (1951), *55* (1952), and *77* (1953) prepared by the committee on land acquisition and control of highway access and adjacent areas of the Highway Research Board; and the releases of this committee through the Highway Research Correlation Service of the Highway Research Board.

PROPERTY ACQUISITION

Procedures for acquiring property

Highway agencies, along with many other public bodies or quasi-public corporations like railroads and public utilities, are vested with the power of "eminent domain." This is the right of the government to take private property for public use, with or without the owner's consent. The owner, in turn, if not satisfied with the payment offered for the property, has recourse to the courts to secure just compensation. . Most highway agencies avoid using eminent domain when at all possible. Instead, property is obtained by direct negotiation with the owners. Condemnation is resorted to only when the owner refuses to sell or when his demands are unreasonable.[5]

The taking of property under eminent domain is not limited to rights of way of a definite width. For example, the California law states that "the department may acquire any real property which it considers necessary for state highway purposes." It specifically mentions real property that may be exchanged for other property needed for highway purposes; quarries; borrow pits for fill materials, sand, or gravel; site for offices, shops, and storage yards; and space needed to accommodate cut or fill slopes, drainage channels, and access roads. Locations providing scenic views or park sites are also included.

Procedures for forcibly acquiring property are far from uniform among the various highway agencies. Many of the methods are extremely cumbersome and time-consuming. Some agencies employ different techniques under different circumstances. In any event, the evidence is strong that in many jurisdictions efficiency could be greatly improved by a drastic revision of present laws and practices.[6]

Where property must be obtained by condemnation, the procedure may be long drawn out. This is particularly true when the findings of the trial court are reviewed by the higher courts. There are many instances where completion of a highway improvement has been delayed for several years because of tangles over rights of way. At times, property owners have forced exorbitant payments by the threat

[5] The California Division of Highways reports that direct settlement is made with the owner in 97% of its cases.

[6] For more on this subject see *Public Land Acquisition for Highway Purposes*. Reports on New York, Texas, and Minnesota acquisition practices appear in *Highway Research Board Bulletins 4*, pp. 18–27, and *30*, p. 5. Details of California practice may be found in the *California Right of Way Manual* published by the Division of Highways of that state (1950).

of litigation. To avoid these losses in time and money, a number of states have now enacted legislation permitting highway agencies to take almost immediate possession of needed land. Details of these arrangements vary from state to state. In general, they require that taking the land first be justified to the proper court. Next, money or bond equal to the value of the land is deposited with the court for the landowner. The highway agency is then free to begin construction while the final settlement is worked out.[7]

Payment for acquired property

Fair payment for rights of way would, on the one hand, provide just compensation to the owner and, on the other, represent a proper and fair use of public funds. However, it is often impossible to provide full compensation to property owners, for public officials are prevented by law from paying for certain losses that a property owner may suffer. For example, the courts have ruled that the owners of business property taken for public purposes cannot be compensated for such things as loss of goodwill, inability to locate an acceptable substitute location, loss of profit caused by moving or by interruptions during construction, or the cost of moving goods or other personal property. This is but one illustration of the basic principle that government is not required to make payment for all injuries that it imposes on persons or property.

Payment when entire property is taken. When property is taken in its entirety, just compensation is usually based on the *market value* of the property. The AASHO defines market value as "the highest price for which property can be sold in the open market by a willing seller to a willing buyer, neither acting under compulsion and both exercising reasonable judgment."[8] This definition would permit land value to be set at the "highest and best use" which is defined as "the most productive use, reasonable but not speculative or conjectural, to which property may be put in the near future." Thus a vacant parcel of land located in an industrial area, but currently being farmed, could be priced as industrial land. On the other hand, farmland at

---

[7] For further discussion and court rulings for and against immediate possession see *Public Land Acquisition*, p. 7, and *Highway Research Board Bulletins 10, 30, 38, 55,* and *77*, pp. 1, 8, 5, 5, and 3, respectively. An exhaustive study titled *Immediate Possession of Highway Right-of-Way* was prepared by the committee on right of way of the AASHO in 1951.

[8] This definition and others that follow are from *Highway Definitions*, part IV, *Right of Way Terms,* adopted by the AASHO on January 1, 1952.

some distance from town will be paid for as such, and not on the basis that it might, in the future, become business or commercial property.

Market value may be approached in four ways, as follows: [9]

1. *Market-Data Approach.* Comparison of property being appraised with similar properties being sold or listed for sale.

2. *Replacement Cost New Less Depreciation Approach.* The market value of the land is determined by the study of market data; to this is added the estimated cost of replacing the improvements today less the proper depreciation from all causes. On improved property, this method supplements the market-data approach. An alternative within this method may be to determine the cost of the land and add to it the cost of moving the buildings and other improvements to another site.

3. *Income Approach.* For types of property where income is important, the actual and fair earnings of the property are compared to earnings of comparable properties that have been sold, and from this an estimate of value is obtained. The courts have generally ruled that possible future use and profits, if only hypothetical or speculative, cannot be considered as evidence of value.

4. *Historical Cost New Less Depreciation Approach.* Actual cost is generally the best evidence of value for both land and improvements of new property. In older properties, historical cost becomes less and less important.

An appraisal to determine market value, based on one or more of the approaches outlined above, is the first step toward securing property for highway rights of way. Armed with this appraisal, a negotiator attempts to make a settlement with the property owner. If agreement cannot be reached, condemnation proceedings are instituted in the courts. Condemnation cases are much like other civil court procedures. Representatives of each party present appraisals and other measures of the worth of the property to the jury, or judge sitting in place of the jury. Disputes over the admissibility of evidence are settled by the judge. The jury then weighs all the facts and sets the amount of the settlement.

Appeals to higher courts generally concern the rulings of the trial judge as to admissibility of evidence. Decisions on these points by the higher courts establish much of the precedent for future appraisal practices in each jurisdiction.

[9] Based on *Right of Way Manual,* California Division of Highways.

Payment for partial takings

When only a portion of a property is to be acquired, payment is usually set as the difference in value of the property "before and after taking." Part of the settlement is for the property actually acquired and the remainder for "severance" damages. Under certain circumstances, "benefits" to the remaining property are offset against damages in reaching the final settlement.

Value of property taken may be determined by the approaches outlined in the preceding section. For farmland, a price per acre may be appropriate. For business property, where value per unit of area decreases from front to rear of the property, "depth factors" are sometimes employed as a guide.

The AASHO defines severance damage as "the loss in value of the remainder of a parcel resulting from the acquisition." It occurs, for example, if a remaining piece of farmland is too small to be tilled economically or if a lot in a business area is shortened to a point where the enterprise operates less efficiently. Severance damages may also include losses resulting from impairment of access, light, air, and view.[10]

In most jurisdictions the courts have ruled that property abutting a road has no right to the continuation or maintenance of traffic in front of it. Accordingly, loss in land value when a highway improvement diverts the main flow of traffic vertically or horizontally or both is not a compensable damage.

Benefits to adjoining property and to surrounding areas often result from highway improvement. For legal purposes, these are grouped into two classes, "general" and "special." The AASHO defines a general benefit as "advantage accruing from a given highway improvement to a community as a whole, applying to all property similarly situated." An example would be a general rise in property values in an area made accessible by a new road. Special benefit is defined as "advantage accruing from a given highway improvement to a specific property and not to others generally." Examples of special benefits are: opening a street giving additional frontage or making a corner lot; opening a new road or changing the grade of an existing road, making the property more accessible or providing ingress and egress where none was provided before; and improving the road fronting a property by grading, paving, or drainage. Note that in each of these

[10] See discussion on p. 131.

examples a particular piece of property benefits, as contrasted to benefits accruing to the community in general.[11]

The extent to which the courts have permitted benefits to offset damages varies so widely among states that no generalization can be made.[12] In some instances, special benefits, but not general benefits, may be offset against severance damage and also against the value of the land taken. In others, special benefits alone may be offset against severance damages to remaining property but not against the value of the property taken. There are instances, too, where general benefits have been offset against severance damages.

SETTLEMENTS WHEN NO PROPERTY IS TAKEN

A highway improvement sometimes impairs the usefulness of lands abutting a proposed location or in the area penetrated. Injury from this cause is called "consequential damage," defined by the AASHO as "loss in value of a parcel, no portion of which is acquired, resulting from a highway improvement." The most common causes of consequential damage are impairment of access, light, air, and view.

In general, the courts do not distinguish between severance and consequential damages. Thus, in a given jurisdiction, benefits would be offset against consequential damages to the same degree as against severance damages.

EXCESS CONDEMNATION

Excess condemnation is the taking of more property than is actually required for a highway improvement. In some states the statutes permit taking small fragments that have little value. In some this authority extends further, so that a whole property may be taken when its cost is less than that of the partial taking plus severance damages

[11] There is substantial evidence that highway improvement increases the value to abutting property and that it also raises property values in the areas penetrated. Business activity generally increases on city streets that have been relieved of through traffic. A number of California case studies of the effects of freeways on land values have been published in *California Highways and Public Works,* beginning with the issue of May–June 1948. Results of a study on land values along the Gulf Freeway in Houston were published by the Texas Highway Department in 1952. Data on the effect of bypasses on property values in two Indiana locations appear in a paper by A. K. Branbaw, A. D. May, and H. L. Michael, published in *Highway Research Board Bulletin 67* (1953).

[12] See *Highway Research Board Bulletins 55,* p. 3, and *77,* p. 8.

to the remainder. In these cases, legal means are also established for the sale of the excess to private owners, usually by auction.

The taking of continuous strips of rights of way along highway margins is permitted by the constitutions of a few states. Under this authority, marginal lands may be acquired for one or more of three purposes: (1) to provide space for future development, if needed, (2) to protect the highway from objectionable or unsightly developments, and (3) to recoup at least a part of the cost of the road improvement by selling the land at a higher price after the new road is completed. In certain other states, the legislatures have passed statutes that permit the acquisition of marginal lands, but these, unlike constitutional provisions, must be tested in the courts. David R. Levin suggests that condemnation to carry out the first two purposes listed above probably would be found valid as in the public interest. He indicates, however, that "the courts seem to frown upon condemnation of land for recoupment." [13] Excess condemnation to provide for public rather than private gain from increases in land value has been little used in the United States, although many highway officials seriously propose its employment.

RIGHTS OF ACCESS, LIGHT, AIR, AND VIEW

Control of access

In the past, business, commercial, and other developments along conventional highways and streets often have practically destroyed their usefulness as traffic arteries. As an illustration, Garvey Road, which carries U. S. Highways 60 and 70 east from Los Angeles for 30 miles, was built in the middle 1930's through open fields away from the then developed towns. Access from adjoining property was not controlled. Within one year, congestion caused by roadside development had decreased the capacity by about 25%. Within 4 years, ribbon development was almost continuous, and speed zoning was in effect over much of the road's length. Like examples may be found throughout the country.

By 1953, 31 states had employed the "controlled-access" or "freeway" principle to prevent repetitions of these earlier experiences.[14]

---

[13] See *Public Control of Highway Access and Roadside Development*, pp. 59–67.

[14] Controlled access by statutory enactment, judicial decision, or constitutional provision was in effect in Arkansas, California, Colorado, Connecticut, Delaware, Florida, Georgia, Illinois, Indiana, Kansas, Kentucky, Louisiana, Maine, Mary-

Control of access has been defined by the AASHO as "that condition where the rights of owners or occupants of abutting land or other persons to access, light, air, or view in connection with a highway are controlled by public authority." Under this principle, highway agencies are free to select conditions under which access to highways is permitted. Entrances, exits, and crossings for existing roads and outlets for abutting property may or may not be provided, at the discretion of the highway agency. With this authority, it is possible to prevent ribbon development with its attendant evils. Further, access, egress, and crossing facilities can be located and designed primarily to meet traffic and other engineering considerations rather than to satisfy local demands.

The development of freeway-type facilities may be seriously hampered where access control legislation is lacking. In these states, owners of abutting property cannot be denied access to any highway, old or new. Various strategems have sometimes proved helpful in providing a measure of control. For example, by the combination of wide rights of way and outer highways, indiscriminate entry to or crossing of the through lanes can sometimes be prevented. Again, access at points of hazard may be denied under the police power. However, experience to date has proved beyond question that access control legislation is a "must" of modern highway practice.

Payment for rights of access, view, light, and air

The legal right of the public to convenient and safe travel over public roads and streets is firmly established in the United States. On the other hand, abutting property also has certain legal rights, among them rights to reasonable access and egress to existing highways, reasonable view of the property from the highway and of the highway from the property, and a flow of light and air to the property from the highway. These private rights are protected by the "due process" clause of the Constitution. They can be taken only for public purposes and then only by payment of just compensation, with final determination in disputed cases made by the courts.

Freeway-type facilities involve access control and grade separation,

land, Massachusetts, Michigan, Minnesota, Mississippi, Missouri, Nebraska, New Hampshire, New Jersey, New York, North Dakota, Ohio, Oklahoma, Oregon, Pennsylvania, Rhode Island, South Dakota, Texas, Utah, Virginia, Washington, West Virginia, Wisconsin, and Wyoming. For brief descriptions of controlled-access statutes in effect in 1947 and for a model law see *Public Control of Highway Access and Roadside Development*, Public Roads Administration (1947). See also *Highway Research Board Bulletin 77*, pp. 17–20.

both of which often bring public and private rights into direct conflict.   In each state, the courts must distinguish among situations
where (1) public rights are paramount so that no compensation is
due the property owner, (2) private rights are taken under eminent
domain so that the owner is entitled to compensation, and (3) private
rights are infringed, but under the police power, so that the owner
is not entitled to compensation.   As yet, these limits are poorly defined in most jurisdictions, since disputes involving control of access
are of fairly recent origin.   Furthermore, legal precedent is established
only from court cases arising in each state and usually from the few
of these that are reviewed by that state's higher courts.[15]   Some time
yet must elapse before this phase of right-of-way law is defined with
any certainty.

In many states, the courts have awarded property owners the actual
damage sustained when access to an existing highway was denied or
impaired.   In cases of partial takings, loss or impairment of access
was considered with other damages to the remaining property in
reaching the value "after taking."   Where no property was taken,
damages were permitted for loss of access alone.[16]   In two states at
least, however, the courts have denied awards for loss of access where
the arrangements offered by the new highway were equal to those in
effect earlier.   However, the decisions on this general subject have been
conflicting and often irreconcilable in principle, even within a single
state.

In some states, but not in others, the courts have held that construction of controlled-access highways on new locations creates a vested
right of access from adjoining lands to the freeways.   Highway
agencies affected by these rulings are forced to purchase access rights
along the new freeway just as they would along existing highways.
Often the costs of extinguishing the access rights are practically equal
to those of the property taken.   Highway officials and the courts in
increasing numbers feel that this view creates a windfall for land-
owners at public expense and is therefore prejudicial to the public
interest.[17]

Numerous claims for loss of light, air, and view have been occasioned
by grade-separation structures and other improvements where the

[15] Before reaching a conclusion, the courts review the findings of courts in
other states, but are not bound by them.

[16] See Frank K. Wall, *Highway Research Board Bulletin 10,* for a discussion
of the value of access rights.

[17] See papers by J. B. Hutton, Jr., in *Highway Research Board Bulletin 51,*
pp. 38–61 (1951) and by H. B. Reese in *Bulletin 77,* pp. 36–50 (1953) for careful

roadway grade was altered. Here again, some courts have ruled that public rights transcend private rights so that no compensation need be paid; others have taken the opposite view. To illustrate, certain courts have held that compensation need not be paid abutting owners when the change involved a legitimate street use.[18] In particular cases, the construction of bridges, viaducts, and their approaches, and other changes in street or highway grade have all been classed as proper street uses. On the other hand, the Iowa Supreme Court has ruled for the property owners in a case where a viaduct constructed in the street as part of a railroad grade separation left a narrow and circuitous means of access and also impaired light, air, and view.[19] The court stated, in effect, that abutting owners were entitled to compensation for the destruction, substantial impairment, or interference with their rights of access, light, air, or view by any work or structure built for the improvement of the highway. The California Supreme Court in the Riccardi case went even farther. Here one major street was depressed under another to provide grade separation. The property in question was to be served by a local way 30 ft wide at ground level. It was ruled by a 4–3 decision that abutting property owners were entitled to compensation for the loss of direct access to and reasonable view of their property from the through portions of the highway. The majority ruling in the Riccardi case is far-reaching as it greatly extends the rights of abutting property at the expense of the public's right to the use of the highways. Many authorities consider that this decision is contrary to precedent and sound public policy. Certainly its widespread adoption would greatly increase the cost of modern highways.[20]

CIRCUITY OF TRAVEL—CUL-DE-SACS

Modern highway designs that employ outer highways, center medians, and traffic interchanges almost always lengthen the route to or from some parcels of abutting or nearby property. One-way streets, U-turn prohibitions, and many other traffic-control measures have a like effect. Many courts have held that this "circuity of travel" may

and detailed studies of court rulings on the subject in the United States and England. The articles also suggest legislative and judicial remedies.

[18] See, for example, *Highway Research Board Bulletin 38,* pp. 54–55.

[19] See *Highway Research Board Bulletin 30,* p. 18 (1950).

[20] For an abstract of the Riccardi case and a discussion of its implications see *Legal Aspects of Controlling Highway Access,* pp. 16–17, 33–34, and 43–44.

be imposed under the police power and therefore is noncompensable unless public officials have acted in an arbitrary manner.

It is also reasoned that circuity of travel does not substantially impair ingress and egress. Further, any interference that does result is one of the prices of road improvement shared in common with the general public. The courts will seldom award damages unless access to the particular property in question is substantially impaired as compared with other property in the vicinity.[21]

Limited-access highways often cut across and block off existing roads and streets. Property that earlier had access to cross streets in either direction is placed on a dead-end street, commonly called a "cul-de-sac." In numerous instances, owners of property so affected have sued for damages. In a majority of cases, the courts have denied such claims when adequate means of access was left. Often the reasoning has been that the principal factor was mere "circuity of route" which is not compensable, as explained in the preceding paragraph. In other cases, the ruling was based on the argument that the injury, if any, differed only in degree but not in kind from that suffered by the public in general. Another court held the damages to be *damnum absque injuria*, which means injury without violation of a legal right. In some states, however, the courts have granted damages. For example, in the Bacich case in California, a three-story apartment house located at about mid-block was placed on a cul-de-sac when the grade of one of the adjacent cross streets was lowered 50 ft. The State Supreme Court permitted damages by a 4–2–1 decision which held that reasonable egress and ingress to urban property embraces access in both directions to the next intersecting street. Thus, in California, property owners may sue for damages if highway improvement places their property on a cul-de-sac. However, in four cases since tried in that state, property owners who sued for damages were denied them by trial juries.[22]

RESERVING RIGHTS OF WAY FOR FUTURE HIGHWAY IMPROVEMENTS

Almost all highway agencies select locations and prepare tentative plans for highway improvements several years before funds become

[21] See *Legal Aspects of Controlling Highway Access*, pp. 17–18 and 28–33, and *Highway Research Board Bulletins 38*, pp. 11–13 (1951), and *55*, pp. 10–11 (1952).

[22] For added information on this subject, see *Legal Phases of Highway Access*,

available to purchase rights of way for them. During this time lapse, buildings and other improvements often are constructed on the property. The result is economic waste as well as high right-of-way costs. Early purchase of rights of way is the ideal solution to this problem, but funds for that purpose are usually lacking.[23]

Highway development rights, purchased from a property owner, give a highway agency the right to limit the uses of or developments on land abutting a highway. Reservation agreements as employed in Ohio and special easements authorized by statute in Maryland are forms of development rights. Each has the fault that compensation must be paid at the time that the rights are obtained. In a few states, authority to establish *ultimate right-of-way widths* is vested in the state highway department or local government as an extension of the police power. By giving proper public notice, the erection of structures and other detrimental practices within the ultimate right of way can be prohibited. In a number of states, local government has been given the power to institute an *official map procedure.* This authority permits local officials to adopt an official map showing, among other features, contemplated highways and streets. When the map is approved after public hearings, it becomes binding on public authorities and private property owners alike. *Subdivision regulations* and *zoning* are other devices by which local officials may control developments on the sites of future highways.

The techniques mentioned above all have at times proved effective in reserving rights of way for future highways. However, each of them is circumscribed by statutory limitations, judicial rulings regarding private rights, or local customs and pressures. A search for more effective legal means, begun in 1951 by the committee on land acquisition and control of adjacent areas, Highway Research Board, is actively under way.[24]

pp. 15–16, 18–28, and 34–49, and *Highway Research Board Bulletin 55,* pp. 15–17 (1952).

[23] There are a few instances where funds for advanced acquisition of rights of way have been provided. For example, in California in 1952 the legislature provided $10 million in an advance right-of-way acquisition and protection fund. This sum was soon expended, and in 1953 a revolving fund of comparable proportions was established.

[24] See *Highway Research Board Bulletins 38,* pp. 13–16 (1951), *55,* pp. 1–3 (1952), and *77,* pp. 3–8 (1953). Also see papers by L. C. Moser and R. B. Sawtelle, pp. 51–72 of *Bulletin 77.*

8 ——————————— Highway Design

INTRODUCTION

Highway designs are dictated by the physical characteristics and limitations of the motor-vehicle driver and of the vehicle that he operates. Good designs will be efficient and safe in daylight and dark and in good and bad weather. They will be consistent, so that the driver is not confronted unexpectedly with different and serious situations. Most important of all, they will be adequate for tomorrow's as well as today's traffic.[1]

The designer in planning a highway facility is concerned among other things with capacity, or how many vehicles the road can and will carry, with roadway and lane widths, with vertical and horizontal alinement and their effects on sight distances and speeds, and with intersection and interchange layout. These and many other aspects of the problem must be weighed in terms of first cost, over-all economy, convenience, and safety before the design of the project is finally completed.

DRIVER CHARACTERISTICS

The human mechanism

After a person's eyes register a given happening, a period of time elapses before muscular reaction occurs. This period, called *reaction time*, is appreciable, and differs among persons. It also varies for the same individual, being increased by fatigue, drinking, and other causes. A simple eye-to-finger reaction, which requires depressing the finger after a light flashes, usually takes about three-eighths of a second. Eye-to-foot reaction called for in depressing the brake pedal

---

[1] For a review of past changes in design standards as a guide to the future see A Choice of Guides, by Thomas H. MacDonald, *American Highways*, January 1953, p. 6.

of a motor vehicle requires a longer period, usually about six-tenths of a second, but more than a full second for some individuals. The subjects of these tests were expecting the signal to which they were to respond, whereas the average motor-vehicle operator is not. Thus another interval of time, called *perception time,* is required to alert the driver before reactions can begin. Field tests have shown that combined perception and reaction time is five to seven times that required for eye-to-foot reaction. Perception plus reaction time assumed by the AASHO ranges from 2 sec for drivers traveling 70 mph to 3 sec for those traveling 30 mph.[2]

Often drivers face situations much more complex than those requiring application of the brakes. For example, at a typical right-angle intersection with vehicles approaching from all directions, the driver must look to both sides and possibly ahead, determine a course of action, and then carry out the appropriate muscular response. In other words, the procedure becomes preception–judgment–reaction. In this instance perception requires considerable time. The eyes see acutely in an arc covering about 5 degrees, but only vaguely over the remaining spread of vision. They must be focused individually in each direction, sometimes requiring 0.6 sec for each. After this, time ranging from 1 to 3 sec is needed to judge the appropriate action. Then the muscles must respond. Thus, in complex situations, 3 or more seconds may elapse before any of the controls of the vehicles are changed.[3] This clearly indicates the desirability of confronting vehicle operators with only one decision at a time, and that one should be simple rather than complex.

Other driver characteristics

Fear of accident controls many driver decisions. Operating speeds are ordinarily set instinctively at the highest level consistent with a feeling of security and comfort. The decision to pass another vehicle or conduct other maneuvers is similarly affected. Since different drivers exercise different degrees of caution, the speeds at which they

[2] See *A Policy on Sight Distances for Highways,* AASHO, p. 2 (1940). This "policy" pamphlet is one of several on highway design published by the AASHO. The entire "policy" series, bound in one volume, has been released by the AASHO under the title *Policies on Geometric Highway Design* (1950). Publication of a revised edition is scheduled for late 1954. For the remainder of this chapter, references will be to the particular pamphlet in question.

[3] See T. W. Forbes in *Transactions American Society of Civil Engineers,* p. 416 (1941).

drive will not be the same. Operators also tend to follow the path that involves the least change of speed and least discomfort. Cutting of corners by motorists who approach intersections too fast and do not slow down is an illustration. Setting the brakes when confronted with any danger is another involuntary response.

Drivers almost invariably veer away from fixed objects like walls or railings set close to the roadway edge. Likewise they stay at considerable distances from unpaved, depressed, or rough shoulders. If these conditions exist, the effective width of the roadway is reduced by the driver's natural reactions.

Fear of arrest and punishment also affects driver behavior. In heavily policed urban areas excessive speed and other reckless practices occur less frequently than on suburban or rural roads where the chance of detection is remote. For the same reason, traffic-control devices are more effective in urban than in other areas; likewise designs used may differ between urban and rural situations.

SIZES AND WEIGHTS OF MOTOR VEHICLES

Almost all highways carry both passenger automobiles and trucks, and design standards must be set to meet the requirements of both. Usually the size, weight, and other characteristics of legally permitted trucks govern. In each state the legislature prescribes the limits for each characteristic of all vehicles operating there, although local authorities sometimes permit greater loads or interpose more severe restrictions on particular roads or streets. Table 1 lists some of the more important size and weight features for which maximums are prescribed by law and gives the extreme upper and lower values set by the individual states. Also shown are recommendations of the AASHO as presented in *A Policy concerning Maximum Dimensions, Weights, and Speeds of Motor Vehicles to Be Operated over the Highways of the United States* (1946). The last 4 columns of Table 1 give, for each item, the number of states whose requirements are higher than, equal to, or lower than those recommended by the AASHO and the number of states having no requirement on particular items.

In many states, the desire of the trucking industry for more economical operation through the use of larger and heavier vehicles has resulted in demands for upward revisions of existing limits. At times legislatures have yielded to these pressures without fully appreciating the results. It must be emphasized that the AASHO recommendations represent the carefully weighed judgment of engineers from the state

TABLE 1. SUMMARY OF STATE LIMITATIONS ON TRUCK DIMENSIONS, AXLE LOADS, AND WEIGHTS

Item	AASHO Uniform Standard	Max. in Any State	Min. in Any State	Number of States * Having Limits			Number of States Having No Such Requirement
				Higher than AASHO	Same as AASHO	Lower than AASHO	
Width, in.	96	102	96	2	47	0	0
Height, ft	12.50	14.00	12.50	12	35	0	2
Length, ft							
Single unit truck	35	55	35	13	35	0	1
Truck tractor and semitrailer	50	65	45	10	17	21	1
Any combination †	60	65	45	3	10	35	1
Axle load, lb							
Single axle	18,000	22,400	18,000	15	34	0	0
Tandem axles	32,000	40,000	28,000	16	25	8	0
Maximum practical gross weight on any permissible vehicle	71,900	108,800	42,000	16	2	31	0

Data condensed from tabulation published in *American Highways*, April 1952.

* Includes District of Columbia.

† Full trailers not permitted in 5 states, full trailers coupled to semitrailers not permitted in 34 states nor by the AASHO recommendations.

highway departments and the Bureau of Public Roads. Upward or downward revision of some of these standards may appear desirable at a later date, but only after the results of current and projected engineering and economic research have been carefully interpreted. A further argument against raising the recommended requirements at present is the large mileage of existing roads that are substandard even for the vehicles now permitted.[4]

HIGHWAY CAPACITY

Traffic estimates

The traffic on a highway is measured by the number of vehicles passing a "traffic station" and is stated as the "volume" of traffic. Twenty-four-hour counts taken periodically on different days of the week permit calculation of the average annual daily traffic (ADT) which is a standard index. In urban areas the maximum traffic day is usually a weekday; on rural highways it frequently is Sunday. Variation in metropolitan or urban area flow with hours of the day, days

[4] For two authoritative presentations on this subject see H. S. Fairbank, Motor Vehicle Sizes and Weights, *Civil Engineering*, June 1949, pp. 40–43, and *A Factual Discussion of Motor Truck Operation, Regulation, and Taxation*, U. S. Bureau of Public Roads (1951).

of the week, months of the year, and by classes of vehicles is illustrated by San Francisco–Oakland Bay Bridge traffic counts shown in Fig. 1. On more heavily traveled roads and streets *hourly counts*

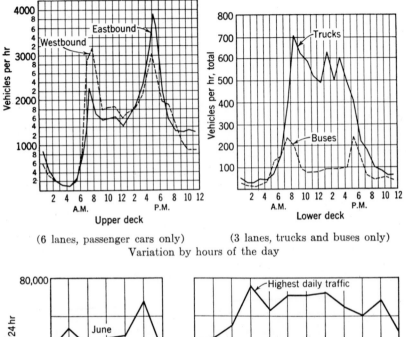

(6 lanes, passenger cars only)   (3 lanes, trucks and buses only)

Variation by hours of the day

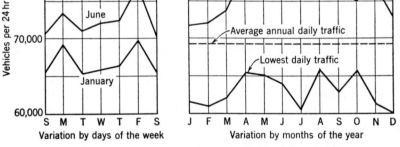

Variation by days of the week   Variation by months of the year

Fig. 1. Traffic flow on San Francisco–Oakland Bay Bridge

of peak traffic may be of very great importance. They are sometimes made by multiplying 5-min or 15-min counts, respectively, by 12 or 4.

It is not economically sound to design a facility to be congestion-free every hour throughout the year. However it has been established that for many hours each year the traffic volume approaches that of the 30th heaviest hour, which is the hourly volume exceeded only 29 hr per year. As a rule it is considered sound practice to design roads to carry this volume, called the *30th-hour volume* (see Fig. 2). Unfortunately, the ratio between average daily traffic and 30th-hour (or other design-hour) traffic is not constant for all roads, so that added data must be collected at each location if the relationship is to be firmly established. It has been determined that this ratio remains

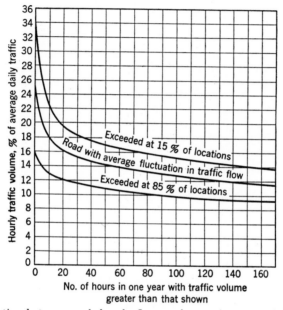

FIG. 2. Relation between peak hourly flows and annual average daily traffic on rural highways (Courtesy U. S. Bureau of Public Roads)

substantially constant from year to year at a given location. Also a range of values is known. Figure 2 shows that for 70% of our roads and streets 30th-peak-hour volume falls between 12 and 18% of the average daily traffic. Recorded extremes show 30th-hour traffic ranging from 8 to 38% of the average daily traffic. For rural locations the average is about 15%, while for urban facilities it is about 12%.

Separation of traffic-count data by direction of travel is important where heavy flow occurs in one direction at one time of day and in the other at another time. At times, economy in final design may be realized by using the same lane for traffic in opposite directions. For example, on Chicago's Outer Drive, special curbs that may be raised and lowered divide the roadway so that more than half the lanes can be used for travel in the direction of heavier flow. In other cities, similar results are obtained with less costly traffic signals over all lanes or by employing special signs and markers (see also p. 279).

For urban freeways or major highways, traffic counts on the present streets in the area may not fully measure the volume that develops on the new facility. Vehicles from some distance away may be attracted and, at times, entirely new traffic may be generated. Under such circumstances, information like that developed from origin-and-destination surveys is needed if estimates are to be accurate.

On October 12, 1949, the AASHO subcommittee on factual surveys issued a report concerning the diversion of traffic from city streets to expressways and freeways. This stimulated interest and led to studies in a number of places, including Hartford, Conn.; Columbus, Ohio; Charleston, W. Va.; St. Louis, Mo.; Shirley Highway, Va.; and Houston, Texas.[5] The methods used included origin-and-destination surveys and roadside, screen-line, and home interviews. M. Earl Campbell of the Highway Research Board in a progress report [6] indicates findings as follows:

1. A higher percentage of traffic is attracted to the controlled-access expressway than to the boulevard type of thoroughfare.

2. At the point of equal time by either route, up to 50% of the drivers will use the high-type expressway although the distance may be approximately twice as great.

3. About 5% of the drivers will use the high-type expressway where travel time is 1.5 times the travel time by city street, and the travel distance may be nearly three times as far.

4. Up to about 15% of drivers having a choice will use the expressway when travel time is 1.2 times that by the city streets.

5. About 5% of the drivers will use the city streets even though the travel distance by city street is longer and travel time by city streets is twice as great.

The report indicated a need for much added research on the subject, and also for study on the parallel problem of new traffic generation by freeway-type facilities.

Traffic-lane capacity

Traffic-lane capacity has been a subject for continuing study for many years. In the past many equations or other expressions for capacity have been offered, but these were unsupported by sufficient

---

[5] For a review of the studies on the Shirley Highway, Va., see *Public Roads*, February 1952, pp. 241–250.

[6] See Diversion of Traffic from City Streets to Expressways as a Basis for Traffic Assignment, *Highway Research Board Correlation Service Circular 139*, July 1951. See also *Highway Research Board Bulletin 61* (1952).

field observation and gave widely different results. However, the report titled Highway Capacity, Practical Applications Of Research, prepared by O. K. Normann and W. P. Walker of the U. S. Bureau of Public Roads, is authoritative.[7] Its findings are supported by tremendous masses of data collected by Federal, state and city traffic engineers. The following paragraphs in part summarize this report:

Basic capacity. *The basic capacity of a traffic lane is the maximum number of passenger cars that can pass a given point on a lane or roadway during one hour under the most nearly ideal roadway and traffic conditions that can possibly be attained.* It assumes that all vehicles travel at the same velocity and at the minimum spacing allowed by the average driver when trailing another vehicle.[8] Observed relations between vehicle spacing and velocity are shown in Fig. 3 for several roadway conditions. Basic capacities computed from these spacings are given in Fig. 4. It is to be observed that the basic capacity of a traffic lane is approximately 2000 passenger vehicles per hour; furthermore, this capacity occurs at speeds between 30 and 40 mph.

Only if all of the following conditions are met can a traffic lane reach the basic capacities shown in Fig. 4:

1. There must be at least two lanes for the exclusive use of traffic traveling in one direction.

2. All vehicles must move at approximately the same speed, which is governed by the slowest drivers and lies between 30 and 40 mph.

3. There must be practically no commercial vehicles.

4. The widths of traffic lanes, shoulders, and clearances to vertical obstructions beyond the edge of the traffic lane must be adequate.

---

[7] This report, which was prepared under the auspices of the Highway Research Board committee on highway capacity, was first published in *Public Roads,* October and December 1949. It is available also as the *Highway Capacity Manual* (147 pp.), and can be had from the Superintendent of Documents Washington 25, D. C.

[8] Improvements over the years, such as four-wheel brakes, have made closer vehicle spacing possible with a resulting increase in capacity. Other improvements will be made. However, when operating under high traffic densities, most drivers follow preceding vehicles too closely. One study showed that under these conditions 28% of the drivers could not have avoided rear-end collisions had the drivers of the preceding cars set their brakes suddenly. This assumed good brakes and the extremely low value of one second for perception plus reaction time. Capacity figures given herein are based on current operating habits, whether entirely safe or not.

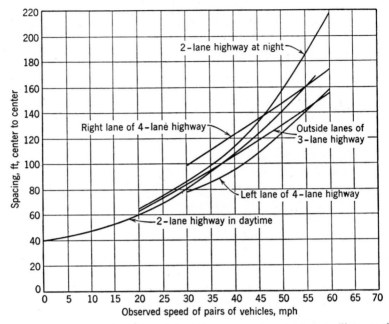

F<small>IG</small>. 3. Minimum spacing allowed by the average driver when trailing another vehicle at various speeds (Courtesy U. S. Bureau of Public Roads)

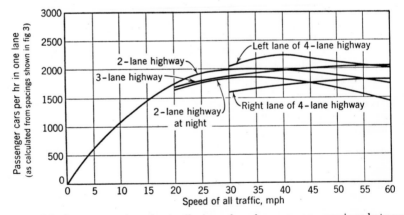

F<small>IG</small>. 4. Maximum capacity of a traffic lane, based on average spacings between pairs of vehicles traveling at the same speed (Courtesy U. S. Bureau of Public Roads)

5. There must be no restrictive sight distances, grades, improperly superelevated curves, intersections, or interference by pedestrians.

Multilane Roads. Multilane roads can be designed to meet all five conditions listed above. Therefore, the basic capacity for a multilane highway is 2000 cars per hour per lane, regardless of the number of lanes. Until recently, general opinion was that no more than three lanes in one direction should be used because added lanes did not contribute proportionally to capacity. Experience on the Lake Shore Drive in Chicago, however, has shown that with six lanes in one direction high capacity per lane is maintained.[9]

Two-Lane Roads. On two-lane roads, with few opposing vehicles, traffic can fill one lane by immediately passing into the gaps that form. This single lane might reach the basic capacity of 2000 vehicles per hour. However, as passing is restricted by vehicles from the opposite direction, the spaces that develop in the lane cannot be filled by passing maneuvers. Instead, queues of vehicles form in each direction until the spaces between queues become long enough to permit passing. Then new queues form. Basic capacity in one direction, then, is affected by volume in the opposite direction. It has been established that the basic capacity of a two-lane road *in both directions* is 2000 vehicles per hour. This might be 2000 vehicles in one direction and none in the other or 1000 in each direction.[10]

Three-Lane Roads. The center lane of a three-lane road serves vehicles performing passing maneuvers in either direction, and its use is therefore entirely different from that of an added lane on a multilane facility. When other conditions are ideal, vehicles can completely fill the outside lanes by utilizing the center lane for passing. Thus, the basic capacity of a three-lane, two-way road is 4000 vehicles in both directions.[11] The basic capacity in one direction is limited to 2000 passenger cars per hour on any section with even a single restriction in sight distance.

[9] With four lanes in one direction, an actual count of 1958 passenger vehicles per lane per hour has been recorded. With six lanes in one direction the maximum count was 1640 per lane per hour. Differences might be explained (*a*) that the six-lane facility was not loaded as close to capacity and (*b*) that increased difficulty of turning on and off might cause a true decrease in capacity.

[10] The Posey Tube in Alameda, Calif., is the only facility that, by actual count, has exceeded the basic capacity of 2000 vehicles in both directions. Under close traffic direction it has carried somewhat in excess of 2600 vehicles per hour on its two lanes.

[11] A total count of 3064 vehicles per hour has been recorded on a three-lane road in New Jersey.

Possible capacity. *Possible capacity is the maximum number of vehicles that can pass a given point on a specific lane or roadway during one hour under the prevailing roadway conditions.* It is less than basic capacity because it recognizes impairment in one or more of the five conditions assumed in establishing basic capacity.

Practical capacity. *Practical capacity is the maximum number of vehicles that can pass a given point on a lane or roadway during one hour without the traffic density being so great as to cause unreasonable delay, hazard, or restriction to the driver's freedom to maneuver under prevailing roadway and traffic conditions.* Unreasonable is a relative term and varies for different locations. In urban areas, for example, a driver is willing to accept regulation of his speed by other traffic to a greater extent than in rural areas. Thus practical capacity for like facilities will be greater in urban than in rural areas.

Three methods for measuring delay and restrictions to driver freedom are developed in the *Highway Capacity Manual* and are reported briefly in the following paragraphs.

Speed Range. When traffic volumes are very low, drivers are free to select their travel speeds. Figure 5 shows that on some high-speed two-lane highways they vary from over 70 to less than 30 mph, a range of 40 mph. As traffic volume increases, interference between vehicles increases also. Top speeds decrease markedly and slowest speeds decrease somewhat. At 1800 vehicles per hour the top speed is reduced to 40 mph and the speed range to less than 15 mph.

If the values for average speeds of Fig. 5 are plotted against traffic volume there results the straight line shown in Fig. 6. This relationship has been proved by extensive investigation. It disproves the prevalent notion that at some volume below possible capacity there is a marked reduction in average vehicle speed. It also eliminates the supposed possibility of setting practical capacity at the traffic volume where speed is suddenly reduced.

As traffic volume increases, vehicles are more closely spaced, whether this spacing is measured in distance or in time units. It has been found that, when vehicles are more than 9 sec apart, the average difference in the speeds of successive ones is about 6 mph. As this spacing falls below 9 sec, the speed difference decreases rapidly. In other words, a driver's actions are unaffected by a vehicle that is over 9 sec ahead; they are affected if the preceding vehicle is closer than 9 sec. Thus speed difference offers the most sensitive index to traffic congestion. However, vehicle spacing is not regular and the speeds of some vehicles are influenced by the preceding ones; others are not. For a two-lane highway carrying 800 vehicles per hour in both directions, 72% of the drivers are closer than 9 sec to the preceding car, and their speed is governed in part by the speed of the other vehicle. For 900 vehicles per hour the percentage is about 75.

Passing Opportunity. On a two-lane road carrying few vehicles, a driver can pass another vehicle almost at will, but as traffic volume increases oppor-

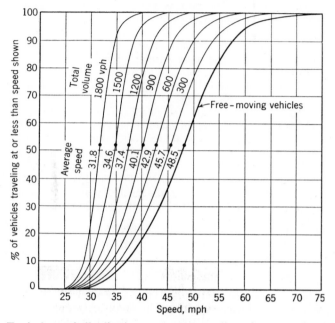

Fig. 5. Typical speed distributions at various traffic volumes on level, tangent sections of 2-lane, high-speed highways (Courtesy U. S. Bureau of Public Roads)

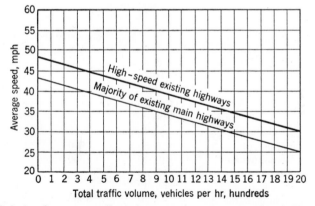

Fig. 6. Relation between traffic volumes and average speeds of all vehicles on level, tangent sections of 2-lane rural highways (Courtesy U. S. Bureau of Public Roads)

tunities to pass decrease. The ratio of the number of passings required per
mile of highway for drivers to maintain a desired speed to the number of
passings that they can actually perform is another measure of traffic congestion. Figure 7 shows for a typical situation the relation between passings
required to maintain speed and those actually accomplished. It is to be noted
that the total number of passings required to maintain speed increases as the
square of traffic volume. Actual total passings, however, increase up to 1300
vehicles per hour and decrease thereafter.

Operating Speed. As far as the individual driver is concerned, over-all or
running speed is the most significant index of congestion. Figure 8 shows the
influence of traffic volume on the actual speed that can be maintained by
drivers who desire to travel 70, 60 and 50 mph, respectively. It is to be observed that, as traffic volume increases and passing opportunity decreases,
actual speeds fall far below desired speeds. For example, if the volume on a
two-lane road is 1300 vehicles per hour, the maximum attainable speed is about
38 mph, whether the driver wishes to drive 70, 60 or 50 mph.

Setting practical capacities. The three factors of speed difference,
passing opportunity, and operating speed are all measures of congestion. Using the data summarized above it is possible to relate
traffic volumes to operating conditions satisfactory to the majority
of motorists. This in turn must be weighed against the financial means
of the particular highway agency. The committee on highway capacity makes no positive recommendations regarding practical capacities
of traffic lanes. Suggested values are shown in Table 2.

TABLE 2. SUGGESTED PRACTICAL CAPACITIES OF TWO-, THREE-, AND
MULTILANE HIGHWAYS UNDER IDEAL TRAFFIC AND ROADWAY CONDITIONS

		Capacity in Passenger Vehicles per Hr	
Type of Facility	Operating Speed,* Mph	Total, Regardless of Distribution between Directions	Per Lane, in Direction of Heavier Flow
Two-lane, rural	45–50	900	
Two-lane, urban	35–40	1500	
Multilane, rural	45–50		1000
Multilane, urban	35–40		1500
Three-lane, rural	45–50	1500	
Three-lane, urban	35–40	2000	

* The average speed for the average driver traveling as fast as possible with
safety.

Vehicle speeds 30 mph or greater must be maintained or capacity will
decrease. This is illustrated in a general way in Fig. 4, which shows that the

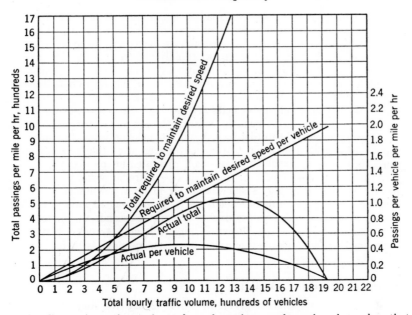

FIG. 7. Comparison of actual number of passings performed and number that would be required at various traffic volumes for all vehicles to maintain their free speed on a 2-lane highway with two thirds of the total traffic in one direction (Courtesy U. S. Bureau of Public Roads)

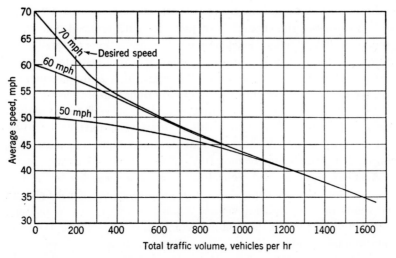

FIG. 8. Average speeds for drivers traveling at their desired speeds wherever possible on 2-lane level highways with no restrictive sight distances (Courtesy U. S. Bureau of Public Roads)

maximum capacity of a two-lane road is cut almost in half when vehicle speed decreases to 10 mph. If, for any reason, traffic is greatly slowed or momentarily stopped on a road loaded almost to capacity, congestion immediately results. Vehicles will stack up rapidly. Even though the cause of congestion lasts but a few seconds, additional vehicles may continue to be stopped for a considerable time after the cause of the restriction has been removed. A queue will form which moves down the highway in a direction opposite to that in which the vehicles are moving. In some cases these have been observed several miles from the scene of the original restriction, although traffic was apparently operating in a normal manner between the queue and the point of original restriction. Methods for measuring the factor of safety against such complete traffic stagnation are presented in the Manual.

Careful distinction should be made between traffic volume and traffic density. To illustrate, Fig. 3 shows that at 30 mph the minimum spacing of vehicles (center to center) is about 80 ft, whereas at 10 mph it is 45 ft. Capacity in the first case is about double that in the second. In photographs, heavy congestion creates the illusion of high volume. Actually, pictures of free-flowing, high-volume roads show wide vehicle spacings, with few vehicles in the field of view.

Factors that reduce capacity

The practical capacities given in Table 2 are for ideal traffic and roadway conditions. These must be reduced to correct for departures from the ideal.

Effect of lane width and edge clearance. Twelve-foot lanes and 6-foot shoulder widths and lateral clearances are assumed as perfect conditions. A reduction in either or both of these decreases capacity. Table 3 expresses the capacities of facilities with reduced lane widths, shoulder widths, or edge clearances, or of combinations of these as percentages of the capacity of an ideal facility. To illustrate its use: If vertical obstructions are placed at the edges of a 24-ft pavement, its capacity drops 24% because of the obstructions; also, it has the same capacity as an 18-ft road with 6-ft shoulders on each side. Another example: If a bridge 18 ft in width is retained as part of a two-lane road designed to the highest standards, the possible capacity of the road is set by the bridge at only 58% of that of the roadway.

Effect of commercial vehicles. Under all conditions, a truck utilizes more highway capacity than a passenger car. On level multilane roads one commercial vehicle [12] has the effect of two passenger cars; in rolling terrain the factor becomes four (see Table 4); and in mountainous country, about eight. For two-lane highways each of these values is increased about 25%. However, care must be exercised

---

[12] Those vehicles having dual tires on the rear wheels.

TABLE 3. COMBINED EFFECT OF LANE WIDTH AND EDGE CLEARANCES ON
HIGHWAY CAPACITIES *

Capacity Expressed as a Percentage of the Capacity of
Two 12-Ft Lanes with No Restrictive Lateral Clearances

Clearance from Pavement Edge to Obstruction, Ft	Obstruction on One Side				Obstruction on Both Sides			
	12-Ft Lanes	11-Ft Lanes	10-Ft Lanes	9-Ft Lanes	12-Ft Lanes	11-Ft Lanes	10-Ft Lanes	9-Ft Lanes
Possible Capacity of Two-Lane Highway								
6	100	88	81	76	100	88	81	76
4	97	85	79	74	94	83	76	71
2	93	81	75	70	85	75	69	65
0	88	77	71	67	76	67	62	58
Practical Capacity of Two-Lane Highway								
6	100	86	77	70	100	86	77	70
4	96	83	74	68	92	79	71	65
2	91	78	70	64	81	70	63	57
0	85	73	66	60	70	60	54	49
Possible and Practical Capacities of Two Lanes for One Direction of Travel on Divided Highways								
6	100	97	91	81	100	97	91	81
4	99	96	90	80	98	95	89	79
2	97	94	88	79	94	91	86	76
0	90	87	82	73	81	79	74	66

* Effects of lane widths and lateral clearances on driver comfort, accident
rates, etc., are not included in these relations.

TABLE 4. EFFECT OF COMMERCIAL VEHICLES ON PRACTICAL CAPACITIES OF
MULTILANE FACILITIES

Commercial Vehicles, %	Capacity Expressed as a Percentage of Passenger-Car Capacity on Level Terrain, %	
	Level Terrain	Rolling Terrain
None	100	100
10	91	77
20	83	63

in determining the percentage of trucks; usually it is lower at peak hours than for average conditions.

Effect of imperfect alinement. Imperfect alinement and breaks in the profile reduce the distance that a driver can see ahead along the road. If on a two-lane road this distance is less than 1500 ft, it will not be safe to make many passing maneuvers that could otherwise be performed. This reduced passing opportunity in turn decreases capacity, as shown in Table 5.

TABLE 5. EFFECT OF PASSING SIGHT-DISTANCE RESTRICTION ON PRACTICAL CAPACITIES OF TWO-LANE HIGHWAYS WHEN ADEQUATE STOPPING SIGHT DISTANCES ARE ALWAYS PRESENT *

Percentage of Total Length of Highway on Which Sight Distance is Restricted to Less than 1500 Ft	Practical Capacity, in Passenger Cars per Hr	
	For Operating Speed † of 45–50 Mph	For Operating Speed † of 50–55 Mph
0	900	600
20	860	560
40	800	500
60	720	420
80	620	300
100	500	160

* The data in this table apply to sections with 12-ft traffic lanes, shoulders adequate for parking disabled vehicles clear of the traffic lanes, and a continuous stopping sight distance corresponding to the design speed. Also, the sight distance on the restricted portions of the section must be uniformly distributed between the required stopping sight distance for the design speed and 1500 ft.
† Average speed for drivers trying to travel at maximum safe speed.

Effect of grades. Brakes are assisted by gravity on upgrades and opposed by gravity on downgrades. On uphill stretches, vehicle spacings can therefore be smaller, which permits increased capacity. With grades often go restricted sight distances, which decrease capacity.

Speeds of passenger cars are little influenced by grades up to 6 or 7%. However, those of trucks are markedly affected. This is illustrated [13] by Fig. 9. Distance-speed relationships for an approach speed of 40 mph are shown by solid lines, those for an approach speed of 10 mph by dotted lines. As noted, capacity of the road is unaffected until vehicle speeds fall below 30 mph. Assuming that the curves of

[13] See the *Highway Capacity Manual* for like curves for lighter vehicles and for similar data for light-powered trucks and combinations.

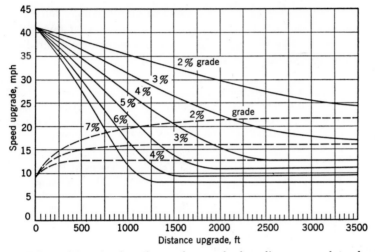

FIG. 9. Effect of length of grade on the speed of medium-powered trucks and combinations of 40,000 lb gross weight (Courtesy U. S. Bureau of Public Roads)

Fig. 9 fit the vehicles being considered, capacity will be unaffected, for example, by a 5% grade less than 625 ft long. But, to maintain full capacity on 5% grades longer than 625 ft, a lane for trucks must be added to the upgrade half of the road, starting below that point and continuing to the summit. Table 6 shows, for two-lane highways,

TABLE 6. EFFECT OF COMMERCIAL VEHICLES AND GRADES ON THE CAPACITY OF TWO-LANE HIGHWAYS WITH UNINTERRUPTED TRAFFIC FLOW WHEN THE GRADE DOES NOT CAUSE A RESTRICTION IN THE PASSING SIGHT DISTANCE

Length of Grade, Miles	Equivalent of One Dual-Tired Commercial Vehicle, in Terms of Passenger Cars, on a Grade Averaging				
	3%	4%	5%	6%	7%
0.1	3.9	4.1	4.2	4.2	4.4
0.2	4.1	4.3	4.5	4.7	5.1
0.4	4.3	4.6	4.9	5.3	5.5
0.6	4.4	4.8	5.2	5.8	6.5
0.8	4.6	5.1	5.7	6.4	7.1
1.0	4.6	5.3	6.0	6.7	7.4
1.5	4.8	5.6	6.3	7.0	7.7
2.0	5.0	5.8	6.5	7.2	8.0
3.0	5.0	6.0	6.6	7.3	8.2
4.0	5.1	6.0	6.7	7.4	8.3
5.0	5.1	6.0	6.7	7.6	8.3
6.0	5.1	6.0	6.8	7.6	8.3

the number of passenger cars required to create congestion equal to that caused by one truck. This assumes, of course, that no truck lane has been added. Table 7 gives like data but recognizes sight-distance restrictions as well as grades.

TABLE 7. EFFECT OF COMMERCIAL VEHICLES AND GRADES ON THE CAPACITY OF TWO-LANE HIGHWAYS WITH UNINTERRUPTED TRAFFIC FLOW, WITH PASSING SIGHT DISTANCE RESTRICTED FOR 1500 FT AHEAD OF THE CREST AND A TYPICAL ALINEMENT ELSEWHERE ALONG THE GRADE

	Equivalent of one Dual-Tired Commercial Vehicle, in Terms of Passenger Cars, on a Grade Averaging				
	3%	4%	5%	6%	7%
% of highway with restricted sight distance (assumed as typical)	30	40	50	60	70
Capacity of highway with restricted sight distance, as % of unrestricted capacity	87	81	75	69	62
Length of Grade, Miles					
0.1	5.8	7.1	8.6	10.2	12.5
0.2	6.0	7.4	9.0	10.9	13.6
0.4	6.3	7.8	9.6	11.6	14.6
0.6	6.5	8.2	10.1	12.5	16.1
0.8	6.6	8.5	10.6	13.0	16.8
1.0	6.7	8.7	11.0	13.5	17.4
1.5	6.9	9.0	11.5	14.1	18.2
2.0	7.0	9.3	11.9	14.5	18.4
3.0	7.1	9.4	12.0	14.7	19.0
4.0	7.1	9.4	12.1	14.7	19.1
5.0	7.2	9.5	12.1	14.8	19.1
6.0	7.3	9.6	12.1	14.9	19.1

Summary. Suggested practical capacities for roads or traffic lanes of ideal design were given in Table 2. To find the capacities of actual or contemplated roads, reductions to recognize their limitations must be made. Appropriate adjustment factors for typical situations have been given in Tables 3 to 7. From these or like data the capacity of a two-, three- or multilane road may be found, assuming no interruptions of flow from intersections, traffic-control devices, or pedestrians.

Table 8 expresses the capacity of typical highway facilities in terms of average annual daily traffic volumes for ideal facilities. These values likewise could, by proper adjustment, be made appropriate for other road conditions.

TABLE 8. AVERAGE ANNUAL DAILY TRAFFIC VOLUMES CORRESPONDING TO
THE PRACTICAL CAPACITIES OF DIFFERENT TYPES OF HIGHWAYS, AS BASED
ON THE NATIONWIDE AVERAGE RELATIONSHIP BETWEEN THE 30TH HIGHEST
HOURLY VOLUME AND THE AVERAGE ANNUAL DAILY TRAFFIC VOLUME *

Type of Traffic		Average Annual Daily Traffic Volume on					
% of Pas-senger Cars	% of Com-mer-cial Vehi-cles	Two-Lane Rural Roads		Four-Lane Rural Roads †		Four-Lane Urban Expressways †	
		In Level Terrain	In Rolling Terrain	In Level Terrain	In Rolling Terrain	In Level Terrain	In Rolling Terrain
100	0	5750	5750	19,250	19,250	37,500	37,500
90	10	5200	4450	17,500	14,800	34,000	29,000
80	20	4800	3600	16,050	12,000	31,000	23,500

* Except for the presence of commercial vehicles, roadway and traffic conditions are assumed to approach the ideal, including 12-ft traffic lanes, tangent
alinement, and uninterrupted flow.

† Assuming two-thirds of traffic in heavier direction during peak hour.

Street capacity [14]

The capacity of important intersections rather than the capacity
of the street itself usually determines how many cars a major metropolitan artery can accommodate. Between intersections the street
is alternately heavily loaded and largely unoccupied. These intersections, where grade separation has not been made, are almost universally controlled by traffic signals, stop signs, or directing officers
without which traffic would become completely snarled.

The accepted unit for stating intersection capacity is "vehicles per
10 ft of street width per hour of green light." From this, the capacity
per clock-hour for a particular direction may be obtained by applying
the ratio of green time per signal cycle for that direction to the total
cycle time. Street width is measured from curb to curb, even though

[14] Data presented here are from the *Highway Capacity Manual.* For a graph-
ical presentation of the arithmetic processes used in the Manual, see J. E. Leisch,
Design Capacity Charts for Signalized Street and Highway Intersections, *Public
Roads,* February 1951.

some space may be devoted to parking, car tracks, and loading platforms, as allowance for these conditions is made in determining capacity. It is preferable to state capacity in terms of 10 ft of street
width rather than per lane because lane widths differ among situations
and agencies. Further, the evidence is conclusive that capacity varies
almost directly with lane width so that results are unaffected by the
adoption of a single standard unit.

Basic capacity. The basic capacity of a 12-ft traffic lane under
free-flowing conditions has previously been stated as 2000 vehicles
per hour per lane. This requires operating speeds of 30 mph or more
which cannot be achieved at intersections where one or more vehicles
are stopped against the red light. Instead, basic capacity occurs
when every green interval is fully utilized by waiting vehicles. Many
observations have established that, for each 12-ft lane, a vehicle passes
the intersection every 2.4 sec of green at an average speed of 10 to
15 mph.[15] From this, basic capacity of a 12-ft lane per hour of green
is computed at 1500 vehicles. Converted to the standard unit, the
basic capacity is 1250 vehicles per 10 ft of street width per hour of
green.

Possible capacity. Both basic and possible capacities are based on
the assumption that traffic volume is great enough to tax the intersection to its capacity during every signal interval. However, possible capacity falls below basic capacity whenever one or more of
the following factors appear:

1. Parked vehicles and vehicles entering or leaving parking spaces.
2. Turning movements.
3. Commercial vehicles, including streetcars.
4. Pedestrian interferences.
5. Inclement weather conditions.

Practical capacity. Practical capacity of a given intersection approach has been defined as the maximum volume that can enter the
intersection from that approach during one hour of green light with
most of the drivers being able to clear the intersection without waiting
for more than one signal cycle. In general it is about 80% of the
possible capacity.

Possible and practical capacities of intersections have been related

---

[15] The time interval for the first two vehicles in line is considerably greater
than 2.4 sec but decreases progressively until it reaches an average minimum of
2.1 sec between the fifth and sixth cars.

to average observed values reported from cities throughout the country. These observed values for various street widths are shown [16] in Figs. 10 and 11. Figure 10 is for two-way streets and gives volumes for one approach. Figure 11 is for one-way streets. Different curves are given to show the effects on capacity of location (downtown, intermediate, or rural) and of the presence or absence of parking. A normal turning movement of 20% and a representative number of

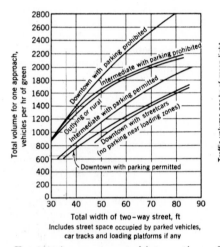

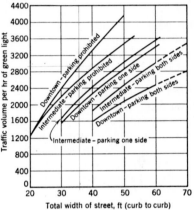

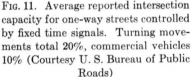

FIG. 10. Average reported intersection capacities for undivided two-way streets controlled by fixed time signals. Turning movements total 20%, commercial vehicles 10% (Courtesy U. S. Bureau of Public Roads)

FIG. 11. Average reported intersection capacity for one-way streets controlled by fixed time signals. Turning movements total 20%, commercial vehicles 10% (Courtesy U. S. Bureau of Public Roads)

commercial vehicles of 10% are assumed. From these curves it is evident that parking reduces capacity by percentages far exceeding the percentage of street width devoted to it. Comparison of Figs. 10 and 11 shows beyond question that, as far as capacity is concerned, one-way streets make much better use of available width than two-direction streets.

Possible capacities are 10% higher and practical capacities are 10% lower than those of Figs. 10 and 11.

[16] Actually there was considerable variation in the capacities reported for each of the several conditions. These data, when plotted, offer a frequency-distribution curve. Figures 10 and 11 present the interpretation placed on these curves.

Corrections to capacities. The influences of parking, turns, and pedestrians on capacity are interrelated and extremely complex. To illustrate, consider the following factors regarding left turns which influence capacity: (1) If two or more vehicles immediately following one after the other desire to turn left, the effect per vehicle on the capacity of the street is not so great as if the vehicles turn separately. (2) The effect of left-turning vehicles is related to the number of oncoming vehicles going straight through and turning left. (3) Each left-turning vehicle crosses the path of pedestrians moving with the green light, and therefore the effect of a left turn is to some extent dependent on the number of pedestrians. (4) A vehicle waiting to make a left turn causes a greater relative reduction in capacity on a narrow street than on a wider one or on one having a wide center-dividing island.

Because of space limitations, none of the correction factors presented in the reference can be given in this text. Also omitted are solutions to typical problems.

Other capacity problems

Weaving sections. Weaving sections are compromises between conventional crossings at grade which operate on a stop-and-go basis and expensive grade-separation structures which permit uninterrupted traffic flow. They are crossings at grade on which traffic streams moving in the same general direction cross by merging and diverging. The traffic circle (see Fig. 33, p. 205) is merely a series of weaving sections.

A chart and formulas for the design of weaving sections appear as Fig. 12. From the data presented, the length of the weaving section and the number of lanes can be found in terms of the number of weaving vehicles, traffic-lane capacity, and desired operating speed.

Regarding the use of weaving sections the report on highway capacity states: "Any weaving section, regardless of its length or number of lanes, will become badly congested when the number of weaving vehicles approaches the possible capacity of two traffic lanes. Operating conditions will seldom be entirely satisfactory unless the traffic on the approach roadways is well below the practical capacities of these approaches and the weaving section has one more lane than would normally be required for the combined traffic from both approaches. For this reason, weaving sections are considered practical only where the two intersecting one-way roadways each carries less than the normal capacity of two lanes of a one-way roadway and the total number of vehicles required to weave does not exceed 1500 per hour."

Ramps and their terminals. Ramps provide access to the through lanes of freeways and expressways. Improperly planned entrances can seriously limit traffic volumes on the through facility. Exits incapable of accommodating the vehicles desiring to leave at given points can cause complete congestion of the main artery.

Ramps usually have sharp curvature which restricts speed. Often practical capacities are about those obtained on tangent sections at speeds less than 20 mph, or in the order of 1200 passenger vehicles per lane per hour. Thus, two-lane ramps (widths normally 28 to 30 ft) should accommodate about 2400 automobiles per hour at speeds of 12 to 15 mph. Often, even on some modern facilities, there is a tendency for traffic to move in a single line at some point on the ramp, usually the entrance or exit. Then capacity falls to 1200 vehicles per hour.

If entry to an "on"-ramp is through a signalized intersection, the capacity will be limited to that of the intersection. Likewise, restricted provision for discharge from the end of an exit ramp may govern its capacity.

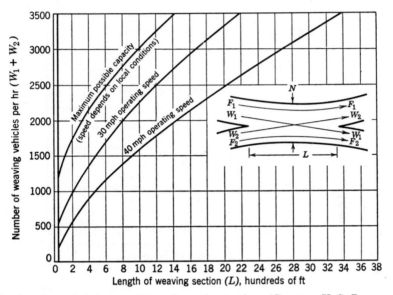

Fig. 12. Operating characteristics of weaving sections (Courtesy U. S. Bureau of Public Roads)

$$N = \frac{W_1 + 3W_2 + F_1 + F_2}{C}$$

N = number of lanes
W_1 = vehicles per hour in the larger weaving movement
W_2 = vehicles per hour in the smaller weaving movement
F_1 and F_2 = vehicles per hour in outer flows
C = normal capacity in vehicles per hour of lanes on approach and exit roadways

In general, when an outer flow exceeds 600 passenger cars per hour, the section should be wide enough to provide a separate lane for this movement

The number of vehicles that can enter an expressway from a given ramp depends on the amount of through traffic on the expressway. Figure 13 illustrates this relationship for a ramp of particular design. Vehicles from ramps must find openings in the streams of through traffic. These are more numerous when volumes are low. Furthermore, when through traffic is low, more vehicles move toward the inside expressway lane or lanes as they approach the ramp location, leaving the outer lane relatively free for entering traffic. For high ramp volumes, a separate lane on the expressway exclusively for ramp traffic must be provided. Then ramp capacity will be 1200 vehicles for this lane plus the number that can enter the stream of through traffic.

Capacity of off-ramps is affected by the number of through vehicles using the right-hand expressway lane. Slow-moving passenger cars and most commercial vehicles stay in this lane, thereby occupying spaces that otherwise

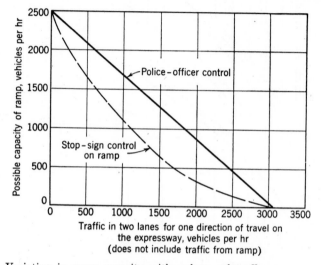

Fig. 13. Variation in ramp capacity with volume of traffic on an expressway. Ramp is 20 ft wide with no acceleration area (Courtesy U. S. Bureau of Public Roads)

would be available for access to the exit ramp. By careful signing, the number of these through vehicles that stay in the outside lane can be greatly reduced. For most installations, exit-ramp volumes cannot exceed 1200 passenger cars less the number of through vehicles using the outside lane. If an expressway lane exclusively for off-ramp traffic is provided, total ramp capacity then is 1200 vehicles plus the number of leaving vehicles accommodated in the outside through lane.

DESIGN SPEEDS

Design speed is defined by the AASHO as "a speed determined for design and correlation of the physical features of a highway that influence vehicle operation. It is the maximum safe speed that can be maintained over a specified section of highway when conditions are so favorable that the design features of the highway govern." Approved design speeds are 30, 40, 50, 60, and 70 mph. The selection of the proper design speed is extremely important, for this choice sets the limits for curvature, sight distance, and other geometric features. Since available funds are often limited, there is the temptation to reduce design speeds in order to save money. Regarding this, the AASHO design standards say, "It is urged that when economy is necessary it be practiced on some feature of highway design other than the geometric features. The roadway section can always be improved and widened at reasonable cost. The paving surface can be widened and strengthened at any future date that finances will permit. But the geometric features of alinement, grade, and sight distance, when once molded into the landscape and tied down with paving surfaces and rights of way, are most difficult and expensive to correct."

Highways are classified by the AASHO as interstate, primary, and secondary and feeder. Topography is classed as flat, rolling, and mountainous.[17] Recommended design speeds for the interstate and for secondary and feeder roads, classified by topography and traffic volume, appear in Table 9. Specific values are not offered for primary highways but range from 30 to 70 mph. The maximum design speed that appears in the table is 70 mph. However, some engineers argue that, wherever possible, design speeds up to 100 mph should be used. They contend that, even though driver and vehicle limitations appear to preclude operation at such speeds, the higher standard of design provides some guarantee against future obsolescence as well as an increased margin of operating safety.[18]

Sudden changes in design speed along a highway should be avoided, particularly on high-speed roads. Some designers prefer to make this change in 5-mph increments, rather than in the 10-mph steps suggested by the AASHO.

[17] The Arizona Highway Department defines these terms as follows:

Flat topography: Cuts and fills up to 10 ft are common. Grades of 3% or less can be obtained without affecting alinement appreciably.

Rolling topography: Cuts and fills up to 80 ft are called for. Short runs of maximum grades.

Mountainous topography: Terrain with precipitous canyons and escarpments. Extended maximum grades required.

[18] At speeds above 80 mph factors like the gyroscopic action of the flywheel, motor, and wheels tend to take control of the vehicle from the driver. Also, perception plus reaction time becomes critical; on curves requiring maximum superelevation, responses are too slow to permit control of a vehicle in a 12-ft lane.

TABLE 9. DESIGN SPEEDS IN MILES PER HOUR FOR INTERSTATE AND
SECONDARY AND FEEDER ROADS

As Recommended by the AASHO

Design Control	Interstate System		Secondary and Feeder Roads, Annual Average Daily Traffic				
	Mini-mum	Desir-able	Under 100	100 to 400		400 to 1000	
			Mini-mum	Mini-mum	Desir-able	Mini-mum	Desir-able
Rural sections							
Flat topography	60	70	40	45	55	50	60
Rolling topog-raphy	50	60	30	35	45	40	50
Mountainous topography	40	50	20	25	35	30	40
Urban sections	40	50					

DESIGN OF THE CROSS SECTION

Cross sections of typical multilane highways of modern design are shown in Fig. 14. Each dimension is based on careful analysis of the volume, character, and speed of traffic and of the characteristics of motor vehicles and their operators. Each element of the cross section is discussed individually in the paragraphs that follow.

Lane widths

In meeting oncoming vehicles or passing slower ones, the position selected by a driver depends primarily on the paved or surfaced width of the highway. Originally this surfaced width was only 15 ft, which was ample for horse-drawn vehicles. With the increase in motor-vehicle traffic the width increased first to 16 ft, then to 18 ft. Later two 10-ft lanes became a standard width for first-class paved high-ways and now, with increased vehicle speeds, 22- and 24-ft widths of pavement are regarded as necessary for "primary" rural highways.

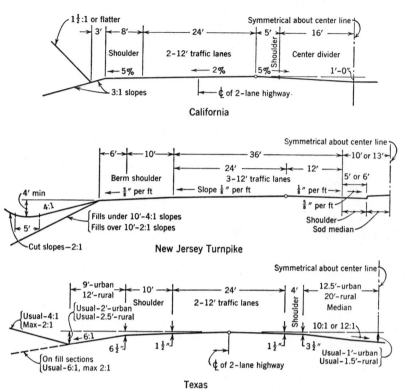

Fig. 14. Typical cross sections of modern highways

Until 1945, over half of our primary highways were surfaced for less than 20 ft.[19]

On highways and streets carrying 1000 or more motor vehicles daily, transverse position of vehicles on the pavement becomes important with respect to efficiency and safety. The report of studies by the Bureau of Public Roads on speed and placement on straight level concrete pavement is sufficient to cover the general situation.[20]

[19] Thus the movement of truck manufacturers and operators in 1946 to increase over-all truck-body widths from 96 to 102 in. was confronted with the fact that 8.5-ft bodies in passing on 18-ft pavements would leave only 12 in. of total free pavement for edges and center clearance.

[20] See New Techniques in Traffic Behavior by E. H. Holmes and S. F. Reymer, *Public Roads,* April 1940, and *Proceedings Highway Research Board* (1943); also Effect of Roadway Width on Vehicle Operation by A. Taragin, *Public Roads,* October 1945, pp. 143–160.

The conclusions were that hazardous traffic conditions exist on pavements less than 22 ft wide, even with moderate volumes of traffic of mixed trucks and passenger cars.

On 18-ft pavements with grass or gravel shoulders, passenger cars pass commercial vehicles at body clearances averaging 2.6 ft. The passenger car usually does not move to the right to increase the clearance nor does it reduce speed.

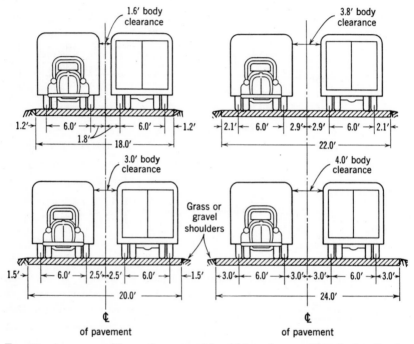

Fig. 15. Average positions of commercial vehicles when meeting during the day on 2-lane concrete pavements having grass or gravel shoulders (Courtesy U. S. Bureau of Public Roads)

Correspondingly, on 20-ft pavements the average clearance is only 3.5 ft, which also is unsafe. For 1 meeting in 8 on 18-ft pavement, and for 1 meeting in 20 on 20-ft pavement, the clearance is 1 ft or less. On 18-ft pavements 5% of the passenger cars and 11% of the trucks fail to keep within the proper lane when meeting oncoming traffic. When two commercial vehicles meet, average clearances are even less than those stated above (see Fig. 15). Figure 15 also shows that trucks passing trucks remain centered in their lanes only when lane widths reach 12 ft.

It is amply demonstrated that, when two-lane pavements are of adequate widths for opposing vehicles to meet, then the provision for passing overtaken vehicles also is adequate. The average clearance of passenger cars when overtaking and passing other passenger cars increases from 2.3 ft on 18-ft pavement to 4.8 ft on 24-ft pavements. These clearances are less than the corresponding meeting clearances of 3.2 and 5.2 ft for 18- and 24-ft pavements, respectively. Apparently, regardless of pavement width, the passing vehicle allows about 1.5 ft clearance to the left of the center line and the passed driver moves scarcely 6 in. to the right.

Standards for the interstate system set lane widths at 11 ft for rural roads when traffic density is less than 200 vehicles per lane per hour. For other rural and all urban facilities, widths are 12 ft. For primary highways carrying over 200 vehicles per hour, lane widths are 11 or 12 ft, depending on design speed and the number of commercial vehicles. For secondary roads, desirable lane width is placed at 10 ft.

Shoulders

The shoulder is that portion of the roadway between the outer edge of the outer traffic lane and the inside edge of the ditch, gutter, curb, or slope. Where guard rail is provided, widths are measured to the face of the rail. Shoulders provide a place for vehicles to park for changing tires or when otherwise disabled, or to stop for any other reason. If designs omit shoulders or if they are narrow, roadway capacity decreases and accident opportunity increases.

Shoulders on rural highways were originally 2, 3, or 4 ft wide, usually unpaved. Sometimes they were surfaced with gravel or like material to provide hard standing at all times, but often they were of earth and not usable in poor weather. Shoulder widths and surfaces have improved progressively, and widths of 10 ft are now preferred for high-type facilities. It is common to pave the inside 18 in. to 3 ft with bituminous material, or at least to apply a bituminous-surface treatment. In some instances, the full shoulder width is paved or treated. In the East, South, and Middle West where rainfall is sufficient and frequent enough to support grass, turfed shoulders are widely employed.

For 18- to 20-ft pavements, "black top" or like shoulders 4 or more feet in width serve to increase the effective pavement width by about 2 ft. Drivers, when passing, will squeeze down the center clearance on narrow pavements having unpaved shoulders. However, if the shoulder is bituminized, they will travel closer to the pavement edge. There seems to be little difference whether untreated shoulders are gravel or grass.[21]

[21] For a progress report on research now under way to determine the effects of shoulder widths and types on vehicle speeds and placements, see Report of

The recommended clear shoulder width for the interstate system is 10 ft. Widths as low as 4 ft are permitted, however, in mountainous topography where added widths would be extremely costly. On primary highways, with traffic greater than 200 vehicles per hour, recommended width is 8 ft in cuts and on fills with side slopes 1 on 4 or flatter, and 10 ft with steeper slopes. For primary roads of lower traffic volumes shoulders 4 to 10 ft in width are recommended. For secondary and feeder roads, widths of 4 to 5 ft satisfy the minimum requirements.

Median strips for divided highways

Positive separation between opposing traffic streams is essential for efficient and safe operation on all roads four lanes and wider. Such division is required by the design standards for interstate highways, and only a few exceptions are permitted by the standards for primary highways.[22] Where median strips are narrow, separation is usually provided by raised curbs; where greater widths are available, curbs may or may not be used. Often in rural areas the wide division alone serves, and no raised barrier is employed.[23]

Wide median strips are to be preferred. With them the chance of freak accidents which might produce head-on collisions over a narrow median is reduced. Headlight glare from opposing vehicles is less troublesome. At intersections, a wide median provides a refuge for cross traffic which may cross each half of the road as a separate maneuver. Likewise there is space for special left-turn lanes, sometimes called pocket lanes, inside the through lanes. These permit vehicles turning left to decelerate and if necessary stop to wait for an opening in opposing traffic without disrupting through traffic (see

the Committee on Influence of Shoulders on Traffic Operation, *Highway Research Abstracts,* May 1950.

[22] Four-lane roads without division are permissible under the AASHO standards for primary roads "(a) on 2- or 3-lane roads only where lengths with sight distance less than the safe passing minimum are widened to four lanes, (b) in urban areas where there are frequent cross streets and width is limited by extensive adjacent improvement, and (c) on long structures where increased width would be prohibitive in cost."

[23] The AASHO standards for primary highways state that the use of curbs should be avoided on rural highways except where necessary to control traffic or drainage. Where curbs are used, they should be low and flat with the incline not steeper than 45 degrees so that vehicles may mount them without difficulty. All vertical or nearly vertical curbs greater than 3 in. in height shall be placed at least 2 ft from the edge of the traffic lane.

Fig. 32, p. 203). Wider medians permit narrower openings through the center divider, which results in closer control of traffic. Often median strips of variable width are employed. If rights of way are expensive, medians may be narrow except for added widths where left turns or cross traffic are to be accommodated. Medians often are narrowed at grade separations in order to reduce the length or width of structures.

For divided highways on the interstate system, desirable median widths are set at 40 and 12 ft for rural and urban roads, respectively. Recommended comparable minimums are 15 and 4 ft. A median width of 2 ft is permitted under extreme conditions. For the primary system, a minimum of 4 ft has been established.[24]

Side slopes

Earth fills of usual height stand safely with side slopes[25] of 1½ to 1. The side slopes of cuts through ordinary undisturbed earth remain in place with slopes of 1 to 1. Rock cuts as steep as ½ to 1 and sometimes ¼ to 1 are stable. In the past, these slopes were standard for many highway agencies because they involved a minimum of earthwork. In recent years, however, side slopes generally have been flattened to provide for safer operation and decreased maintenance.

Steep side slopes on fills create a serious accident hazard. If one wheel of a vehicle goes over the edge, the driver loses control. Overturn may result. With flat slopes the car can often be directed back into the road or continue safely down the slope. Steep slopes on gutter ditches create similar accident hazards. Good practice now demands flat slopes on the roadway side of such ditches. Also, flat fill slopes are visible from the vehicle for their full extent, so that the road takes on a safer appearance. The driver is assured that if necessary he may direct his vehicle onto or down the slope. As a result, vehicle positioning on roads with visible side slopes is closer to the edge and farther from opposing traffic.

Steep slopes erode badly, thus creating serious maintenance problems. Furthermore, it is difficult to grow plants or grasses on them to aid in erosion control. Thus the saving in original excavation and

[24] See Highways with Narrow Medians, *Highway Research Board Bulletin 53* (1951) for reports from seven states that have installed narrow medians.

[25] When slopes are expressed as 1½ to 1, 2 to 1, or the like, the first figure represents horizontal measurement, the second vertical measurement. Many prefer to express slopes by ratios stated as 1 on 2 or 1 on 4. In this instance the first figure represents the vertical and the second the horizontal dimension.

embankment costs may be more than offset by increased maintenance through the years; and in addition the slopes will be unsightly.

Standards for the interstate system recommend that side slopes in cuts be no steeper than 2 to 1 except in solid rock or other special soils. For fills less than 10 ft in height, side slopes are set at 4 to 1 or flatter. Where cut or fill slopes intersect the original ground surface, slopes are to be rounded to blend with the natural ground surface. Standards for primary highways are similar.

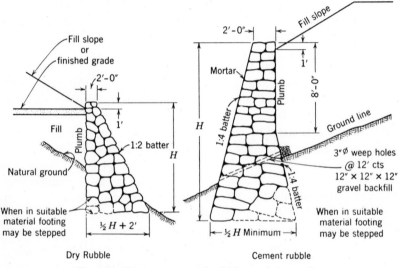

Fig. 16. Cross sections of rubble retaining walls

Sometimes in steep country the side slopes of the original ground approach $1\frac{1}{2}$ to 1 (about 34 degrees from the horizontal), and fills will not "catch" unless unduly extended down the mountain. This is objectionable, as it results in an unsightly scar. These long fill slopes may be eliminated by shifting the road into the mountain until the full cross section is "benched" into the hillside, but this requires increased excavation and end hauling and leaves extensive scar above the roadway. Often it is preferable to contain the embankment with a suitable retaining wall. This may be hand-placed stone, cement rubble masonry, conventional reinforced-concrete T sections, or cribs assembled from precast concrete or metal elements. Figure 16 presents details of stone retaining walls. Figure 17 shows a crib wall of precast reinforced concrete. In urban areas, similar measures are often em-

Fig. 17. A crib wall of precast reinforced concrete in New York State (Courtesy Universal Concrete Pipe Co.)

ployed where narrow rights of way, small clearances, or appearance require that the fill slopes be contained.

Cross slopes

Cross slope is introduced in all tangent sections of roadway. Except where superelevation of curves directs all water toward the inside, slopes usually fall in both directions from the center line of two-lane highways. Each half of a divided roadway is sloped individually, usually with the outside edges lower than the inside ones (see Fig. 14). For high-type pavements, this cross slope (or crown) is often ⅛ in. per ft. On shoulders cross slopes are usually greater, sometimes ½ in. per ft or more.

The cross sections of city street surfaces often are laid out with the pavement surface conforming to a parabola. This procedure makes the inside lanes which accommodate high-speed traffic flatter than the outer lanes. Also it places the steepest slopes adjacent to the gutters, which narrows the width devoted to carrying surface water. On very wide streets a parabolic crown makes the middle lanes almost flat unless gutters are unusually deep. Then some combination of uniform slope with a parabolic curve is used in place of the parabolic section.

Right-of-way widths

In the past, originally acquired rights of way have usually been too narrow.[26] Thus, when it became necessary to add lanes or otherwise widen a road or street, developed property along one or both sides often had to be purchased at high cost. Sometimes several takings have been made at different times from the same property, each at considerable expense. Because of such experiences in the past, engineers now consider it good practice to acquire rights of way wide enough to accommodate the ultimate expected development.

Standards for the interstate system recommend, for rural areas, rights of way as follows:

Facility	Right-of-Way Width, Ft	
	Minimum	Desirable
Two-lane highways	120	220
Divided highways	150	250

For urban areas no specific widths are indicated. It is recommended, however, that the acquisition be wide enough to be adequate for the ultimate design.

SIGHT DISTANCE [27]

Nonpassing sight distance

At times large objects may fall or drop onto a roadway. These will do serious damage to a motor vehicle that strikes them. Proper

[26] In the Middle West and West, rural property was divided by the public lands surveys into sections one mile on a side. Around the boundaries of each section a strip 33 ft wide was dedicated to the public for land access. Most early roads followed these rights of way, and in time this 66-ft width became accepted as standard for all rural roads. This practice continued until the fairly recent past.

[27] Sight-distance computations combine some of the fundamental principles of dynamics with observed characteristics of vehicle, road, and driver. The principles developed in the following pages are entirely valid, but the observed data and numerical results are under critical scrutiny.

design requires that such objects become visible at distances great enough that drivers can stop before hitting them. Furthermore, it is unsafe to assume that the vehicle may avoid trouble by leaving the lane in which it is traveling, for this might result in loss of control or collision with another vehicle. In highway design, this minimum safe stopping distance is known as the nonpassing sight distance.

Nonpassing sight distance is the sum of two distances. The first is that traveled after the obstruction comes into view but before the driver applies his brakes. During this period of perception and reaction, the vehicle travels at design velocity. The second distance is consumed while the driver brakes the vehicle to a stop. Expressed in formulas, the distances covered are:

$$\text{Perception + reaction distance (ft)} = tv = 1.47tV \qquad (1)$$

$$\text{Braking distance (ft)} = \frac{v^2}{2gf} = \frac{V^2}{30f} \qquad (2)\ [28]$$

in which v = design speed, feet per second.
    V = design speed, miles per hour.
    t = perception plus reaction time, seconds.
    g = acceleration of gravity, feet per second^2.
    f = coefficient of friction between tires and pavement.

Table 10 gives values recommended by the AASHO for perception plus reaction time and for safe coefficients of friction. Furthermore, it presents the answers obtained by substituting these values in the formulas given above. Regarding the recommended values for perception plus reaction time, it is to be observed that all but the longest of them (3.0 sec) are less than the averages found in driver tests.[29] The adopted coefficients of friction, even including the factor of safety, assume that the pavement surface is free of mud or ice and that brakes are good. It must be concluded that the stated nonpassing sight distances represent minimums below which it would be unsafe to go in design.

The coefficient of friction between tires and pavement varies considerably with factors like tire condition and pressure, vehicle speed, character of the pavement surface, and the presence of oil, moisture, ice, and snow. Tests by

[28] Derivation of this formula will be found in any standard textbook in engineering mechanics.
[29] See the earlier discussion on driver characteristics, p. 136.

TABLE 10. MINIMUM SAFE NONPASSING SIGHT DISTANCES

Braking

Assumed Design Speed		Perception plus Reaction		Coefficient of Friction Skidding	Factor of Safety	Safe Coefficient of Friction, f	Braking Distance on Level, Ft, $V^2/30f$	Total Safe Stopping Distance, Ft	AASHO Approved Nonpassing Sight Distances
Mph, V	Ft per Sec	Sec	Ft						
10	14.67	3.5	51	0.68	1.25	0.55	6	57	
20	29.3	3.25	95	0.65	1.25	0.525	25	120	
30 *	44	3.0	132	0.62	1.25	0.50	60	192	200
40 *	59	2.75	162	0.59	1.25	0.47	113	275	275
50 *	73	2.50	183	0.56	1.25	0.45	185	368	350
60 *	88	2.25	198	0.53	1.25	0.42	286	484	475
70 *	103	2.0	206	0.50	1.25	0.40	408	614	600
80	117	1.75	205	0.47	1.25	0.375	570	775	
90	132	1.50	198	0.44	1.25	0.35	771	969	
100	147	1.25	183	0.41	1.25	0.325	1025	1208	

* Data for these speeds from AASHO publication, *A Policy on Sight Distance*. Remainder from Arizona Highway Department standards.

R. A. Moyer [30] on clean wet pavements resulted in coefficients of friction for skidding straight ahead varying from 0.6 to 0.8 at 10 mph to 0.4 to 0.6 for 40 mph. Lower values are to be expected for higher speeds. For muddy pavements and ice conditions, respectively, coefficients of 0.1 and 0.05 or less are the rule.

Engineers of the U. S. Bureau of Public Roads found that average braking distances on dry concrete at speeds from 30 to 90 mph fell below those given in Table 10. However, braking distances for 15% of the drivers exceeded the values of Table 10 for speeds of 70 and 90 mph by 25 and 33%, respectively. These results suggest that design braking distances for high speeds may be too low.[31] For other research reports on braking see T. E. Shelburne and R. L. Sheppe, *Highway Research Board Research Report 5-B* (1948), and R. A. Moyer, John W. Shupe, and A. D. Morgan in *Bulletin 37* (1951) of the same agency.

Tests conducted by the Bureau of Standards indicate that the maximum comfortable deceleration rate is 16.1 ft per sec [2] (or ½g). This is produced by a coefficient of friction of 0.5 and indicates a force equal to one-half of the driver's weight trying to slide him from the vehicle seat.

Formula 2 for braking distance assumes a level roadway. If the vehicle is traveling uphill, braking distance is decreased, for gravity forces aid in slowing the car. For downhill operation, braking distance is increased. Braking distance on slopes is expressed by the approximate formula

$$\text{Braking distance} = \frac{v^2}{2g(f + s)} = \frac{V^2}{30(f + s)} \qquad (2a)$$

where s = longitudinal slope of the roadway, or $\dfrac{\% \text{ grade}}{100}$.

[30] See Skidding Characteristics of Automobile Tires on Roadway Surfaces, *Iowa Engineering Experiment Station Bulletin 120*.

[31] See O. K. Normann, *Public Roads*, June 1953, pp. 159–169.

Uphill grades are positive (+) and downhill grades, negative (−). For flat grades and low speeds, braking distance is little influenced by this correction. For example, for 40 mph and a 3% grade, braking distance changes only 7 ft. For 70 mph and a 6% downgrade, however, the change is appreciable, amounting to about 70 ft.

Passing sight distance

On two-lane and three-lane highways, opportunity to pass slow-moving vehicles must be provided at intervals. Otherwise capacity decreases and accidents increase as impatient drivers risk head-on collisions by passing when it is unsafe to do so. The minimum distance ahead that must be clear to permit safe passing is called the passing sight distance. Minimum passing sight distances from the design standards of the AASHO are given in Table 11.

TABLE 11. Minimum Safe Passing Sight Distances

From AASHO Design Standards

Safe Passing Minimum, Feet

Design Speed, Mph	2-Lane		3-Lane *	
	Desirable	Absolute	Desirable	Absolute
30	600	500		
40	1100	900		
50	1600	1400	1100	900
60	2300	2100	1500	1300
70	3200	2900	2000	1800

* Based on assumption that two vehicles are being passed.

For two-lane highways, passing sight distance represents the sum of three distances (see Fig. 18):

d_1 = distance traveled during perception time.

d_2 = distance traveled by the passing vehicle while passing.

d_3 = distance traveled by opposing vehicle during the passing operation.

Assumptions regarding speed of passed and opposing vehicles, speed and acceleration of passing vehicle, and spacing between passing and passed vehicles at the beginning and end of the maneuver must be made. All of these have marked influence on the final result. For three-lane highways, it is assumed that the passing vehicle will have unchallenged use of the center lane; thus d_3, the distance traveled by opposing vehicles, may be neglected. Passing two vehicles rather than one is assumed.

Passing-sight-distance requirements do not apply to four-lane highways, since passing operations need not be performed in lanes occupied

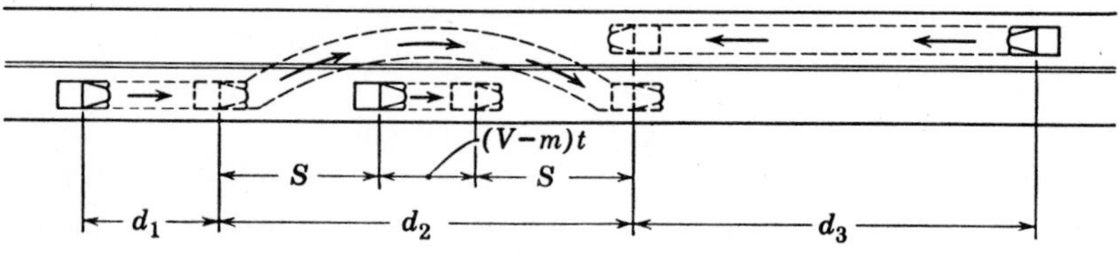

	30			40			50			60			70		
V, Assumed mph, design speed	30			40			50			60			70		
m, Difference between V and speed of passed vehicle, mph	10	15	20	10	15	20	10	15	20	10	15	20	10	15	20
$V - m$, Speed of passed vehicle, mph	20	15	10	30	25	20	40	35	30	50	45	40	60	55	50
$S = V - m + 20$, Spacing, ft	40	35	30	50	45	40	60	55	50	70	65	60	80	75	70
a, Acceleration rate, mph per sec	2.6	2.9	3.2	2.1	2.3	2.6	1.7	1.9	2.1	1.3	1.4	1.7	1.0	1.1	1.3
$t = \sqrt{2.73S/a}$, Time, sec	6.5	5.7	5.0	8.1	7.3	6.5	9.8	8.9	8.1	12.1	11.3	9.8	14.8	13.6	12.1
$d_1 = 4.4(V - m)$, ft	88	66	44	132	110	88	176	154	132	220	198	176	264	242	220
$d_2 = 2S + 1.47(V - m)t$, ft	270	195	134	455	358	270	696	568	455	1028	876	696	1460	1250	1028
$d_3 = 1.47Vt$, ft	285	251	220	473	439	382	719	654	596	1068	1000	863	1512	1400	1245
$d = d_1 + d_2 + d_3$, ft	643	512	398	1060	907	740	1595	1376	1183	2316	2074	1735	3236	2892	2593

For three-lane highways d_3 is dropped and $d = d_1 + d_2$.

When $d = d_1 + d_2$, ft	358	261	178	587	468	358	872	722	587	1248	1074	872	1724	1692	1248

FIG. 18. Diagram and typical computations for passing sight distance (Courtesy Arizona Highway Department)

by vehicles traveling in the opposite direction. Only nonpassing sight distance has to be provided (see Table 10). For high-speed roads in rough country these decreases in sight-distance requirements result in economies so great that often a four-lane divided highway has a lower first cost than a two- or three-lane one.

In computing safe passing sight distance for two-lane highways, the following assumptions regarding driver behavior are made:

1. The overtaken vehicle travels at uniform speed.

2. The passing vehicle is forced to travel at the same speed as the overtaken vehicle while traversing the section of highway where sight distance is unsafe for passing.

3. When the safe passing section is reached and the road opens up to view, the driver of the passing vehicle requires a short period of time (perception time) to look over the situation, watch for opposing traffic, and decide whether or not it is safe to pass.

4. Passing is accomplished by accelerating during the entire operation.

5. Opposing traffic appears at the instant the maneuver of passing begins and arrives alongside the passing vehicle just as the maneuver is completed.

Figure 18 shows definitions, formulas, and computed values for passing sight distance for two- and three-lane roads, based on the assumptions stated above. It covers design speeds ranging from 30 to 70 mph. It should be noted that acceleration rates are based on tests conducted before 1940.

DESIGNING THE GRADE LINE

The grade line is shown on a profile taken along the road center line and is a series of straight lines connected by parabolic vertical curves to which the straight grades are tangent (see Fig. 8, p. 120). In laying this grade line, the designer must secure economy by keeping earthwork quantities to the minimum consistent with meeting sight-distance and other design requirements. In mountainous country the grade may be set to balance excavation against embankment as a clue toward least over-all cost. In flat or prairie country it will be approximately parallel to the ground surface but sufficiently above it to allow surface drainage and, where necessary, to permit the wind to clear drifting snow. Where the road approaches or follows along streams, the height of the grade line may be dictated by the expected level of flood waters. Under all conditions, smooth, flowing grade lines are preferable to choppy ones of many short straight sections connected with short vertical curves.

Maximum grades

As mentioned, passenger-car speeds are little affected by grades up to 6 or 7%, but truck speeds are reduced by much flatter grades with the effect increasing as the grades become longer. This indicates that short or "momentum" grades may be steeper than long or "sustained" grades. Furthermore, grades acceptable where traffic volume is light and passing is possible are not satisfactory where high volumes reduce passing opportunity. Also, steeper grades are more tolerable in mountainous terrain than in flatter country. In this connection it is to be noted that within reasonable limits nothing is gained by lengthening a road to reduce its steepness.

AASHO design standards do not set exact limits for maximum grades. For the interstate system they state: "The maximum gradient preferably shall not exceed 5 percent and in any case shall not exceed 6 percent. On short lengths only, 7 percent may be used." The standards for primary highways give no maximums.

Grades on urban freeways and expressways should be flatter than those suggested above. Recommendations of the AASHO [32] are as follows: "For a high-type road such as a freeway designed for commercial traffic, maximum gradients of 3 percent are in order. On modern parkways limited to passenger vehicles, gradients in a range of 4 to 6 percent are variously used as maximums. Maximum grades of 4 and 5 percent are currently accepted as design standards for modern mixed traffic even though a 3 percent limitation is known as preferable."

Vertical curves over crests [33]

All vertical curves should be as long as conditions permit, and under no circumstance should they be shorter than certain established minimums. Over crests these minimums are almost always dictated by sight-distance requirements. On occasion, where the difference in grades is small, ease of riding and appearance may demand longer curves than does sight distance. No set minimums are prescribed by the AASHO. Some engineers prefer that no vertical curve be shorter than 1000 ft. Others suggest, for high-speed roads, that the length of curve in stations be not less than the algebraic difference in grades.

---

[32] See *A Policy On Grade Separations For Intersecting Highways*, p. 26.

[33] No detailed explanation of the methods for computing elevations of points on vertical curves is included in this book. Complete descriptions will be found in all standard textbooks in route surveying. Briefly, the vertical distance from the intersection of the straight grade lines to the curve is equal to one-eighth the product of the algebraic difference in grades and the length of the curve in stations. This is called the maximum correction. The rate at which the curve departs vertically from both tangent grade lines is proportional to the square of the horizontal distance from the end of the curve. Any intermediate correction, then, is obtained by (1) multiplying the maximum correction by the square of the horizontal distance between the near end of the curve and the point and (2) dividing this product by the square of one-half the length of the curve.

Nonpassing sight distance over crests.   Figure 19a shows the approved method for measuring nonpassing sight distance over crests. It is the longest distance that a driver whose eye is 4.5 ft above the pavement can see the top of an object 4 in. high on the road.   On Fig. 20 are given the equations that express nonpassing sight distance in terms of algebraic difference in grades and length of vertical curve. Solutions to these equations are given in the chart, from which can

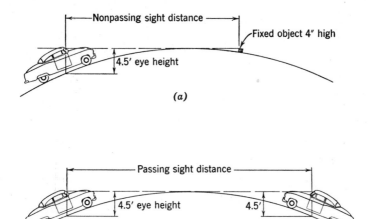

FIG. 19.   Procedure for measuring nonpassing and passing sight distances over crests

be found the length of vertical curve to provide a given nonpassing sight distance for algebraic differences in grades up to 20%.   An added vertical scale on the right margin of the chart gives a direct solution for minimum lengths of vertical curves in terms of design speeds and algebraic differences in grades.

Passing sight distance over crests.   Figure 19b shows the approved method for measuring passing sight distance over crests.   It is the longest distance that a driver whose eye is 4.5 ft above the pavement can see the top of an object 4.5 ft high on the road.   In reality, the 4.5-ft-high object represents an oncoming vehicle.   On Fig. 21 appear the equations that express passing sight distance for two- and three-lane highways in terms of the algebraic difference in grades and length of vertical curve.   Solutions to these equations are given in the chart, from which the length of vertical curve to provide a given passing sight distance can be found for algebraic differences in grades up to

20%. An added vertical scale on the right margin of the chart makes it possible to determine directly the *desirable* minimum length of vertical curves for *two-lane highways* in terms of design speeds and algebraic differences in grades. Absolute minimum vertical curve

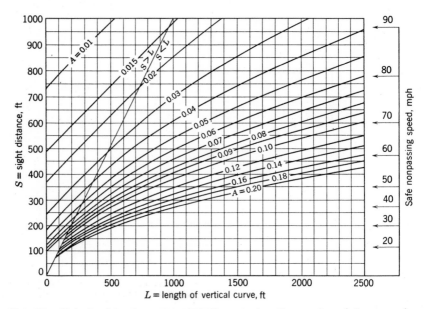

Fig. 20. Relationships between vertical curve lengths, grades, and nonpassing sight distances (Courtesy American Association of State Highway Officials)

A = algebraic difference of grades, % ÷ 100

When $S > L$, $S = \dfrac{7.28}{A} + \dfrac{L}{2}$

When $S < L$, $S = 3.82 \sqrt{\dfrac{L}{A}}$

Height of eye 4.5 ft; height of object 4 in.

lengths for two-lane highways and desirable and minimum curve lengths for three-lane highways are found by using Table 11 and Fig. 21.

Much longer vertical curves are required to provide passing than nonpassing sight distance. Consider, for example, a crest formed by a 2% grade upward followed by a 2% grade downward. On a two-lane highway, for a design speed of 50 mph, a 2900-ft vertical curve must be used to provide passing sight distance, whereas a 300-ft curve will furnish nonpassing sight distance (see Figs. 21 and 20). Vertical distances downward from the intersection of the tangent grades to the

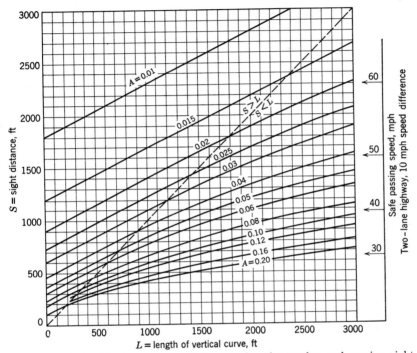

Fig. 21. Relationships between vertical curve lengths, grades, and passing sight distances (Courtesy American Association of State Highway Officials)

A = algebraic difference of grades, % ÷ 100

When $S > L$, $S = \dfrac{18}{A} + \dfrac{L}{2}$

When $S < L$, $S = 6\sqrt{\dfrac{L}{A}}$

Height of eye and height of object 4.5 ft

vertical curves are 14.5 and 1.5 ft, respectively. Or, stated differently, over the crest the road must be cut 13 ft lower to provide passing sight distance than if nonpassing sight distance only is provided. This example illustrates why, in rough country, it is extremely expensive to provide continuous passing sight distance on two-lane roads. It also illustrates why, if continuous passing opportunity is desired, a four-lane design may be cheaper than a two-lane one with the saving in excavation more than offsetting the cost of the extra lanes.

Passing practice studies [34] show that a sight distance of 1500 to 2000 ft is required by most drivers to pass a vehicle traveling 45 to 50 mph. Furthermore, sight distances greatly in excess of 2000 ft are of no more aid to the average driver than those between 1500 and 2000 ft. Likewise, a high percentage of the passing maneuvers made during normal operation can be performed when the sight distance is between 1000 and 1500 ft. These facts explain why the percentage of highway having passing sight distance of 1500 ft or more was adopted as the measure of the ability of a two-lane highway to satisfy passing requirements. For example, Table 5, page 152, shows the effect on capacity of sight distances less than 1500 ft.

Vertical curves in sags

At night, headlight reach usually determines the distance ahead that the driver can see. On sag vertical curves, the beam is directed into the roadway instead of along it and headlight reach is reduced. Extremely sharp sag vertical curves also limit the driver's visibility of the road ahead.

AASHO standards do not prescribe the lengths of vertical curves in sags, except to state that they be as long as possible. Rules of thumb setting minimum lengths in terms of the algebraic difference in grades are often used.[35] Another approach is to specify a minimum curve length, regardless of grade difference. Sight-distance charts based on headlight reach were used in designing the Pennsylvania Turnpike. Assumptions were that the headlights were 2.5 ft above the pavement and that the tops of the beams were slanted one degree upward when the vehicles were on level road.

ALINEMENT DESIGN

The alinement of a road is shown on the plan view and is a series of straight lines called tangents connected by circular curves. In modern practice it is common to interpose transition or spiral curves between tangents and circular curves (see Fig. 8, p. 120).

[34] See *Highway Capacity Manual*, p. 58.

[35] A typical rule for high-type rural highways is that the lengths of sag vertical curves in stations be not less than the algebraic differences in grades. Where curbs are provided, shorter lengths are employed to expedite drainage.

The sharpness of a given circular curve is indicated by its radius. However, among highway engineers sharpness is usually expressed in terms of *degree of curve*, which is the central angle subtended by a 100-ft length of curve. Degree of curve is inversely proportional to the radius, a relationship expressed by the formulas

$$D = \frac{5729.58}{\text{radius}} \qquad (3)$$

$$\text{Radius} = \frac{5729.58}{D} \qquad (4)$$

where D = degree of curve.

Solutions to these equations, for typical curves, give the following results:

Degree of Curve	Radius, Ft	Degree of Curve	Radius, Ft
0° 30'	11,459.16	6° 00'	954.93
1° 00'	5,729.58	10° 00'	572.96
2° 00'	2,864.79	20° 00'	286.48

More precisely, degree of curve may be expressed under either the *arc* definition or the *chord* definition. For the arc definition, the degree of curve is the central angle subtended by a 100-ft *arc* of the curve. Radii for various degrees of curve, arc definition, are inversely proportional to the degree of curve and are given by formula 4.

Under the chord definition, the degree of curve is the central angle subtended by a 100-ft *chord*. From this definition it follows that the precise relationship between radius and degree of curve is

$$\text{Radius} = \frac{50}{\sin \frac{1}{2}D} \qquad (5)$$

For flat curves of any stated degree, the radii obtained by arc and chord definitions are almost equal. However, as the curves become sharper, the results diverge. This divergence is not enough to affect geometric design standards, but must be recognized in computing and surveying the curves.[36]

A few highway agencies, among them the California Division of Highways, use "even-radius" curves, for which the radius is expressed in even figures like 1000, 1500 or 2000 ft. When degree of curve for even radius curves is computed by formula 3, the result does not come out in whole numbers. For example, D for a curve of 2000-ft radius is 2° 51.88'.

Alinement must be consistent. Sudden changes from flat to sharp curves and long tangents followed by sharp curves must be avoided;

[36] Space limitations preclude the inclusion here of the methods for computing and surveying circular curves. These will be found in any standard textbook in route surveying.

otherwise accident hazards will be created. Likewise, the use of compound [37] or broken-back curves is poor practice unless suitable transitions between them are provided. Long curves of very small degree are preferable at all times, as they are pleasing in appearance and decrease the possibility of future obsolescence. However, alinement without tangents is undesirable on two-lane roads because some drivers hesitate to pass on curves. Long, flat curves should be employed for small changes in direction, as short curves appear as "kinks."

Superelevation and side friction

A vehicle traveling a curved path on a flat surface is held in that path by side friction between tires and pavement. The total of these

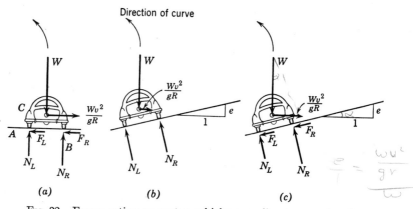

FIG. 22. Forces acting on motor vehicles traveling in curved paths

friction forces (F_L and F_R of Fig. 22a) equals the centrifugal force Wv^2/gR. Expressed in terms of the coefficient of friction f and the normal forces between pavement and tires, this relationship is

$$\frac{Wv^2}{gR} = (N_L + N_R)f = Wf$$

When velocity is stated in miles per hour and the equation is reduced, the relationships of coefficient of friction, velocity, and radius are

$$f = \frac{V^2}{15R} \tag{6}$$

[37] Two circular curves of different radii placed end to end.

Centrifugal force acts above the roadway surface through the center of gravity of the vehicle (see Fig. 22a) and creates an overturning moment about the points of contact between the outer wheels and the pavement (point B). Opposing overturn is the stabilizing moment created by the weight W acting downward through the center of gravity. Overturn can occur only when the overturning moment exceeds the stabilizing moment. Modern passenger cars have low centers of gravity, and consequently the overturning moment is relatively small. As a result, they will slide sidewise rather than overturn. Many trucks have high centers of gravity so that relatively large overturning moments can be created. They may overturn before they slide.

Curved sections of modern highways are almost always superelevated; that is, the roadway surface is sloped upward toward the outside of the curve. By this means, the tendency of vehicles to slide outward or to overturn can be partially or entirely offset. For each combination of radius of curve and speed of travel, there is a specific superelevation that will exactly balance centrifugal force. In this idealized situation, the reactions between tires and pavement act in a direction normal to the pavement surface. Forces acting on the vehicle are illustrated in Fig. 22b. The relationship among superelevation, velocity, and radius of curvature, expressed in feet and second units, is as follows:

$$\frac{e}{1} = \frac{Wv^2/gR}{W}$$

where e is the superelevation stated in feet of rise per horizontal foot across the roadway. With velocity expressed in miles per hour this equation reduces to

$$e = \frac{V^2}{15R} \tag{7}$$

When a vehicle travels at speeds greater than those at which the superelevation balances all centrifugal force, side friction again is needed to keep it in the curved path. Forces acting on the vehicle are shown in Fig. 22c. The coefficient of friction developed as the vehicle follows the curved path is

$$f = \frac{V^2}{15R} - e \tag{8}$$

Maximum coefficients of side friction on dry pavements as determined by circle or curve tests normally range between 0.4 and 0.5. Somewhat lower coefficients are developed on wet pavements. However, drivers become uncomfortable long before side friction approaches values at which slipping impends, unless the pavement is icy or muddy. The AASHO standards, based on studies of driver discomfort, place the maximum coefficient of side friction at 0.16 for design speeds up to 60 mph, and at 0.14 for 70 mph.[38]

The centrifugal forces that act on slow-moving vehicles are relatively small. When these vehicles travel around superelevated curves, side-friction forces acting outward from the center of the curve must be developed between tires and pavement; otherwise the vehicles will slide inward. For standing vehicles there is no centrifugal force, so that in this instance the coefficient of side friction must equal the superelevation. Since highways are used throughout the year, maximum superelevation must never exceed the minimum coefficient of friction that will develop under the most adverse weather conditions. Maximum superelevation permitted by the AASHO is 0.12 ft per ft. If ice and snow conditions prevail, this maximum is reduced to 0.08 ft per ft.[39] In recent practice, up to 0.16 ft per ft have proved satisfactory on ramps at interchanges, particularly on down-ramps where design is for higher speeds than on up-ramps.

Standards for curvature

Standards for the interstate and primary systems base maximum curve sharpness on design speed (see Table 12). Values were computed using formula 8 rearranged and restated in terms of degree of curve, as follows:

$$D_{max} = \frac{85,950(e + f)}{V^2} \tag{9}$$

[38] Superelevation and maximum safe speeds around curves have been the subject of intensive study. A paper by R. A. Moyer and D. S. Berry titled Marking Highway Curves with Safe Speed Indications in *Proceedings Highway Research Board*, pp. 399–428 (1940), is of particular interest. See also Curve Design and Tests for the Pennsylvania Turnpike by K. A. Stonex and C. M. Noble, pp. 429–454 of the same volume. A discussion of tire squeal on curves by Joseph Barnett, R. A. Moyer, and R. D. Evans appears in *Highway Research Board Bulletin 51* (1952). An important conclusion is that squeal of tires should not be used as a criterion for determining maximum safe speed around curves.

[39] On icy surfaces, the coefficient of side friction may be 0.05 or less. Then skid-prevention measures must be taken by vehicle operators or maintenance personnel.

TABLE 12.   SHARPEST PERMISSIBLE HORIZONTAL CURVES

From AASHO Design Standards

Design Control	Degree of Curvature									
	Interstate System		Primary Highways		Secondary and Feeder					
					Average Annual Daily Traffic					
					Under 100		100 to 400		400 to 1000	
	Desirable	Max.	Desirable	Max.	Desirable	Max.	Desirable	Max.	Desirable	Max.
Design speed, mph										
30			20	25						
40	11	14	11	14						
50	7	9	7	9						
60	5	6	5	6						
70	3	4	3	4						
Flat topography					..	14	7	11	6	9
Rolling topography					..	25	11	18	9	14
Mountainous topography					..	56	18	36	14	25

For the sharpest permissible curves, superelevation and coefficients of side friction are set near the maximums stated above. For desirable curvature limits, the same friction factors are used, but the maximum superelevation is reduced by one-half. Maximum and desirable curvature limits for secondary roads are based on topography and traffic (see Table 12).

For curves flatter than those requiring maximum permissible superelevation and side friction, either or both may be reduced. The AASHO design standards make no specific recommendations in this regard, and practice varies among agencies. The book, *Transition Curves for Highways*,[40] and the report, *Interregional Highways*,[41] recommend that curves sharper than 1 degree shall be superelevated. On all curves the superelevation shall be such as to counterbalance completely the centrifugal force of a vehicle traveling at three-fourths of the design speed of the road, except that it shall not exceed the

[40] This 211-pp. book, written in 1940 by Joseph Barnett of the (then) Public Roads Administration, was printed by the U. S. Government Printing Office.
[41] See p. 12 for further description of this report.

appropriate maximum limit.[42] This recommendation, reduced to graph form, appears as Fig. 23. In using such a chart superelevation is commonly read only to the nearest 0.01 ft. On Fig. 23 the superelevation practice of the Texas Department of Highways has also been shown. The superelevation applied to primary highways balances about three-

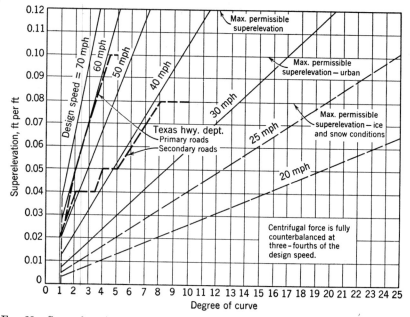

FIG. 23. Superelevation chart, based on recommendations in *Interregional Highways* and on standards of the Texas Highway Department

fourths of the centrifugal force developed at a vehicle speed of 60 mph. That applied to secondary highways balances about three-fourths of the centrifugal force at 40 mph.

As shown by Fig. 23, 1-degree and flatter curves are not superelevated by some highway agencies. Instead, normal crown is continued around the curve, which results in reverse superelevation in the outer lane or lanes. The coefficient of side friction that must be developed is low; for 70 mph and a 1-degree curve normally crowned, it is only 0.07 or 0.08. Some highway engineers consider that even this is objectionable and superelevate all curves

[42] *Transition Curves for Highways* recommends a maximum superrelevation of 0.10 ft per ft. The Interregional report, for rural areas, sets these maximums at 0.12 and 0.08, depending on climate, as does the AASHO. For urban areas the Interregional report sets maximum superelevation at 0.10 ft per ft.

to the minimum required to provide cross drainage. Others avoid the problem. For example, the Louisiana Department of Highways on a 70-mph design uses no curves of sharpnesses between 0° 46′ and 1° 29′. Flatter curves carry normal crown, sharper ones are spiraled and superelevated.

Transition sections

Tangent sections of highways carry normal crown; curved sections are superelevated. Provision must be made for gradual change from one to the other. This usually involves maintaining the center line of each individual roadway at profile grade while raising the outer

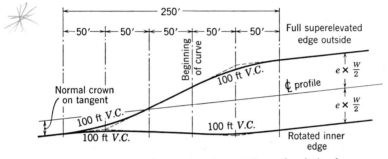

Fig. 24. Application of superelevation at the ends of circular curves

edge and lowering the inner edge to produce the desired superelevation.[43] Where the alinement consists of tangents connected by circular curves, introduction of superelevation is begun on tangent before the curve is reached, and full superelevation is attained some distance beyond the point of curve. A satisfactory transition appears to be a uniform grade along each edge of the road with vertical curves to connect at its ends (see Fig. 24). Some engineers prefer to increase the lengths of the vertical curves and to eliminate the intervening straight grades. Others merely use straight grade lines, without the vertical curves. In any event, the transition must be made smoothly without bumps or holes in the shoulder grade lines. The AASHO

[43] Where the roadway lies in a cut and the grade line is nearly flat, lowering its inner edge may create a sag from which surface water will not drain. Then it may be advisable to accomplish all superelevation by raising the outer edge. This, of course, means that this edge must be elevated twice the usual distance.

With divided highways it sometimes is better to rotate each roadway about the edge adjoining the median strip rather than its individual center line. Otherwise the two sides of the median may be at considerably different elevations; this creates numerous problems, particularly when the median strip is narrow.

design standards do not recommend specific transition lengths, such as those indicated in Fig. 24. Instead, they state that "In attaining superelevation it is desirable that the slope of the outer edge of the pavement with respect to the profile of the center line should not be greater than 1 in 200."

Easement (spiral) curves

If a vehicle travels at high speed on a carefully restricted path made up of tangents connected by sharp circular curves, riding is extremely uncomfortable. As the car approaches a curve, superelevation begins and the vehicle is tilted inward but the passenger must remain vertical since there is no centrifugal force requiring compensation. When the vehicle reaches the curve, full centrifugal force develops at once, and pulls the rider outward from his vertical position. To achieve a position of equilibrium he must force his body far inward. As the remaining superelevation takes effect, further adjustment in position is required. This process is repeated in reverse order as the vehicle leaves the curve. When easement curves are introduced, the change in radius from infinity on the tangent to that of the circular curve is effected gradually so that centrifugal force also develops gradually. By careful application of superelevation along the spiral, a smooth and gradual application of centrifugal force can be had and the roughness described above avoided.

Easement curves have been used by the railroads for many years, but their adoption by highway agencies has come only recently. This is understandable. Railroad trains must follow the precise alinement of the tracks, and the discomfort described above can be avoided only by adopting easement curves. On the other hand, the motor-vehicle operator is free to alter his lateral position on the road and can provide his own easement curves by steering into circular curves gradually. However, this weaving within a traffic lane (but sometimes into other lanes) is dangerous. Properly designed easement curves make weaving unnecessary. It is largely for safety reasons, then, that easement curves have been widely adopted by highway agencies.[44]

For the same radius circular curve, the addition of easement curves at the ends changes the location of the curve with relation to its tangents; hence the decision regarding their use should be made

[44] For an excellent and detailed discussion of easement curves, see Analytical Method for Determining the Length of Transition Spirals, *Transactions American Society of Civil Engineers*, pp. 155–185 (1951).

before the final location survey. This difference in position is illustrated by Fig. 25. Changes made in providing an easement curve
are as follows:

1. The entire circular curve (dashed curve on Fig. 25) is shifted
inward on a line connecting the tangent intersection *PI* with the

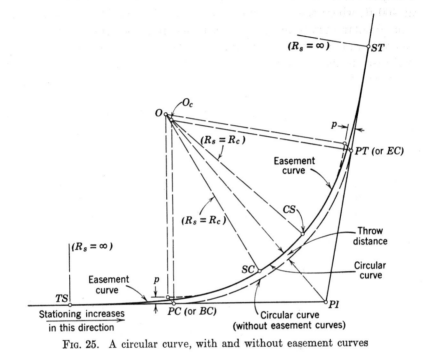

FIG. 25. A circular curve, with and without easement curves

radius point of the circular curve O_c. This shift is designated as the
"throw distance."

2. The ends of the shifted circular curve are removed (dotted curves
in Fig. 25) and appropriate easement curves substituted.

The point of beginning of an ordinary circular curve is usually
labeled the *PC* (point of curve) or *BC* (beginning of curve). Its end
is marked the *PT* (point of tangency) or *EC* (end of curve). For
curves that include easements, the common notation is, as stationing
increases: *TS* (tangent to spiral), *SC* (spiral to circular curve), *CS*
(circular curve to spiral), and *ST* (spiral to tangent).

The sharpness of easement curves, measured in terms of degree of
curvature, increases uniformly from their beginnings. If, for instance,

easement curves 400 ft long are selected to connect each end of a 4-degree circular curve to its tangents, the sharpness of the easement curves will increase by one degree each 100 ft. At the TS or ST, where the curve begins, the degree of curve is zero and the radius infinite. At 100 ft along the curve, the spiral has the same radius as a 1-degree curve; at 200 ft its radius equals that of a 2-degree curve; at 400 ft, where the easement curve ends (SC or CS), both easement and circular curves have the sharpness of a 4-degree curve and a common radius point. If length is added to this identical spiral, it will also fit sharper circular curves. Thus, if it is extended to 1000 ft, it will fit a 10-degree curve. A particular sharpness of easement curve, then, may be designated by its increase in degree of curve per 100-ft station, which is denoted by some writers with the letter k.[45] For the curve described above, k equals 1 degree.

The sharpness or k value of an easement curve, and consequently its length L_s, depends on design speed. As mentioned earlier, motor-vehicle operators control the rate of application of centrifugal force by steering into curves gradually. If drivers are to follow easement curves closely and retain their proper position on the roadway, this change in centrifugal force must not be excessive. Based on "the few observations available," the minimum length of easement curve was set at [46]

$$(L_s)_{min} = 1.6 \frac{V^3}{R} \tag{10}$$

This value for easement-curve length is also recommended by the AASHO design standards for primary highways.[47] Formula 10 can be rearranged to state directly the maximum increase in sharpness of spiral for any given design speed. The result is

$$k = \frac{350,000}{V^3} \tag{11}$$

Solutions for formulas 10 and 11 as applied in design by the Arizona Highway Department appear in Table 13.

[45] The symbols used in the various books and pamphlets on easement curves are not uniform. Others use the symbol a to designate this rate of increase in sharpness.

[46] See Transition Curves for Highways, p. 8.

[47] The proper length for easement curves is still an unsettled question. The reference given near the beginning of this section presents several viewpoints.

TABLE 13. MINIMUM LENGTHS OF EASEMENT CURVES FOR VARIOUS DESIGN
SPEEDS AND SHARPNESS OF CIRCULAR CURVES

Design Speed, Mph	Increase in Sharpness of Spiral per 100 Ft of Curve Length, Degrees	Minimum Length of Easement Curve, Ft									
		Sharpness of Circular Curve, Degrees									
		1°	2°	3°	4°	5°	6°	8°	10°	12°	14°
40	5	20	40	60	80	100	120	160	200	240	280
50	2½	40	80	120	160	200	240	320			
60	1⅔	60	120	180	240	300	360				
70	1	100	200	300	400						
80	⅔	150	300	450							
90	½	200	400								
100	⅓	300	600								

Data from Standard Drawings of the Arizona Highway Department.

Easement curves are usually omitted from 1-degree and flatter circular curves as the inward shift of the main curve to accommodate the spiral is small.[48] AASHO standards for the interstate system recommend that curves sharper than 2 degrees be spiraled. Those for primary highways call for easement curves when the radial offset distance (dimension p on Fig. 25) is greater than 1 ft.

Computations and field surveys for combined circular and easement curves are somewhat more difficult and time-consuming than those for circular curves alone. This explains, at least in part, why the adoption of easement curves by American highway agencies has been slow. Detailed explanations, formulas, and tables of useful functions and dimensions for easement curves will be found in all standard textbooks in route surveying and in the standard drawings of many highway agencies. They also appear in *Transition Curves for Highways*. Because of space limitations, such information is omitted from this book.

The procedure for applying superelevation along the length of easement curves is not standardized among highway agencies. The method proposed by Barnett in *Transition Curves for Highways* is shown as Fig. 26. Note that the maximum difference in slope between normal or profile grade and that of the pavement edge is 1 to 200. This applies for design speeds of 50 mph or more. This may be steepened to

---

[48] For a 100-mph design speed, 1-degree curve, and 300-ft spiral length, the radial offset distance (dimension p on Fig. 25) is only 0.65 ft. This is too small to be of practical significance.

1 to 175 for design speeds of 40 mph and to 1 to 150 for design speeds of 30 mph. It is also to be noted that the normal crown of the outer half of the roadway, which is in a direction opposite to that required for superelevation, is removed on tangent before the easement curve is reached. Figure 26 indicates no vertical curves at breaks in the

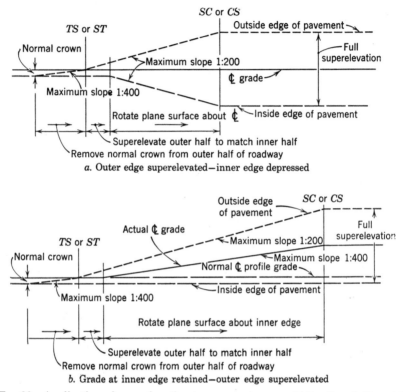

a. Outer edge superelevated—inner edge depressed

b. Grade at inner edge retained—outer edge superelevated

FIG. 26. Application of superelevation to easement curves (After Joseph Barnett)

grade lines because the difference in grades is slight. However, they are included in some design standards.

At times, particularly in rough country, a curve in one direction is followed by one turning the opposite way. In the past the *reverse curve* was often used, with the end point of one circular curve (*PT*) also the beginning point (*PC*) of the next. At this "point of reverse curve" (*PRC*) the roadway was made flat or with normal crown, and all superelevation was developed on the respective curves. For the low-speed operation of early days there was little objection to this practice, but with the higher speeds of modern vehicles reverse curves produced a very "rough-riding" roadway. Also, high-speed drivers cannot closely follow the intended path, which results in an accident hazard. Reverse circular curves are little used on modern highways. However, reverse curves which incorporate proper length easements between them are perfectly acceptable. If no easement curves are provided, curves in opposite directions should be separated by a tangent several hundred feet in length. Some earlier roads likewise have compound curves that change abruptly from one sharpness to another at a "point of compound curve" (*PCC*). Where the radii of the compounded curves are markedly different, the sudden change confuses and deceives the driver so that he shifts his position within the lane, and sometimes veers out of it. For this reason, compounding circular curves of greatly different radii is considered poor practice. Compound curves may be employed, however, if a connecting easement curve is provided which introduces the change in radius gradually. Superelevation is changed along this transition section. Rules for determining curve length correspond to those stated earlier for spirals connecting tangents with circular curves. Computations and field layout are somewhat difficult. Explanations will be found in most writings on easement curves.

As with circular curves, easement curves may be computed by either the arc or the chord definition. The basic assumption, that degree of curve increases uniformly along the length of the spiral, is the same for either. However, for curves of considerable length or sharpness, a slight difference in some of the dimensions results when the length of the spiral is measured as a series of chords rather than along the curve itself. This difference is not great enough to affect the relation between spiral length and design speed (equation 10), but must be recognized in computing and laying out the curves. Of course arc-definition easement curves are used with arc-definition circular curves and chord-definition easements with chord-definition curves.

The American Railway Engineering Association (AREA) spiral, used by most railroads, is based on the chord definition. It is known as the ten-chord spiral because, regardless of its total length, it is laid out in ten equal segments. Points on other types of spirals are often staked out at convenient intervals along the roadway, such as 10, 25, or 50 ft, regardless of the number of segments that result. Another type curve, the lemniscate, advanced by F. G. Royal-Dawson in his book, *Road Curves*, has been used in England to some extent.

The transition curve described in the preceding paragraphs was originally developed by the railroads. Some highway engineers doubt that this form of curve best meets highway needs. A discussion in this vein appears in *Transactions American Society of Civil Engineers*, pp. 868–900 (1948).

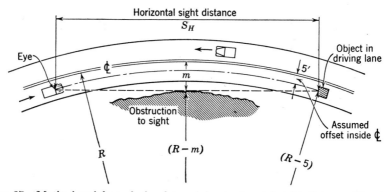

FIG. 27. Method and formula for determining horizontal sight distance (Courtesy Arizona Highway Department)

$$S_H = 2\sqrt{(R-5)^2 - (R-m)^2}$$

Eye is assumed to be 4.5 ft above road and object is assumed to be 4 in. high

Horizontal sight distance

As a vehicle travels around a horizontal curve, any obstruction near the inside edge of the road blocks the driver's view ahead. Any particular combination of sharpness of curve with position of obstruction establishes a horizontal sight distance, which is the greatest distance at which a driver can see an object lying in the roadway ahead. If the design is to provide safe operation, this horizontal sight distance must equal or exceed the safe stopping distance for each design speed (see Table 10, p. 172).

The AASHO pamphlet, *A Policy On Sight Distance* (1940), in measuring horizontal sight distance placed the driver's eye and the object to be avoided at the roadway center line. Some highway agencies that have established their standards for measuring horizontal sight distance at a later date have set eye and object on an arc 5 ft inside the center line. The method and formula adopted by the Arizona Highway Department for measuring horizontal sight distance are shown as Fig. 27. Its design chart, from which the relationship between obstruction location, degree of curvature, and horizontal sight distance can be determined, is presented as Fig. 28. Figure 28 does not apply if required sight distance exceeds curve length, at the ends of circular curves, or along easement curves. For these and like situations, the offset distances may be obtained easily by scaling from the plans. When computing the distance that a cut slope must be set back, it

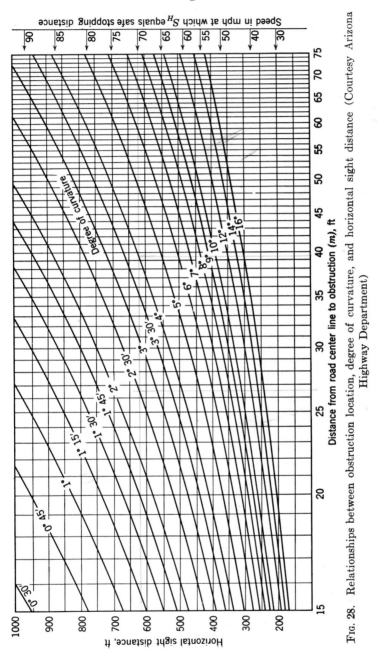

FIG. 28. Relationships between obstruction location, degree of curvature, and horizontal sight distance (Courtesy Arizona Highway Department)

should be recognized that the line of vision passes the critical point of the bank at a level higher than the roadway shoulder. The required bank setback should be provided at this height.

To provide safe horizontal sight distance, it is at times necessary to set back buildings, fences, or signs. Where there is a cut bank along the inside of a curve, the backslope often must be moved outward beyond its location in the normal tangent cross section. If the design speed is high, this setback is large for sharp curves, and the consequent excavation costs are high. This is one reason why design speeds on mountain roads are often low. Where high design speeds are to be maintained regardless of cost, flat curves may be provided at little added cost, since much of the excavation must be provided anyway to meet the horizontal-sight-distance requirement.

Night driving around sharp curves introduces an added problem related to horizontal sight distance. Motor-vehicle headlights are pointed directly toward the front and do not provide as much illumination in oblique directions. Even if adequate horizontal sight distance is provided, it has little useful purpose at night because the headlights are directed along a tangent to the curve, and the roadway itself is not properly illuminated.

Curve widening

Drivers tend to shy away from the roadway edge when traveling around curves. Furthermore, the following wheels of vehicles do not precisely trail the leading ones.[49] Most highway agencies recognize these factors by widening the roadway on sharper curves. No specific recommendations on curve widening are made by the AASHO design standards, and the actual practice varies among highway agencies. Barnett, in *Transition Curves for Highways*, recommends the following formula:

$$W_4 = n(R - \sqrt{R^2 - 400}) + \frac{V}{\sqrt{R}} \tag{12}$$

in which W is the widening in feet and n is the number of lanes being widened. It is suggested that no widening be used on two-lane pavements when W from

[49] Tracking characteristics of vehicles vary with speed, superelevation, and with many features of individual vehicles. To develop side friction, side slipping must occur, and rarely is this equal for front and rear wheels or for truck and trailer. Seldom is the axis of the vehicle tangent to the curve being followed. For more on this subject see R. A. Moyer, Skidding Characteristics of Vehicles and Their Relation to Highway Safety, *Iowa Engineering Experiment Station Bulletin 120;* Moyer and Berry, Marking Highway Curves with Safe Speed Indications, *Proceedings Highway Research Board*, pp. 399–428 (1940); and *Transition Curves for Highways*, pp. 42–49.

formula 12 is less than 2 ft. If this rule is followed, no widening is called for on curves flatter than 4 degrees for a design speed of 70 mph, 5 degrees for 60 mph, and 6 degrees for 50 mph.

Where transition curves are not used, all widening is added to the inside edge of the pavement. With transitions it may be placed entirely on the inside or half inside and half outside. At curve ends, the transition from normal to extra width is made gradually, in a manner like that used to apply superelevation.

Combined curvature and grade

Horizontal curvature increases operating resistance. Also, as superelevation is added and taken off a road of constant grade, some sections along the actual vehicle path become steeper and others flatter than the profile grade. Where grades are relatively flat, no recognition is made of these factors in roadway design. In mountainous country where the combination of sharp curves with steep grades occurs along the best located highway, the effect of curvature on vehicle operation deserves attention. The practice of some agencies is to reduce the grade for the length of the curve, thus compensating for the increased resistance caused by curvature. Many formulas have been used to determine the magnitude of this grade reduction. One simple rule is [50]

$$\text{Compensation in per cent of grade} = \frac{250}{R} \qquad (13)$$

From this, for example, on a curve of 250-ft radius, the grade would be reduced by 1%, as from 6 to 5%. The use of grade compensation is commonly restricted to curves sharper than 6 degrees and to grades 5% or greater. The breaks in grade line are placed on the tangents, about 50 ft from the ends of the circular curve. Short vertical curves at these grade breaks may be incorporated into the design.

CHANNELIZATION

Purposes of channelization

In modern highway practice, color and surface-texture differences in pavements, painted stripes, raised bars, curbings, raised islands, and road guards are widely employed to direct or control vehicle and pedestrian movements. When properly placed, they have increased intersection capacity, improved traffic-flow conditions, and decreased vehicular and pedestrian accidents. Appropriate channelizing devices are included as an integral part of any new intersection or interchange. In addition, they offer an extremely useful and relatively inexpensive tool for correcting some of the deficiencies of existing roads and streets.

[50] See Hewes, *American Highway Practice*, John Wiley & Sons, vol. I, pp. 122–123 (1942), for other suggested methods.

Among the more important purposes of channelization are the following: [51]

1. By channelization, vehicles can be confined to definite paths. When drivers or pedestrians have free choice of routes through large all-paved intersections, their actions cannot be predicted by others. This creates confusion and congestion and often leads to accidents.

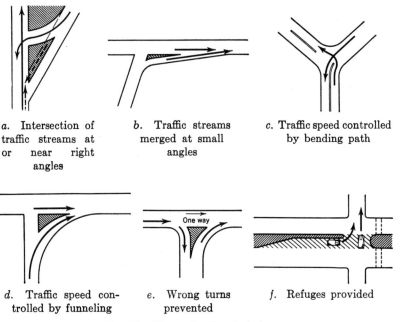

a. Intersection of traffic streams at or near right angles

b. Traffic streams merged at small angles

c. Traffic speed controlled by bending path

d. Traffic speed controlled by funneling

e. Wrong turns prevented

f. Refuges provided

FIG. 29. Channelization techniques

In addition, accidents are more likely, since each vehicle is exposed for longer distances to others making conflicting movements.

2. By channelization, the angle between intersecting streams of traffic can be made more favorable. When cross traffic meets at flat angles (see the dashed arrows of Fig. 29a) the accidents that occur usually are serious ones, just as head-on collisions are. The relative speed between the two vehicles is high, and practically all the kinetic energy of both is dissipated by damaging the vehicles or their oc-

[51] This discussion is based on *Highway Research Board Special Report 5* (1952) titled Channelization. This publication offers a detailed discussion of channelizing principles and 59 typical examples.

cupants. As the direction of meeting swings away from head-on, accidents generally become less severe. It has now been established that, all things considered, the intersection of traffic streams at about right angles (75° to 105°) is most favorable (see Fig. 29a). Besides decreasing accident severity, meeting at this angle reduces the distance and time during which opposing vehicles can be in conflict, and thus reduces accident opportunity. The right-angle crossing also provides drivers with the most favorable condition for judging the relative position and speed of approaching vehicles.

3. By channelization, drivers can be forced to merge into moving traffic streams at flat angles (10° to 15°) and proper speeds (see Fig. 29b). Entry in this manner causes little disruption to traffic or decrease in capacity on the main thoroughfare. Where traffic enters at larger angles, accident hazard is greater, and fewer vehicles are accommodated since the gap in the moving stream must be longer before entry can be made. Access other than by merging usually should be subject to stop-sign control.

4. By channelization, speed control can be established over vehicles entering an intersection. One method of accomplishing this is to bend the traffic stream (Fig. 29c). Another is to funnel the vehicles into a narrowing opening (Fig. 29d). This causes the driver to feel hemmed in, and he reacts by reducing his speed. Funneling also is effective in preventing overtaking and passing in a conflict area. In cases where speed control is the aim, carefully planned superelevation is an important adjunct to channelizing.

5. By channelization, prohibited turns may be prevented (Fig. 29e).

6. By channelization, refuge may be provided for turning or crossing vehicles and for pedestrians. This is illustrated by the provision of turning lanes and of protected areas for cross traffic and pedestrians at the center of the street (see Fig. 29f).

7. By channelization, points of conflict may be separated in such a way that the driver faces only one decision at a time. This reduces confusion and accidents because the driver can reach the proper decision in a shorter period of time.

8. Channelizing devices provide protected locations for essential traffic-control devices.

Channelizing devices

The various channelizing devices exert different degrees of control over driver and vehicle. On the one hand, striping and changes in pavement surface merely suggest the appropriate path and speed. On the other hand, nonmountable road guards, curbs, or bumper blocks like those sometimes used on the exposed ends of streetcar loading zones positively prohibit encroachment by the vehicle. Between the extremes fall such devices as raised bars made of concrete or bituminous mixtures or mountable curbs over which a vehicle may pass if the driver so desires. In selecting the device that will work best in a given situation, the designer must weigh such factors as the space available for the installation, its cost, traffic volumes and speeds, the

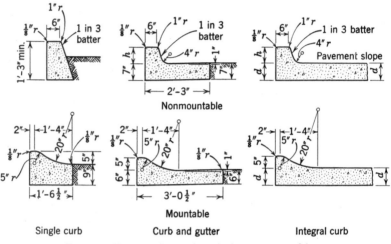

Fig. 30. Cross sections of typical concrete curbings

seriousness of the accidents that may result from vehicles entering the prohibited area, and the influence of police supervision on driver behavior. For example, all these conditions differ greatly between rural and urban locations, and designs appropriate for one may not fit the other.

Curbing and raised islands bounded by curbs are particularly important channelizing devices. Figure 30 shows typical curb cross sections.[52] The given dimensions are intended merely as guides, as curb details are not standardized among highway agencies. If curbs border bituminous pavement, single curb[53] or combined curb and

[52] The standard drawings of each highway agency include details of many curbing types, each of which is assigned a code number or letter. The roadway designer selects the type that meets the particular situation and designates it on the plans by giving its number.

[53] Some highway and street agencies use single curbs of granite or other quarried stone rather than of concrete.

gutter is used. Generally, where water is to flow along the gutter, combined curb and gutter is to be preferred. With concrete pavement, combined curb and gutter or integral curb is generally chosen. Curb and gutter is placed first as a separate operation, and thus provides an excellent means for establishing proper pavement grades. Careful control of grades and pavement smoothness is more difficult if the designs call for integral curb.

In many situations, high visibility is an important requirement for curbings. In these cases it is common practice to use white Portland cement in the concrete or to paint the curbing. Many agencies further increase visibility by providing indentations in the curb face which will reflect headlight rays back to the driver. Installing special reflectors in the curb face offers another method of increasing visibility.

The height of nonmountable curbings seldom exceeds 7 in., as greater heights catch fender edges or other low-hanging parts of passenger cars. Vehicles striking such curbs straight-on will pass over them, but those hitting at small angles usually will be deflected back into the roadway again without serious damage to the vehicle.

Road guards provide a positive means of confining vehicles to designated roadways. They are usually 2 ft or more in height, and vehicles striking them will suffer some damage, at least to body parts. Road guards appear most frequently on rural roads in rolling or mountainous country where the combination of high fills and tortuous alinement is common. They consist of a continuous "rail element" supported at intervals by sturdy posts. Approved rail elements include steel-wire cable, woven steel-wire tape, steel strip, steel plate, woven steel-wire fabric, steel-plate beam, or timber. Posts may be of treated or untreated timber, steel, or precast concrete.[54]

DESIGN OF INTERSECTIONS AT GRADE [55]

Most highways intersect at grade, which makes the intersection area a part of both roads. In this area must occur all crossing and turning movements. Figures 31 and 32 show typical intersections at grade,

[54] For detailed information about guard rails, see the standard specifications and drawings of the several highway agencies. Also see *Specifications for Highway Guards,* AASHO (1951).

[55] For detailed information on intersection design see *A Policy on Intersections at Grade,* of the AASHO (1940), and the *Traffic Engineering Handbook* published by the Institute of Traffic Engineers.

ranging from simple to complex.   Figure 31*a* illustrates the simplest
intersection design.   Here the roadway has been extended out to meet

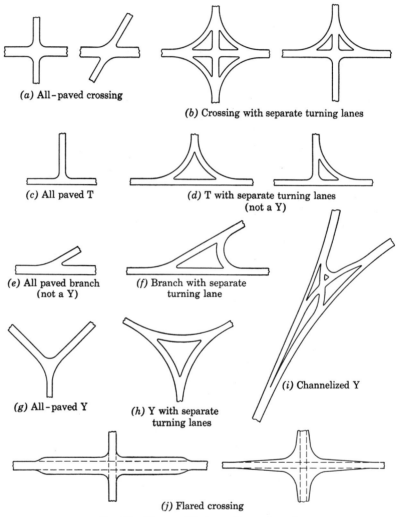

(*a*) All-paved crossing

(*b*) Crossing with separate turning lanes

(*c*) All paved T

(*d*) T with separate turning lanes
(not a Y)

(*e*) All paved branch
(not a Y)

(*f*) Branch with separate
turning lane

(*i*) Channelized Y

(*g*) All-paved Y

(*h*) Y with separate
turning lanes

(*j*) Flared crossing

FIG. 31. Types of intersections at grade

a circular arc connecting the road edges in order to provide pavement
under vehicles turning to the right.   For intersections of roads or
streets carrying little traffic, no further treatment is needed, with the
possible exception of signs or other traffic-control devices.   However,

as the importance of one or both of the thoroughfares increases, other features must be added to the design. For example, in Fig. 32*b*, which shows the intersection of a cross street with a divided expressway with frontage roads, the following devices have been used: acceleration and deceleration lanes to clear the through lanes of both right-turn

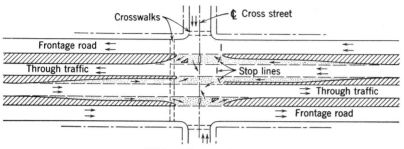

a. With traffic-signal control

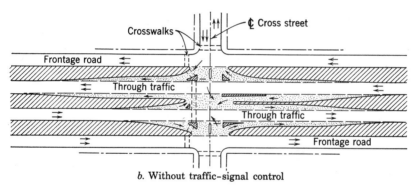

b. Without traffic-signal control

FIG. 32. Typical intersection at grade between an expressway with frontage roads and a cross street

and left-turn vehicles, channelizing islands, pedestrian islands, and striping of pedestrian lanes.

A careful traffic count and estimate for the future, including data regarding each turning movement, must precede the design of an important intersection. Only in this way can those movements that are heavy be favored in the design. Traffic information coupled with knowledge of lane capacities leads to decisions regarding the number of lanes to be supplied. The speeds at which vehicles will approach and move through the intersection will govern many dimensions, particularly minimum sight distances in various directions and the radii of curves. Likewise, a decision regarding the need for traffic signals currently or in the future will affect certain features of the design.

In laying out intersections, characteristics of driver and vehicle and the possibility of accidents and their frequency and severity must be always kept in mind. As stated earlier, drivers should be confronted with but one decision at a time. Further, they should be guided into the proper channels for their intended routes and prevented from doing wrong or unpredictable things. It is important that spacious areas which permit "open-field running" be eliminated by the provision of directional islands that leave little choice of route. Pavement and islands that supply direction to converging streams of traffic should lead to blending at very small angles. It is preferable to use single large islands rather than several small ones, as single large ones are less confusing to drivers.

Most important intersections must accommodate large trucks and the radii of all curves made long enough for them. For the inside edge of 90-degree turns at low-speed intersections, the AASHO recommends as a minimum a three-centered compound curve with radii successively 120, 38, and 120 ft. Because the vehicle does not track and its front overhangs, minimum lane width near the center of the curve [56] approaches 20 ft.

Sometimes a study of traffic-flow data indicates that relatively few vehicles perform a particular turning movement at a given intersection. If this movement complicates the design or increases congestion, it should be eliminated completely and provision made for it in some other way. For example, vehicles desiring to make left turns often are directed to the right completely around an adjacent block; then they pass through the intersection with normal cross traffic.

Certain design features of complicated intersections often require testing by actual use. In such cases it is common to place temporary channelizing islands made of sandbags which can be easily shifted around. Sand sprinkled over the roadways will indicate vehicle

---

[56] See *A Policy on Intersections at Grade* for further details of this layout, and for recommendations concerning those to fit other central angles, vehicle types, and speeds. The California Division of Highways has made extensive tests on the turning radii of large trucks now in common use in that state. For a report of these tests and design recommendations based on them see J. C. Young, Truck Turns, *California Highways and Public Works*, March–April 1950. For a report on model studies to determine turning radii, see L. F. Heuperman, *Highway Research Board Bulletin 72*, pp. 14–49 (1953).

paths. After the design has been proved, the permanent installation is made.

ROTARY INTERSECTIONS [57]

A rotary intersection is one in which all traffic merges into and emerges from a one-way road around a central island (see Fig. 33). An authoritative statement regarding them is as follows: [58]

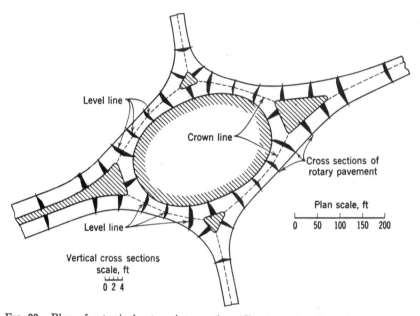

Fig. 33. Plan of a typical rotary intersection (Courtesy American Association of State Highway Officials)

Because of the relatively large area required for their development, the extra travel distance within them, the necessary speed reduction on the part of all entering vehicles, and the limited capacity of the weaving sections, rotaries are not being used today except in special instances. It is found possible to handle greater volumes than formerly was thought feasible in at-grade intersections, combining channelization and traffic signal controls. It is found that partial-cloverleaf grade separations are comparable in over-all development and operating costs to rotaries properly designed. Thus the range of traffic volume conditions wherein the rotary is considered most suitable has

[57] For detailed information see *A Policy on Rotary Intersections*, AASHO (1942).

[58] From *Highway Practice In The United States*, Public Roads Administration, p. 102 (1949).

narrowed considerably during the last decade. Many existing rotaries in urban and suburban areas have been made operable under increasing traffic volumes only through installation of traffic signal controls and stop-and-go operation for which their over-all shape is poorly suited.

Some recent interchange designs for freeways have combined over- or undercrossings for through traffic with rotaries at ground level to distribute traffic to local streets.

GRADE SEPARATIONS [59]

When one highway crosses another at grade, capacity is reduced to that of the intersection. Furthermore, some or all of the vehicles must slow down or stop to permit the passage of crossing and turning traffic. There are many points of conflict, with accompanying accident opportunity. A grade separation structure eliminates these difficulties. Capacity will rise to that of the traffic lanes. Vehicles can travel at uniform speed, which reduces both travel time and operating costs. Accident opportunity is almost entirely eliminated. On the other hand, since right-of-way, construction, and maintenance costs of grade-separation structures are great, they can be afforded only on high-type facilities which carry large volumes of traffic.

Provisions for grade separation between freeways and the ordinary streets selected to carry traffic across are relatively simple. They consist merely of bridges to carry one facility over the other (see Figs. 34 and 35a). Arrangements for smooth access and egress between cross streets and ground-level or depressed freeways likewise are not difficult if sufficient right-of-way width can be had. Figure 34 illustrates such provisions. As a rule connections to elevated freeways present more difficulties.

In settled areas, freeway crossings solely for pedestrians often are needed. These offer no serious problem if the freeway is either elevated or depressed. If the freeway is near ground level the solution is less satisfactory. Since the minimum vertical clearance above a roadway is 14 ft, users of an overcrossing must climb a stairway or ramp rising 15 ft or more. With undercrossings, vertical clearances total only about 8 ft, but policing becomes a serious problem since the walkways are not visible until the approach ramp or stairway has been descended. A compromise solution that raises the freeway grade some 4 ft at the undercrossing has sometimes proved best. The pedestrian must still

[59] For detailed information see *A Policy on Grade Separations for Intersecting Highways*, AASHO (1944).

descend a short stairway or ramp, but the entire length of the walkway is visible from the approach sidewalks.

At the intersection of two freeways or where a freeway intersects a major highway, an *interchange* may be required. An interchange not only offers grade separation between the two traffic arteries, but in

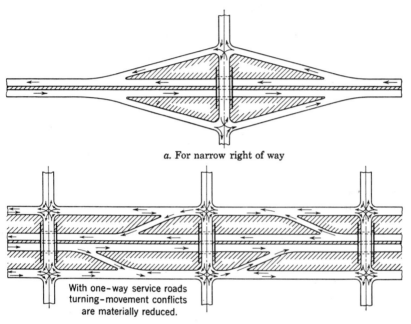

a. For narrow right of way

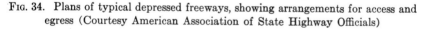

With one-way service roads turning-movement conflicts are materially reduced.

b. Combined with outer highways

Fig. 34. Plans of typical depressed freeways, showing arrangements for access and egress (Courtesy American Association of State Highway Officials)

addition provides easy routes for vehicles transferring from one through facility to the other. A few of the many possible patterns appear in Fig. 35.

The most common interchange is the *cloverleaf*, illustrated by Fig. 35*d* (see also Fig. 7, p. 37). With it, the intersecting arteries are separated, and in addition all eight turning movements are accomplished free of intersections where vehicle paths must cross. Turning vehicles peel off the right side of the roadway on which they enter the interchange and blend from the right into the roadway being entered. A serious objection to the cloverleaf design is that vehicles desiring to turn left must execute 270-degree right turns and travel

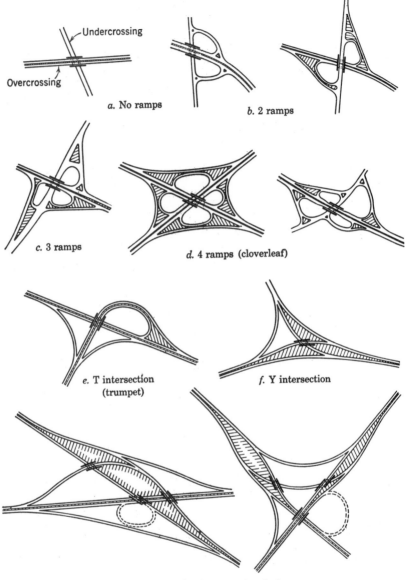

g. Direct-connection designs

FIG. 35. Types of grade separations (diagrammatic) (Courtesy American Association of State Highway Officials)

substantially greater distances. Another flaw is that large ground areas are covered. Figures 35*b* and *c* show modifications of the cloverleaf pattern with one and two quadrants omitted. If all turning movements are to be accomplished with these designs, left turns at grade across at least one of the traffic arteries are required.

Figure 35*e* shows an interchange pattern suitable for T intersections. Note that traffic from lower to upper left must traverse a 270-degree turn but that all other turning movements are accomplished with curvatures not much greater than 90 degrees. Figure 35*f* shows a layout for a Y intersection. Only one grade separation is required to eliminate all crossings at grade. It should be noted, however, that no provision is made for vehicles traveling from lower to upper left. The designs outlined by Fig. 35*g* illustrate the combination of direct connections for heavy left-turning movements with indirect connections (270-degree right turns) for others. Note that provision for some of the eight possible turning movements has been omitted. Figure 35*g* nicely illustrates the range of layout choices available to the designer.

A grade-separation layout providing direct paths in all quadrants is illustrated by the four-level structure shown in Fig. 36. As with the cloverleaf, straight-through traffic is separated, and all turning vehicles leave and enter by the right-hand lanes. However, by having roadways at four different levels, all left turns are accomplished at slightly greater than 90 degrees, as against the 270-degree right turn on the cloverleaf. Left-turn traffic must be extremely heavy before the elaborate structure can be justified economically. Cost of the pictured interchange was $4 million, including $1,600,000 for right of way totaling 35 acres. In 1953, the upper deck of this structure carried a daily traffic of 125,000 vehicles.

Interchange design must begin with a traffic estimate showing the number of vehicles that will be performing each maneuver. Only in this manner can important movements be favored. Design speed on through roadways should conform to that of the approaching freeways, but that on ramps and connections may be considerably lower. Several tentative layouts generally are made, from which estimates of right-of-way, construction, maintenance, and user costs are developed. Design details evolve from studies of capacity, sight distance, grade, curvature, superelevation, and channelization as discussed earlier in this chapter. The provision of adequate sight distance

offers particularly troublesome problems and demands special attention. Helpful means for increasing sight distance include open-type
handrails that do not block the view between adjoining roadways and

Fig. 36. Four-level interchange in Los Angeles, Calif. (Courtesy California Division of Highways)

ramps and the substitution of small unconnected columns for continuous walls as supports for the upper levels of grade-separation
structures.[60]

[60] See p. 252 for clearance and loading standards for highway structures.

RAILROAD-HIGHWAY GRADE SEPARATIONS

Grade separation between highways and railroads is extremely desirable. The AASHO design standards for interstate highways recommend that, "Where railway operation involves two or more main-line tracks, separation should be provided regardless of traffic volumes on the interstate highway. Where the railway operates six or more regular train movements per day on a single track, separation of grades may be justified regardless of traffic volume on the interstate highway. Where the railway has five or less regular train movements per day, grades should be separated when an economic analysis indicates justification, proper weight being given to both hazard and delay." Without question, rail-grade separations for all freeways and many major streets can be justified by like warrants.

The major design question is usually whether the highway should go over or under the railroad. Where the railroad track lies in fairly deep cut or on a high fill, the answer is usually apparent, but when it is near ground level the decision becomes more difficult. If the highway goes over the railroad, the structure itself may be lighter as highway loads are much smaller than railroad loads. However, clearance must be greater, the usual minimum vertical distance from top of rail to underside of structure being about 23 ft, as against the 14-ft clear distance to be supplied above a highway. Then, too, the roadway passes over a crest, which requires a long, sweeping vertical curve to meet sight-distance requirements. These two facts make an overcrossing and its approaches much longer than an undercrossing at the same location. In settled areas, and particularly in business and residential districts, overcrossings are objectionable from an aesthetic point of view, and their construction may lead to objections and damage suits by property owners.[61] If the highway goes under the railroad, other problems arise. Special provision must be made for removal of rainwater that falls within the crossing area. If the groundwater table is high in the area of the crossing, the water level must be lowered or the roadway must be sealed against leakage and made heavy enough that it will not float. At undercrossings, provision for uninterrupted train service during construction is both expensive and troublesome. Often many underground utilities must be relocated and support provided for adjacent buildings. In all such cases, the problem requires careful study before a decision concerning type of

---

[61] See p. 132.

crossing is reached. Detailed design follows accepted standards as previously outlined.

RESEARCH ON HIGHWAY DESIGN PROBLEMS

Much valuable research on highway design problems has been carried out by the engineers of our highway agencies and research organizations. However, as the reader of this chapter can well recognize, gaps still exist in our knowledge of almost every aspect of this important subject. Intensive research is under way on many of these problems, and is certain to continue in the years ahead. Other problems are bound to develop as highway transportation grows and evolves.

The committee on geometric design of the Highway Research Board has listed 26 subjects on which research is needed. A statement of each problem in terms of the factors involved, research and data needed, and selected references appears in *Highway Research Board Special Report 12* (1953). This publication furnishes a clear demonstration of the challenge and opportunity that a career in highway design offers the young engineer.

9 ——————— Highway Drainage

INTRODUCTION

This chapter discusses means for collecting, transporting, and disposing of surface water originating on or near the highway right of way or flowing in streams crossing or bordering that right of way. On an average, 25 cents of the highway construction dollar is spent for culverts, bridges, and other drainage structures. Substantial added expenditures are demanded on rural roads for ditches, dikes, channels, and erosion-control installations. In urban and suburban locations, major capital investment goes into storm drains and their appurtenances. In addition, routine cleaning and repair of drainage facilities coupled with the expense of rebuilding after heavy storms takes a substantial share of maintenance funds. A conservative estimate is that over \$1 billion is spent annually for highway drainage and erosion control.

The attack on surface-drainage and erosion-control problems must begin with the location survey. Ideal locations from a drainage standpoint would lie along the divides between large drainage areas. Then all streams flow away from the highway, and the drainage problem is reduced to caring for the water that falls on roadway and backslopes. In contrast, locations paralleling large streams are far less desirable as they cross every tributary where it is largest. Again, ideal locations avoid steep grades and heavy cuts and fills as they create difficult problems in erosion control. Admittedly, surface drainage is only one among many considerations in highway location, but it warrants careful attention.

Once the highway location is established, treatment of surface drainage problems falls into 2 basic steps: (1) hydrology—estimating the peak rates of runoff to be handled, and (2) hydraulic design—selecting the kinds and sizes of drainage facilities to accommodate the

213

estimated flows. In the past, hydrologic data of value to highway engineers have been fragmentary, and hydraulic designs based on them often seemed pointless. For this and other reasons, drainage design before about 1940 was largely by rule-of-thumb methods, many of them of doubtful validity. Since that time, and particularly since World War II, highway engineers have devoted increasing attention to drainage problems. Research already completed or under way will greatly extend present knowledge. The results of these efforts are already and will be increasingly apparent in better and more economical highway drainage.

✳ ECONOMY IN DRAINAGE

True economy in drainage design means finding the solution that is cheapest in the long run. The first step is to estimate the first cost, maintenance outlay, and anticipated loss and damage for each reasonable solution. These are then compared by one of the methods outlined in Chapter 4. In these computations, the annual charge for possible flood damage or economic loss equals the estimated loss that a flood of given magnitude will cause, multiplied by the probability that the flood will occur in any one year. For example, if losses from a flood exceeding the design flow total $50,000, and hydrologic studies indicate that such a flood will occur once in 25 years, the annual charge for possible flood damage equals [1] $50,000 × $\frac{1}{25}$, or $2000.

Economy problems in drainage are diverse, and do not lend themselves to any single set of assumptions or rules. The most common unknown in such problems is the flood frequency on which the design should be based. For a major highway carrying large volumes of heavy traffic, losses to motorists and to the economy in general may be tremendous if the road is closed frequently by floods and washouts. On the other hand, on a lightly traveled rural road, economic losses alone will not justify large capital expenditures to prevent occasional interruptions to traffic. For the major highway, studies might prove that drainage facilities should accommodate a 50-year flood, whereas designs based on a 5-year flood would be more reasonable for the rural road. In another instance, capacity to accommodate infrequent floods would be appropriate if smaller waterways resulted in flooding of valuable property. However, it might be cheaper in the long run to inundate bottom lands every few years rather than to provide

[1] For further discussion of the "cost of risks" see E. L. Grant *Engineering Economy*, 3d edition, Ronald Press, pp. 268–273 (1950).

channels and structures large enough to protect them. As a third example, damage to embankments overtopped by flood waters will generally be much more severe in arid regions where the slopes are unprotected than in humid regions where they are covered with grass or other growth. Thus, other things being equal, more generous designs to prevent overtopping would be appropriate in arid regions than in humid ones.

Where drainage problems of any magnitude have alternative solutions, economy studies based on reasonable estimates of costs and possible future damage represent the best approach. It is true that flood frequencies and some of the costs must be roughly approximated. Even so, the findings will be better than hunch decisions based on no study at all. They are better also than rigid rules applied in all cases without consideration of cost in the long run.

LEGAL RESPONSIBILITY FOR DRAINAGE

Highway agencies have legal responsibility for damage to private property resulting from changes they make in natural drainage patterns. For example, damage claims against an agency could be established if erosion, silting, or flooding of private property resulted when the flow of several small streams was concentrated into a single structure or channel. Again a cause of action would be created if water backed up against a highway structure or embankment and inundated lands or property. However, liability is restricted to those damages that are a direct consequence of the highway improvement. In each case, responsibility of the highway agency would be determined by negotiation or court proceedings. The important point is that improper or inadequate drainage designs may bring not only criticism and charges of incompetence, but damage suits as well.

HYDROLOGY

Hydrology is that branch of physical geography dealing with the waters of the earth. The branch of hydrology of particular concern to highway engineers deals with the frequency and intensity of precipitation and the frequency with which this precipitation brings peaks of runoff that equal or exceed certain critical values. Of importance also is the distribution of precipitation through the seasons, insofar as it influences the growth of grasses, shrubs, and other plants useful for erosion control.

It should be understood at the outset that predictions regarding future rainfall or runoff from accumulated records rest on the laws of probability: in other words, the chance that a given event will or will not take place. To illustrate, consider the statement that a culvert is designed to carry a "50-year" flood. This means that, if past experience is repeated, the chances are 1 in 50 that the structure will flow full or be overtaxed once in a particular year. It does not mean that the design flood or a larger one will occur exactly one time in 50 years; in fact, the chances are only 64 in 100 that a flood of this magnitude will occur in a given 50-year period. On the other hand, several floods of this or greater magnitude could occur in successive years or in a single year, but the chance for either combination is extremely small.

Precipitation occurs as rain or in frozen form, particularly as snow. It results when warm, moisture-laden air is cooled as it flows over a mountain barrier (orographic lifting), is forced upwards by a cold-air mass (frontal lifting), or rises through cooler air (convective lifting) as in summer thunderstorms. The duration and intensity of precipitation produced by these storm types is markedly different. Many other factors also have pronounced influence. Among them are geographical position in the general circulation of the earth's atmosphere, the moisture content of the air, wind velocity and direction, elevation, and the steepness and aspect of slopes. It follows that rainfall data collected at scattered gages offers only an approximation of the precipitation in the immediate area of each gage. Variations will be even greater along the length of a highway.

Of the moisture that falls, some is returned to the atmosphere by evaporation from land and water surfaces and by transpiration through plants. Another portion percolates through the ground, sometimes emerging as springs. This underground water travels slowly and generally adds little to extreme floods. The remaining precipitation flows overland in a thin sheet until it reaches streams or channels. These in turn deliver the water to larger streams that take it to the ocean. As would be expected, the ratios of runoff to precipitation show wide variation. Most of the rain that falls on rocky or bare, impervious slopes, roofs, or pavements runs off quickly. At the other extreme, only a small percentage of that falling onto plowed land or heavy forest litter may run off at all, and that at a slow rate. Slope and surface moisture at the time of rainfall introduce added variables. Again, the snow melt rarely causes major floods on small streams, as the water comes off in long sustained moderate flows. As drainage areas become larger, increasing amounts of water are devoted to swelling the streams to flood stage, and this "channel storage" slows the rush of water downstream. For these and other reasons, the determination of peak runoff from rainfall records is difficult.

The uncertainties inherent in predicting runoff from rainfall records would be of no concern if long-time, country-wide records of the flow from representative drainage areas were available. To date, however, such records exist only for the larger streams. There are very few gaging stations on streams draining areas less than 20 square miles. Only 21% of the gages in operation in 1950 were for areas smaller than 100 square miles. Observations in conjunction with research projects have been started on a relatively small number of lesser streams, but the data are too few to furnish reliable information for design purposes. As further stream-flow records become available, increased certainty in runoff predictions will become possible.

The following paragraphs present four methods now employed for estimating peak flows. In using them, the engineer must recognize the uncertainty of the basic data on which the final answer is based. Next, he must realize that predictions regarding future runoff are subject to the laws of chance. Finally, he must understand the limitations of each method and select the one or ones most suitable for his particular purpose.

Runoff from stream-flow records

Where a gaging station on the stream in question has accumulated records for a considerable time, these data are reduced to a graph showing the frequency of recurrence of floods equal to or exceeding given magnitudes.[2] Methods for estimating flood frequencies on un-gaged streams from the records of gaged streams have also been advanced. This is possible even though the drainage areas are of considerably different size if they are hydrologically similar.[3]

As mentioned earlier, there are few gaging stations on streams serving small watersheds so that direct determination of flood frequencies

---

[2] Several methods for reducing stream-flow records into graphs of discharge versus recurrence interval are in use. Each gives somewhat different results. For details of these methods, see the standard textbooks in hydrology and hydraulic engineering. Examples and a bibliography on the subject will also be found in papers by Tate Dalrymple, in *Proceedings Highway Research Board*, pp. 163–179 (1946), and *Research Report 11-B* (1950) of the same agency.

[3] See the last reference in the preceding footnote; also Rainfall and Topographic Factors That Affect Runoff, by W. D. Potter, *Transactions American Geophysical Union*, February 1953, pp. 67–73.

for them is not possible. Studies conducted by the Soil Conservation Service, U. S. Department of Agriculture, have led to a method for expressing runoff in terms of geographical position, drainage area, and land use.[4] Figure 1 presents these findings as adapted to highway purposes by Carl F. Izzard of the U. S. Bureau of Public Roads. Application is limited to watersheds smaller than 1000 acres and to farmed or wooded lands in the eastern and midwestern United States. A typical solution appears on the figure. As yet, values of some of the factors are tentative and subject to change; so the results must be used cautiously.

Data like those shown in Fig. 1 have not as yet been developed for the western United States. Records of runoff from smaller watersheds are not extensive enough to furnish proof that the same empirical relationships apply in arid and in humid regions. Also, assuming the approach to be valid, rainfall frequency, land use, and slope factors are yet to be developed.

Runoff data also are almost wholly lacking for watersheds in the general range between 1½ and 20 square miles, so that estimates of flood frequency for such areas must be made by other less reliable methods. Records of peak flows for these and smaller areas could be obtained at relatively little expense through efforts within the individual highway agencies. These efforts would be well repaid in improved and more economical design of drainage facilities.

The rational method

The rational method may be reduced to the formula:

$$Q = ciA_d \tag{1}$$

in which Q = runoff, cubic feet per second.

c = a "runoff" coefficient expressing the ratio of rate of runoff to rate of rainfall.

i = intensity of rainfall, inches per hour, for a duration equal to the time of concentration.

A_d = drainage area in acres.

This expression, as written, is not dimensionally correct. It gives numerically correct results, however, because 1 in. per hr per acre

[4] See Surface Runoff from Agricultural Watersheds by W. D. Potter, *Highway Research Board Research Report 11-B*, pp. 21–35 (1950). Also see Peak Discharge for Highway Drainage Design, by Carl F. Izzard, *Proceedings American Society of Civil Engineers*, Separate 320, October 1953.

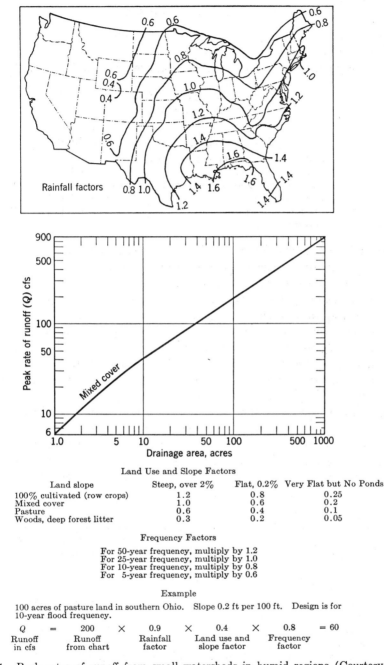

Land Use and Slope Factors

Land slope	Steep, over 2%	Flat, 0.2%	Very Flat but No Ponds
100% cultivated (row crops)	1.2	0.8	0.25
Mixed cover	1.0	0.6	0.2
Pasture	0.6	0.4	0.1
Woods, deep forest litter	0.3	0.2	0.05

Frequency Factors

For 50-year frequency, multiply by 1.2
For 25-year frequency, multiply by 1.0
For 10-year frequency, multiply by 0.8
For 5-year frequency, multiply by 0.6

Example

100 acres of pasture land in southern Ohio.   Slope 0.2 ft per 100 ft.   Design is for 10-year flood frequency.

Q	$=$	200	$\times$	0.9	$\times$	0.4	$\times$	0.8	$= 60$
Runoff in cfs		Runoff from chart		Rainfall factor		Land use and slope factor		Frequency factor	

Fig. 1.   Peak rates of runoff from small watersheds in humid regions (Courtesy U. S. Bureau of Public Roads)

and 1 cu ft per sec represent the same amount of water per unit of time, within 0.8%.

Coefficients c for the rational formula are given in Table 1. Where

TABLE 1. VALUES OF COEFFICIENTS OF RUNOFF (c) FOR USE IN THE RATIONAL FORMULA

Type of Drainage Area	Coefficients of Runoff, c
Concrete or bituminous pavements	0.8–0.9
Gravel roadways, open	0.4–0.6
Bare earth (higher values for steep slopes)	0.2–0.8
Turf meadows	0.1–0.4
Cultivated fields	0.2–0.4
Forested areas	0.1–0.2

ground cover is dissimilar, the drainage area is sometimes subdivided and a composite coefficient obtained by weighting the coefficients for each section according to area. Rainfall intensity i is obtained from records of nearby stations of the U. S. Weather Bureau. These records are reduced to a graph showing rainfall intensity versus rainfall duration for various recurrence intervals [5] (see Fig. 2). Actual selection of the value for rainfall intensity rests on estimates of the acceptable frequency of occurrence of the design flood and on the time of concentration for the area. The latter is the interval required for water to reach the outlet from the most remote point in the basin. Some data are available on the time of overland flow to the defined channels.[6] Approximations of times of channel flow can be made from observed or computed velocities. Formulas for expressing time of concentration in terms of watershed characteristics have been developed by some agencies.[7] The drainage area A_d is determined from

[5] For detailed information see particularly V. T. Chow, *Illinois Engineering Experiment Station Bulletin 414*.

[6] See Carl F. Izzard, *Proceedings Highway Research Board*, pp. 129–150 (1946).

[7] For example, the California Division of Highways, for watersheds up to 10,000 acres, determines time of concentration by the equation

$$T = \left(\frac{11.9L^3}{H}\right)^{0.385}$$

where T is the time of concentration in hours, L is the developed length of the channel from the head of the watershed to the site in miles, and H is the fall in the basin from the head of the watershed to the site in feet. See G. A. Tilton and R. R. Rowe, *Proceedings Highway Research Board*, p. 169 (1943), for this equation and for a nomograph offering a complete solution to the rational equation. The entire paper has been printed by the Division under the title California Culvert Practice.

topographic maps, aerial photographs, or rough field surveys comparable in accuracy to compass and pacing. Greater precision is not justified.

The rational method rests on a number of assumptions. One of these is that the basin is in equilibrium: outflow equals rainfall less

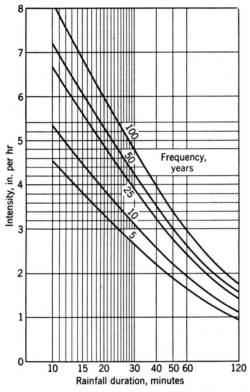

FIG. 2. Rainfall intensity, duration, and frequency for the southern one third of Ohio (Courtesy Ohio Department of Highways)

all retention in the basin, and this retention is stated solely in terms of surface characteristics. Factors like surface conditions when rainfall begins and the retarding effect of channel storage are neglected. Another assumption is that rainfall is of uniform intensity throughout the area during the time of concentration. This does not recognize that elevation, steepness and aspect of slopes, and other features that affect rainfall may be quite different over the basin. The assumptions just listed and others not mentioned become particularly susceptible to error as the size of drainage area increases. With correct values for rainfall and for the runoff coefficient, the rational formula always overstates the runoff, with the error increasing as the size of basin increases. Thus its application should be confined to relatively small areas.[8]

Another assumption under the rational method is that large floods occur with the same frequency as excessive rainfall. For storm drains and other installations in urban areas or in other cases where the surface is nearly impervious, this assumption is probably valid. There are many situations, however, where a large flood follows excessive rainfall only if the surface is already saturated by previous rain. In this case, the maximum runoff will occur only with the combination of excessive rainfall and previous rain. Then, if the design is made for a once-in-10-year rainfall and the ground is wet before such a storm but once in 5 times, the probability of a stated flood is $\frac{1}{10}$ times $\frac{1}{5}$, or $\frac{1}{50}$, or once in 50 years.

Empirical formulas

Formulas expressing the waterway opening to accommodate extreme floods have been widely employed in the past. The most common of these is that of Talbot:

$$a = cA_d^{3/4} \qquad (2)$$

where a = waterway opening, square feet.

c = a coefficient, ranging from 1.0 for steep, rocky ground through 0.6 for hilly country of moderate slopes to 0.2 for level terrain not affected by snow.

The Talbot formula was first proposed before the turn of the century, when practically nothing was known regarding hydrology or hydraulic design. Limited investigation has established that, for certain portions of the midwestern United States, results from the formula approximate the combination of a 10-year flood and a velocity of 10 ft per sec through the culvert. Otherwise the Talbot formula has little scientific verification. Its widespread adoption in the highway field probably can be attributed to its simplicity and the lack of something better.

There are several other empirical formulas that state either waterway opening or peak flow in terms of a coefficient of runoff and a fractional power of the area. Some of them, such as the Burkli-Ziegler

---

[8] Some engineers confine solutions by this method to areas under 1000 acres; others apply it to areas up to 10,000 acres.

formula, contain multipliers to recognize rainfall intensity and slope of the drainage area. All such formulas have the weakness that they offer an easy but not necessarily accurate substitute for hydrologic and hydraulic engineering analysis. Also, in most instances, the answers do not give the flood-frequency data required for economy studies.

Runoff predictions from unit hydrographs

A *hydrograph* is a plot of stream flow as the ordinate against time as the abscissa. A *unit* hydrograph is the hydrograph produced by 1 in. runoff from a given drainage area for a typical or specified rainfall distribution of some specified duration. With the rainfall characteristics specified, the unit hydrograph presents clearly the runoff characteristics of the basin. It has been shown that, within reasonable limits, similar (but not equal) rainfall of the same duration and distribution will produce unit hydrographs of substantially similar shape. It can then be assumed that, for a specified type of storm, the time scale of the unit hydrograph for a basin is constant. The ordinates will be approximately proportional to the volumes of runoff. Thus the unit hydrograph provides a means for relating the runoffs to be expected from storms of like type but of differing intensity.

Unit hydrographs can be extremely useful in predicting flood-recurrence intervals, which are the highway engineer's principal concern. For example, short-term runoff records of a basin can be extended to cover the full period for which rainfall records are available. Again, runoff predictions can sometimes be made for local ungaged areas from the records of similar areas for which the runoff has been measured.[9]

HYDRAULIC DESIGN PRINCIPLES

Hydraulic design for highways employs the basic principles of fluid flow, particularly those relating to open channels and closed conduits.[10] In most cases, solutions are aimed at the single problem of accommodating occasional large volumes of storm water. The methods of

[9] For further information see Hunter Rouse, *Engineering Hydraulics,* John Wiley & Sons, pp. 292–302 (1950), and Linsley, Kohler, and Paulhus, *Applied Hydrology,* McGraw-Hill Book Co., pp. 444–464 (1949).

[10] For the basic concepts and formulas see J. K. Vennard, *Elementary Fluid Mechanics,* 3d edition, John Wiley & Sons (1954); Hunter Rouse, *Engineering Hydraulics,* John Wiley & Sons (1950); or other standard textbooks in these fields.

analysis are the same as for other branches of hydraulic engineering.

Of necessity, highway construction disrupts established drainage patterns. To illustrate, roadway cuts intercept water that earlier had moved overland across the right of way. Again, the flow from several small streams may be collected and passed under the highway at a single location. Often, streams are diverted to channels that differ from their predecessors in length, cross section, and flow characteristics. These examples show that almost every change upsets balances established by countless earlier storms. In particular, there is the possibility of higher velocity of flow which may bring unsightly and costly erosion. Erosion in turn creates debris that is transported downstream and deposited at points where the velocity slackens. A cardinal rule of drainage design could well be that existing drainage patterns be disrupted as little as possible. Necessary changes must not at any point bring velocities that will create new erosion problems. Disregard for this simple rule has created many serious maintenance problems, and, even worse, has made the surroundings of many highways very unsightly.

Water standing in pools along the highway sometimes creates a health hazard by providing a breeding place for mosquitoes. Furthermore, water drawn from roadside ditches by capillary action may soften the subgrade and contribute to pavement failure. Another rule of drainage, then, might be that all water be drained away after every storm. There will be numerous exceptions, but the consequences should be carefully weighed for each of them.

DRAINING THE ROADWAY AND ROADSIDE

Water that falls on the roadway flows laterally or obliquely from it under the influence of cross slope or superelevation in the pavement and shoulders. Figure 3 shows typical cross slopes for rural two-lane highways. (Figure 14, p. 163, is representative of multilane highways.) When the roadway lies on fill, the most common practice is to let the flow continue off the shoulder and down the side slope to the natural ground (see Fig. 3a). Little erosion results if the slopes are protected by turf or if the water flows across the roadway and down the slope as a sheet. Where slopes are unprotected, they may wash badly [11] if irregularities in pavement or shoulder concentrate the water into small streams. A likely place for such concentrations is the low points of

[11] For a discussion of slope-protection methods see p. 261.

sag vertical curves. One technique for preventing washing of side slopes is to retain the water at the outer edge of the shoulder as indicated in Fig. 3a. Another, for concrete pavements, employs a low

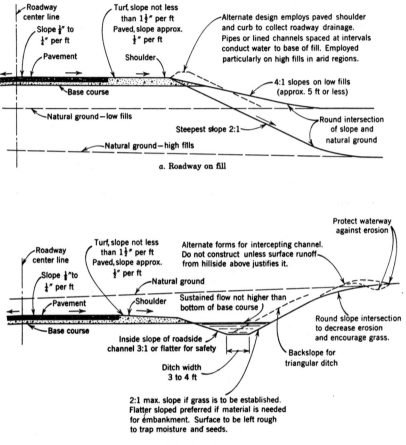

a. Roadway on fill

b. Roadway in cut

FIG. 3. Typical highway cross sections incorporating good drainage features.

lip cast into the outer edge of the pavement slab. In this instance flow to the catch basin or other collecting device is along the pavement itself. This design is gradually disappearing, as it creates a splash and ice problem and is a hazard to traffic.

When roadways are in cut, water from the traveled way and back slopes is collected in a roadside channel commonly of trapezoidal or triangular cross section (see Fig. 3*b*). Dimensions, slope, and other characteristics of this channel are determined by the flow to be accommodated. Particular care must be exercised where roadside channels discharge to prevent erosion of the toe of the fill slope.

Figure 3*b* also indicates that an intercepting channel, sometimes called a crown ditch, may be employed at the top of the cut slope. It prevents erosion of the back-slope by surface runoff from the hillside above. Crown ditches often are constructed with a motor grader that excavates a small channel and forms the spoil into a dike on the downhill side. In cases where the natural ground is already protected by grass, ground cover, or litter, the surface should not be disturbed. Rather, the channel should be formed with the natural ground as its bed and a small dike of topsoil or other imported material as the bank.

It is common practice to build crown ditches as single, continuous channels placed a short distance uphill from the top of the back-slope. This procedure must be used with the greatest caution; otherwise unsightly erosion is bound to result. Evidence of this is abundant along many existing roads. Methods for controlling scour where the entire flow must be retained in the ditch are discussed in the section on channel design. As an alternative, it is sometimes possible to limit the flow to a safe amount by diverting it at intervals. One technique is to drop the water down the slope to the roadside ditch by means of specially designed channels or conduits. In open country there are often situations where diversions can be made at intervals to ditches leading away from the road along contour lines.

ROADWAY DRAINAGE IN URBAN AREAS

Water falling on or near city streets and on urban freeways and expressways generally flows along the gutters to curb or gutter inlets and from them into underground storm drains. Installations of this kind are very expensive compared to those suitable for rural areas. On the other hand, these expenditures have greater justification, as urban highways generally carry larger volumes of vehicular traffic and often serve pedestrians as well. Furthermore, property damage from flooding may well be extremely high in urban areas.

Gutters and inlets on urban streets and highways are generally designed to limit the spread of water over the traveled lanes to some arbitrary maximum. A suggested assumption is that the flow should not encroach on the outside lane by more than 6 ft for a storm of 20 min duration and 1-year return period. It is reasoned that storms of shorter duration have such high intensities that vehicles must travel slowly because vision is obscured by rain pelting on the windshields. The 1-year return period controls the spacing of inlets where the roadway is on a grade. However, designs must be for much longer return periods at low points in vertical curves or at other points where ponding would block traffic or flood adjoining property. Inlets at these points must also be proportioned to handle the extreme flows that fail to enter inlets at higher points along the roadway. Flow along gutters and into inlets generally is computed by the rational formula, using a runoff coefficient of about 0.9 if the entire drainage area is paved.

Storm drains leading from the inlets generally are designed for return periods of at least 10 years. Where flooding may have serious consequences, designs for a 25-year storm return period may be more appropriate. Storm drains usually are proportioned to flow just full or nearly full, although in special situations they may be designed to flow under pressure to take advantage of available head.

A detailed presentation on urban drainage problems is beyond the scope of this book, but may be found in texts and handbooks in hydraulic engineering. However, many of the older procedures are being modified by the results of continuing research by highway engineers. Information has been developed on runoff in overland flow from pavements, roofs, and turf. It has been proved that sizable amounts of water are stored in the gutters, a fact that should be recognized in design. Investigations of the hydraulic properties of storm-drain inlets in gutter or curb have shown that their capacity is limited, and that it is affected by roadway cross section and roadway grade. Substantial changes in many standard inlets appear to be in order. These instances demonstrate that a careful review of the highway literature on urban highway drainage is well worth while.[12]

CHANNELS

Designs for roadside and crown ditches, gutters, stream channels, and culverts flowing partially full are all based on the principles of

---

[12] See particularly Carl F. Izzard, *Proceedings Highway Research Board*, pp. 129–146 (1946), and *Highway Research Board Research Report 11-B*, pp. 36–54 (1950). These papers include extensive bibliographies. Also see papers by J. C. Guillou and C. L. Larson in *Highway Research Board Research Report 6-B* (1948).

flow in open channels. For uniform flow, the basic relationships are commonly expressed in the Manning formula:

$$V = \frac{1.486}{n} R^{2/3} S^{1/2} \tag{3}$$

where V = average velocity in feet per second.

n = Manning's roughness coefficient (see Table 2).

R = hydraulic radius in feet; this is the area of the flow cross section divided by the wetted perimeter.

S = slope of the channel in feet per foot.

TABLE 2. REPRESENTATIVE VALUES OF ROUGHNESS COEFFICIENT n FOR
VARIOUS CHANNEL LININGS

Manning Formula

Type of Lining	Value of n
Ordinary earth, smooth graded	0.02
Jagged rock or rough rubble	0.04
Rough concrete	0.02
Bituminous lining, likely to be wavy	0.02
Smooth rubble	0.02
Well-maintained grass—depth of flow over 6 inches	0.04
Well-maintained grass—depth of flow under 6 inches	0.06
Heavy grass	0.10

Also,

$$Q = VA = \frac{1.486}{n} A R^{2/3} S^{1/2} \tag{4}$$

where Q = discharge, cubic feet per second.

A = area of the flow cross section, square feet.

At times, these equations are modified to state the dimensions of particular channels or conduits more directly, but in all cases the same fundamental concepts apply.

Water progressing down mild slopes in open channels is in "tranquil flow," but that traveling steep slopes is in "rapid flow" (see Fig. 4). The proper solution to many channel problems rests on this distinction. Tranquil flow exists when the depth of water in the channel is greater than the "critical depth," and rapid flow when the depth is less than critical. Physically, critical depth is illustrated by the depth at which water flows over a weir. Mathematically, critical depth occurs when the velocity head ($V^2/2g$) is half the "mean depth."

Mean depth, in turn, is the area of the flow cross section divided by its width at the liquid surface. It follows that critical depth is independent of channel slope and roughness and has a fixed value as long as the quantity of flow and channel dimensions remain constant. It should be noted, however, that channel roughness does enter the calculation for "critical slope," at which uniform flow at critical depth occurs.

The effect of critical depth on flow characteristics is illustrated by Fig. 4. At the crest of the steep slope, the velocity increase between

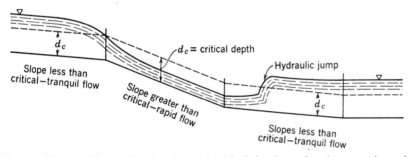

d_c

d_c = critical depth

Slope less than critical—tranquil flow

Hydraulic jump

Slope greater than critical—rapid flow

d_c

Slopes less than critical—tranquil flow

FIG. 4. Diagram illustrating the effect of critical depth on flow in open channels and partially full culverts

tranquil and rapid flow occurs smoothly over some distance. Lowering of the water surface begins upstream from the change in slope. Where the stream grade flattens again, transition from rapid to tranquil flow takes place abruptly in a "hydraulic jump," in which turbulence absorbs some of the energy from the flowing stream. Some distance downstream from the hydraulic jump the channel grade flattens even more. This causes a further decrease in velocity and an increase in stream depth that begins some distance upstream from the grade change. Figure 4 demonstrates that, with tranquil flow, the depth of water at a given point may be altered by downstream conditions: in other words, "control is downstream." Thus, with tranquil flow, the effect of grade change, channel constriction, junction with another stream, and other modifications extends upstream in a "backwater curve." Methods for computing these are offered in the references cited earlier. On the other hand, unless rapid flow is submerged to a depth greater than critical, it is unaffected by downstream conditions. Thus, with rapid flow, "control is upstream." [13]

[13] When velocities become substantially greater than critical, designs for expansions, contractions, and bends in channels and of bridge piers and culvert

The aim in channel design is to find the cross section that will be cheapest to construct and maintain. Side slopes 2 to 1 or flatter are essential except in rock or other hard materials, or where the channel is lined. For unlined channels, it can be generalized that the best cross section requires the least total excavation. However, this rule applies only when construction can be accomplished with conventional equipment. In particular, designs that have numerous changes in dimensions or that must be executed by hand-labor methods will prove costly.

Open-channel designs can be accomplished by solving the Manning equation numerically. As this procedure is tedious and time-consuming, charts have been developed to solve the more common problems. One appears [14] as Fig. 5. Explanations and two examples appear on the chart. Notice that critical depth plays an important part in the analysis.

Channel design is not complete until the possibility of erosion is eliminated, within practical limits. The first step is to check actual velocity against maximum safe values for unprotected earth (see Table 3). Where channel scour is indicated, means for reducing

TABLE 3.   MAXIMUM SAFE VELOCITIES WHEN CHANNEL EROSION IS TO BE PREVENTED

Type of Lining	Allowable Velocity, Ft per Sec
Well-established grass on any good soil	6
Meadow type of grass with short, pliant blades, heavy stand, such as bluegrass	5
Bunch grasses, exposed soil between plants	2–4
Grains, stiff-stemmed grasses that do not bend over under shallow flow	2–3
Earth without vegetation:	
Fine sand or silt, little or no clay	1–2
Ordinary firm loam	2–3
Stiff clay, highly colloidal	4
Clay and gravel	4
Coarse gravel	4
Soft shale	5

entrances demand extreme care. For a detailed discussion see Hunter Rouse, *Engineering Hydraulics*, Chapter VIII, and High Velocity Flow, a Symposium, *Transactions American Society of Civil Engineers*, pp. 265–400 (1951).

[14] This is one of a group of hydraulic charts developed by the U. S. Bureau of Public Roads. Similar charts for other common cross sections can be worked up in a short time from the Manning equation.

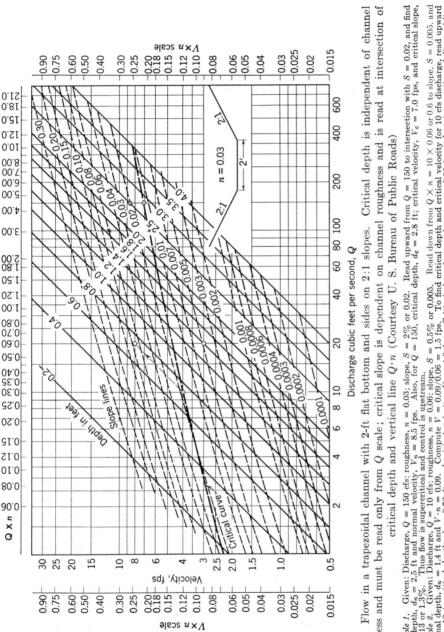

Fig. 5. Flow in a trapezoidal channel with 2-ft flat bottom and sides on 2:1 slopes. Critical depth is independent of channel roughness and must be read only from Q scale; critical slope is dependent on channel roughness and is read at intersection of critical depth and vertical line $Q \cdot n$ (Courtesy U. S. Bureau of Public Roads)

Example 1. Given: Discharge, $Q = 150$ cfs; roughness, $n = 0.03$; slope, $S = 2\%$ or 0.02. Read upward from $Q = 150$ to intersection with $S = 0.02$, and find normal depth, $d_n = 2.5$ ft and normal velocity, $V_n = 8.5$ fps. Also, for $Q = 150$, critical depth, $d_c = 2.8$ ft; critical velocity, $V_c = 7.0$ ft, and critical slope, $S_c = 0.013$ or 1.3%. Thus flow is supercritical and control is upstream.

Example 2. Given: Discharge, $Q = 10$ cfs; roughness, $n = 0.06$; slope, $S = 0.5\%$ or 0.005. Read down from $Q \times n = 10 \times 0.06$ or 0.6 to slope, $S = 0.005$, and find normal depth, $d_n = 1.4$ ft and $V \cdot n = 0.09$. Compute $V = 0.09/0.06 = 1.5$ fps. To find critical depth and critical velocity for 10 cfs discharge, read upward from $Q = 10$ to critical depth, $d_c = 0.72$ ft, and critical velocity, $V_c = 4.0$ fps. Critical slope for roughness, $n = 0.06$ is read at intersection of diagonal line $d_c = 0.72$ and $Q \cdot n = 0.6$ and equals 0.07 or 7%.

velocity to safe levels or for protecting the channel should be adopted.

An effective way to reduce velocity is to reduce the flow by diversion. In some instances this can be done, as has been pointed out in the discussion of crown ditches. In many cases, however, diversion is not possible. A cursory examination of the Manning equation might indicate that substantial velocity reduction could be gained by making channels wider, but unfortunately this is not so. In some instances velocity can be reduced somewhat by increasing channel length and thus decreasing the slope. However, velocity varies as the one-half power of the slope, so that large slope changes are required before velocity is changed appreciably. Further, this solution usually is limited to open country where rights of way or easements for drainage cost little so that ditches can be laid out at an angle to the highway center line. It is also possible to reduce the slope by introducing baffles, checks, or drops into the channel. These devices have been constructed of many materials, including sod, treated timber, corrugated metal, and concrete. However, many drops have washed out during the first severe storm. Those with adequate notch capacity and with suitable provision for energy dissipation on the downstream apron may be more costly in the long run than a continuous smooth lining. Further, drops in roadside channels are a hazard to traffic and, in humid regions, interfere with mowing operations. On the whole, velocity reduction to prevent channel erosion is difficult to attain and may cost more than a suitable lining.

In humid areas, grass offers effective and attractive protection for roadside ditches and other small channels subject to intermittent flow. Grass roughens the channel and raises the safe velocity as compared to unprotected earth (see Tables 2 and 3). Many agencies sow grass on slopes and line the channels with sod promptly after grading operations. Rubble, laid plain or with cement mortar, is another effective means of channel protection, particularly for roadside ditches. It is rough and has high erosion resistance but may be costly, as the individual stones are laid by hand. Paving with concrete or dense-graded bituminous mixtures is often employed with small and large channels alike. As these linings can be placed successfully on steep side slopes and have relatively smooth surfaces, designs employing them can be hydraulically efficient and thus less costly. Where the design results in high velocities, provision for energy dissipation must be made at the lower end of the channel unless discharge is into a rocky streambed or into a pool deep enough to force a hydraulic jump.

Streams carrying sediment bring particularly difficult channel-design problems. It has been established that the ability of water to transport solids along the streambed varies as a power of the velocity greater than the square. It follows that any sizable velocity decrease will cause the stream to drop part of its load. This debris may clog the channel, causing troublesome and sometimes costly overflow and heavy maintenance expense. The most acceptable solution is to so design channels and structures that the upstream velocity is equaled or exceeded throughout. Then the sediments will be transported on past the highway as before. In situations where the initial velocity cannot be maintained, sediments may be trapped in strategically placed debris basins designed for easy cleaning with mechanical equipment.

At times highway improvements require that existing streams be transferred to new channels. For example, stream alinement may be straightened as in Fig. 3, page 111. Again, the road may intersect a stream twice as it cuts directly across a meander or looping bend. Here the first cost is often far less to carry the stream in a channel paralleling the road than to construct two bridges or culverts. Changes like these increase the slope of the channel and often improve its hydraulic properties. Both measures bring increased velocity unless the excess energy is absorbed by means of drops or other devices. Without such controls, unstable conditions are set up in streams having erodible beds. During succeeding storms, the current will cut and fill until a new balance is established. Often these adjustments in grade and alinement are sizable in amount and extend far up and down stream. It follows that channel changes on streams with erodible beds must be planned with extreme care.

DIKES

Dikes are earth embankments employed to contain or divert stream flow. Where all construction is to be above the level of the existing ground, dikes are used alone. Often, however, dike-channel combinations represent the most economical solution, as the dike can be made of spoil from the channel. In the past, dikes were often built by casting or dumping the materials loosely into place; but modern practice demands that construction be in compacted layers as for roadway embankments.[15]

Unprotected dike faces exposed to swiftly moving water are subject

[15] See pp. 381–390.

to erosion. Defensive measures include those previously mentioned for channels. Also, bank-protection installations of rock and brush encased in wire baskets have proved effective on small streams. Special care must be taken to extend the basket a distance below streambed so that the water cannot undercut it. A wide variety of measures appropriate on larger streams have been devised but cannot be offered here.

Often where dikes are employed to turn the flow of a stream, the need for face protection can be eliminated by placing the dike some distance back from the channel proper. Then an area of dead water cushions the bank and prevents scour.

CULVERTS

The term "culvert" encompasses practically all closed conduits employed for highway drainage with the exception of storm drains. Culverts might be classed as stock products, in that standard designs are used repeatedly. This is in direct contrast to the situation for bridges that span larger streams, for which special designs are made in almost every case. Culverts are far more numerous than bridges, and more money is spent on them. In fact, about 15 cents of the highway construction dollar goes for these smaller drainage structures. Clearly, culvert design warrants the serious attention of highway engineers.

Culvert types

The more common culvert types and the materials of which they are made are shown in Fig. 6. For smaller openings, pipe in stock sizes is generally employed, with the pipe arch as a substitute where headroom is limited. For openings of moderate size, pipe and box culverts compete for favor. For larger openings, single- or multiple-span box culverts are generally used, although one or more large-diameter pipes of reinforced concrete or bolted metal plates sometimes are preferred. Bridge culverts replace box culverts when the foundation is nonerodible and a paved floor is unnecessary. Arch culverts may be economical under high fills where loading is heavy.

Under normal circumstances, selection of culvert type and material is based on comparative costs. At times, however, other factors may control. For example, the presence of corrosive agents in the soil may bar certain materials unless a means of protection can be devised. Again, if the structure location is remote, the portability and ease of erection of light, prefabricated metal sections may make them particularly desirable. At times, factors like the availability of skilled labor or time limitations may govern. In any event, the decision must be based on careful study of all pertinent factors.

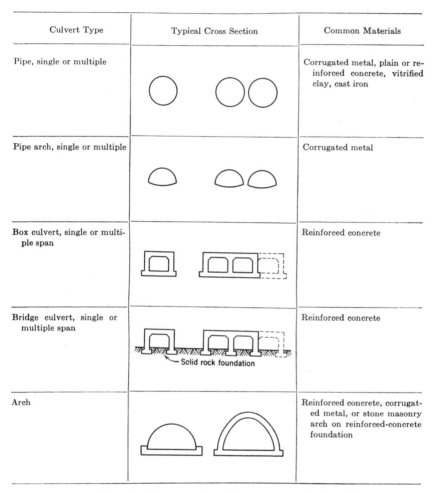

Culvert Type	Typical Cross Section	Common Materials
Pipe, single or multiple		Corrugated metal, plain or reinforced concrete, vitrified clay, cast iron
Pipe arch, single or multiple		Corrugated metal
Box culvert, single or multiple span		Reinforced concrete
Bridge culvert, single or multiple span	Solid rock foundation	Reinforced concrete
Arch		Reinforced concrete, corrugated metal, or stone masonry arch on reinforced-concrete foundation

Fig. 6.   Common culvert types and materials

Materials in culverts

Accepted materials for corrugated metal culverts, as listed [16] by *AASHO Specification M36–47* are pure iron, copper-bearing iron, cop-

[16] See *Highway Materials*, part I, *Specifications*, and part II, *Tests*, published by the AASHO, for this and subsequent references.

per–iron, copper–molybdenum–iron, and copper–steel. All have high resistance to corrosion. This resistance is increased further by galvanizing the individual sheets before they are shaped. In forming the pipe, individual sheets (usually wide enough to provide 2-ft culvert lengths) are bent to the selected cross section. Joints are lapped and fastened with cold-driven rivets of the base metal. During forming, circumferential corrugations about 2½ in. crest to crest and ½ in. or more deep are pressed into the metal. Individual sections are lap-riveted together at the shop into lengths convenient for transportation and field handling. Field connections between these lengths are made with corrugated metal bands pulled tight with galvanized bolts. Large-diameter pipes, arches, and arch culverts of corrugated metal are made up into segments of manageable size that can be assembled and bolted into a unit on the site. Sometimes the specifications require that pipe sections be coated with bituminous material to provide added protection. For situations where the stream carries sand, gravel, or other abrasives, the invert may be paved with bituminous mastic.

Culvert pipe of plain or reinforced concrete, cast iron, or vitrified clay is made at the plant in standard lengths. Jointing between individual sections, using specified materials and methods, follows bedding of the pipe.[17]

Culvert loads and stresses

Culverts are loaded vertically by vehicle wheels and superimposed fill and horizontally by passive or active earth pressure. Particularly for pipe culverts, the magnitudes of these loads are uncertain. Major factors influencing them are depth of cover, nature and density of the overlying and adjacent soils, trench width and depth (if the pipe is set in a trench rather than on a flat surface), deformation of the pipe under load, and field construction procedures.

Stress analysis for pipe culverts is laborious because they are indeterminate structures subject to complex loadings. Also, stress calculations are based on assumptions regarding the method of support under the pipe, and results are far different between point support in a flat-bottom trench and distributed support when the pipe is carefully bedded or is cradled in concrete. It must be concluded that theoretical analysis can define the range in which loads and stresses lie,

---

[17] See *AASHO, Designations M41–49, M64–42,* and *M65–49* for specifications for these types of pipe. See the standard specifications and drawings of the state highway departments for details of jointing practice.

but that the results may not be quantitatively correct for particular situations.

Corrugated metal pipe is more flexible than pipe of other materials and can tolerate considerably greater deformations. Under vertical loads, the sides of corrugated metal pipe tend to deform laterally against the adjacent backfill. The resulting horizontal earth pressure substantially increases the load-carrying ability of the pipe. Many agencies require that large-diameter pipe of corrugated metal be distorted vertically by temporary shores before backfilling is begun. Removal of the shores after backfill results in large horizontal pressures against the pipe and creates a more favorable stress distribution.

Because of the difficulties and uncertainties outlined above, highway agencies seldom make structural designs for pipe culverts. Instead, using research findings and past experience as a guide, they have developed standard plans to fit all usual situations. Thus, for corrugated metal pipe, highway agencies prescribe plate thickness for various pipe sizes and fill heights. For concrete, vitrified clay, and cast-iron pipe they specify the particular strengths of pipe to be employed in each situation. Strong reliance is placed on the recommendations of the various manufacturers.[18]

Design and construction of box, bridge, and arch culverts of reinforced concrete follow the fundamental rules developed in courses in structural engineering and will not be discussed here. It should be noted, however, that each highway agency has standard drawings covering culvert designs appropriate for the more common heights and widths of openings, fill heights, and skew angles.[19]

Culvert installation

Standard procedures for installing culverts are outlined in the specifications of each highway agency. Particular attention is devoted to bedding and to backfill in order to protect the culvert and to prevent subsequent settlement in the roadway surface. Many agencies specify

[18] For further information on loads and stresses in pipe culverts generally and for bibliographies, see M. G. Spangler and others in *Transactions American Society of Civil Engineers,* pp. 316–374 (1948); M. G. Spangler and R. L. Hennessy, *Proceedings Highway Research Board,* pp. 179–214 (1946); and Tilton and Rowe, *Proceedings Highway Research Board,* pp. 186–192 (1943). For a report on the supporting strength of flexible pipe, see M. G. Spangler, *Public Roads,* February 1938, pp. 217–231.

[19] For an example of box culvert design procedures and tables of dimensions for culverts, see C. R. Burky, *Journal American Concrete Institute,* September 1942, pp. 35–52.

that backfill materials be brought to the proper moisture content, placed in small lifts, and compacted with power-driven tampers. Some permit the substitution of clean sand or gravel for the regular backfill material, in which case careful jetting or puddling produces satisfactory compaction.

Culverts through embankments demand particular attention to protect them from damage by construction equipment and to secure proper soil compaction around them. Some agencies require that the embankment first be constructed above the level of the culvert crown, after which a trench is dug for the culvert.

Headwalls and endwalls

Most culverts begin upstream with headwalls and terminate downstream with endwalls. Headwalls direct the flow into the culvert

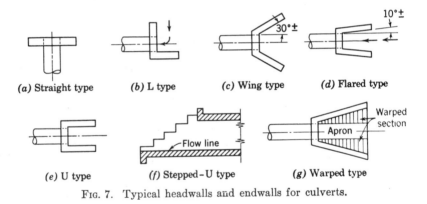

(a) Straight type   (b) L type   (c) Wing type   (d) Flared type

(e) U type   (f) Stepped-U type   (g) Warped type

FIG. 7. Typical headwalls and endwalls for culverts.

proper while endwalls provide a transition from the culvert back to the regular channel. Both protect the embankment from washing by flood waters. Common types are diagrammed in Fig. 7. Most headwalls and endwalls are cast in place of reinforced concrete, although rubble masonry and timber have been employed at times. Units prefabricated of corrugated metal or precast of concrete are sometimes installed with pipe of the same materials. In all cases, cutoff walls extending below the level of expected scour should be incorporated in the design. Often a paved apron extending beyond the cutoff wall is a wise addition.

Straight-type headwalls and endwalls are employed mainly with smaller pipe culverts (see Fig. 7a). They are hydraulically inefficient as entrances, unless the corners are well-rounded. In recent years, some agencies have been omitting endwalls and sometimes headwalls from small pipe culverts. Instead, the pipe is extended beyond the toe of the embankment.[20] L-type headwalls (Fig. 7b) direct the flow from roadside ditches into culverts under the road. They create a serious accident hazard, and many agencies are replacing them with gutter inlets covered with grates. For large culverts, wing-type walls (Fig. 7c) are most widely employed. Entrance losses with them are about 0.15 of a velocity head as contrasted with a loss of 0.05 with hydraulically designed entries. Flared, U, and warped walls (Figs. 7d, e, f, g) have special applications.[21]

Energy dissipators

Culverts on steep slopes always discharge at supercritical velocities and create serious erosion problems in unprotected channels. One method of dissipating the excess energy is to place a sill across the end of the culvert apron to produce a hydraulic jump.[22] Another device is the SAF (St. Anthony Falls) stilling basin that combines a downstream pool with baffles and sills.[23] The greater flow resistance offered by corrugated metal pipe likewise can sometimes be employed to advantage in reducing velocity through the culvert. Drops in the upstream channel or drop inlets to the culvert proper, if designed to produce free fall in the stream, sometimes offer an economical means for velocity control.

Debris control

Streams in flood often carry brush and occasionally transport large branches, whole trees, or other sizable objects. There are many instances where this floating debris has clogged culvert entrances and raised the headwater elevation till the road was overtopped. Where possible, culverts should be designed to pass expected debris. For

[20] The entrance loss for a projecting thin-walled pipe flowing full is about 0.8 velocity heads.

[21] Space limitations prevent a discussion of headwall and endwall design. It should be realized, however, that the two serve opposite functions and that identical designs may not be appropriate. For more on this subject see Tilton and Rowe, *Proceedings Highway Research Board,* pp. 178–186 (1943).

[22] For details regarding sill and apron proportions, see J. F. Forster, R. A. Skrinde, and others in *Transactions American Society of Civil Engineers,* pp. 973–1022 (1950).

[23] See F. W. Blaisdell and others, *Transactions American Society of Civil Engineers,* pp. 483–561 (1948).

example, where a stream may carry large floating objects, a single large-span box culvert is preferable to a multispan structure of the same total opening. As a possible alternative, the curtain wall separating the barrels of the multispan culvert might be extended upstream, with its top slanting downward. Debris will ride up on this wall, or at least be turned to pass more easily through the opening. In many cases, upstream debris racks of wire, timber, steel rails, piling, or other materials may offer the most reasonable solution to the problem. With such installations, maintenance crews must remove the debris following each flood.

In mountainous areas, flood waters often tumble large rocks and boulders along the streambed. Here also provision must be made either to pass such objects through the structure or to trap them upstream where they will do no harm.[24]

Culvert location

Culverts usually are installed in the original streambed with their grades and flow lines conforming to those of the natural channel. In this way, disturbance to stream flow and the erosion problems it creates are held to a minimum. In rolling and mountainous country in particular, marked departures from channel alinement either upstream or downstream may direct the current to one side of the channel, causing erosion there and deposition on the opposite side. On the other hand, culverts on substantial skews are longer and more costly than those at right angles or on small skews. Often the best solution involves reducing large skews somewhat and providing a channel change and erosion protection at one or both ends of the structure.

In rough country, culverts can sometimes be advantageously located on a bench on the side of the canyon rather than in the channel. Culverts under high fills are costly as they are very long and carry heavy loads, and use of the sidehill location reduces both length and load. On the other hand, the erosion threat at the outlet may require expensive control measures. Also, objections to ponded water because of health or safety hazards and threats to stability of the fill must be overcome. Where the streambed is steep, a compromise solution with the culvert entrance lowered to the streambed level and the culvert on the sidehill may be most satisfactory. Curvature or breaks of grade

---

[24] For debris-control measures of the California Division of Highways, see Tilton and Rowe, *Proceedings Highway Research Board*, pp. 192–196 (1943).

to make the culvert conform to the channel should be employed if the design is cheaper and is hydraulically and structurally sound.

Inverted siphons should be avoided whenever the water carries sediment or debris. Even though the velocity at peak flow may keep the barrel clear, deposits may collect as the discharge decreases. Also, stagnant water trapped in the sag may be objectionable.

Hydraulic design of culverts

The aim in hydraulic design is to find the type and size of culvert that will most economically accommodate the flow from a storm of stated frequency. In almost all cases, the primary control is the permissible level of the headwater pool upstream from the structure. Under certain circumstances, high headwater may have serious consequences, and cannot be tolerated. For example, in settled areas high headwater may inundate valuable property. Again, a relatively low fill may be overtopped, bringing lengthy interruptions to traffic and serious damage to pavement and embankment. Sometimes high velocities through the culvert may produce erosion problems downstream or threaten damage to the culvert or its appurtenances. On the other hand, there are many situations where high headwater will cause little damage or inconvenience. In these cases the extra head can be recognized in the design, with an accompanying reduction in culvert size and cost. In effect, then, culvert design becomes an economic problem in which structure costs for various headwater elevations are balanced against the estimated costs of possible damage or inconvenience.

Some highway agencies have established design criteria for culverts in terms of the height of the headwater pool. This approach, as typified by the practice of the California Division of Highways, requires that "a culvert just pass a 10-year flood without static head at the crown of the culvert at entrance, and that design of culvert appurtenances be balanced to avoid serious damage from head and velocity obtaining in a 100-year flood." Headwalls are proportioned for zero freeboard against a 100-year flood.

Flow through conventional culverts having square-edge inlets may occur in numerous fashions, some of which are illustrated in Fig. 8. The diagrams under case I demonstrate three flow patterns with low headwater. The most significant characteristic is the free water surface at the entrance and through the culvert barrel. Notice that this free water surface exists even when the headwater pool is somewhat above the crown of the culvert. Flow under case I is roughly comparable to flow over a weir. Case II depicts three common situations where the culvert entrance is submerged. In case IIa the headwater surface is above the crown of the culvert by something more than one-fifth the culvert height. Flow is comparable to that through a square-edge orifice: the barrel does not flow full and will not do so, regardless

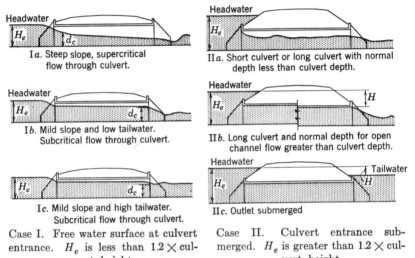

Ia. Steep slope, supercritical flow through culvert.

Ib. Mild slope and low tailwater. Subcritical flow through culvert.

Ic. Mild slope and high tailwater. Subcritical flow through culvert.

Case I. Free water surface at culvert entrance. H_e is less than $1.2 \times$ culvert height

IIa. Short culvert or long culvert with normal depth less than culvert depth.

IIb. Long culvert and normal depth for open channel flow greater than culvert depth.

IIc. Outlet submerged

Case II. Culvert entrance submerged. H_e is greater than $1.2 \times$ culvert height

Fig. 8. Typical flow patterns for culverts with square-edge entrances (Courtesy Carl F. Izzard)

of the head on the culvert. In case IIb the culvert flows full because the barrel slope is too flat to overcome friction losses. In case IIc tailwater submerges the outlet, which causes the barrel to flow full at the outlet and, under most circumstances, to flow full for its entire length. Cases IIb and IIc are practically identical with problems of flow in closed conduits as treated in fluid mechanics.

For designs combining low headwater, low tailwater, and steep culvert slopes (Fig. 8, case Ia), flow through the culvert will be supercritical. Unless downstream channel flow is also supercritical, a hydraulic jump will occur near the culvert outlet. For this flow pattern, control is at the culvert entrance, which functions much like a weir. The lower part of Fig. 9, which refers to circular pipe culverts, gives experimentally determined relationships among pipe diameter, discharge, and headwater elevation. Figure 10 offers like comparisons for box culverts.

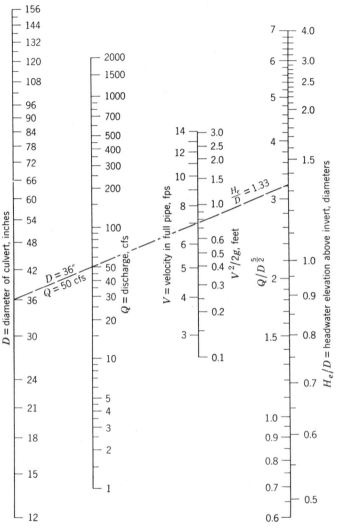

Fig. 9. Headwater depth for pipe culverts not flowing full (Courtesy U. S. Bureau of Public Roads)

Where low headwater, low tailwater, and culvert slopes less than critical are combined (case I*b* of Fig. 8), flow in the barrel is subcritical but passes through critical depth at the outlet, which becomes

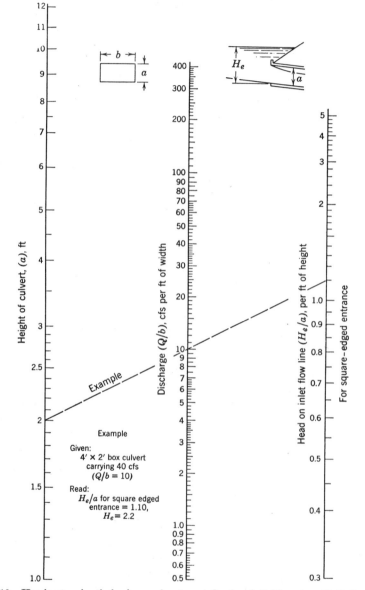

FIG. 10.   Headwater depth for box culverts not flowing full (Courtesy U. S. Bureau of Public Roads)

the control section. A backwater curve and headwater elevation can be computed as a problem in nonuniform flow by methods outlined in textbooks in fluid mechanics. However, for culverts of normal length, an approximate solution can be taken from Figs. 9 and 10. The combination of low headwater, high tailwater without outlet submergence, and mild barrel slope (case Ic of Fig. 8) is seldom found in practice. If it is encountered, headwater elevation can be determined by computing backwater curves from a point of beginning in the outlet channel.

Where culverts are to operate with submerged entrances, the first design step is to determine whether or not the culvert in question will flow full. If there is a free outlet (cases IIa and IIb of Fig. 8), the culvert will flow full if the normal depth as computed for open-channel flow is greater than the depth of the culvert. If normal depth is less than the culvert depth, it will flow partially full with control at the entrance.[25] If the outlet is submerged (case IIc, Fig. 8) the culvert will always flow full at the outlet, and in most cases will flow full for its entire length.

The upper portion of Fig. 9 gives the relationships of discharge, culvert diameter, and headwater elevation for pipe culverts with square-edge entrances that are not flowing full. Figure 10 offers like data for box culverts with square-edge entrances.

For culverts flowing full, headwater elevation is computed by applying the Bernoulli equation:

$$H = \left(1 + K_e + \frac{29n^2L}{R^{4/3}}\right)\frac{V^2}{2g} \tag{5}$$

where H = difference in elevation between the surfaces of the headwater and tailwater pools (Fig. 8, case IIc), or between the surface of the headwater pool and the crown of the culvert outlet (Fig. 8, case IIb).

$V^2/2g$ = velocity head in feet.

K_e = coefficient of entrance loss, ranging from 0.4 for square-edge entrances to 0.1 or less for carefully rounded entrances.

n = Manning's roughness coefficient (see Table 4).

L = length of the culvert in feet.

R = hydraulic radius in feet.

[25] Nomographs for flow in circular or rectangular conduits are very helpful in solving this problem. These diagrams are similar to Fig. 5, p. 231.

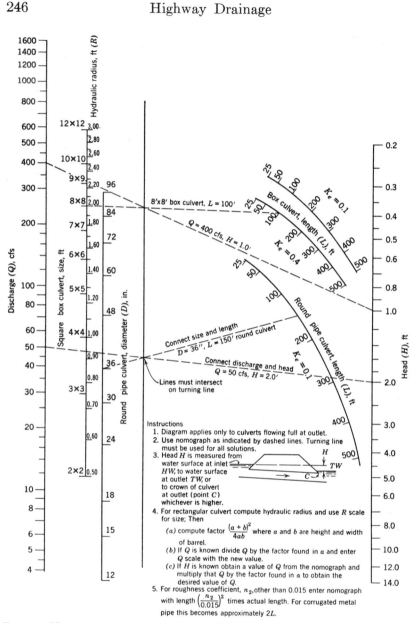

Fɪɢ. 11. Nomograph for culverts flowing full (Courtesy U. S. Bureau of Public Roads)

Figure 11 is a nomograph which solves the Bernoulli equation for full flow in round and square concrete culverts of usual size. Instructions for using the chart and for applying it to rectangular culverts and to those having a roughness coefficient other than 0.015 appear on the figure.

Modifications in culvert design

In hydraulic engineering terms, the entrances of pipe culverts of standard design would be classed as square-edge, as contrasted with rounded or bell-mouthed.[26] However, it has been proved that headwater elevation can sometimes be markedly reduced by rounding the culvert entrance. In applied culvert design where headwater elevation is the primary control, rounding the entrance may permit a substantial reduction in culvert diameter and thus in culvert cost.

TABLE 4. VALUES OF ROUGHNESS COEFFICIENT (n) FOR VARIOUS CULVERT MATERIALS

Kind of Culvert	Value of Manning's n
Concrete pipe with rough joints	0.016–0.017
Concrete pipe, ordinary joints, reasonably smooth	0.015
Concrete pipe, excellent joints, steel forms	0.012–0.014
Concrete box culverts, plywood forms, smooth	0.013–0.014
Concrete box culverts, ordinary formwork	0.014–0.015
Concrete box culverts, rough, with sediment deposits	0.016
Vitrified clay pipe	0.013–0.014
Corrugated metal pipe	0.024
Corrugated metal pipe, paved invert	0.019–0.021

Comparisons of the flow characteristics of culverts with square-edge and rounded inlets [27] are shown in Figs. 12 and 13. Figure 12 is for short culverts. As indicated on the figure, the culvert with a square entrance does not flow full. The culvert with a rounded entrance flows full when the ratio of H to D exceeds 1.5. The tremendous improvement in flow conditions is illustrated by the graph. Figure 13 is for

26 The upstream end of corrugated metal pipe is flared slightly, and concrete pipe is generally laid with a bell end at the culvert entrance, so that neither have square-edge entrances. However, these modifications do not provide a fully rounded entrance.

27 These curves are based on model studies made at the St. Anthony Falls laboratory of the University of Minnesota. For further details see the paper by L. G. Straub, A. G. Anderson, and C. E. Bowers, in *Highway Research Board Research Report 15-B* (1953).

long culverts on steep slopes. For this example the ratio of length to depth is 105. As with short culverts, rounding the entrance causes the culvert to flow full when the inlet is submerged. In this situation, the fall in the culvert barrel is added to the effective head on the culvert. The graph illustrates the resulting spectacular improvement in flow characteristics.

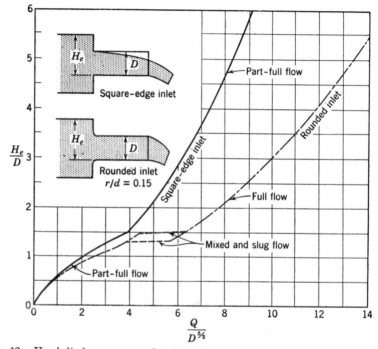

Fig. 12.   Head-discharge curves for short circular culverts with square-edge and rounded inlets (After Straub, Anderson, and Bowers)

Research with culvert models of square and rectangular cross section has indicated that results much like those shown in Figs. 12 and 13 can be produced by tapering the inlet end of the barrel.[28] The area at the entrance should be about double that of the barrel proper. Tapers may be in sides alone or in both sides and top. The rate of offset from the straight barrel section should be about 1 in 4.

Rounding or tapering the culvert entrance does not always produce results so spectacular as those shown by Figs. 12 and 13. When the

[28] See paper by R. H. Shoemaker and L. A. Carpenter in *Highway Research Board Research Report 15-B* (1953).

ratio of H to D is less than 1.2, the barrel will not flow full, and head reduction from inlet improvement is limited to the saving in entrance loss. Again, long culverts on mild slopes will flow full, regardless of entrance type, and most of the head is consumed by barrel friction. Here again the saving is limited to reduction in entrance losses (see the dotted curves in Fig. 13).

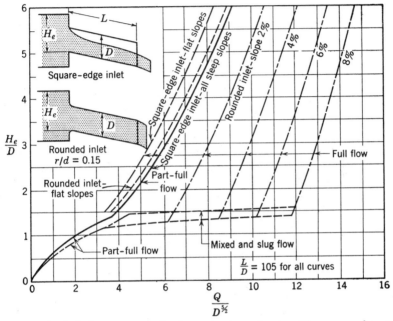

FIG. 13.   Head-discharge curves for long circular culverts with square-edge and rounded inlets (After Straub, Anderson, and Bowers)

Figures 9, 10, and 11 provide an approximate method for appraising the value of culvert entrance improvement. With Fig. 9 or 10, culvert size for a stated headwater elevation can be determined for a square-edge inlet and culvert partially full. Culvert size for an improved inlet and full barrel can be determined from Fig. 11. Whether or not inlet improvement is worth while depends on a cost comparison between the two solutions.

   Culvert size on very flat slopes often is determined by the tolerable head loss through the structure. This head loss has three parts, as indicated by equation 5. The first loss is the energy of flow of 1 velocity head. If the outlet is submerged, this head can be partially regained by flaring the outlet not more than 10 degrees. The second loss, K_e, occurs at the entrance and can be reduced from 0.4 to 0.1 by tapering or rounding the entrance. The third loss, barrel friction, can be reduced by careful attention to construction methods, as indicated by Table 4.

Dips

A dip is formed by lowering the roadway grade to the level of the streambed from bank to bank of the stream. Vertical curves at each end form transitions back to the regular grade line. Washing of the roadway surface is prevented by a curtain wall of concrete, timber, or cement rubble masonry along the downstream edge of the traveled way.

In arid regions where streams flow at infrequent intervals, dips often provide an economical substitute for culverts on roads carrying low volumes of traffic. They offer a large waterway area at little cost. If properly designed, they are little damaged by flood water and are self-cleaning, so that maintenance costs are low. With long transitions at the ends, they ride smoothly. Principal disadvantages are interruptions and hazard to traffic when the dip is flowing.

A dip-culvert combination has sometimes been employed to good advantage. Here the grade line is only partially lowered. Pipe culverts under the road surface at streambed level carry small flows without inconvenience to traffic. The larger waterway capacity of the dip comes into play during major floods. Dip-culvert combinations must have carefully streamlined profiles, and the downstream side must be protected by pavement. Provision for energy-dissipation at the downstream toe is also required.

BRIDGES [29]

Highway bridges carry vehicular traffic and pedestrians over larger streams and other bodies of water. Although bridges are relatively few in number, each structure presents unique problems and involves a large expenditure. In American highway practice, bridge design is considered a distinct function and usually is done in a separate department of the highway agency. At times, private consulting engineers are called in to advise on particularly difficult problems. Occasionally a private engineering firm undertakes the complete design.

[29] See pp. 110 to 113 for a discussion of bridge location.

Highway bridge engineers employ the same analytical tools as other structural engineers. Principal differences are in clearance and loading requirements. The student who is aiming toward highway bridge design should devote his major attention to structural engineering. Among other subjects, he must master the analysis of indeterminate structures.[30]

Hydraulic problems

Stream-flow records provide the best method for estimating discharge under bridges.[31] This and other methods were discussed earlier in this chapter. An analysis of the channel to determine the relations among peak flow, waterway opening, water-surface elevation at the structure and upstream from it, and flow velocity must then be made. A major factor is the degree of contraction of the flowing water in the approach channel. Final determination of structure proportions and required channel modifications results from this study.[32] Where bridges cross navigable waters, span lengths and structure heights may be set by the clearances required for vessels.

Where bridge piers must be set into streams with erodible beds, possible undermining by scour becomes a primary consideration. To date, little is known regarding the depths to which streambeds will be disturbed by flood waters. If the estimate is oversafe, the foundation is more costly than necessary; but, if scour is underestimated, the foundation may be undermined, bringing destruction to the entire bridge. Basic research on scour is now under way, particularly at the State University of Iowa. Among the findings to date are that the least scour occurs when the pier offers the least resistance to flow, which means that piers alined with the flow and of the smallest possible cross section are superior where scour is a problem. It is also known that scour increases with depth of flow, and thus is a greater problem in streams having high ratios between flood stage and normal

[30] A new era in structural engineering began in 1932 with the publication of a paper by Hardy Cross on the moment-distribution method for analyzing statically indeterminate structures (see *Transactions American Society of Civil Engineers,* vol. 96, pp. 1–156). This technique and other "relaxation" methods that stem from it provided a workable means for analyzing continuous frames and led to their widespread adoption in the highway as well as other fields.

[31] Flood frequency reports are being compiled in many states by the U. S. Geological Survey in cooperation with the state highway departments.

[32] For an excellent discussion of this subject see Tate Dalrymple, *Proceedings Highway Research Board,* pp. 163–179 (1946).

stage. Studies of the effect on scour of flexible mats surrounding bridge piers have also been carried out.[33]

Clearances for highway vehicles

Recommendations of the AASHO for horizontal and vertical clearances for highway vehicles are summarized [34] in Fig. 14. The left-

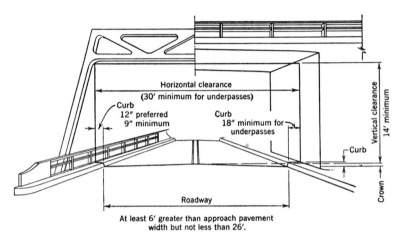

Fig. 14. Clearance requirements for highway bridges and underpasses (Based on *AASHO Standard Specifications for Highway Bridges*)

hand side of the figure pertains to bridges and the right-hand side to underpasses. The AASHO specifications also state that, for bridges less than 50 ft in length, horizontal clearances should conform as nearly as practicable to the shoulder-to-shoulder width of the roadway. Vertical clearance of 14 ft should be maintained for the full roadway width when curbs are not employed.

Bridge loadings

Highway bridges are designed to resist loads produced by the weight of the structure (dead load), the weight and dynamic effect of moving loads (live load and impact), and wind loads. Structures on curves must resist centrifugal forces developed by moving vehicles. Under certain circumstances, stresses resulting from temperature change,

[33] For further information see E. M. Laursen and Arthur Toch, *Proceedings Highway Research Board*, pp. 82–87 (1952).

[34] Figure 14 is based on Figs. 1 and 3, pp. 151 and 153, of *Standard Specifications for Highway Bridges*, 6th edition (1953).

earth pressure, buoyancy, shrinkage, rib shortening, erection, ice and current pressure, and earthquakes must also be considered.

Trucks and other heavy vehicles that produce the larger live loads have a wide variety of total weights, axle loads, and axle spacings. For design purposes the AASHO has adopted standard vehicles that produce representative loadings. Figure 15 shows two alternative vehicles employed for bridge design for trunk highways. The H–20–S

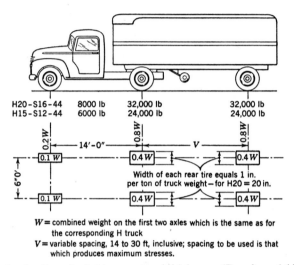

Fig. 15. Design loadings for bridges on trunk highways (Based on *AASHO Standard Specifications for Highway Bridges*)

16–44 designation, for example, is for a truck-semitrailer combination having a total weight of 36 tons distributed as shown in Fig. 15. The 44 indicates the year in which the loading standard was adopted. For secondary highways, the standard vehicles are trucks weighing 20 tons (H–20), 15 tons (H–15), and 10 tons (H–10). Distribution of these total weights among the four wheels of the truck is as indicated in Fig. 15. For longer span lengths, a combination of a uniform lane load and a single moving concentrated load governs the design.[35] Selection of the loading standards for particular bridges is based on long-range predictions by highway planning agencies. The trend is toward heavier loadings, because of the rapid increase in truck numbers and weights. Fortunately, bridge costs do not increase in direct proportion to live load.

[35] For details, see *ibid.*, pp. 155–175.

Bridge types

In the simplest terms, bridges consist of substructures of abutments and piers under superstructures carrying the roadway between these supports. Types include, among others, slab, girder, truss, arch, and suspension bridges, each with a distinctive form of superstructure. Rigid frames are bridges in which the substructure and superstructure are rigidly joined. A further distinction is made in terms of materials, the most common of which are reinforced concrete, steel, and timber.

The suitability of the various bridge types is governed primarily by the length of individual spans. Short-span structures, ranging up to about 60 ft, are generally either (a) reinforced-concrete rigid frames with slab decks (similar in cross section to the bridge culverts shown in Fig. 6, p. 235), (b) T beams of reinforced concrete, or (c) steel I beams with reinforced-concrete decks. Precasting and prestressing of the reinforced-concrete portions of these structures are among the newer developments. A combination of timber stringers with timber or reinforced-concrete deck is sometimes employed for spans of less than about 20 ft. Bridges of somewhat longer spans are often (a) girder-type rigid frames of reinforced concrete or steel, (b) T beams of reinforced concrete, or (c) steel-plate girders or pony trusses with reinforced-concrete decks. As spans reach 200 to 300 ft, steel trusses or arches of steel or reinforced concrete are usually favored. Spans greatly in excess of 500 ft are generally cantilever trusses or suspension bridges. Where provision is made to pass ships through rather than under the roadway level, the channel span generally is selected from the vertical-lift, swing, or bascule types.

Combination of several bridge types in a single structure is illustrated by the Chesapeake Bay bridge pictured in Fig. 16. Beginning in the immediate foreground is a series of 60-ft spans carried on steel I beams. Following these are 100- and 200-ft spans supported by steel-plate girders. Next are deck trusses with 250- and 300-ft spans. The adjoining cantilever structure covers 1450 ft in three spans. The suspension bridge across the main ship channel has a center span of 1600 ft and end spans each of 661 ft. Beyond the suspension bridge are a series of deck cantilever trusses, a through cantilever structure over the secondary ship channel, and shorter spans leading to the opposite shore.

One of the important design principles illustrated by the Chesapeake Bay bridge is that, for economy, increases in pier height are accompanied by increases in the lengths of individual spans. Thus, other things being equal, low bridges have short spans and high bridges long spans. Another rule is that, where clearance above the stream-bed or water surface is not a factor, deck-type structures with the roadway above the upper chord of truss or girder are superior to through structures. With deck-type designs, lateral bracing is simpler and cheaper and the view is not obstructed by structural members.

Fig. 16. Chesapeake Bay Bridge (Courtesy *Highway Magazine*)

Bridges should harmonize with their surroundings. For example, exposed steel girders may be entirely appropriate on a structure crossing an industrial artery, but a rigid frame with exposed surfaces of concrete or stone may be more suitable on a landscaped parkway. Again, in mountainous country, large bridges often are visible from the approach roadway or from roadside areas and other vantage points. Here, graceful arches of steel or reinforced concrete may well be most appropriate from an aesthetic if not from a cost point of view.[36]

[36] For detailed drawings of bridge superstructures of the more common types designed for several loadings see *Standard Plans for Highway Bridge Superstructures* (1953). This work was prepared by the U. S. Bureau of Public Roads and is available from the Superintendent of Documents, Washington 25, D. C.

Obsolescence of bridges

Many bridges built before 1930 had lane widths less than 10 ft. Design live loads sometimes were 5 tons. Until 1941, the AASHO specifications permitted 10-ft lane widths and 10-ton truck loadings on certain state highways. Many bridges of these designs are still in service, and they must be used until funds for replacement become available.

Vehicle operation over substandard bridges is regulated by the appropriate highway authority. Among the controls are posted weight and clearance limits and one-way passage for trucks and buses. There are many instances where drivers have unwittingly or willfully imposed overloads on posted bridges, damaging them or wrecking them completely. Through trusses with narrow roadways or tortuous approach alinement have proved particularly vulnerable, since collision with a main truss member brings complete collapse of the span.

10 ———— Roadside Development

INTRODUCTION

Roadside development deals with the entire right of way, except for the traveled way. It also is concerned with growth or change on abutting lands that affects the appearance or utility of the road. In the past, roadside development was generally thought of as roadside beautification, to be accomplished after the road itself was completed, if at all. It has become apparent, however, that early attention to "naturalizing" the roadside not only provides a more pleasing environment for the motorist but results also in lower maintenance costs and safer highways. Today, roadside development is given careful consideration in every phase of the highway program. By 1950, 29 state highway departments included personnel for roadside development in their organizations.[1]

[1] Reports and other papers of the committee on roadside development of the Highway Research Board are the most important source of reference material on this subject. For a bibliography covering offerings before 1950 see, *Index to Publications*, 1921–49, of the Highway Research Board. For listings of later writings, refer to the index of papers and reports given in the annual *Proceedings Highway Research Board*. (Through 1947 most of these papers appeared in the annual *Proceedings*. After that, they were released separately.) For a brief but authoritative statement on roadside improvement for rural and urban freeways see the chapter on landscape design in *Interregional Highways*, House Document 379, 78th Congress, 2d session. Reports of the Annual Short Course in Highway Development held at Ohio State University offer many valuable articles. The chapter on Highway Landscape in *American Highway Practice*, vol. 1, L. I. Hewes, John Wiley & Sons (1942) outlines the growth of roadside development in considerable detail. This work devotes particular attention to highway landscaping in the national parks and other areas of scenic beauty. For an excellent discussion of erosion-control measures suitable for many western areas see five articles by H. D. Bowers in *California Highways and Public Works* beginning in November–December 1949.

PLANNING FOR ROADSIDE DEVELOPMENT

Early highways were patterned after the railroads of the same period. The principal concern was to fashion the cheapest roadway that would carry traffic under all conditions of weather. Little attention was given to appearance. Horizontal and vertical alinement consisted of long straight sections connected by short curves. Shoulders were narrow or nonexistent, and side slopes were as steep as soil or rock would stand. Rights of way were narrow. Drainage ditches, channels, and structures were designed to provide protection for the roadbed without regard for erosion outside the roadway limits. These economies in first cost inevitably brought unsightly conditions and high maintenance costs. With the passage of time, design standards have been gradually modified, and now are far different from those outlined above.

Location practices have marked effects on the appearance of the finished highway. Often a pleasing vista or a view point can be developed with little sacrifice in cost or distance. Long sweeping horizontal curves are preferable to short curves connected by long tangents. Choppy or broken-backed grade lines should be flattened and smoothed even though they meet the demands of geometric design. In rough country, cut depths and fill heights should be as small as possible to reduce scar and slope erosion to a minimum. Sometimes retaining walls (see p. 168) are helpful. In many other ways also the locator can by careful attention improve the attractiveness of the road.

Modern highway design provides wide shoulders; shallow, wide gutter ditches; and flat back-slopes in cuts and flat side slopes on fills. Tops of cut banks and toes of fills are rounded to blend into the original ground (see Fig. 1. Also Fig. 3, p. 225). These features provide a safer roadbed and one of more pleasing appearance. Furthermore, erosion occurs more slowly or can be more easily prevented on the flatter slopes. One result is decreased expenditures for cleaning gutters and ditches. In addition, ditches and slopes can be dressed or mowed with power equipment, and this further reduces maintenance costs.

Wide rights of way are extremely important in roadside development. In rural areas, they permit blending the road into the natural landscape and provide space to plant screening in front of objectionable signboards and other unsightly objects. Also, access to necessary service facilities can be more easily controlled when they are some distance from the traveled way. In urban areas, wide rights of way on freeways and like facilities make room for planting to screen adjoining property from the sounds of heavy traffic or, in other cases, separate the road from unsightly industrial developments.

Several means exist for extending roadside development outside the right of way proper. These include control of access, the acquisition of "development rights" that bar undesirable growth on adjoining

Fig. 1.   Highway in Florida with well-rounded cross section and good turf cover
on slopes (Courtesy U. S. Bureau of Public Roads)

property, and zoning ordinances to prevent indiscriminate changes in land use. Some jurisdictions also have laws or ordinances that place restrictions on the erection of signs on adjacent lands. All such measures, although very effective, create legal questions of serious concern to highway administrators.[2]

[2] For more on this subject see Reports of the Committee on Land Aquisition and Control of Highway Access and Adjacent Areas, *Highway Research Board Bulletins 4, 18, 38, 55,* and *77.* Other references include four publications of the Public Roads Administration prepared by David R. Levin titled *Public Land Acquisition for Highway Purposes* (1943), *Public Control of Highway Access and Roadside Development* (revised 1947), and *Legal Aspects of Controlling Highway Access* (1945). See also *Roadside Protection,* published by the American Automobile Association.

CONSTRUCTION PRACTICES AND ROADSIDE DEVELOPMENT

Careful examination of construction practices is an important aid in roadside development. Where possible, taking soil for fills from along the right of way (called side borrow) should be avoided in favor of sources out of sight of the roadway. Grading operations must be so planned that suitable topsoil is salvaged for future erosion-control work. Boulders or rock fragments resulting from blasting should be buried in the fills or otherwise disposed of. Natural, flowing lines rather than plane surfaces are highly desirable on all cut and fill slopes. Transitions between cuts and fills deserve special treatment.[3] "Daylighting" small cuts on the downhill side of the roadway to provide better views or small roadside parking areas is an excellent practice. Trees and shrubs suitable for retention should be protected from construction machinery and from damage during blasting. Objects of interest like rock outcrops in cut slopes or particularly attractive trees lying near the toes of fills often can be preserved to add variety.

Final cleanup after construction demands particular attention. Ragged slopes in borrow areas and along the roadside must be dressed to encourage the return of native plants and shrubs. However, the common practice of applying a "sandpaper" finish to cut and fill slopes is to be avoided, for with the first heavy rain they will erode badly. The best practice is to leave a series of small benches that will trap seeds and water and offer a foothold for plant growth.

VEGETATION AND ROADSIDE DEVELOPMENT

Over the continental United States, soil, topography, temperature, and amount and character of rainfall are very different.[4] Plants that grow well in one area may not be suitable in another. Yet the use of turf, ground cover, shrubs, or trees in roadside development is appropriate throughout the country.

[3] Forming cut and fill slopes in "bell mouths" offers a pleasing transition. The end of each cut slope conforms to a cone with its apex located a suitable distance above the roadway at the intersection of the slope and the ground surface. For fills the cone is inverted. Contours of these transitions have a bell-mouthed appearance. See articles by R. S. Dubois and F. W. Cron, *Report of Committee on Roadside Development*, pp. 20–49 (1949).

[4] For a detailed discussion and bibliography see the *Report of Committee on Roadside Development*, Highway Research Board, pp. 12–63 (1950).

Turf

That portion of the United States roughly east of San Antonio, Texas (longitude 97 West), and the coastal areas of Oregon and Washington are classed as "humid." In humid regions, turf or other ground cover can be rapidly established and relied upon to prevent erosion of flat slopes.[5] Recommended practice is to sow grasses immediately after grading. In the past this was not possible because the planting season was limited. However, grass varieties are now available for sowing through the spring and summer and to fit most conditions of exposure and soil type.

Turf is most commonly developed by *seeding*, farm-type equipment often being used. Another technique is *sprigging*, the planting or broadcasting of sprigs taken from established grass. *Sodding*, solidly or in strips, with grass already growing at another location, is a third common method. Because of high cost, sodding must be employed sparingly. A typical application would be the lining of a drainage channel where severe erosion could occur before seeded or sprigged grass could become established.

Topsoiling, or covering the surface with soil containing dormant seed, soil micro-organisms, and plant food, has been widely employed to provide favorable conditions for plant growth. Topsoiling is expensive, and the trend is toward conditioning the existing soils by mulching (see below) and with fertilizers. Before topsoil is placed on steep slopes, the underlying material must be roughened; otherwise the thin soil layer will slump down when softened by rain. On inclines steeper than 1½ to 1, it is common practice to hold topsoil in place by means of wooden frames or with longitudinal boards staked normal to the surface. Where rains are heavy, these measures may prove unsatisfactory unless the topsoil is covered with straw or other vegetable matter. This, in turn, is held down by wire mesh staked to the slope.

Mulching, with or without topsoil, is a highly recommended practice. Straw, hay, roadside cuttings, or local materials like pine branches, leaf litter, moss, sawdust, tobacco stems, cottonseed hulls, or threshed soybean plants are spread uniformly over the surface, often by passing them through a special blower. The spread material is then worked into the previously loosened surface by means of disks,

[5] *Ibid.*, p. 24, states that seeded or planted vegetation can be established on 3-to-1 slopes and on 2-to-1 slopes that have been liberally rounded at crest and toe.

soil pulverizers, or with sheepsfoot or similar tamping rollers.   On banks too steep for ordinary equipment, rollers are often propelled up and down the slope by winches mounted on trucks or tractors. Mulching retards washing of the soil, adds organic material, and holds moisture between rains.

Mulching is extremely effective for erosion control as it binds the soil together and provides favorable conditions for the growth of native plants.   Whether or not it offers the best use of limited funds on rural roads in isolated areas is a debatable question.

On high, steep slopes in rough country where rainfall is intense, mats of brush, embedded in the slopes, are sometimes used to supplement mulching.   California practice places horizontal layers of brush 6 in. thick and 5 ft wide at 6-ft vertical intervals.   The stalks are laid normal to the roadway center line with the leafy ends out.   Grain and alfalfa seed are sown in the mulch, and live cuttings of plants indigenous to the area are planted to form permanent cover.

On the basis of preliminary field testing, the Monsanto Chemical Company has reported that Krilium and other resins show promise in preventing soil erosion and in holding mulches against the action of wind and water.   The tests also showed that "the 'performance level' of the resin approximates that of straw mulch." [6]

Turf shoulders [7]

Turf shoulders are widely employed throughout the East, Middle West, and South.   They are pleasing in appearance, furnish effective erosion and dust control, and are cheaper than other permanent shoulder surfacings in first cost and maintenance.[8]   Stated disadvantages include a tendency in some cases to build up higher than the adjacent pavement and in others to subside below it.   Turf will not resist continued traffic, and, at turnouts or where pavements are narrow, a paving of some kind must be substituted.

Another disadvantage of turf shoulders has been that they softened badly during rainy weather.   Since World II, extensive research on this problem has been conducted by highway agencies in New York,

[6] See *Report of Committee on Roadside Development*, pp. 15–25 (1952).   See also L. J. Goodman, *Highway Research Board Bulletin 69* (1953).

[7] See particularly *Report of Committee on Roadside Development*, pp. 58–94 (1949), pp. 59–74 (1951), and pp. 8–11 (1952).

[8] Untreated gravel and oiled shoulders are cheaper, but cannot be classed as permanent.

New Jersey, Michigan, Illinois, and other states. Many problems remain to be explored. Results to date indicate, however, that stable shoulders with satisfactory turf can be constructed. Recommended material is a compacted, stabilized surface course meeting AASHO requirements[9] with organic materials added to the extent permitted by stability. Fertilizers and ground limestone (as required) are also included. Mowing should be no lower than 3 in.

Ground cover [10]

"Ground cover" has been defined by the Highway Research Board committee on the subject as "low-growing herbaceous or woody plants. not·more than 3 feet high at maturity." Both low shrubs and vines are included. Ground cover is an alternative to grass in controlling erosion by wind and water. It also serves as insulation that reduces sloughing caused by freezing and thawing. For protecting slopes and other roadside areas the best ground covers are thicket or mat-forming plants, those that root from decumbent branches, and those that spread from suckers and shoots. Bushy, dense-foliaged plants and those producing litter with great water-holding capacity afford the greatest protection against erosion. Rapid-growing species with inconspicuous flowers to prevent distraction and vandalism are to be preferred. Fire resistance or the ability to sprout after burning is important. Plants that are subject to disease and insect damage, that crowd out more desirable species, that are poisonous or irritating to the skin, or that may become agricultural pests are not acceptable. For median strips and islands, erosion control is but one of the functions of ground cover. Properly selected plants will prevent headlight glare without affecting sight distance and will provide a contrasting background that implements traffic direction.

Trees and shrubs

Trees and shrubs offer an effective means for providing interest, variety, and beauty to the roadside. For rural roads, the objective is the preservation or, where necessary, the re-creation of a natural foreground in harmony with the distant view. Existing, well-placed

---

[9] See p. 398.

[10] See *Report of Committee on Roadside Development,* pp. 34–37 and 84–99 (1951), for a more detailed discussion of ground cover and a list of ground-cover plants. Also see *Highway Research Board Correlation Service Circular 166,* June 1952.

trees should be preserved, while unpleasing or view-obstructing growth should be removed. Replanting should be considered only where irregular introduction of trees and shrubs will serve to highlight the natural beauty or where it is particularly desirable to screen unsightly or distracting objects or activities. Trees and shrubs native to the area generally are more desirable than imported varieties. Row planting along rural roads is not considered good practice as it spoils distant views and is monotonous.   It is better to create occasional points of interest or to call attention to intersections, bridges, or other points of hazard by carefully planned group planting.

Formal arrangement of trees and shrubs is more appropriate on urban freeways and expressways than in rural areas. Often continuous planting is desirable to screen unsightly roadside conditions or to insulate residential areas against vehicle noise from the road. Serious effort should be made, however, to avoid monotony and sameness over long stretches of the route. One effective means is to group flowering trees and vines at appropriate locations.

PARKING TURNOUTS AND REST AREAS [11]

Parking turnouts to permit stopping off the traveled way by school buses, mail carriers, and others are an important adjunct to major rural highways. As these roads approach urban areas and on urban expressways and streets, off-road stops for public-transportation vehicles also become necessary. Provision for parking clear of the road at points of scenic or historical interest serves to prevent road obstruction and accidents.

A number of states (16 by 1949) are developing statewide systems of wayside rest areas. Ohio now has over 300 such areas in operation, and Michigan contemplates over 500. Important elements in site selections are natural features that make the area attractive, easy accessibility at safe locations, sufficient area (usually 1 to 3 acres), and existing shade. Locations where public use will create a fire hazard or otherwise affect adjoining property should be avoided. Experience to date indicates that locations close by cities and towns are not satisfactory as they are monopolized by townspeople. In developing sites, adequate driveways and parking space separated from the

[11] See *Report of Committee on Roadside Development*, pp. 66–94 (1950), and *Highway Research Board Special Report 7, Publication 230* (1952), for further information on this subject.

traveled way, bumper rails or curbs to confine vehicles, and possibly fencing should be provided. Benches, water supply, and comfort facilities are highly desirable. Without question, the provision of highway rest areas is worth while. However, many highway officials resist their establishment because users are untidy and sometimes vandalic, which makes maintenance difficult and expensive.

11 ———————— Traffic Engineering

INTRODUCTION

Traffic engineering deals with the direction and control of vehicular and pedestrian traffic on existing highways and streets. Thus it is concerned with the planning, design, and operation of all devices that aid the flow of traffic. Among these are pavement markings, traffic markers, signs, and traffic signals. Traffic engineering also deals with means for improving the efficiency of the existing system by the designation of arterial routes and one-way streets, and by controlling the use of these and other facilities. The integration of street and highway lighting into the over-all highway plan generally is considered a traffic-engineering responsibility. Interwoven into all the functions listed above is accident reduction; and traffic engineers usually are assigned the responsibility for accident investigation and for maintaining and analyzing accident records and statistics. Parking likewise falls within the province of the traffic engineer because of the impact that parking problems have on street and highway operation.

Many highway agencies have now created traffic-engineering departments to handle problems like those outlined above. Sometimes, traffic-engineering functions are expanded to deal with problems in geometric design and highway planning. Several universities offer advanced training and many give courses in traffic engineering.[1]

[1] For detailed treatment and an extensive bibliography on traffic engineering see the *Traffic Engineering Handbook*, 2d edition, a reference book published by the Institute of Traffic Engineers, New Haven, Conn. (1950). Also see *Traffic Engineering Functions and Administration*, the Public Administration Service (1948). Many excellent presentations on current topics appear in *Traffic Engineering*, a periodical published by the Institute of Traffic Engineers. Other sources include *Traffic Quarterly* and other offerings of the Eno Foundation for Highway Traffic Control, Saugatuck, Conn., and publications of the Yale Bureau of Highway Traffic and the Institute of Transportation and Traffic Engineering, University of California.

TRAFFIC-CONTROL DEVICES

Pavement markings

Among the earliest pavement marking was the longitudinal center stripe which reputedly appeared first in Wayne County, Mich., in 1911. Today painted or built-in pavement markings are one of the most helpful instruments for traffic direction and control. Stripes are employed to delineate roadway center lines, lane boundaries, no-passing zones, pavement edges, roadway transitions, the approach of obstructions, streetcar clearances, turns, stop lines, crosswalks, railroad crossings, and parking-space limits. Symbols, words, or numbers convey pertinent information such as that about speed limits and the nearness of schools.

Patterns and colors for pavement markings differ among highway agencies, but there is substantial progress toward uniformity. Recommended pavement markings for all usual situations are described on pages 75–97 of the 1948 edition of the *Manual on Uniform Traffic Control Devices,* hereafter referred to as the Manual. This 223-page volume, published by the Bureau of Public Roads [2] is the latest revision by a joint committee representing the American Association of State Highway Officials, the Institute of Traffic Engineers, and the National Committee on Uniform Traffic Laws and Ordinances.[3] A typical plate from this publication is reproduced as Fig. 1.

Typical variation in marking practice is to be seen in the patterns for center-line delineation on two-lane rural highways. The most common design is that suggested by the Manual, which has 15-ft dashes separated by 25-ft spaces. Other dash-space combinations range from 9–15 to 70–70. A few agencies employ continuous lines. Width of line usually is 4 in., although 3- and 6-in. stripes appear. Color generally is the recommended white, but some agencies use yellow. Further standardization based on research findings appears highly desirable.[4]

Most agencies employ specialized mechanical equipment and trained crews for pavement striping. Some units are capable of covering 60

[2] Available for purchase from the Superintendent of Documents, Government Printing Office, Washington 25, D. C.

[3] See also *Traffic Engineering Handbook,* pp. 171–189.

[4] An excellent example of research on the effectiveness of highway markings is reported by C. W. Prisk in *Public Roads,* June 1952, p. 21. As indicated in Fig. 1, the standard marking for no-passing zones on two-lane highways is a solid barrier line alongside the center stripe in the lane from which passing is

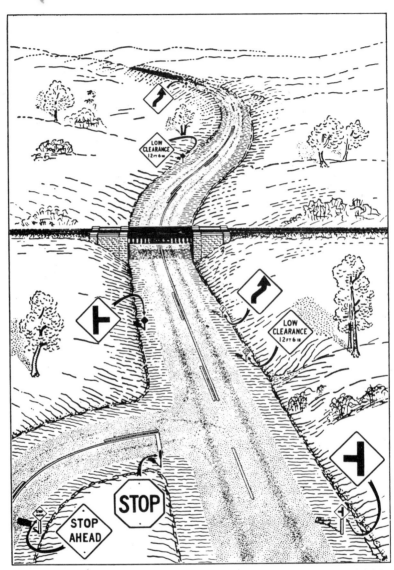

Fɪɢ. 1. Typical application of marking and signing to a 2-lane rural highway
(Fig. 5, page 36 of *Manual of Uniform Traffic Control Devices*)

to 70 miles per day. Hand painting by spray or brush is, of course, necessary in tight quarters. Paints are fast drying, but almost all states use signs or protective devices to prevent vehicles from tracking them. In 15 states, motorists crossing newly painted lines are subject to arrest. Normal service life of stripes is 6 to 9 months.

A variety of paint mixtures are employed for striping. Worthy of particular notice is the strong trend toward the inclusion of glass beads to increase night visibility. In 1950 more than half of the 1½ million gallons of paint applied was beaded.[5]

Traffic markers

Reflector markers of single or clustered buttons or small panels covered with reflecting coatings serve as "hazard markers" to mark obstructions and as "delineators" to outline the edges of the roadway at vertical and horizontal curves. Hazard markers reflect yellow light; delineators are uncolored. Both commonly are set about 3½ ft above the roadway.[6]

Signs

The most common device for warning, regulating, and informing drivers is the traffic sign. Although signs are not needed to confirm the drivers' knowledge of the recognized rules of the road, they are essential wherever special regulations apply or where directions or

prohibited. In Missouri and Iowa the practice has been to place the barrier line in the center of the affected lane. A cooperative research project of the Missouri Highway Department and the Bureau of Public Roads studied vehicle placements and speeds in sections marked in these manners. It was found that "some of the traffic operation characteristics differed but little on the two types of markings. In critical conditions for transverse placements, however, particularly for vehicles traveling in the no-passing zone in the face of oncoming traffic or where wide vehicles were involved, the advantage was consistently with the national standard marking. The national standard also showed favorable performance in the comparison of daylight and night driving, and in the extent to which drivers complied with the no-passing restriction."

[5] Pavement Marking, *Highway Research Board Bulletin 36* (1951), gives the results of a survey of methods and application procedures of the state highway departments. It also discusses current preferences in traffic paints both plain and beaded, and gives specifications for them. *Bulletin 57* (1952) titled Pavement Marking Materials discusses research, testing, and field techniques and offers an extensive bibliography. For a research report and bibliography on glass beads see V. H. Lyon and D. L. Robinson, *Proceedings Highway Research Board*, pp. 245–273 (1949).

[6] For further details on construction and location of traffic markers see *Manual on Uniform Traffic Control Devices*, pp. 99–101.

notice of approaching hazards must be communicated to the driver (see Fig. 1). Signing practice is not uniform among highway agencies. However, the recommendations of the *Manual on Uniform Traffic Control Devices*, pages 7–74, can be accepted as standard.

Authority to install signs is vested by law with highway or police officials. Placing of signs by other persons or organizations should not be permitted since these installations have no legal significance and will reduce the effectiveness of authorized signs. Under no circumstances should any sign or its support carry commercial advertising. Regulatory and warning signs should be installed sparingly, for excessive use decreases their authority.

Table 1 states the purpose and gives shape, color combination, and minimum dimensions for typical signs. Notice that both shape and color emphasize the message. Warning signs are diamond-shaped, except the round railroad-crossing sign. Stop signs are octagonal. Informational and regulatory signs are rectangular. Warning signs are in black on a yellow background. Informational signs are black on white or, for certain oversize signs, white on black. Sign dimensions given in Table 1 represent minimums. Larger sizes are desirable

TABLE 1. PARTIAL DATA ON RECOMMENDED SIGNING PRACTICE

Purpose of Sign	Shape	Colors	Minimum Dimensions, In.
Warning of hazard	Diamond	Black on yellow	24 x 24
Railroad crossing	Disk	Black on yellow	30 (diam.)
Regulatory	Vertical rectangle	Black on white	18 x 24
Stop	Octagon	Black on yellow or white on red	Rural 30 x 30 Urban 24 x 24
Parking	Vertical rectangle	Red on white or green on white	12 x 18
Informational	Horizontal rectangle	Black on white or white on black	
Route markers	Shield or special	Black on white	

Based on *Manual on Uniform Traffic Control Devices*.

where speed, hazard, accident experience, or competition from lights or other signs is extreme. Excessive use of large signs is to be avoided because it makes the regular sizes less effective.

Permanent signs are commonly of metal protected by a rust-resistant coating, although waterproof plywood and wooden boards are sometimes employed. Bolts, screws, and fittings must be non-corrosive to avoid discoloration. Signs having significance at night should be illuminated or reflectorized.[7] Illumination may be by lights in or behind the sign or by independently mounted floodlights. Reflectors include reflector buttons, strips of polished metal, and paint containing glass beads.

Sign positioning depends on the purpose of the sign and the circumstances peculiar to each location. Recommended positions for all usual situations are given in the Manual. For example, warning signs for rural roads should be placed 6 to 10 ft from the pavement edge and the bottom of the sign 30 in. (or more) above the roadway. On high-speed roads, warnings should be posted 500 ft ahead of the hazard. In urban areas where vehicles may park along the curb, a horizontal clearance not less than 1 ft between curb face and near edge of sign and a 7-ft height above the curb are prescribed. On multilane roads, destination signs often are suspended above the roadway to make them visible from the inside lanes.

According to the Manual, lettering on signs should be in clear, open, rounded capitals.[8] However, the effects on legibility of letter size, shape, and spacing, and the comparative effectiveness of upper- and lower-case letters are the subject of continuing research.[9]

Signals [10]

All power-operated devices (except signs) for controlling, directing, or warning motorists or pedestrians are classed as traffic signals. Particular installations will serve one or more of the following functions:

[7] Nonreflectorized signs would be appropriate for most school-zone markings, for parking control effective only in the daytime or illuminated by street lighting, and for "Men Working" and other temporary warnings. Where speed limits differ between day and night, the Manual suggests that two signs, one black on white, unreflectorized, and the other white on black, reflectorized, be mounted on the same standard.

[8] Detailed drawings for these are supplied by the U. S. Bureau of Public Roads.

[9] For discussions of several aspects of this subject and bibliographies covering earlier work in this field see T. W. Forbes and Karl Moscowitz, and discussion by D. W. Loutzenheiser, *Proceedings Highway Research Board,* pp. 355–373 (1950); A. R. Lauer, *Proceedings Highway Research Board,* pp. 360–371 (1947); and H. W. Case, J. L. Michael, G. E. Mount, and R. Brenner in *Highway Research Board Bulletin 60,* pp. 44–58 (1952).

[10] See *Manual on Uniform Traffic Control Devices,* pp. 103–169, and *Traffic Engineering Handbook,* pp. 216–289, for a detailed treatment and bibliography.

1. Provide for orderly movement of traffic.

2. Reduce the frequency of certain types of accidents.

3. Coordinate traffic so that it flows nearly continuously and at selected speeds.

4. Control speed on through highways and main routes.

5. Interrupt heavy traffic to permit crossings by other vehicles or pedestrians.

6. Direct traffic into particular routes or lanes.

7. Warn and control traffic at railroad crossings, drawbridges, and other points of hazard.

The Manual offers standards of design, application, location, and operation for traffic signals.

If the directions given by signals are to be enforceable, they must be erected under legal authority, and the intention of each must be stated in detail in laws or ordinances. Model legislation will be found in the Uniform Vehicle Code and in the Model Traffic Ordinance, both prepared by the National Committee on Uniform Traffic Laws and Ordinances and published by the Bureau of Public Roads.[11]

There is widespread belief among laymen that traffic signals offer the solution to all traffic-control and accident problems, particularly those at intersections. In many instances, signals have been installed without careful study by qualified engineers. The consequences often have been excessive delay, disobedience of signals, diversions to alternate routes, and increased accident frequency. As a guide to the proper use of signals, the Manual offers minimum "warrants" for signal installations based on vehicular and pedestrian volumes, accident hazard, coordinated movement, and interruption to continuous traffic. Separate recommendations are given for rural locations where traffic normally is light and speeds high and for urban locations where these conditions are usually reversed. To illustrate, the suggested minimum requirements where traffic volume alone is to justify a signal installation are as follows:

	Urban	Rural
Minimum vehicular volume entering intersection from all approaches (average per hour for any 8 hr)	750	500
Minimum vehicular volume entering intersection from the minor street (average per hour for the same 8 hr)	175	125

[11] Available from the Superintendent of Documents, Washington 25, D. C.

Signals for intersection control

Characteristics of signals. Modern signals for intersection control operate by electricity. Individual units have separate red, yellow, and green lenses, 8 in. or more in diameter, each illuminated from behind by its own light source. Often lenses directing separate movements to left or right and for pedestrian control are added. Lens assemblies are mounted on pedestals or brackets outside the roadway limits, or are suspended above the intersection by cables or other supports. The recommended height for signals mounted at the side of the roadway is 8 to 10 ft above the sidewalk, or above the crown of the pavement where there is no sidewalk. Signals suspended over the roadway should have a minimum vertical clearance of 14½ to 15½ ft.

For rural areas one or more signal faces should be visible to traffic on each approach. In urban areas or at rural intersections having high pedestian volume, two or more signal faces on each approach are prescribed. With only one signal face, drivers of vehicles following immediately behind trucks or buses may be unable to see the signal indication as they approach the intersection. For proper pedestrian regulation, a signal face must be clearly visible to the pedestrian for the entire length of the crosswalk. Thus, if vehicular signals are located on the near side of the intersection, another signal face or a separate pedestrian signal must be placed on the far side. On expressways and other facilities where signals must interrupt fast-moving traffic, a common practice is to install three and sometimes four signal faces on each approach.

The Manual assigns positive meaning to each color and its use. The green light should be given only when traffic is permitted to proceed straight ahead or turn in either direction. When certain movements are permitted and other prohibited, the regular circular red lens facing traffic should be illuminated together with a separate green arrow for each permitted movement. Solid red alone means to stop and wait for a green indication while flashing red has the same meaning as an arterial stop sign. Flashing yellow means proceed with caution. The use of steady yellow for caution is not recommended, except as a warning between green and red indications.

Signal locations. For typical right-angle intersections, far-side, near-side, mast-arm, and center-suspended locations each offer certain advantages and are favored by some engineers. That signal location is controversial is indicated by the following quotation from the Manual:

"Thirty-six outstanding traffic engineers could not develop a majority for the first choice for either rural or urban intersections, although the greatest number of votes was cast for the center-suspended location in rural areas and the far-right, far-left location in urban areas."

Apparently there is a trend toward suspending at least one signal face over the roadway on mast arm or cable. This action is attributed in part to the increasing number, brilliance, and color of illuminated advertising signs that decrease the nighttime effectiveness of signals placed above the sidewalk.[12] The Manual makes no specific recommendation regarding signal location; instead it leaves determination to the engineers who plan the installation. It does caution against undue variation along the same street.

[12] In some localities, projecting signs that throw light along the roadway are prohibited by law or ordinance.

Fixed-time traffic signals. "Fixed-time" traffic signals are set to repeat regularly a given sequence of signal indications. They are contrasted with "traffic-actuated" signals that are controlled wholly or in part by the approach of vehicles from the various directions. Fixed-time operation has the advantage that, with a series of interconnected signals, vehicles can move through a series of intersections with a minimum of stops and other delays. Its disadvantage is that it cannot adjust to short-time variations in traffic flow and often holds vehicles from one direction when there is no traffic in the other. This results in inconvenience and delay and sometimes in a decrease in capacity.

"Cycle length," the time required for a complete sequence of indications, ordinarily falls between 30 and 120 sec. Short cycle lengths are to be preferred, as the delay to standing vehicles is reduced. With short cycles, however, a relatively high percentage of the total time is consumed in clearing the intersection and starting each succeeding movement. As cycle length increases, the percentage of time lost from these causes decreases. With high volumes of traffic, it may be necessary to increase the cycle length to gain added capacity.

On the average, each traffic lane of a normal signalized intersection will pass one vehicle each 2.4 sec of green light.[13] The yellow (caution) interval following each green period is between 3 and 5 sec, depending on street width. To determine an approximate cycle division, it is common practice to make a short traffic count (15 to 30 min), during the peak period. Simple computations give the number of vehicles to be accommodated during each signal indication and the minimum green time required to pass them. With modern control equipment, it is possible to change the cycle division at intervals during the day to fit the traffic pattern better.[14]

At many intersections, signals must be timed to accommodate pedestrian movement. The *Traffic Engineering Handbook* recommends a "go" interval of at least 5 sec in which pedestrians may start. In addition, time for crossing at 3.5 to 4.0 ft per sec must be allowed before the caution period protecting the crosswalk expires. Where streets are wide, the time of pedestrian crossings probably will govern the minimum permissible cycle length. The caution period may be lengthened considerably beyond the 3 to 5 sec needed with motor vehicles unless separate pedestrian signals are provided or a pedestrian refuge is placed in the center of the street. Long clearance periods encourage driver violations of the red indication.

In downtown locations where pedestrian movements are unusually heavy, a so-called "scramble" system for fixed-time signals has sometimes proved effective. A separate interval is provided solely for pedestrians during which they may cross either street or proceed diagonally across both.

Coordinated movement. Fixed-time traffic signals along a street or within an area usually are coordinated to permit compact groups of vehicles to move along together. Under normal traffic volumes, properly coordinated

[13] About 4 sec of green time is used by the first vehicle, but this time soon decreases to about 2 sec as succeeding vehicles pass. If turning movements are frequent or heavy vehicles numerous, these headways increase.

[14] See *Traffic Engineering Handbook*, pp. 223–229, for more precise timing methods.

signals at intervals no greater than 1200 ft are very effective in producing a smooth flow of traffic. However, coordinated movements are shattered if the street is overloaded.

Four systems of coordination, simultaneous, alternate, simple progressive, and flexible progressive all have been or are now in use. The *simultaneous system* makes all color indications on a given street alike at the same time. It produces high vehicle speeds between stops but low over-all speed and leads to blocking of cross streets when the main streets are filled with traffic. These and other faults severely limit the usefulness of simultaneous timing.

The *alternate system* has all signals change their indication at the same time, but adjacent signals or adjacent groups of signals on a given street show opposite colors. The alternate system works fairly well on a single street that has approximately equal block spacings. It also has been effective for controlling traffic in business districts several blocks on a side, but only when block lengths are approximately equal in both directions. With the alternate system, green and red indications must be of approximately equal length. This cycle division may be satisfactory where two major streets intersect, but it gives too much green time to minor streets crossing major arteries. Other criticisms are that at heavy traffic volumes the later section of the group is forced to make additional stops, and that adjustments to changing traffic conditions are difficult.

The *simple progressive system* retains a common cycle length but provides "go" indications separately at each intersection. This permits continuous or nearly continuous flow of vehicle groups at a planned speed and discourages speeding between signals. Flashing lights may be substituted for normal signal indications when traffic becomes light.

The *flexible progressive system,* the most advanced now in use, has a master controller mechanism that directs the controllers for the individual signals. This arrangement not only gives positive coordination between signals but also makes predetermined changes in signal indication by remote control. For example, the cycle length of the entire system can be lengthened at peak hours to increase capacity and shortened at other times to decrease delays. Flashing indications can be substituted when normal signal control is not needed. Also the offsets in the timing of successive signals can be adjusted to favor heavy traffic movements, such as inbound in the morning and outbound in the evening. Again, changes in cycle division at particular intersections can be made.[15]

Timing progressive traffic signals. The timing of progressive signals on a given street must be carefully fitted to the traffic. Field counts at appropriate times, both for the street in question and for important cross streets, represent the first step. From these counts an appropriate cycle length for the entire system and cycle divisions for each intersection can be worked out.

[15] Progressively timed traffic signals are sometimes combined with directional channelization to relieve severe congestion and to decrease traffic delays at congested intersections. For a detailed description of such an installation near Jersey City, N. J., see W. R. Bellis, *Proceedings Highway Research Board,* pp. 377–395 (1950). Reports on three added intersections are offered in *Highway Research Board Bulletin 72,* pp. 1–13 (1953).

Also the most desirable travel speed along the street must be found. A "floating car" which moves with the traffic stream offers an excellent means for gaging actual speeds.[16] Starting with these basic data, the "offsets" in timing between the signal indications of the different streets can then be worked out by graphical or analytical methods.

The graphical solution is based on a space-time diagram that has distance along the street as its ordinate and time in seconds as the abscissa (see Fig. 2). On this graph the slope of any straight line represents velocity, since the units are distance and time. To illustrate, the slope of the straight lines running from upper left to lower right in Fig. 2a indicates a speed of 18 mph. The lines themselves show the location-time relationship for vehicles traveling at given speeds. For example, in Fig. 2a the two diagonal straight lines each represent the progress with time of an automobile traveling from Turk toward Mont at 18 mph. The heavy dashed horizontal lines opposite each street show the signal timing at that intersection. The wide, open spaces represent "go" time, the narrow, open ones "caution" intervals, and the solid black segments are "stop" time. On a working model of the diagram these signal indications would be drawn separately on narrow strips of tracing paper or tracing cloth. By shifting the strips laterally, all possible combinations of signal offsets could be investigated on a single chart. Also the sloped lines representing speed might be marked out with black thread for easy moving.

Figure 2 shows three combinations of offsets, each selected to fit a peculiar traffic-flow pattern. Timing for the morning peak hours (Fig. 2a) favors the heavy flow of inbound traffic by giving it a through band of 27 sec, which is the maximum possible. Signal offsets are timed for the most favorable speed of 18 mph. On the other hand, the light flow of outbound traffic receives a narrow through band, which means that some of the vehicles will be delayed at O'Farrell. Figure 2c shows the timing for the afternoon peak period, when heavy outbound traffic is favored. Timing for "off-peak" periods appears in Fig. 2b. In this case traffic flows with equal ease in either direction at the higher speed of 22 mph. However, the through bands are only 15 sec wide, which limits the number of vehicles that can travel in a given squad.

The experienced traffic engineer can add many refinements to the procedure outlined above. As an example, by lagging or leading the signals at particular intersections, the main artery can be cleared in both directions to permit vehicles and pedestrians to cross at intermediate unsignalized locations. In the same way, main arteries can be cleared in one direction to permit easy left turns by vehicles traveling the other way. Often left turns can be reduced or prohibited at important intersections by providing for them at adjacent unsignalized locations. Other techniques are based on the adjustment of cycle division at less important intersections. To illustrate, vehicles can be encouraged to move in squads by limiting the green time at these locations.

Timing patterns for traffic signals are often severely criticized by the uninformed on the grounds that they do not provide wide through bands in both directions. In most cases, this is physically impossible. Only in rare instances is the proper combination of block spacing and vehicle speeds to be found.

[16] See D. S. Berry, *Proceedings Highway Research Board,* pp. 429–440 (1952), and (with F. H. Green), pp. 311–318 (1949).

King Street signal timing

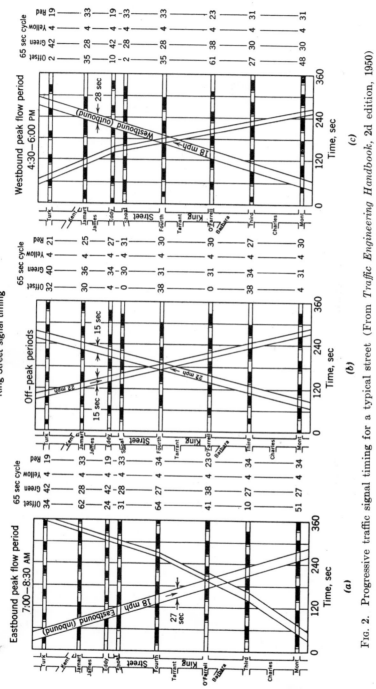

Fig. 2. Progressive traffic signal timing for a typical street (From *Traffic Engineering Handbook*, 2d edition, 1950)

Provision of through bands in both directions is particularly difficult where block spacings are irregular. This can be convincingly demonstrated by diagrams similar to Fig. 2.

Traffic-actuated signals. Traffic-actuated signals respond in a predetermined manner to the approach of vehicles from one or more legs of an intersection. In general, they are most effective at widely spaced or isolated locations where coordination with other signals is unimportant. Where traffic on heavy-volume or high-speed arteries must be interrupted for relative light cross traffic, *semi-traffic-actuated* signals are often installed. For them, detectors are placed only on the minor street. The signal indication normally is green on the main road and red on the cross street. On actuation, the indications are reversed for a predetermined interval after which they return to the original colors. Pushbutton signals at pedestrian crossings often operate in a similar way.

Full traffic-actuated signals have detectors located on each approach and assign the right of way to the various traffic movements on the basis of demand. With modern control equipment, signal operations can be adapted to many situations. As one example, consider an intersection between major and minor arteries. Here the green indication will normally remain with the main street. On demand from the cross street, the signal indication will change at once if the main street has no traffic. With continued flow on the main street, the green indication will remain until all vehicles have been cleared or until some predetermined period has elapsed. The minimum green period for the cross street will permit the passage of one vehicle. However, this interval is extended up to a set maximum by continued traffic on the cross street. Full traffic-actuated controls also have been applied successfully to intersections having three or four signal phases. "Go" indications are offered to the various movements in rotation, except that those with no traffic demand are skipped.

Several combinations of traffic-actuation control with progressive signals have also proved successful. To illustrate, in downtown Denver, a master controller keeps a constant count of traffic volumes and movements and alters signal-light timing each 6 min. Cycle lengths are adjusted automatically in a range between 40 and 120 sec, and cycle splits are changed to favor heavier traffic flows. There are other traffic-actuated devices for such purposes as to control speed at intersections and other points of hazard and to direct one-way movements where the road is too narrow to permit two-way operation.

Several types of detectors for traffic-actuated signals are in use. These include pressure-sensitive devices, magnetic indicators embedded in or under the pavement, sound-sensitive mechanisms; and light-sensitive instruments. All refer their signals to the controller electrically. Detector placement depends on several factors, including the type of installation and vehicle approach speed. As an illustration, for two-way full traffic-actuated installations and a vehicle approach speed greater than 50 mph, the detector should be placed at least 225 ft ahead of the stop line.

ARTERIAL ROUTES

Arterial routes are those especially designed to carry through traffic. Wherever possible, new arterials should be designed as freeways or expressways. Of necessity, however, most arterials are existing through highways or streets along which cross traffic is regulated by signals or stop signs. By installing a properly selected network of arterials it is usually possible to increase the capacity of the entire street system, reduce delays to through and local traffic, and decrease accidents.

Arterial routes and through streets are usually incorporated into the master plan for the community. Although there are no fixed rules regarding selection of routes, studies of traffic volumes, origins and destinations, and accident experience are basic tools for planning them. The *Traffic Engineering Handbook* offers helpful suggestions, among them that:

1. Arterials must carry at least one lane of traffic in each direction and be at least half a mile in length.

2. Arterials should skirt neighborhood areas rather than penetrate them.

3. In a grid system of streets, arterials should be spaced about 2000 ft apart.

4. Where accident hazard is not a factor, minimum volumes to justify arterials are 300 vehicles per average hour during the day and 450 vehicles hourly during peak periods.

In many instances, peak-hour traffic volumes on arterial streets exceed the capacity of the conventional two-way streets; however, several techniques have been devised to increase their capacity. Among these are:

1. Prohibition of parking during peak hours on one or both sides of the street. Sometimes this parking ban extends throughout the day.

2. Provision of an extra lane adjacent to signalized intersections to bring intersection capacity nearer to street capacity between intersections. This is often accomplished by eliminating parking for several hundred feet on each side of the intersection.

3. Special provision for right-turn vehicles outside the through lanes and elimination of left turns at congested intersections.

4. Reversing the direction of traffic in the center lanes to provide more lanes in the direction of heavier flow. This has been accom-

plished in several ways. On the Pulaski Skyway, N. J., and Lee Highway, Va., red and green signals are suspended directly over the affected lanes. In Detroit signs stating the hours that lane use is permitted are suspended overhead. In Los Angeles movable signs are placed in the streets by crews of men traveling carefully outlined routes four times daily. On a 2-mile stretch of the eight-lane Outer Drive in Chicago, three sets of special metal fins were installed along the roadway. These can be raised by hydraulic jacks to form a curb or lowered to become a part of the roadway surface. When the center set of fins is raised, the eight lanes are divided equally between opposing traffic. By raising one of the outer sets, six lanes are set off for inbound traffic and two lanes for outbound vehicles. The other set provides the same lane distribution, but favors outbound traffic.

Four-way stop signs are sometimes employed at the intersection of two arterials where volumes do not warrant traffic signals. The *Manual on Uniform Traffic Control Devices* recommends that this arrangement be employed only where traffic on the cross streets is nearly equal or where there is a serious accident hazard.

Large industrial plants, commercial enterprises, or amusement facilities such as drive-in theaters almost always front on arterial streets. These create sudden traffic peaks, and often present serious congestion and accident situations. Often highway officials lack authority to cope with the resulting problem. In any event, they must be given serious consideration in the future. A discussion of these problems and suggested solutions to many of them appear in *Policy on Drive-In Theatres*, American Association of State Highway Officials (1949).

ONE-WAY STREETS

One-way streets are those on which vehicular traffic moves in only one direction. In many cities much of the downtown street grid is operated on a one-way basis with opposing traffic using alternate streets.[17] In numerous other locations, pairs of one-way streets serve as major traffic arteries.

The widespread adoption of the one-way traffic plan stems from a number of important advantages over two-way operation, some of which are:

Greater capacity. More vehicles can be accommodated by the same street system (see Figs. 10 and 11, p. 157).

[17] In New York City about 1000 miles of street are one-way.

Increased Average Speed. Progressive signals can be timed to give a full-width through band on each one-way street, even where block spacing is irregular. There are fewer delays at intersections because the number of possible conflicts is greatly reduced. This is illustrated for two-lane streets by Fig. 3. At intermediate unsignalized intersections traffic can cross freely during the breaks in through traffic.

Improved Pedestrian Movement. At signal-controlled intersections of two one-way streets, one crosswalk is completely free from turning vehicles during each phase of the signal. Turns across the opposite

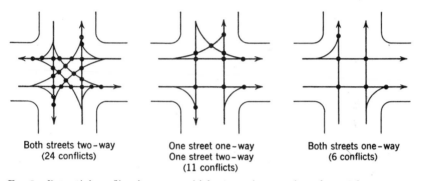

Both streets two-way
(24 conflicts)

One street one-way
One street two-way
(11 conflicts)

Both streets one-way
(6 conflicts)

Fig. 3. Potential conflicts between vehicles at an intersection of two 2-lane streets. Two-way vs. one-way operation

crosswalk are from one direction rather than from two (see Fig. 3). At unsignalized intersections and mid-block locations, pedestrians can cross during the breaks in traffic.

Reduction in Accidents. By the elimination of conflicts, as listed above, one-way operation reduces most types of accidents.

Other Advantages. Among these are the elimination of headlight glare, greater ease of movement for emergency vehicles, and a reduction in police attention to traffic.[18]

One-way operation often presents difficulties of at least temporary nature. Transit routings must be revised, usually with attendant confusion.[19] Travel distances to reach certain locations are often increased, a condition that may seriously affect particular businesses.

[18] The *Traffic Engineering Handbook* cites several examples where policing time was cut to one-half or less by the introduction of one-way streets.

[19] In New York, attempts to make a pair of streets one-way was prevented by court action by the transit company that had a 99-year franchise for two-way operation.

For example, a food store may lose most of its patrons if the street on which it fronts is made one-way inbound. Sometimes accidents increase, particularly when traffic is speeded up.

Proposals to install one-way streets often meet with opposition from businessmen and others who fear that their interests will be adversely affected. Sometimes the initial step is to try one-way operation on one pair of streets. Only after these have been accepted by the public can permission be obtained to expand the plan. There have been numerous instances where objections have prevented so much as a trial of a one-way street plan. In other cases public opposition has forced city officials to abolish the plan after a trial. In at least one large city one-way streets were installed, forced out by business interests, and finally restored after motorists had deluged city officials with protests.

HIGHWAY ILLUMINATION [20]

Motor-vehicle headlights provide the only illumination for most of the rural road mileage, but fixed lighting at important intersections and points of hazard is becoming more and more common. Because of the cost, however, only a few principal rural arteries have been provided with continuous illumination. In urban areas, on the other hand, fixed lighting for main arteries and residential streets alike is widely employed. Here, where the population density is much greater, added benefits like improved police protection offer further arguments favoring street lights.

Without question, the most compelling reason for improved highway illumination is the present high nighttime accident rate. Roughly half the highway fatalities occur during daylight and half during darkness. On the basis of vehicle-miles driven, however, the accident rate in both urban and rural areas is about three times as great at night as during the day. This is explained in part by limited studies,[21] which indicated little change in driving speed between lighted and unlighted roads although visibility was much lower on unlighted roads. Also, certain unsafe practices were more prevalent on unlighted roads, particularly following too closely and failure to stay in the proper lane

[20] The committee on night visibility of the Highway Research Board has been active in this field for a number of years. Recent offerings of this committee include *Bulletins 56* (1952) and *68* (1953).

[21] See *Proceedings Highway Research Board,* p. 513 (1944), for a report of driver behavior on lighted and unlighted sections of a rural two-lane highway.

when meeting opposing traffic. In any event, highway lighting as a means of accident reduction offers a fruitful field for further study.

Principles of highway and street lighting

When an object appears darker than its background, discernment is by *silhouette*. If the object is brighter than its immediate background, seeing is by *reverse silhouette*. When direct illumination of about one foot-candle intensity is provided on the side facing the driver, variations in brightness permit discernment by *surface detail*, without general contrast with the background.

The aim in most street and highway lighting is to illuminate the roadway surface to provide seeing by silhouette. Where traffic volume and pedestrian numbers are small, an average surface brightness of about 0.2 horizontal ft-candle is sufficient. Intensities should be increased for more important highways and at intersections. The maximum recommended brightness is for business streets and is 1.2 horizontal ft-candles. For highways where access is fully controlled, the level recommended by the AASHO is 0.6 ft-candle. These values are for pavements having average reflectance. Where reflectance is poor illumination should be raised as much as 50%, but where it is excellent values can be decreased by about 25%.

Reverse-silhouette lighting of curb ends, piers and abutments, and other obstructions is obtained by direct illumination of the hazard in a manner that outlines it against the surrounding darkness. On brightly lighted streets or where vehicles are numerous, seeing is largely by surface detail.

Under headlight illumination, the upper portions of persons and vehicles appear in reverse silhouette. Here the reflective quality of the object being viewed assumes particular importance. According to F. W. Hurd [22] the reflection factor of a white, diffusing surface is about 98%. Most objects encountered on highways have reflection factors of about 7%, but dark clothing reflects only about 2% of the light. Studies in Massachusetts in 1934, using the type of headlight then available, indicated that persons in white clothing against dark backgrounds could be seen twice as far away as those in dark clothing.[23] The reflecting quality of the pavement also has great impor-

[22] *Traffic Engineering*, June 1950, p. 345.

[23] These figures demonstrate the value of reflectors on fixed objects and bicycles. They also show that pedestrians are much more visible if part of their clothing is light in color. Pedestrians whose clothing is all dark can walk with increased safety if they display an unfolded pocket handkerchief.

tance under headlight illumination since the lower portions of persons and vehicles and most dark objects first appear in silhouette against the roadway. A light-colored pavement or a seal coat that reflects light back to the driver is highly desirable. Surfaces that become mirror-like when wet are particularly to be avoided, for almost no light reflects back from them toward the light source.

Effectiveness of headlights

Experiments conducted by General Electric Company [24] indicate that alerted drivers employing the upper beam of sealed-beam headlights perceived a dummy dressed in dark clothing at a distance of 500 ft. Under like conditions except that the drivers were not alerted, perception occurred at a distance of 250 ft. This finding and many like studies demonstrate conclusively that 50 mph represents the safe top nighttime speed when illumination is solely by headlight.[25] The General Electric tests also investigated the effects of headlight glare on perception distance. It was reported that, when both vehicles depressed their headlights on meeting, alerted drivers saw the dummies at about 300 ft during all phases of the passing maneuver. When the test driver used the lower beam and the approaching vehicle did not dim its lights, the perception distance for alerted drivers fell from 250 ft to about 150 ft as the vehicles approached each other.

Intensive research to improve headlights has been conducted by vehicle and lamp manufacturers and others. The polarized-headlight system has received particular attention and has its strong proponents and opponents. In general, the motor-vehicle manufacturers oppose its adoption. Space limitations preclude the inclusion of the arguments here.[26] The effect of tinted windshields on night visibility is also under study.[27]

[24] See The Polarized Headlight System, *Highway Research Board Bulletin 11,* pp. 30–36 (1948).

[25] This statement can be proved by substituting a reaction time of 0.75 sec for the 2.5-sec perception and reaction time in Table 10, p. 172.

[26] For pro and con discussions see The Polarized Headlight System, *Highway Research Board Bulletin 11* (1948). Also see *Traffic Engineering,* April–July and October–November 1950.

[27] See articles by Warren Heath and D. M. Finch and by Val J. Roper in *Highway Research Board Bulletin 68,* pp. 1–30 (1953).

Highway lighting installations [28]

Light Sources. Light sources for street and highway lighting are usually of the filament, sodium-vapor, mercury-vapor, or fluorescent type. All of these produce about the same visibility for the same level of illumination since color differences do not materially affect vision. Of the four types, the *filament lamp* has the greatest usage. It produces a pleasing color, is inexpensive, and is available in a variety of sizes from 1000 to 25,000 lumens. On the other hand, it consumes more power than the other types. *Sodium-vapor lamps* produce a distinctive yellow-orange color. They are particularly adapted for marking hazardous locations since drivers are familiar with yellow-orange as an indication of caution. Sodium-vapor lamps have high efficiency and long life, a highly desirable quality under certain conditions. *Mercury-vapor lamps* are being employed increasingly because of their high efficiency. Their light is bluish white, with little of the red component. *Fluorescent lamps* often are mounted below eye level to provide continuous lighting along the sides of a roadway. Sometimes they are employed overhead in tunnels and underpasses. Luminaires are available for fluorescent lighting for streets and highways. Because of the length and number of lamps, these fixtures are quite large. On the other hand, they offer a "warm white" light, less direct glare, and wider bands of direct reflection from the pavement surface to the driver's eye.

Luminaires. Luminaires distribute light from the sources into definite patterns that best suit particular situations. Descriptions of the five general types appear in Fig. 4. Recommended practice places luminaires 20 to 30 ft above the roadway, with 25- and 30-ft heights preferred for all except the smallest lamp sizes. With high mountings, uniform illumination can be maintained even though individual units are widely spaced. High mounting also greatly reduces the blinding effect of direct glare. For example, for the same candlepower, a lamp mounted 10 ft above the pavement produces 13 times the glare of one at 30 ft. Of necessity, individual lamps are larger with wide spacings. For the higher mountings, recommended spacing is approximately 120 ft. At high levels of illumination lights are installed on both sides of the road. For lower surface brightness, successive units are placed on opposite sides of straight roads. On curves, more than half and sometimes all the units are placed on the outside. The usual practice is to suspend the luminaires over the roadway, sometimes on cables and again on mast arms extending outward from the roadside. Sidewalk illumination is gained by proper luminaire selection.

Trees are a definite asset to a community and their mutilation or removal to provide adequate street lighting is usually unwarranted. Much can be done by cooperation between the agencies charged with the two responsibilities. For example, luminaire position, height, and spacing can be fitted to tree-

[28] For authoritative recommendations see the 1953 *American Standard Practice for Street and Highway Lighting* (D12.1–1953) of the American Standards Association. Much of the 1947 Standards appear in the *Traffic Engineering Handbook*, pp. 449–471. The 1953 Standards (tentative) and an extensive bibliography appear in *Illuminating Engineering,* August 1952, pp. 449–471.

planting patterns.   Again, new trees can be selected from the globe-headed or upright types that do not conflict so seriously with lighting installations.[29]

Type	General Description	Pattern of Light Distribution	Typical Applications
I	2-way (or 4-way) light distribution	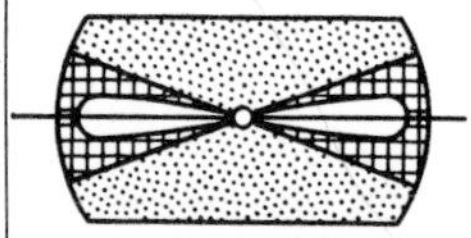	For mounting over center of street or (4-way) in the center of intersections
II	Narrow asymmetric lateral distribution (2-way or 4-way)	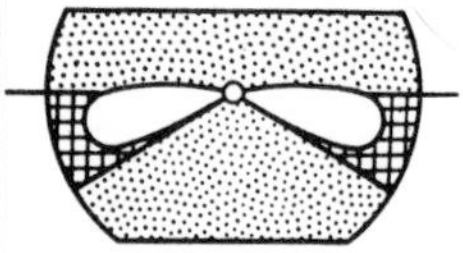	For mounting on one side of a relatively narrow roadway or (4-way) at one corner of a right-angle intersection
III	Medium-width asymmetric lateral distribution	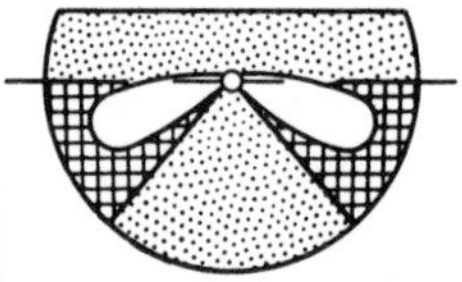	Wider-spread beam for mounting on one side of wider roadways
IV	Wide asymmetric lateral distribution	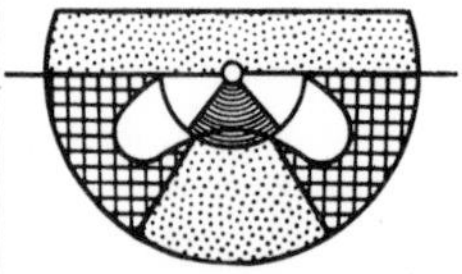	For side of road mountings
V	Symmetrical distribution	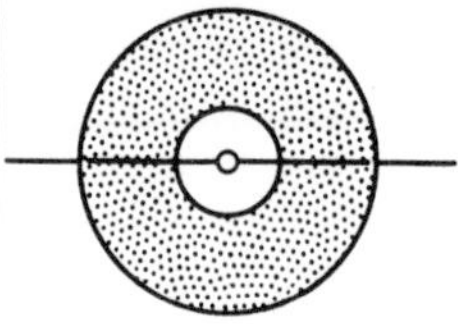	For mounting near the center of roadway or at intersections

FIG. 4.   Types of luminaires employed for street and highway lighting

MOTOR-VEHICLE ACCIDENTS

Motor-vehicle accidents claim an appalling toll in the United States. In 1952, 38,000 people were killed [30] and 1,350,000 others injured.   In addition, 8.6 million property-damage accidents were reported.[31]

[29] For more on this subject, see E. H. Scanlon and K. M. Reid, *Illuminating Engineering,* March 1948.

[30] Of these deaths, 11,000 occurred in cities and towns and 27,000 in rural areas. Pedestrian fatalities totaled 5450 in urban areas and 3150 in rural locations.

[31] Of these, 5.2 million caused property damage less than $25.

Stated differently, there was one reported accident for each five motor vehicles. Deaths each year have remained above 30,000 almost continuously since 1928, except for the World War II years when driving was curtailed. In all, motor-vehicle accidents claimed their millionth victim late in 1951. On the other hand, death and injury rates stated in terms of vehicle-miles driven have decreased over the years. Much is still to be done, however, to disprove the jaundiced statement that 35,000 lives per year is the price that must be paid for automotive transportation.

Highway safety is a joint responsibility and must be approached from several directions. To illustrate, the President's Highway Safety Conference, meeting at intervals in Washington, is organized into eight committees, as follows: laws and ordinances, accident records, education, enforcement, engineering, motor-vehicle administration, public information, and organized public support. Again, highway accident prevention is often subdivided into the three E's: Engineering, Education, and Enforcement.

Accident reports and statistics

Most motor-vehicle accidents have multiple causes, and repetitions under like circumstances can often be prevented if one of these causes is removed. Accident reports, to be of value in planning remedial action, must show all the circumstances surrounding each accident. The data should include exact location and time, vehicle speeds and paths, light, weather, and road situations, and driver and vehicle condition. In many cases there may be other factors of great significance that would be recognized by an experienced observer. Accident reports must be free of bias. In particular, the reporter must resist the temptation to assign the accident to a single cause or to fix legal responsibility. Otherwise he may overlook some hazard that, if uncorrected, will cause a like accident at a later time.

As a means of gaining complete and accurate accident reports, the National Conference on Uniform Traffic Accident Statistics has developed standard accident report forms for drivers and investigators.[32] As yet, however, accident reporting is far from uniform or complete in the United States. Almost all the states have laws that require vehicle operators to report injury or property-damage accidents.[33]

[32] These forms are available from the National Safety Council. The form is reproduced in the *Traffic Engineering Handbook*, p. 116.

[33] All injury accidents must be reported. In most states, property damage less

As of 1949, only 17 states had legislation requiring officers to report accidents investigated in the course of duty.

Accident reports are collected at designated central locations like the city or state law-enforcement agency or state motor-vehicle department. Sometimes duplicate copies are provided for traffic engineers. Pertinent data for accident statistics are transferred to tally sheets or to punch cards for mechanical tabulation. The reports themselves are most effectively used if filed by location, although a chronological file with a location cross index is often employed.

The National Safety Council serves as a clearing house for traffic accident statistics. Its annual publication, *Accident Facts*, offers a detailed and authoritative analysis of great usefulness to all who are concerned with the problem.

Summaries of data from accident reports, often combined with figures on mileage driven, population, or vehicle registration, provide extremely useful measures of accident conditions. Table 2 shows, for several classes of highways and streets, the mileage death rate in deaths per 100 million vehicle-miles and the mileage accident rate in accidents per million vehicle-miles. Table 3 is a directional analysis of motor-vehicle accidents. These tables are representative of the many ways in which accident data may be broken down for engineering analysis.[34] It must be borne in mind that generalizing from accident statistics is dangerous unless all factors are taken into account.

Studies to express a mathematical relationship between accident expectation and traffic volume, population, or number of vehicles have been published.[35] It was suggested, for example, that the number of single-car accidents should be proportional to the number of vehicles using the system, the number of two-car accidents proportional to the square of the number of vehicles, and the number of vehicle-pedestrian accidents proportional to the product of vehicle numbers times pedestrian numbers.

than a stated amount (mostly commonly $50) need not be reported. However, a few states require reports on all property-damage accidents.

[34] See *Uses of Traffic Accident Records*, published by the Eno Foundation for Traffic Control (1947). For the procedures of the Connecticut Highway Department see R. E. Jorgensen and R. G. Mitchell, *Proceedings Highway Research Board*, pp. 336–348 (1949).

[35] See, for example, R. J. Smeed, Some Statistical Aspects of Road Safety Research, *Journal Royal Statistical Society*, section A, vol. 112, part I, pp. 1–32 (1949), D. M. Belmont, *Proceedings Highway Research Board*, pp. 383–395 (1953), and John W. McDonald, *Highway Research Board Bulletin 74*, pp. 7–17 (1953).

TABLE 2. MILEAGE ACCIDENT RATES FOR TYPICAL HIGHWAYS AND STREETS

Description of Facility	Period of Record	Mileage Accident Rate	
		Fatalities per 100 Million Vehicle-Miles	Accidents per Million Vehicle-Miles *
National average, all streets and highways	1951	7.6	20 †
National average, all streets and highways	1951	7.6	9.5 ‡
National average, rural	1951	10.8 §	....
National average, urban	1951	4.4 §	....
Average for 2 states with worst accident experience (largely rural)	1951	12.9	....
Average for state with best accident experience (largely urban)	1951	3.0	....
Connecticut, U. S. 1 and 1A, N. Y. line to New Haven, urban and rural, no access control	1940–49	9.4	5.0
Connecticut, Merritt and Wilbur Cross Parkways—rural—full-access control	1940–49	3.5	2.2
Virginia—U. S. 1—Sec. 1, rural, no access control	1950	12.9	5.1
Virginia—Shirley Highway—Sec. 1, rural—full-access control	1950	0	0.9
California, all highways and streets	1951	7.6	....
California, 2-lane rural state highways	1951	11.9	2.5
California, 82 route sections, rural, partial-access control	1949–50	10.0	2.1
California, 3 route sections, rural—full-access control	1949–50	3.9	1.4
California, Arroyo Seco Parkway, urban—full-access control	1941–49	1.8	1.1
California, Bayshore Freeway, urban—full-access control	1948–49	2.7	1.1

* These figures are approximate at best, because of the wide differences in reporting practice.

† Based on National Safety Council estimate of total number of accidents.

‡ Based on National Safety Council estimate, excluding property-damage accidents of less than $25.

§ Assuming vehicle-miles are equally divided between rural and urban.

TABLE 3. DIRECTIONAL ANALYSIS, MOTOR-VEHICLE TRAFFIC ACCIDENTS, 1951

		Urban		Rural	
Location and Movement	Statewide Fatal, 17 States	All Accidents, 313 Cities	Fatal, 313 Cities	All Accidents, 11 States	Fatal, 11 States
Total Accidents	*100.0%*	*100.0%*	*100.0%*	*100.0%*	*100.0%*
Pedestrian Intersection Accidents	*5.0*	*3.0*	*24.0*	*0.2*	*1.0*
Car going straight					
Entering intersection	2.0	0.8	7.7	0.1	0.6
Within intersection	0.8	0.3	3.1	*	0.2
Leaving intersection	1.4	0.7	9.6	0.1	0.2
Car turning right					
Entering intersection	0.1	0.1	0.2	*	*
Within intersection	0.1	0.1	0.3	*	*
Leaving intersection	0.1	0.2	0.9	*	*
Car turning left					
Entering intersection	0.1	0.1	0.4	*	*
Within intersection	0.1	0.1	0.1	*	*
Leaving intersection	0.3	0.5	1.3	*	*
All others	*	0.1	0.4	*	*
Pedestrian Nonintersection Accidents	*17.0*	*3.0*	*32.0*	*1.1*	*11.0*
Car going straight	16.3	2.8	30.6	1.0	10.6
Car backing	0.2	0.1	0.6	*	*
All others	0.5	0.1	0.8	0.1	0.4
Two Motor-Vehicle Intersection Accidents	*11.0*	*44.0*	*17.0*	*19.6*	*12.0*
Entering at angle					
Both going straight	7.2	19.1	12.8	5.3	7.0
One right, one straight	0.2	1.8	0.4	0.8	0.2
One left, one straight	0.5	3.3	0.7	2.0	0.6
All others	0.1	0.8	0.1	0.5	0.3
Entering from same direction					
Both going straight	0.1	3.9	0.3	0.8	0.1
One right, one straight	0.1	1.5	0.1	0.9	0.2
One left, one straight	0.6	2.3	0.2	3.7	0.6
One stopped	0.6	5.1	0.3	2.3	0.7
All others	*	0.9	0.1	0.2	0.1
Entering from opposite direction					
Both going straight	0.5	1.3	0.9	0.5	0.8
One left, one straight	1.0	3.6	1.0	2.0	1.3
All others	0.1	0.4	0.1	0.6	0.1
Two Motor-Vehicle Nonintersection Accidents	*24.0*	*41.0*	*7.0*	*47.2*	*30.0*
Opposite directions					
Head-on collision	8.9	1.2	2.7	2.9	11.9
Sideswipe collision	6.7	2.4	0.8	12.2	8.2
Same direction					
Rear-end collision	2.4	6.9	0.7	7.3	2.5
Sideswipe collision	1.3	5.3	0.5	4.8	1.7
One car parked					
Proper location	1.0	10.5	1.6	2.7	0.6
Improper location	1.1	0.6	0.2	1.5	1.2

TABLE 3. DIRECTIONAL ANALYSIS, MOTOR-VEHICLE TRAFFIC ACCIDENTS,
1951 (*Continued*)

Location and Movement	Statewide Fatal, 17 States	Urban All Accidents, 313 Cities	Urban Fatal, 313 Cities	Rural All Accidents, 11 States	Rural Fatal, 11 States
One car stopped in traffic	0.6	5.1	0.2	6.0	0.8
One car leaving parked position	0.2	4.7	*	0.9	0.2
One car entering alley	*	0.2	*	*	*
One car leaving alley	*	0.3	*	*	*
One car entering driveway	1.0	1.0	*	5.5	1.4
One car leaving driveway	0.3	1.6	0.1	1.4	0.1
All others	0.5	1.2	0.2	2.0	1.4
Other Accidents	*43.0*	*9.0*	*20.0*	*31.9*	*46.0*
Collision with nonmotor vehicle					
Intersection	1.3	1.1	3.2	0.1	0.4
Not at intersection	4.9	0.9	2.0	1.4	4.1
Collision with fixed object in road					
Intersection	0.5	0.6	0.8	0.2	0.2
Not at intersection	5.0	1.3	2.0	3.5	6.1
Overturned in road					
Intersection	0.2	0.1	0.3	0.1	0.2
Not at intersection	2.4	0.1	0.6	·1.3	2.1
Left road at intersection					
Then overturned	0.9	0.1	0.2	0.8	1.3
Then struck fixed object	1.0	0.9	1.2	1.1	1.1
Then struck other vehicle	*	*	0.1	0.1	0.1
Then struck pedestrian	*	*	0.1	*	*
Left road at curve					
Then overturned	6.1	0.1	0.8	4.5	7.5
Then struck fixed object	4.5	0.4	1.9	2.5	3.4
Then struck other vehicle	0.1	*	0.1	0.1	0.3
Then struck pedestrian	0.1	*	0.1	*	*
Left road on straight road					
Then overturned	8.2	0.2	0.7	8.7	11.1
Then struck fixed object	4.8	1.9	3.2	5.1	4.7
Then struck other vehicle	0.1	0.1	0.1	0.4	0.3
Then struck pedestrian	0.1	*	·0.3	*	0.2
Fell from vehicle					
Boarding, alighting in traffic	0.2	0.1	0.2	*	0.1
Not boarding or alighting	2.1	0.2	1.0	0.2	2.0
Injured within vehicle	*	0.1	0.1	*	*
Mechanical failure (no other event)	*	*	*	*	*
Fire (no other event)	*	*	*	0.1	*
All others	0.5	0.8	1.0	1.7	0.8

From *Accident Facts*, 1952 Edition, courtesy National Safety Council.

Source: Reports of state and city traffic authorities. Urban based on reports from cities over 10,000 population.

* Less than 0.05%.

Accident data applied to highway design

One of the strongest arguments for freeways is that they reduce accidents, a fact demonstrated by Table 2. More convincing proof can
be found by a study of Table 3, which is a directional analysis of
motor-vehicle accidents. On freeways there are no pedestrian accidents because pedestrians and vehicles are separated. Almost all
head-on or sideswipe collisions between opposing vehicles are prevented by positive center separation. Elimination of parking, except
by disabled vehicles, and the provision of wide shoulders reduces conflicts between moving and standing vehicles. Limiting access to a few
carefully selected points reduces collisions with entering vehicles.
Fixed illumination at danger points eliminates many of the accidents
caused by poor night visibility. Thus, on roads developed to freeway
standards, the opportunity for a large percentage of the usual accidents
is completely eliminated or greatly reduced. It must be recognized,
however, that freeway-type designs do not eliminate rear-end collisions
and sideswipes that result when drivers fail to adjust their speeds to
safe values where visibility is limited by rain, fog, or snow.[36] Neither
can it eliminate damage resulting when vehicles leave the traveled way.

Special analyses of accident data have had marked influence on design practices. One instance is the study begun in 1944 by the U. S.
Bureau of Public Roads and the National Safety Council. It considered the relation between accidents and such factors as roadway type,
traffic volume, pavement width, and number and sharpness of curves.[37]
It was found, for example, that if bridge width on two-lane roads exceeded pavement width by less than 1 ft, there were 10 accidents in
each 10 million passings. Where bridge width exceeded pavement
width by more than 5 ft, there were less than 2 accidents per 10 million
passings.

Accident data applied to existing roads and streets

Accident spot maps offer a very convenient visual device for recording accidents. Various colored pins or pasted spots are posted to large

[36] Many drivers feel secure when trailing another vehicle at a safe following
distance, even though visibility is far short of the safe nonpassing sight distance
for their speed of travel. Under these circumstances, collision with a stopped
vehicle can be avoided only by swinging around it. There have been instances
where more than 100 vehicles have been involved in a succession of rear-end
pile-ups which began when a single vehicle became disabled on the roadway.

[37] See *Traffic Engineering Handbook*, pp. 123–128. Also see M. S. Raff in
Public Roads, June 1953, pp. 170–186 and in *Highway Research Board Bulletin
74*, pp. 18–45 (1953).

maps to indicate accident locations, types, and severity. Accidents on rural roads or freeways may be plotted on strip maps with engineer's stations as the abscissa. Many agencies rely heavily on these visual means to indicate locations of high accident frequency. Some require field investigation of all locations where more than one accident occurs.

For detailed studies of particular locations, _collision diagrams_ and _condition diagrams_ are extremely helpful. The collision diagram (see Fig. 5) shows schematically the details of all the accidents that have occurred at the intersection within the study period. On most of these diagrams, the time of each occurrence is printed along one of the arrows. The condition diagram is a plan view of the location. With all pertinent information before him on the two diagrams the engineer can develop improvements by employing striping, signing, signals, channelizing islands, lighting, or other devices that have been effective in like situations. The evidence is conclusive that these techniques can reduce accidents and congestion on existing roads and streets. Figure 5 is offered as a single illustration. It is one of a set of case studies provided by the Association of Casualty and Surety Companies.[38]

Education and enforcement

Education and enforcement activities normally are not counted as traffic-engineering functions; so they can be given only brief mention in this book. However, their importance must not be underestimated. In 1951 a law violation or unsafe driving practice was a contributing factor in three-fourths of the accidents that brought death or personal injury. The most frequent charge was _exceeding the speed limit_. It represented 39% of the infringements. Among the others were _violating right of way_ 25%, _wrong side of road_ 10%, and _reckless driving_ 9%. In each of these instances, proper driving might have broken the chain of circumstances that resulted in the accident. Alcohol, which slows the reflexes but increases a driver's confidence, contributes to many accidents. Reports in 1951 from about half the states showed that 17% of the drivers in fatal accidents and 21% of adult pedestrians killed had been drinking.[39] Fatigue also appears to be a factor, as evidenced by the many accidents occurring very late at night or after long hours of driving.

An educational activity that appears particularly fruitful is driver education in the high schools. Cleveland, Ohio, was among the first to offer such courses,

[38] By July 1954, 121 case studies had been prepared. They may be obtained at nominal cost from the accident-prevention department of the Association, 60 John Street, New York 38, N. Y. Sixteen of the illustrations were reproduced in _Traffic Engineering_ between September 1949 and October 1950.

[39] These data are from _Accident Facts_, published annually by the National Safety Council. They also may be found in the _Book of Highway Accident Data_, released each year by the Travelers Insurance Companies.

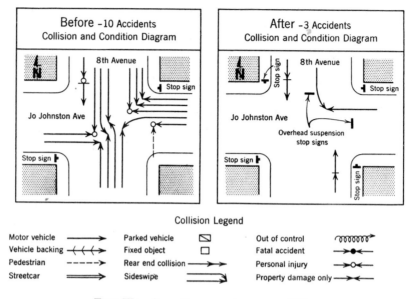

Collision Legend

Motor vehicle	Parked vehicle	Out of control
Vehicle backing	Fixed object	Fatal accident
Pedestrian	Rear end collision	Personal injury
Streetcar	Sideswipe	Property damage only

FOUR-WAY STOP REDUCES ACCIDENTS 70%

Case Study 98

FIG. 5. Typical example from *Getting Results through Traffic Engineering*

PROBLEM. A two-way stop intersection in Nashville, Tenn., had been a high-accident-frequency location for a number of years.

FACTS. The intersection of 8th Avenue and Jo Johnston Avenue is a normal right-angle intersection. However, visibility on all approaches is critically restricted by existing buildings on each corner.

Traffic control consisted of 24-in. reflectorized stop signs on Jo Johnston Avenue. Traffic volumes range from 500 to a maximum of 800 vehicles per hour during daylight hours, divided almost equally between the two streets.

There were 10 accidents at this location during a 7-month period, of which 4 resulted in personal injuries. Due to the high accident experience, there had been considerable agitation in the past for the installation of traffic signals.

SOLUTION. ·The installation of traffic-control signals could not be justified under any of the warrants in the *Manual on Uniform Traffic Control Devices* except possibly that of accident hazard. An analysis of the 10 accidents occurring during a 7-month period revealed that 9 of these accidents resulted from a type of conflict—right angle, vehicle-pedestrian and left-turning—that could be expected to be eliminated or materially reduced by modern traffic signals if properly obeyed by both drivers and pedestrians.

Traffic signals, however, are one of the most restrictive types of control devices and should not be installed until an adequate trial of less restrictive remedies with satisfactory observance and enforcement had failed to correct the situation. It was therefore decided to try correcting the accident problem by making this a four-way stop intersection.

and the accident records of graduates who took them have been twice as good as for those who were untrained. Driver training in high school reaches the age group with the worst accident record. In 1951, 15% of the drivers were under 25 years of age, but they must accept the blame for 25% of the fatal accidents and 21% of the nonfatal accidents.[40] Safety programs in the trucking industry, training in grammar and adult schools, and community safety organizations like local chapters of the National Safety Council are typical of other very effective education measures.

Without question, consistent enforcement of traffic laws brings a decrease in accidents. However, many obstacles make such enforcement difficult. Among these are the archaic traffic laws in force in many jurisdictions. For example, many states prohibit arrests for speeding based on evidence from electronic speed-measuring devices. Again, the fact that arrested drivers often escape with light penalties or none at all brings disregard for laws and for law-enforcement officials. A public awareness of the importance of traffic-law observance and greater support for those charged with law enforcement are imperative.

Scientific procedures for driver licensing to eliminate those who are physically or mentally unfit offer another means of accident reduction. Chronic drinkers or persons with epilepsy, serious heart disease, or drug addiction should not drive; yet few states require a physical report as a condition for licensing, except where there is outward evidence of physical disability. Care-

---

[40] This accident experience is reflected in higher insurance rates on vehicles driven by persons in the 18–24 age group.

Fig. 5. *Continued*

Reflectorized 24-in. signs reading "4-Way Stop" were installed on the 8th Avenue approaches to the intersection and the legend "4-Way" was added to the 24-in. stop signs on Jo Johnston Avenue. Because of the blind corners, it was decided to call attention to the four-way stop requirement in addition to that furnished by the stop signs located on each corner.

This additional emphasis was provided by the installation of 48-in. reflectorized stop signs, made out of all-weather plywood, which were suspended from span wires over the center of each roadway. The legend "4-Way Stop" was placed on both sides of these signs, thus necessitating the installation of only two signs —one on each roadway. Thus a near-side indication is given traffic on one approach and a far-side indication on the opposite approach.

CHECKBACK. There have been only three accidents involving property damage in the 7 months following initiation of this four-way stop—a 70% reduction. Two of these were rear-end collisions occurring within a few days of the installation before drivers had become familiar with the control.

COST. The total cost of materials for this project was $34.

Prepared by:
Accident Prevention Department
Association of Casualty and Surety Companies

                              Contributed by:
                              WILLIAM H. MANN
                              Member, Institute of Traffic Engineers
                              Traffic Engineer
                              Nashville, Tenn.

ful examination of "chronic violators" and "accident repeaters" would locate many persons whose faulty attitudes or emotional instability make them extremely poor drivers. Tests for defective side vision and depth perception, and for eye dominance, muscular imbalance, and other faults in vision could well be added to the licensing procedure. Applicants whose eyes showed serious weaknesses could be instructed in techniques for compensating for them.[41]

 PARKING

Widespread automobile ownership has brought serious parking problems to all urban locations. Cars on the streets overnight in residential sections make street cleaning and policing difficult. Suburban business and shopping centers have been forced to provide extensive parking facilities to attract business. Street congestion and the parking problem have been particularly acute in the central business areas of the larger cities as more and more people have chosen to drive downtown rather than to travel by mass transportation.[42]

It is sometimes argued that limited decentralization of business from downtown areas is beneficial. In most large cities, however, the rapid and unordered shift to suburban areas to avoid downtown congestion has created grave difficulties. Decreased property values in downtown areas represent a serious economic loss. In some cases, assessed valuation has fallen by one-third in 10 years. Furthermore, these sections carry a major share of the city tax burden, with less than one-half of the contribution being returned in municipal services. With the reduction of property values, there has been a corresponding decrease in city income. During the same period, the relative cost of police, fire, and other protective measures has risen in the deteriorated areas.

Many cities are substantially increasing off-street parking facilities. This will make street space now used for parking available for traffic movement and also meet, in part, the presently unsatisfied demand for added parking stalls. Efforts to improve mass transportation and thus

[41] Two publications of the Eno Foundation, *The Motor Vehicle Driver: His Nature and Improvement* (1949), and *Personal Characteristics of Traffic-Accident Repeaters* (1948), offer excellent discussions and bibliographies on driver training, law enforcement, and driver licensing. See also *Highway Research Board Bulletins 60* (1952) and *73* (1953), and Bibliography on Highway Safety, Annotated, *Bibliography 2* (1947) and *Supplement 1* (1949).

[42] A study by S. T. Hitchcock and R. H. Burrage (see *Public Roads*, June 1950, pp. 25–32) showed that demands for parking space in the downtown areas of two cities of over 500,000 population were 4.7 times the supply. In four cities in the 250,000 to 500,000 size, this ratio was 3.3 to 1. Even for towns having less than 25,000 residents, the demand exceeded the supply by 34%.

reduce the number of vehicles coming downtown have been much less successful.

Among the reasons for today's serious condition is that parking has often been an "orphan," with responsibility divided among property owners, merchants, private investors, and such governmental units as city council, police, traffic engineer, and the courts. Widespread and concerted efforts to create agencies whose primary concern is parking offer a hopeful sign of improvements to come.

On-street parking

Figure 6 shows the space requirements for storage and maneuver when parking is parallel, at right angles, or diagonal to the curb. Al-

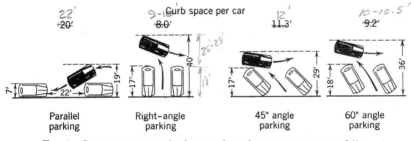

Fig. 6. Street space required to park and maneuver automobiles

though parallel parking accommodates fewer vehicles, it offers much less disruption to moving traffic and is recommended except where volume is light or the streets are more than 70 ft wide.

In the congested downtown areas of cities of all sizes, the curb space devoted to parking is being continually reduced to accommodate moving traffic better. There are many instances where parking on certain principal arteries is banned entirely, at least during morning and evening rush hours. Also, more and more curb space is being reserved for mass-transit and commercial-loading zones.

Legally, the right of the government to regulate on-street parking is firmly established. In 1805 in England, Lord Ellenborough, a famous British jurist, asserted that "the King's highway is not to be used as a stable yard." He established the principle that streets are primarily for the free passage of the public and anything that impedes that passage, except in an emergency, is a nuisance that may be abated. Parking, even in front of one's own property, was classed as a privilege subject to control and not as a right.[43] In the United States, authority

[43] Rex V. Russell, 6 East 427, 102 Eng. Rep. 1350.

to regulate parking stems from the *police power*, the right of government to legislate to protect health, safety, and morals. Under it, public officials are free, within reasonable limits, to establish rules to control on-street parking and to set penalties against violators.[44] The police power can be exercised without compensation to property owners or others who may suffer loss as a result. In many instances, the courts have permitted severe limitations to property access under the police power. For example, the laws of many states require property owners to secure permits for driveways connecting to state highways. On the other hand, the police power is not so broad that access to private property can be completely denied without recompense to the owner. Its limits in each state must finally be defined by court decision.

✗ *Parking meters* are an effective means for regulating on-street parking. First installed in Oklahoma City in 1935, by January 1952 they were in use in 1200 cities with populations greater than 10,000 and in 16,000 smaller cities as well.[45] Parking meters offer an accurate time check on parkers, thus discouraging overtime and all-day users.[46] Short-time parking as contrasted with longer space use is encouraged, with the turnover often 2 to 3 times as great with meters. Police time for parking enforcement is cut approximately in half. Often double parking is substantially decreased. On the other hand, motorists may resent both the charge for parking and the nuisance of carrying small coins. This feeling is sometimes expressed by a refusal to trade in areas where meters are employed if meter-free parking is also available nearby.

Parking meters produce substantial revenues. As of January 1952, some 1,113,000 on-street meters produced an annual revenue of $76 million, or more than $70 per meter.[47] Cost of meter operation and policing is 15 to 20% of the income. About 80% of the cities place meter revenues in the general fund and use them for ordinary city

[44] Recommended curb-parking legislation will be found in the Uniform Vehicle Code and the Model Traffic Ordinance.

[45] These and other parking-meter data are from *Parking Meters, Highway Research Board Bulletin 81* (1954), a joint study by the American Municipal Association, the Highway Research Board, and the Bureau of Public Roads.

[46] Checks in 11 cities indicated that in unmetered zones 37.6% of all parkers stayed overtime while in metered zones 24.3% were offenders.

[47] One disadvantage of meters is that, with earnings so great, city officials will sacrifice traffic improvements in order to retain parking spaces.

expenses. The remainder apply this income to traffic improvement and the development of off-street parking.

Authority to install parking meters stems from the police power, and apparently cannot be challenged as long as the charges reasonably approximate the cost of street space, including rights of way, construction and maintenance, and the expense of regulation. It has been intimated, however, that the profit from meters must go to further alleviate parking difficulties; otherwise the courts may invalidate parking meters as a regulatory device.[48]

Off-street parking

General requirements. The gross space per car in parking lot or parking garage usually ranges between 225 and 300 sq ft per vehicle. In general, less floor space is required where cars are positioned by attendants, as contrasted with driver parking. Other variables like lot or building dimensions and layout also have important bearing. First cost per parking space has a wide spread, from a few hundred dollars for lot parking where land is inexpensive to $3500 or more for multistory elevated or underground facilities.

Provision for all possible demands for parking in downtown areas does not appear economically feasible. As already indicated, approximately 250 sq ft of floor space per vehicle is required. On the other hand, the average office worker occupies less than 100 sq ft. Thus, if all office workers drove downtown, two persons per car, parking space would exceed office space. Neither can downtown parking be furnished for all shoppers as is done in modern suburban shopping centers. There parking space exceeds floor area by 2.5 to 3 times.

Location and layout of parking facilities must be fitted to traffic conditions on adjacent streets. For example, if parking lots or garages are designed to discharge onto heavily traveled, narrow streets, both street traffic and parkers are seriously inconvenienced. On the other hand, by connecting off- and on-ramps of freeways directly into parking installations, the adjoining streets can be completely freed of many vehicles.

Selection of the kind of parking installation for a given location or area is usually an economic matter. First costs of land, building, and accessories, amortized over an assumed useful life, plus annual charges

[48] See Use of Parking Meter Revenues, *Highway Research Board Bulletin 33* (1951).

for operation, maintenance, and taxes [49] must be determined for each appropriate design. These are weighed against the annual estimated income to determine the financial solvency of the project.

In estimating income, the willingness of users to walk from parking place to destination is of particular importance. Data on this subject are fragmentary. Studies in Washington, D. C., in 1946 indicated that all-day parkers would walk 8 blocks to work from a free parking lot but less than 1 block if parking cost 50 cents. It is sometimes assumed that shoppers and other short-time parkers will walk as far as 800 ft. However, in small cities less than 10% walk this distance, but in large cities 30% walk farther. Actually such factors as the nearness of competing shopping areas or parking locations, the charge for parking, and the type of goods being bought may influence potential parkers equally as much as does walking distance.

Parking lots. The parking lot is the simplest off-street parking facility. Usually the area is subdivided with curbs or bumpers, surfaced with a bituminous or concrete pavement, and marked out into parking stalls and driveways. On private lots attendants often park and return vehicles and collect fees. In many cases public lots are equipped with parking meters and are operated in conjunction with on-street parking.

Advantageous sites for parking lots often are found in the interior of large blocks or facing on back streets where property values are low. At times, by careful planning, small or irregular-shaped lots can be developed to good advantage.

Fringe parking on lots located outside the downtown areas of high property value has been tried as a solution to downtown congestion and parking difficulties. Motorists travel from the lots on mass-transportation vehicles or by special shuttle buses. Data collected in 1948 by F. W. Lovejoy [50] show that, of the 19 cities that had established fringe parking lots, 9 had abandoned them. The reasons for failure were varied, but indicated that, at least for shoppers, fringe parking lots are not satisfactory.

Careful consideration should be given to the appearance of parking lots fronting on the streets. Often, for example, by setting the pave-

[49] Taxes, as such, would be paid only on privately owned facilities. However, the construction of publicly owned parking removes property from the tax rolls and thus reduces income from taxes. Sometimes public parking agencies make "in-lieu payments" equivalent to the taxes that would otherwise be assessable.

[50] See Parking, *Highway Research Board Bulletin 19* (1949).

ment a few feet back from the sidewalk, the lot can be screened with a border of shrubs or other planting.[51]

Multistory parking buildings. Multistory parking buildings of an open-walled type have been constructed in many urban and suburban locations where land values are high (see Fig. 7). At times, the valuable ground floor has been devoted to stores or other businesses

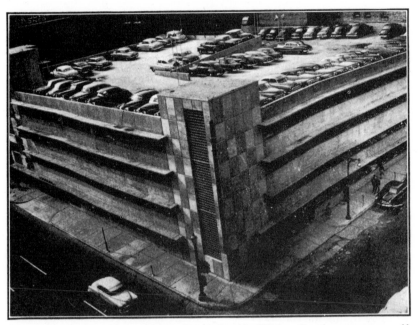

FIG. 7. Municipal parking garage, Grand Rapids, Mich. Continuous ramp, self-service (Courtesy Grand Rapids Police Department)

and the remainder to parking. Access and egress to parking garages is by fairly steep ramps. In some, vehicle spotting is by attendants; in others, customers park their own cars. Often gasoline and lubrication sales and washing, greasing, and mechanic services add supplementary income.

Parking buildings are relatively cheap. Often the walls are open, the ceilings low, and heating, ventilating, and certain other refinements omitted. Maintenance costs also are low.

[51] For examples of parking-lot location and layout see *Parking Manual,* American Automobile Association (1946), and *Parking* (1946), and other publications of the Eno Foundation.

Designs of parking garages are fitted to customer requirements. For service to all-day parkers, provision must be made to receive and discharge almost all the vehicles in short periods of time.[52] Different designs would be more suitable for shopper parking, where loading and unloading peaks are not so sharp.[53]

Underground parking garages. The first cost per stall for underground parking garages generally is higher than for aboveground structures. However, in downtown areas where property values are extremely high, underground facilities built under parks or plazas may offer the most economical way to provide off-street parking. The first large garage of this kind, with a capacity of 1500 cars, was completed under Union Square in San Francisco in 1942. It has been a marked success financially. A like structure accommodating 2000 cars was completed in 1952 under Pershing Square in Los Angeles.[54] Both cities plan to develop other sites in the same way. A garage under Grant Park, Chicago, holding 2350 cars, will be in service in 1954. Other cities with plans for like facilities include Boston, Detroit, Pittsburgh, and Cincinnati.

Mechanical parking garages. Since World War II, private investors have built a number of garages equipped with mechanical devices that park and retrieve cars. Most of these installations employ elevators that move both vertically and horizontally. Labor costs are low as only one attendant is needed for each elevator. Tiers of stalls the height and width of the building on each side of the shaft are serviced by a single elevator. In some instances, the elevator is equipped with a device that reaches under the cars, grips them by front and rear bumpers, and rolls them into or ejects them from the elevator. Another type of installation consists of an all-steel building equipped with movable steel ramps. Other patented schemes also have been constructed or are under development.[55]

[52] The General Petroleum garage in Los Angeles, intended largely for company employees, consists of a single continuous ramp 60 ft wide spiraled around a rectangular shaft housing elevators and stairways. Customers drive their cars up the ramp, but attendants turn them around during the day ready to be driven directly out. See *Engineering News-Record*, July 22, 1948, p. 78.

[53] As of 1952, the largest parking garage, with 1600 stalls on 5 levels, was a part of the Hecht Company Suburban Shopping Center, Arlington, Va. See *Engineering News-Record*, July 10, 1952, p. 34, for a detailed description.

[54] See *Civil Engineering*, December 1951, p. 25, for a detailed description.

[55] See, for example, *Engineering News-Record*, December 28, 1950, p. 16, and May 8, 1952, p. 59.

Truck and bus terminals. In many large cities, congestion in commercial and industrial areas is relieved by providing special off-street terminals for trucks and buses. Large and unwieldy over-the-road trucks drive to destinations located out of the congested areas but on or near the main highways into the city. Here loads are sorted for distribution over the city in lighter, more maneuverable vehicles.[56] Off-street bus terminals conveniently situated near entering highways, the downtown area, and local mass transportation are in widespread use. One of the most elaborate was constructed in New York City by the Port Authority. It serves both intercity and commuter buses. Another, constructed by the Greyhound Bus Company in Chicago, combines bus terminal, shops, and off-street parking.[57]

Zoning for parking. Zoning is a legal extension of the police power for preventing haphazard or detrimental land development. Many zoning ordinances state the amounts of off-street parking space to be provided in all new or remodeled buildings. In Detroit, for example, each new family dwelling must have parking for one car; office buildings and retail stores, respectively, must offer a parking stall for each 400 and 333 sq ft of floor area; and industrial plants must provide one space for each 5 employees.[58] Some regulations state that the stalls must lie within the confines of the building or plant whereas others permit off-site parking within walking distance. Often commercial establishments are required to provide on-site space for trucks loading and unloading goods. There is little uniformity between cities in zoning for parking. The regulations are enacted by local governing bodies who are influenced by local situations and political pressures.

It has been suggested that zoning for parking be made retroactive to force owners of existing buildings to provide off-street parking within a stated terms of years. No judicial decisions have been given on such proposals, but there is serious doubt regarding their constitutionality.

The inclusion of off-street parking requirements in zoning ordinances has caused many bitter disputes. Property owners often maintain that they make new construction and remodeling prohibitively expensive. Others assert that, under present ordinances, each new building

[56] Possibly the largest of these, costing $9 million, is located on Manhattan Island close by the Holland Tunnel.

[57] See *Civil Engineering*, April 1951, p. 39, and *Engineering News-Record*, April 9, 1953, p. 41.

[58] These are not precise statements of the regulations. They are given to typify more complex regulations covering parking requirements for all classes of land use.

accentuates the parking problem, as it demands far more parking space than it supplies. In any event, zoning is one of several effective approaches to the parking problem.[59]

Private development of off-street parking. Private interests have developed many off-street parking facilities as an investment or to provide for employees or customers. However, there is widespread belief that private investments alone will not solve the parking problem. One cited reason is that private capital is interested only when investments in parking promise at attractive return, and often this is not so. Again privately owned parking facilities, once constructed, may be withdrawn for other uses that promise greater income. To illustrate, it may be more attractive financially to convert a private parking lot into a building site. Another complaint is that rates are set to gain maximum profit rather than most effective use. For example, greatest revenues may come from all-day parkers or from renting spaces by the month. Most effective use may demand rates that encourage shoppers and other short-time customers, and discourage all-day parkers. Owners of private parking facilities complain that public agencies, free from taxes and the pressure to make money, offer unfair competition to private garages. In some instances they have blocked attempts of public agencies to provide off-street parking.

Without question, private investors and public both have a stake in privately owned parking facilities. One extreme suggestion for protecting the public interest is that governmental agencies take over all private facilities. Another proposal, advanced by David R. Levin, is that private parking facilities be regulated as public utilities.[60]

Public development of off-street parking. A comprehensive study of parking legislation conducted by the U. S. Bureau of Public Roads found .that by 1951 the legislatures of 43 states had granted power to provide off-street parking to state, county, or city officials or to special parking agencies. There are great differences in the authority granted by the various acts. As examples, the agencies may or may not have power to (1) finance by revenue or general-obligation bonds, (2) arrange for commercial uses in public parking facili-

---

[59] For an excellent discussion of the subject and data on zoning ordinances in many cities and counties in the United States see Zoning for Parking Facilities, sections 1 and 2, and Zoning for Truck-Loading Facilities, *Highway Research Board Bulletins 24* (1950) and *59* (1952).

[60] See Parking Facilities as Public Utilities, *Proceedings Highway Research Board,* pp. 15–24 (1950), for a discussion of this proposal and the legal concepts that underlie it.

ties, (3) acquire land by eminent domain, (4) construct facilities, or (5) operate them on completion. David R. Levin, who headed the study, found six distinct trends in off-street parking legislation. These are: (1) an increasing reliance on bond financing, (2) emergence of the "system" concept with on-street and off-street facilities integrated functionally and financially, (3) dedication of parking-meter revenues to alleviate parking difficulties, (4) legal sanction of auxiliary and supplementary commercial uses in parking structures, (5) creation of special parking agencies, particularly the parking authority, and (6) making site acquisition easier by granting the power of eminent domain. Levin concludes that "the choice of method of providing off-street parking accommodations will vary with the size and economic characteristics of the city, its political and business mores, its tax and debt structure, the magnitude of its parking needs, and a host of related factors. It cannot be said categorically that a parking authority or government officials or private interests alone can do the job in every place and under every circumstance." [61]

Parking surveys

Factual data regarding parking demands and needs in downtown areas is best determined by means of a parking survey. Field investigation for the survey involves three phases, as follows:

1. *An inventory* to show existing parking facilities. This gives the location, type, capacity, ownership, operation, physical layout, and schedule of fees for all on-street and off-street parking.

2. *Parking interviews* to determine the use of existing facilities and the demonstrated demand. Over a period of several weeks interviewers cover every parking stall for the business hours of one day. License number, vehicle type, and time of arrival and departure, and type and location of parking are recorded. The driver is asked his home address, trip origin, purpose of trip, and its destination.[62] Also included is a count of cars parked in fringe areas.

3. *Cordon counts* on all streets entering the area. These are manual counts that show the number and type of vehicles entering and leaving the area throughout the day.

---

[61] For a more complete statement and details of legislation in various states see Off-Street Parking, *Highway Research Board Bulletin 48* (1952). This is a revision and consolidation of *Bulletins 2* (revised) and *7*, both dated 1947. See also *Highway Research Board Bulletin 77*, pp. 25–32 (1953), and *Engineering News-Record*, February 5, 1953, p. 46.

[62] From which the walking distance can be calculated.

Some of the field data can be easily processed by using calculating or adding machines. However, analysis of the parking interviews is speeded and improved if the information is punched into tabulating cards for machine sorting and totaling.

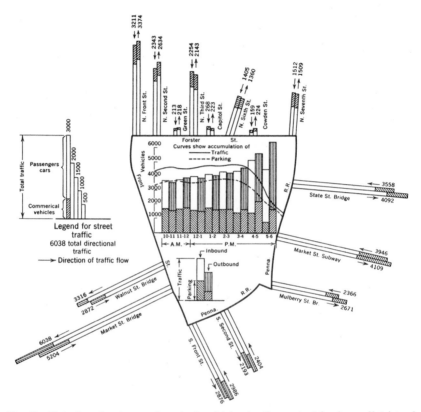

Fig. 8. Entering, leaving, and parked vehicles in the central business district of a city of 175,000 population. Parking and traffic data cover a weekday between 10 A.M. and 6 P.M. (Courtesy U. S. Bureau of Public Roads)

Analysis of the field data from a parking survey accurately depicts current parking practice and indicates the most suitable locations and capacities for added facilities. Figures 8 and 9 offer two of a group of charts that reduce the complex data to workable form.

Prediction of demands for parking in various sectors is the most difficult part of the analysis. Immediate demand is the total of legal and illegal parking in the area, fringe-area parking, and an estimate

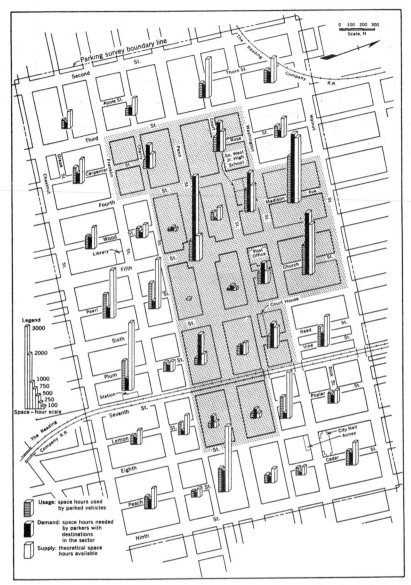

Fig. 9. Diagram showing supply, usage, and demand for parking in various segments of the business district of a city of 175,000 population. Data covers an average weekday between 10 A.M. and 6 P.M. (Courtesy U. S. Bureau of Public Roads)

of added parking that would come with congestion relief. Future demands are measured from predictions of traffic and business growth. An organized publicity campaign to secure the cooperation of the public must precede parking-survey field work. All media of communication including newspapers, radio, and television should be employed.[63]

[63] For a detailed report on the influence of population, sales, and employment on parking see S. T. Hitchcock, *Proceedings Highway Research Board,* pp. 464–485 (1953), and *Public Roads,* December 1953, pp. 248–258. For examples of spot studies on specific parking problems see R. H. Burrage, *Highway Research Board Highway Research Abstracts,* October 1953, pp. 16–40.

12 ——————— Highway Subgrade Structure

INTRODUCTION

Highway subgrade (or basement soil) may be defined as the supporting structure on which pavement and its special undercourses rest (see Fig. 1). In cuts, the original soil lying below the special courses is usually designated as subgrade. In fills, the subgrade is constructed

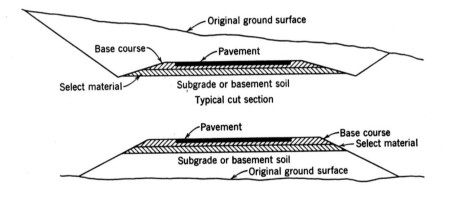

Typical cut section

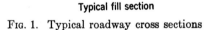

Typical fill section

Fig. 1. Typical roadway cross sections

over the native ground and consists of imported material from nearby roadway cuts or from borrow pits.

Before 1920 attention was focused largely on the pavement or other wearing course, and little notice was given to the materials that made up the subgrade or to the manner in which they were placed or compacted. Soon after that date increased vehicle speeds brought demands for higher standards of alinement and grade, which in turn meant deeper cuts and higher fills. At the same time, the weight and number of vehicles increased, which imposed larger and more numerous wheel loads on the roadway surface. In many instances, subsidence or even total failure resulted. Study of such failures indicated that the fault lay in the subgrade and not in the surface. This in turn led to the investigation of the properties of subgrade soils and of their performance under service conditions. Now most state highway departments and many county and city highway departments have established detailed procedures for the investigation of subgrade materials.

This chapter summarizes present knowledge of the behavior of soils as a highway material and outlines some methods used in design. It is to be observed, however, that explicit answers to all the complex problems discussed are not yet available. Much progress has been made, but research still is needed to improve present methods.[1]

CHARACTERISTICS OF SOIL

Constituents of soils

Soils consist largely of mineral matter formed by the disintegration or decomposition of rocks. The rocks may be of three kinds: igneous, made by the solidification of molten material; sedimentary or bedded, formed from sediments deposited chiefly by water; or metamorphic, formed by the action of heat or pressure or both on one of the other rock forms. The disintegration into soil may be caused by the action of water, ice, frost, or temperature changes, or by plant or animal life. Soils near the surface may contain humus and organic acids resulting from the decay of vegetation. Almost all soils contain water in varying amounts and in free or adsorbed [2] form. Wide variation in soil types is the rule rather than the exception; sometimes five to ten distinct types occur in a mile of road.

Characteristics of soil particles

Certain soil characteristics are useful in predicting the performance of a soil: namely, the grain size, shape, surface texture, and chemical composition.

---

[1] Probably the most complete single volume on highway soil problems and roadway design methods is *Soil Mechanics for Road Engineers,* 541 pp., prepared by the Road Research Laboratory, Department of Scientific and Industrial Research, and published by Her Majesty's Stationery Office, London, England (1952).

[2] See p. 313.

Grain size. The grains of which a soil is composed have been classified in terms of size by the American Association of State Highway Officials as follows:

		U. S. Sieve Series	
Class	Particle Diameter	Passing	Retained
Gravel	76.2 to 2.0 mm	3-in.	No. 10
Coarse sand	2.0 to 0.42 mm	No. 10	No. 40
Fine sand	0.42 to 0.074 mm	No. 40	No. 200
Silt	0.074 to 0.005 mm	No. 200	. . . . . .
Clay	0.005 to 0.001 mm		
Colloidal clay	Smaller than 0.001 mm		

The classifications adopted by other agencies employ different particle diameters for the division points. For example, the U. S. Bureau of Public Roads' classification marks the division between fine sand and silt at the no. 270 sieve: a diameter of 0.05 mm. The International Society of Soil Science places this division at 0.02 mm. The latter agency defines clay as finer than 0.002 mm and colloidal clay as finer than 0.0002 mm. Regardless of the differences in the various grain-size classifications, all have a common aim: to establish a basis for relating particle size to soil behavior.

General characteristics of the various particle size groupings are as follows:

Gravel consists of rock fragments usually more or less rounded by water action or abrasion. Quartz, the hardest of the rock-forming minerals, usually is the principal constituent. Well-rounded pebbles and boulders that have undergone long wear are almost entirely quartz. Gravels that are only slightly worn and therefore rough and angular commonly include other minerals such as granite, schist, basalt, or limestone.

Coarse sand frequently is rounded like the gravel with which it is found and generally contains the same minerals.

Fine sand particles commonly are more angular than coarse sand particles because the film of water that usually surrounds the finer particles has served as a buffer to protect them from abrasion.

Silt grains usually are similar to fine sand and have the same mineral composition. However, they may be produced by chemical decay rather than by grinding. Occasionally, silts contain pumice, loess, or other materials foreign to the associated sand. The presence of silt in fine soils may be detected by its grittiness if a tiny amount is placed in the mouth and bitten between the teeth.

Clays result almost entirely from chemical weathering and are often platelike or scalelike in shape. Because of their small size, their performance is strongly influenced by moisture and chemical composition.

Colloidal clays are finer clay particles that remain suspended in water and do not settle under the force of gravity. When examined under a microscope, they are found to be in a state of unordered motion called "Brownian movement" which is caused by an electric charge in each particle repelling other particles of like charge. Some authorities have stated that clay particles of diameter up to 0.002 mm show Brownian movement.

For most highway purposes coarse-grained materials are preferable. Soils containing any great percentage of clays or colloids are extremely troublesome and can be used only with difficulty. They should never be placed close under the roadway surface. Silty soils also cause difficulties in areas where the ground freezes or where the movement of moisture by capillary action is objectionable.

Grain shape. The shape of the larger soil particles as found in nature often indicates their strength and toughness. Rounded particles found in stream deposits have undergone considerable wear and are probably quite strong. On the other hand, flat and flaky particles probably have not been subject to such treatment and may be weak and friable and not suitable for many highway uses.

Granular soil mixtures like those employed for base courses contain little clay, and the properties of the larger soil particles have an important influence on their behavior. Here, an angular particle shape produced by crushing strong, tough rock or gravel increases the resistance of the soil mass to deformation under load. Many specifications for base courses require that the soil mixture contain a stated percentage of crushed rock particles.

The effect of grain shape on the performance of small particles in the clay size is obscure. Other influences, such as those of free and adsorbed moisture, particle ionization, the presence of lime or other chemicals, and of density, are probably more important.[3]

Surface texture. The surface texture of the larger soil particles greatly influences their performance in granular soil mixtures. For example, the grains of wind-blown and beach sands and of crushed quartz often have slick surfaces. The coefficient of friction developed

---

[3] For a report of a general study of the size, shape, and structure of soil clays by means of the electron microscope see E. R. Kinter, A. M. Wintermyer, and Max Swerdlow, *Public Roads*, December 1952, pp. 89–100.

between these surfaces is low. As a consequence, the soil mixture that contains them has little resistance to deformation under load. Some authorities assert that the rough surface of freshly crushed rock is more important than its angular shape in developing greater strength in soil mixtures.

With soil grains of small size, the effect of surface texture is overshadowed by other factors, as mentioned above.

Chemical composition. There are no common engineering tests to determine the chemical composition of soil particles or to evaluate the influence of chemical composition on the performance of soils as a highway material. It is known that chemical composition has marked effect on the thickness and behavior of the water film that usually surrounds soil particles. Certainly, then, chemical composition indirectly influences the properties of soil masses. Chemical composition also may affect the bond between aggregates and bituminous binders.

Related to chemical composition is the crystal structure of the soil grains, which also influences their performance.

Effects of moisture on the performance of soils

Soil technicians agree that the properties of a soil mixture are influenced more by variations in moisture content than by any other cause. Soils that have ample supporting power under one set of moisture conditions may be entirely unsatisfactory if the percentage of moisture changes.

Soil grains are surrounded by a thin film of adsorbed water (see Fig. 2). The water in these films is attracted by the molecular charge of the soil grains and has a higher boiling point, lower freezing point, and greater cohesion than ordinary water. At the surface of the mineral particle this adsorbed water is almost solid and more nearly like ice. Then as the distance from the particle increases the properties of the adsorbed water change and finally become the same as those of free or gravitational water. This adsorbed moisture can be removed from soils by evaporation, but not by pressure in the range normally encountered in highway work.[4]

The thickness and cohesion of this water film will vary with changes in the amount of water available, with the electrolytic charge and crystal structure of the aggregate, with the chemicals if any in the water, and with pressure and temperature. As the properties of the

[4] T. W. Lambe, *Proceedings Highway Research Board*, p. 491 (1949), showed that, for certain clays, much adsorbed water remained on the soil particles when they were dried in the usual way at 105° C.

Highway Subgrade Structure

water film change, the properties of the soil mass also change. However, for a particular soil under given conditions of service, the principal variable is the total moisture content.

For all practical purposes, the diameter of a very fine soil particle may be considered as that of the mineral plus the adsorbed moisture film. Figure 3 serves to illustrate the relationship between the dimensions of very fine soil particles and this moisture film. It can be

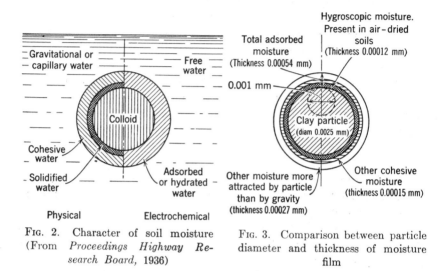

FIG. 2. Character of soil moisture (From *Proceedings Highway Research Board,* 1936)

FIG. 3. Comparison between particle diameter and thickness of moisture film

seen that the effective diameter of the clay particle varies widely with changes in the moisture content of the soil. The particle shown in Fig. 3 has a diameter of 0.0025 mm, which is 2½ times the diameter of the largest colloid. When the diameter of this particle is reduced to that of the largest colloid (dotted circle on Fig. 3) and its thickness is compared to that of the water jacket, the importance of moisture on the effective diameter of a colloid becomes apparent. On the other hand, to represent the finest sand grain, the particle diameter in the figure must be increased 20 times. It follows that the effective diameter of the sand particle changes a relatively small amount with changes in moisture content.

Figure 4 shows how variations in moisture content affect the volume of a typical soil mixture. The chart indicates, for a variation in the thickness of the moisture film, the change in volume of the parts of a sand-clay mixture. It is assumed that the mixture is composed of spherical particles and that the film thickness is uniform over the particle surfaces. The separate volumes include the moisture film attached to each particle. The column at the left shows the mix in an oven-dry state with no moisture present, and with the voids in the material filled with air. The middle column is the same material with the voids now filled with moisture, but with swelling of the ma-

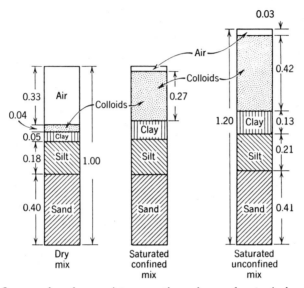

Fig. 4. Influence of surface moisture on the volume of a typical soil mixture (From *Proceedings Highway Research Board*, 1938, somewhat modified)

terial prevented. The column at the right shows the material in an unconfined state, with the moisture demand of the soil particles satisfied, as indicated by the test for field moisture equivalent.[5] The charts indicate that between the dry state and the state where moisture demand is satisfied the volume increases are: for sands 2%, for silts 16%, for clays 160%, and for colloids 950%. Thus the volume of soils predominantly coarse grained is little affected by moisture, whereas the volume of soils predominantly fine grained is greatly affected.

The moisture surrounding soil particles has another property that greatly influences soil performance—the ability to bind the particles

[5] See p. 322.

together by tensile forces in the water film. These forces, called surface tension,[6] tend to pull the soil grains together (see Fig. 5). Their magnitudes vary inversely with the "dimensions" of the particles (often assumed as the diameter of a sphere). In sands the force of surface tension is relatively small, but in colloidal sediments it may exert pressures equal to several hundred atmospheres. It compacts loose colloidal sediments more thoroughly than is possible by artificial means except by using a high-power testing machine in the laboratory.[7]

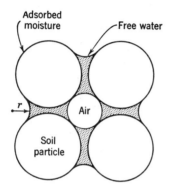

FIG. 5. Diagram illustrating surface tension effects in an unsaturated soil

The force exerted by surface tension decreases as the moisture content increases, since the radius of the moisture surface increases with increased moisture content.[8] When the soil becomes saturated, the forces exerted by surface tension disappear entirely.

In summing up, it may be said that, in general, the properties of soils composed largely of coarse materials are primarily controlled by the characteristics of the particles, but for soils composed largely of clays and colloids the properties are primarily controlled by the characteristics of the moisture film.

Effect of density on the behavior of soils

The density of a soil is its weight per cubic foot. It is sometimes expressed as "wet weight," or the total weight including water. It is more commonly the "dry weight," which is the weight of the soil particles alone, excluding the weight of the contained water. As a

---

[6] The true nature of surface tension is not fully understood as yet. Some writers use the expression "molecular forces associated with surface energy." See, for example, W. S. Housel and others, *Proceedings Highway Research Board*, pp. 465–489 (1950).

[7] A familiar demonstration of surface tension is provided by the stability of moist sand compared with dry sand. When moist sand is molded to a given shape, it will retain that shape until all surface moisture evaporates; then it will crumble and become free flowing. This procedure is used to determine when sand is "surface-dry" (*ASTM Designation C128–42*).

[8] This decrease in force accounts for the fact that soils expand when moisture content is increased above the "shrinkage limit."

particular soil becomes more dense, it will contain a greater number of particles, and the (pore) volume remaining for air and water will be decreased. If the soil contains moisture, and almost all soils do, there is room for less of it, so that the moisture film between particles will be thinner. With this increased density and decreased moisture goes improvement in the physical properties of a soil that are of primary importance in roadbuilding. Strength is increased; consolidation under load, the rate of water movement through the soil, and volume change under variation in moisture are all decreased. Compaction of subgrades and bases to obtain these advantages is accepted practice.[9]

TESTS FOR SOILS

The preceding discussion shows that there is wide variation in the characteristics of different soils and that the performance of each individual soil is affected by its moisture content and density. A number of physical tests have been developed to measure soil performance, the most common of which are described briefly on the pages that follow. Standard procedures for making most of them appear in *Highway Materials,* part II, *Tests,* AASHO (1950). Some also appear in publications of the American Society for Testing Materials. Wherever possible, the appropriate test designations have been given to make reference easier.

Physical tests for particle size [10]

Particle sizes for gravels and for coarse and fine sands are determined by "sieve analysis." A sample of soil is dried and then shaken through a series of sieves ranging from coarse to fine, and the amount (percentage of sample dry weight) retained on each sieve is weighed and recorded.

[9] The density of a soil is usually expressed in pounds per cubic foot, but engineers should understand the meaning of the terms "voids ratio" and "porosity." Voids ratio is the ratio between the volume of voids or pores in the soil and the volume of the solid particles. This ratio may be greater or less than unity, depending on the degree of compaction. Porosity is the ratio of the volume of voids to the total volume of the soil plus its voids, given as a percentage. If the voids ratio is represented by e the porosity will equal $e/(1 + e) \times 100$.

[10] See Sieve Analysis of Fine and Coarse Aggregates, *AASHO Designation T27-46* and *ASTM Designation C136-48;* and Mechanical Analysis of Soils, *AASHO Designation T88-49.*

The standard sieve sizes of the American Association of State Highway Officials for soils testing are as follows:

Sieve description									
In inches *	2	1½	1	¾	⅜				
By number †						4	10	40	200
Opening in milli-meters	50.8	38.1	25.4	19.1	9.52	4.76	2.00	0.42	0.074

* Sieves in this group have square openings of the size indicated.

† Sieves in this group also have square openings. The sieve number designates the number of openings per lineal inch across the sieve.

Sieve analysis is not commonly used for determining particle size of materials which will pass the no. 200 sieve (0.074 mm). Such particle size is found by observing the rate at which the grains will settle through a gas or liquid. This settlement phenomenon is related to grain size by Stokes's law, which states that the rate of settlement of a solid through a given liquid or gas is proportional to the square of the diameter of the solid. The method specified by the AASHO is called the hydrometer test (see *AASHO Designation T88-49*).

In general terms the hydrometer test is conducted as follows: A sample of the material passing the no. 4 sieve is thoroughly wetted by mixing with water. After 18 hr this mixture is placed in a special mixing cup, water and a deflocculating agent (to dissipate electrolytic bonds in the material that might prevent settlement) are added, and the entire mixture is agitated until particles are in suspension in the water. After agitation, the mixture is placed in a graduated flask and the solids are permitted to settle under the pull of gravity. As the larger particles settle out, followed by those of smaller and smaller diameter, the specific gravity of the liquid decreases, and this change is recorded by a special hydrometer that is read at prescribed intervals. This change is specific gravity is then related to the grading of the material by Stokes's law. Precise control of temperature and of other possible variables is required if the results of this test are to be satisfactory.

Sometimes it is desired merely to know the percentage of fines smaller than a given size. For example, control of the percentage smaller than 0.02 mm appears to be critical in preventing frost heave. This can be determined by a simple field test to find the residue that fails to settle out of a sample in a prescribed time.[11]

[11] See Soils Tests for Military Construction, *American Road Builder's Association Technical Bulletin 107* (1946).

F. N. Hveem of the California Division of Highways has developed a "sand-equivalent" test for quick field determination of the presence of undesirable quantities of claylike materials in soil-aggregate mixtures on a volume rather than a weight basis. Essentially the test is performed by shaking vigorously a sample of fine aggregate in a transparent cylinder containing a special aqueous solution that includes calcium chloride as a flocculating agent. The strength of the calcium chloride solution has been adjusted to exaggerate the volume of bentonite clays which have high lubricating effect while not exaggerating the volume of kaolinite clays. After shaking, the mixture stands for 20 min before the relative volumes of sand and partially sedimented clay are noted. The "sand-equivalent" is the ratio between the volume of sand and the combined volumes of sand and expanded, saturated clay, expressed as a percentage. Thus, higher values of the sand-equivalent indicate superior materials. Minimum permissible values are (approximately) 30 for base courses, 45 to 55 for aggregates for plant-mix pavements, and 80 for concrete sand.[12]

HOW USED

Physical tests to evaluate the influence of moisture

By increasing the moisture content of a soil, its consistency can be varied from semisolid to plastic to liquid. Experience has shown that the percentage of moisture at which these changes take place can be directly correlated with the behavior of the material in service. Tests on the portion of the sample that passes a no. 40 sieve, called the soil mortar, determine the percentage of moisture [13] at which each change in consistency takes place. They are called the Atterberg tests after the Swedish scientist who suggested them.

Liquid limit (*AASHO Designation T89–49*). The liquid limit (LL) signifies the percentage of moisture at which the sample changes, with a decrease in moisture, from a viscous or liquid state to a plastic one. If the soil mortar is wetter than the liquid limit, a grooved sample of the soil in a standard cup will flow when lightly jarred 25 times (see Fig. 6). If the sample is drier than the liquid limit, the groove will not change shape when the sample is jarred. At the liquid limit the soil particles have been separated by the water just widely enough to deprive the soil mass of its shearing strength.

[12] For further details see F. N. Hveem in *Proceedings Highway Research Board,* pp. 238–250 (1953), and *Western Construction,* June 1953, pp. 107–113.

[13] Obtained by dividing the weight of water in the sample by the weight of the oven-dry sample.

Plastic limit (*AASHO Designation T90–49*). The plastic limit
(PL) signifies the percentage of moisture at which the sample changes,
with decreasing wetness, from a plastic to a semisolid state. In this
condition the soil mortar begins to crumble when rolled into threads
⅛ in. in diameter (see Fig. 6). At the plastic limit, the moisture will

Divided Soil Cake Before Test

Soil Cake After Test

PHENOMENON OCCURRING DURING LIQUID-LIMIT TEST

Soil Thread Above the Plastic Limit

Crumbling of Soil Thread Below
the Plastic Limit

PHENOMENON OCCURRING DURING PLASTIC-LIMIT TEST

FIG. 6. Diagram illustrating the Atterberg tests for soil mortars

not separate the soil particles but will produce just enough surface
tension to give contact pressure between the soil grains and thus
cause the mass to act as a semisolid. Additional moisture causes the
soil to become plastic or, stated differently, produces "significant"
lubrication.

Plasticity index (*AASHO Designation T91–49*). The plasticity
index (PI) of the sample is defined as the difference between its liquid
limit and its plastic limit. It also is stated as a percentage of dry
weight. It indicates the fineness of the soil mortar. For a coarse-
grained soil, or for a fine-grained soil with few particles of clay or

colloid size, a small increase in moisture above the plastic limit provides enough particle separation to destroy cohesion and shearing strength. This means that the difference in numerical value between the plastic limit and the liquid limit is small so that the plasticity index also is small. On the other hand, for a soil high in clays or colloids this separation moisture becomes somewhat gluey because of the fine particles dispersed in it, and considerable water will be required before the strength of the mass is destroyed. In this case, the numerical value of the plasticity index is high. Thus, the plasticity index is an indirect method for measuring the amounts of clays and colloids in the silt, clay, and colloid fractions of the soil.

Experience shows that soils with high plasticity indices are much less desirable for subgrade or base courses than those having lower indices. Many construction agencies use the PI as a primary control in selecting the materials that go close under the pavement. A common specification for base courses requires that the plasticity index shall not exceed 6; and some agencies insist that it be no greater than 3.

Nonplastic soils (NP designation). Fairly clean sands, some rock dusts, and certain other materials are classed as nonplastic since they cannot be tested in the usual manner for the plastic limit. As a rule, nonplastic soils make excellent road materials when properly confined under a wearing course. Some of them, rock dusts for example, form hard durable surfaces when wet down and compacted. Others, like clean sand, displace easily under load, and their use for base course or fill brings difficult construction problems.

Shrinkage factors of soils (*AASHO Designation T92–42*). This test measures the changes in volume and weight that occur as a pasty mixture of soil mortar and water is dried to constant weight at 110° C. Test results may be reduced to factors like the shrinkage limit, volumetric change, and lineal shrinkage.

Shrinkage limit is the moisture content, expressed as a percentage, at which volume change ceases. The sample shrinks on drying until the shrinkage limit is reached, but its volume remains constant with further drying. At this moisture content, the compressive forces developed by surface tension just equal the resisting forces developed between the soil particles.

Volumetric change is the decrease in volume of the soil mass, expressed as a percentage of dry volume, when the water content is reduced from some assigned percentage (usually the field-moisture equivalent) to the shrinkage limit.

The *lineal shrinkage* of a soil is the percentage decrease in one dimension of a wet soil sample when the water content is reduced from some given value to the shrinkage limit. The test for shrinkage factors has in the main been superseded by the various tests for swell and expansion.

Field-moisture equivalent (*AASHO Designation T93–49*). The field-moisture equivalent of a soil is the percentage moisture at which the demands for adsorbed water are fully satisfied. The test is performed by finding the maximum water content at which a drop of water placed on a smoothed surface of the soil will disappear completely in 30 sec. At higher moisture percentages the drop will spread out over the surface, leaving a thin film of moisture. In fine soils the test determines the moisture content at which the air in the interstices between particles becomes sealed in by the moisture films around individual particles, so that capillary forces can no longer draw moisture into the soil. In coarse-grained soils the test indicates that all voids in the material are filled with water.

Centrifuge moisture equivalent (*AASHO Designation T94–42*). The centrifuge moisture equivalent of a soil represents the percentage of moisture retained against a force of 1000 times gravity. This test has little current use.

Tests for volume change. As already indicated, the volume of most soils increases when they are given a chance to absorb water. Soils that make good subgrade and base courses expand very little while those that are poor swell more. Numerous methods are employed to measure this tendency, among them the AASHO test for volume change (*AASHO Designation T116–49*). For it a sample passing the no. 4 sieve is compacted in a steel mold 4 in. in diameter. Final specimen height is about $1\frac{9}{16}$ in. The change in height that results when the specimen is soaked is measured with an Ames dial. Results are reported as the "per cent volume change," which is based on the ratio between the change in height and the height of the sample before soaking. Other tests for volume change are quite similar. Results may be stated as "per cent expansion" or "per cent swell" which are synonymous terms with per cent volume change.

Many agencies employ a test for volume change as one of the measures of the quality of subgrade and embankment materials. A common specification requirement limits the volume change of base-course materials to 1%.

An alternative to the test for volume change is employed as part of the Hveem stabilometer design method.[14] Here the pressure exerted by a confined sample measures its tendency to expand during soaking.

Strength tests for soils

Soil tests for determining the strength or supporting power of soils may be divided into two groups. One of these is used in foundation investigation and is concerned with measuring the load-carrying capacity and rate and amount of consolidation in the soils that sup-

[14] See p. 350.

port foundations. Tests are conducted on the soils in place or on (almost) undisturbed samples. In highway work the application of these methods is limited to bridge-foundation studies or other special problems. For discussion of them the reader is referred to the standard textbooks in soil mechanics.

The second group of strength tests is designed to measure the supporting power of disturbed soils as recompacted under standard procedures. They represent one of several empirical approaches to the problem of setting layer thicknesses for bituminous pavement, base course, and selected undercourses. Several of these are outlined on pages 346 to 354, under the heading "Design of the Roadway Structure."

Tests for determining the density of soils

Theory of soils compaction. The supporting power of soils increases with density. A road constructed on a given soil may be entirely satisfactory if the soil is properly compacted. On the other hand, the road may fail if the soil is insufficiently compacted, particularly if the voids become filled with water.

The soil density (weight per cubic foot) varies with the peculiarities of the soil itself, the moisture content, and the compactive device and method that are employed. Thus a standard weight per cubic foot cannot be set, but must be determined in each instance. Principal variables in the soil are:

1. Specific gravity of the soil particles themselves. It may vary from 2.0 to 3.3, but usually is between 2.6 and 2.7; therefore the weight of a cubic foot of voidless soil (if such existed) could vary from about 125 to 210 lb. The usual soil weight (voidless) is between 162 and 169 lb.

2. The particle-size distribution of the soil. A mass composed entirely of spheres of one size in the densest possible condition will contain 74% solids and 26% voids. If smaller spheres are introduced into the mass, the percentage of solids will increase. This idea extended to soils indicates that particle-size distribution may greatly affect density.

3. Grain shape of soil particles. Sharp, angular particles will resist shifting from a loose to a more compact state. Flaky particles in soil will cause a decrease in density as they cannot easily be compacted.

The influence of moisture content on the density of a soil is illustrated by curve A, Fig. 7. This curve was obtained as follows. Designated percentages of water were added to dry samples of a particular soil. Each sample was then compacted by the same procedure, and the weight of soil per cubic foot of compacted material was obtained. Curve *A* shows that the densest sample was obtained when 9% (by weight) of water was added to the dry material. It also shows that 129 lb of dry material would be needed to make a cubic foot of soil, under the stated conditions.

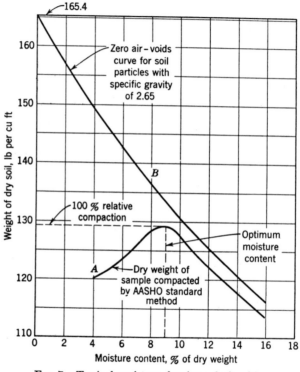

FIG. 7. Typical moisture-density relationships

Although the curve in Fig. 7 is for a particular soil and for a designated compaction method, similar tests have proved beyond doubt that the general form of the moisture-density curve remains the same for other soils and for other compaction methods. For each compaction method, there is an *optimum moisture content* at which a given soil can be compacted to greatest density. For any other moisture content, it will be less dense.

For low percentages of moisture (say, below about 5% for the soil in Fig. 7) water attaches to the individual particles mostly as adsorbed or cohesive water; air fills the remaining voids. Neither the water nor the air lubricates the soil mass. Hence, friction between the grains prevents further consolidation when the compactive effort is applied. But water in larger amounts serves to lubricate the soil somewhat. Then the compactive effort can consolidate the grains further. As the amount of water is increased, this lubricating action becomes more and more effective until at the optimum moisture content the greatest density is obtained.[15]

Above the optimum moisture content the soil weight per cubic foot drops off again, but the reason for the decrease is entirely different. In Fig. 7, curve B shows the dry weight of soil (of specific gravity 2.65) in a cubic foot of a voidless mixture of soil and water.[16] For this voidless condition, if a certain moisture percentage is assigned, the volumes occupied by water and by soil are fixed. As the amount of water increases, the amount of soil must decrease accordingly, since both water and soil are incompressible. Thus, curve B represents the maximum possible weight of soil that can be forced into a cubic foot of space along with a given percentage of water. Densities obtained in practice do not reach those indicated by curve B, as some air voids are always present in compacted soils. This explains why the actual dry weights shown by curve A are slightly less than the theoretical values at moisture percentages above the optimum. This difference in the ordinates of the two curves represents the small amount of air that always is present in soil-water mixtures.

As mentioned, different soils have different maximum densities and optimum moisture contents. Figure 8 shows the moisture-density curves obtained by compacting a variety of soils in the same standard manner. Likewise, the compactive method or amount of compactive effort expended changes both maximum density and optimum moisture content. This is illustrated by Fig. 9, which shows moisture-density curves for the same soil compacted in several different ways. The solid lines on Fig. 9 give the results obtained by the standard AASHO test and a modification of it that employs 4.5 times as much energy. For this particular soil, the change lowers the optimum moisture con-

---

[15] For a more detailed discussion of this subject, see the writings of Housel and others.

[16] The equation for this curve is

$$\text{Dry weight of soil per cubic foot} = \frac{62.4}{\dfrac{1}{\text{specific gravity of soil particles}} + \dfrac{\% \text{ moisture}}{100}}$$

tent by 5% and raises the dry weight from 105 to 117 lb per cu ft. The dotted lines show the densities obtained with pneumatic and sheepsfoot rollers.

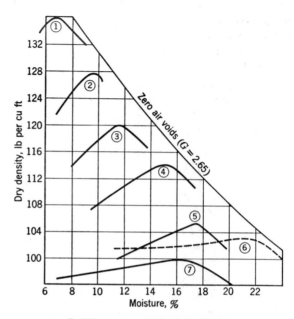

Soil Texture and Plasticity Data

No.	Description	% Sand	% Silt	% Clay	L.L.	P.I.
1	Well-graded loamy sand	88	10	2	16	NP
2	Well-graded sandy loam	72	15	13	16	0
3	Med.-graded sandy loam	73	9	18	22	4
4	Lean sandy silty clay	32	33	35	28	9
5	Loessial silt	5	85	10	26	2
6	Heavy clay	6	22	72	67	40
7	Very poorly graded sand	94	← 6 →		NP	NP

Fig. 8. Moisture-density relationships for seven soils each compacted by the AASHO standard method (After A. W. Johnson)

Figure 9 can be used to demonstrate that an increase in the density of a soil leads to an increase in its "strength" under service conditions. Assume that one sample of this soil, containing 17% moisture, is compacted by the AASHO standard method and a like one by the modified AASHO method. Dry densities of these samples are shown to be 103 and 112 lb per cu ft, respectively. It may be that, as compacted, even the less dense of these will carry the superimposed loads without failure. Suppose, however, that each of these samples becomes saturated, as may well happen in time. Then the moisture content of the samples will be 24 and 19%, respectively, as indicated by the intersection of the horizontal lines *aa'* and *bb'* with the zero air-voids curve. For this soil, the moisture content of the wetter sample exceeds the plastic limit, which means that the material will lose much

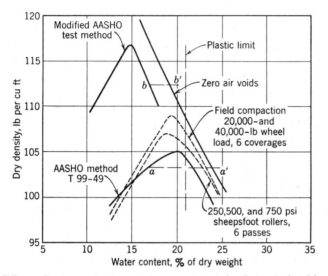

Fig. 9. Effect of compaction method on moisture-density relationships. Tests made on silty clay soil having 10% sand, 63% silt, 27% clay. LL = 36, P.I. = 15, Sp. gr. = 2.72 (After A. W. Johnson, but somewhat modified)

of its supporting power. The more highly compacted one will probably remain stable.

The foregoing discussion of compaction assumes that a soil, once compacted, will remain at almost constant volume in service. For the better soils this is true, or nearly so. However, many of the poorer soils, compacted at optimum moisture content, will swell if added moisture becomes available. They require special treatment. The swelling will not occur if the external pressure on the soil mass is great enough, which in turn means that such materials, if buried deeply enough, will not cause trouble. Where confinement under a weight of fill is impractical, volume change can be reduced by compacting the soil at some higher moisture content at which the desire of the soil for water is more nearly satisfied.

Laboratory tests for soil density. Tests for density may be divided into two classes: laboratory tests to set a standard for density, and field tests to measure the density of a soil in place in the roadway structure. Laboratory tests may in turn be subdivided on the basis of compaction procedure, into "static," "dynamic" or "impact," and "tamping foot" or "kneading" methods.

Static Tests. Some agencies use a static test to determine maximum density of laboratory samples. One such test is conducted as follows: About 4000 grams of soil containing a designated percentage of water are placed in a cylindrical mold 6 in. in diameter and 8 in. high. This sample is compressed under a load of 2000 lb per sq in., applied at a speed of 0.05 in. per min. When the full load is reached it is held for a period of 1 min and then gradually released. Using the known dry weight of soil, mold diameter, and the measured height, the dry density of the sample is computed. Enough samples are processed to delineate the peak of the moisture-density curve. This peak value represents the standard.

Dynamic or Impact Tests. Many highway and airport agencies now determine optimum moisture content and maximum density with dynamic or impact tests. Samples of soil, each containing a designated percentage of water, are compacted in layers into molds of specified size. Compaction is obtained with a given number of blows from a free-falling hammer of prescribed dimension and weight. The peak of the moisture-density curve represents standard density.

Details of three impact tests are given in Table 1. For the AASHO

TABLE 1.   DETAILS OF IMPACT COMPACTION TESTS

Name of Test

Test Details	AASHO Standard	Modified AASHO	California Impact
Diameter of mold, in.	4	4	2.86
Height of sample, in.	5 cut to 4.6	5 cut to 4.6	10 to 12
Number of lifts	3	5	5
Blows per lift	25	25	20
Weight of hammer, lb	5.5	10	10
Diameter of compacting surface, in.	2	2	2
Free-fall distance, in.	12	18	18

tests, the volume of the compacted sample is held constant by shaving it to proper height. Density varies with dry weight of the trimmed sample. For the California impact test, sample weight is constant, usually 5 lb, and density varies with the height of the compacted sample. The AASHO standard test [17] (sometimes called the standard Proctor test) is used by most of the state highway departments. The modified AASHO test [18] is employed by the U. S. Engineers and a few highway agencies. The California impact test (nicknamed the "rathole" test) is used by the highway departments of that state and Nevada.[19]

The AASHO standard test is performed on that portion of the soil that will pass a no. 4 sieve.[20] Specifications for the modified AASHO and California impact methods require that material retained on the ¾-in. sieve be removed from the sample but that it be replaced with an equal weight of ¾-in. to no. 4 gravel from the same soil.

 Tamping-Foot or Kneading-Compaction Tests. A group of West Coast engineers working as a subcommittee of the American Society for Testing Materials has standardized a tamping-foot compactor originally developed by F. N. Hveem of the California Division of Highways. Material is fed into a rotating mold and is compacted by many repetitions of load applied through a tamping shoe shaped like a sector of a circle. About one-fourth of the specimen is covered in each application. Compaction comes through a kneading action, as contrasted with static pressure or impact. Proponents of this method have developed substantial evidence that kneading compaction, compared to other laboratory methods, provides better correlation with field densities obtained with tamping or pneumatic rollers. Samples of soil and dense-graded bituminous mixtures that are to be tested in the Hveem stabilometer are prepared in the kneading compactor (see pp. 350 and 474).[21]

Field tests for density of soils in place.[22] Field tests provide a means of comparing the densities of constructed roadways with the standard densities obtained in the laboratory. Usually this comparison is made on the basis of *relative compaction*, which is defined as follows:

[17] *AASHO Designation T99-49.*

[18] See *Transactions American Society of Civil Engineers*, p. 454 (1950).

[19] See Compaction of Embankments, Subgrades, and Bases, *Highway Research Board Bulletin 58* (1952), for details of the practices of the individual state highway departments.

[20] See *ibid.*, pp. 46–50, for methods for correcting the unit weight to recognize coarse aggregate content.

[21] See also J. L. McRae and P. C. Rutledge, *Proceedings Highway Research Board*, pp. 593–600 (1952).

[22] See *AASHO Designation T147-49.*

$$\text{Relative compaction} = \frac{\left\{\begin{array}{l} \text{dry weight per cubic foot of soil in place in} \\ \text{roadway structure} \end{array}\right\}}{\left\{\begin{array}{l} \text{dry weight per cubic foot for a soil sample at} \\ \text{optimum moisture content compacted in a} \\ \text{prescribed standard manner} \end{array}\right\}}$$

With many highway agencies, relative compaction is the sole measure by which the acceptability of a completed roadway structure is measured.[23]

The procedure for determining relative compaction is as follows:

1. Remove from the fill a small sample of the compacted material through the full depth of the layer to be tested.

2. Obtain the wet and dry weights of the sample. From these also determine the moisture content of the sample.

3. Determine the volume that the sample occupied in the fill by finding how many pounds of a material of known unit weight are required to fill this space. Sand or heavy oil, or water poured in a flexible rubber liner, have served this purpose.[24]

4. From the dry weight of the sample and the known volume that it occupies in the fill, obtain the dry weight per cubic foot.

5. Determine the relative compaction of the soil in the fill by dividing its dry weight per cubic foot by the laboratory standard density.

Densities and moisture content have also been determined experimentally without disturbing the soil. At Rutgers University measurements have been made using X-ray methods which, because of cumbersome and expensive instrumentation, are not readily applicable in the field. At Rutgers, Cornell, and the University of California, investigation of the use of radioactive material to measure these properties is under way.[25]

---

[23] See p. 382 for more on this subject.

[24] Several methods are described in *Public Roads,* vol. 22, no. 12, February 1942, and in *Proceedings Highway Research Board,* part 2, p. 154 (1938). Each highway agency will have a favored method. The method adopted must be rapid in order that delays in construction are minimized. Absolute accuracy is not possible. One authority has indicated that variations in test results in the order of 2 lb per cu ft are to be expected.

[25] See *Highway Research Board Abstracts,* April 1951. See also *Civil Aeronautics Administration Technical Development Reports 161* (1952) and *194* (1953), and Robert Horonjeff and Irving Goldberg, *Proceedings Highway Research Board,* pp. 500–511 (1953).

CLASSIFICATIONS FOR SOILS

Soil classifications, based on physical tests or other information, represent groupings into which all soils of like characteristics can be separated. Once a soil has been classified, its performance should be predictable from the known behavior of others in the same group. Many systems of classification have been proposed and have been very useful for their intended purposes. But no single grouping will fit the many diverse problems of soil science. A classification suited to agricultural or geological uses does not satisfy the requirements of the civil engineer; neither is a classification best suited to the foundation engineer's problem entirely satisfactory for the highway engineer. Descriptions of some of the classifications developed for highway and airport purposes follow.

Textural classification

The textural classification is based purely on grain-size distribution. It was first developed about 1890 before the influence on soil behavior of grain shape, colloidal particles, and other variables was understood. It is simple and widely used and can be applied with little experience. Soils alike under this classification, however, may show widely different performance in service.

A textural classification into three groups—sand, silt, and clay—is often employed. A corresponding "triangle textural classification" diagram (see Fig. 10) is helpful.[26] The sum of the perpendicular distances from any point within an equilateral triangle to the three sides is constant and may be arbitrarily set as 100%. The position of every point inside the triangle then represents the sieve analysis (or three-way textural classification) of a soil of particular grading. After the grain-size distribution of a sample has been determined, the chart is read as follows: spaces vertically upward, starting with zero at the bottom, represent clay percentages; spaces left to right, diagonally downward, starting with zero at the left, represent silt; spaces right to left, diagonally downward, starting with zero at the right, represent sand. For example, the three dotted lines in Fig. 10 represent clay 28, silt 25, sand 47%. The soil described by these percentages (point P) is therefore classified as a clay–loam.

[26] The classification shown was proposed by the U. S. Bureau of Public Roads. Similar classifications have been made by the U. S. Department of Agriculture, the Lower Mississippi Valley U. S. Engineers Department, and others.

Soil descriptions reflected by the triangular classification diagram are much used in engineering work. Soils composed almost entirely of sand and silt are called loams. Thus, with one exception, every

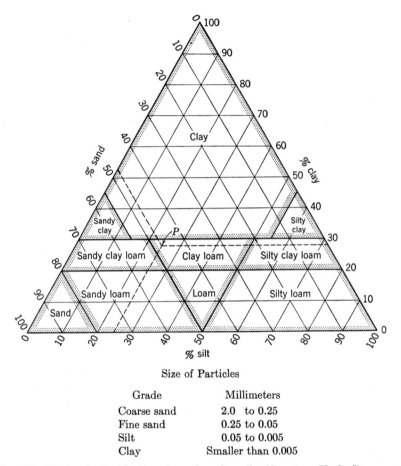

Size of Particles

Grade	Millimeters
Coarse sand	2.0 to 0.25
Fine sand	0.25 to 0.05
Silt	0.05 to 0.005
Clay	Smaller than 0.005

Fig. 10. Textural classification for subgrade soils (Courtesy U. S. Bureau of Public Roads)

soil containing less than 20% clay is a loam, with the prefix "sandy" or "silty" added to indicate which predominates. These names appear along the lower part of the chart. Soils containing 20 to 30% clay are also called loams, with the term "clay" added to indicate the higher clay content. These names appear above the "loam" classifications in the chart. All other soils are designated as "clays," with prefixes of "sandy" or "silty" added to indicate the remainder of the material. The textural classification points up the important principle that the behavior of soils containing 30% or more clay depends solely on the characteristics of the clay.

The Public Roads Administration soil classification [27]

The Public Roads Administration soil classification was developed about 1928 after extensive research. It classified soils on their stability under wheel loads when the soil served as the road surface or as the base beneath a bituminous wearing surface. It divided the soils into eight uniform groups, designated as the A soils, ranged from A-1 for good soil mortars to A-8 for peats and mucks. Classification of non-uniform soils into B groupings was proposed but was later abandoned. Distinctions between the different soils in the A groups were based on the physical tests already described or on relations between them.

Table 2 shows, for each group, the general character of the soil, the test elements, the treatment required in construction, and the indicated performance in service.

American Association of State Highway Officials classification of soils and soil-aggregate mixtures [28]

The AASHO classification shown in Table 3 is an adaptation of the original Public Roads Administration classification. It represents changes that seemed desirable after 15 years' use of the older grouping. It retains the group designations and descriptions employed previously, but otherwise differs markedly from the Public Roads classification. Important improvements are:

1. It divides some of the PRA groups into subgroups so that distinctions not previously possible now can be made.

2. It evaluates the influence of both coarse and fine particles, whereas the PRA classification applied only to material passing the no. 10 sieve.

[27] See *Public Roads,* May 1929, June 1931, July 1931, and February 1942.

[28] This classification was originally presented as the Report of the Committee on Classification of Materials for Subgrades and Granular Type Roads and was published in *Proceedings Highway Research Board,* pp. 375–392 (1945). It was adopted by the AASHO as recommended practice in 1949 and appears in the 1950 *Specifications for Highway Materials* as *AASHO Designation M145–49.*

TABLE 2. PUBLIC ROADS ADMINISTRATION SOIL CLASSIFICATION

Group	A-1	A-2 Friable	A-2 Plastic	A-3	A-4	A-5	A-6	A-7	A-8
General stability properties	Highly stable at all times	Stable when dry; may ravel	Good stable material	Ideal support when confined	Satisfactory when dry; loss of stability when wet or by frost action	Difficult to compact; stability doubtful	Good stability when properly compacted	Good stability when properly compacted	Incapable of support
Physical constants:									
Internal friction	High	High	High	High	Variable	Variable	Low	Low	Low
Cohesion	High	Low	High	None	Variable	Low	High	High	Low
Shrinkage	Not detrimental	Not significant	Detrimental if poorly graded	Not significant	Variable	Variable	Detrimental	Detrimental	Detrimental
Expansion	None	None	Some	Slight	Variable	High	High	Detrimental	Detrimental
Capillarity	None	None	Some	Slight	Detrimental	High	High	High	Detrimental
Elasticity	None	None	Some	None	Variable	Detrimental	None	High	Detrimental
Textural classification:									
General grading	Uniformly graded; coarse to fine, excell. binder	Poor grading; poor binder	Poor grading; inferior binder	Coarse material only; no binder	Fine sand, cohesionless silt, and friable clay	Micaceous and diatomaceous	Deflocculated cohesive clays	Drainable flocculated clays	Peat and muck
Approximate grading limits:									
Sand, %	70-85	55-80	55-80	75-100	55 (max.)	55 (max.)	55 (max.)	55 (max.)	55 (max.)
Silt, %	10-20	0-45	0-45	*	High	Medium	Medium	Medium	Not significant
Clay, %	5-10	0-45	0-45	*	Low	Low	30 (min.)	30 (min.)	Not significant
Physical characteristics:									
Liquid limit	14-35	35 (max.)	35 (max.)	NP †	20-40	35 (min.)	35 (min.)	35 (min.)	35-400
Plasticity index	4-9	NP-3 †	3-15	NP †	0-15	0-60	18 (min.)	12 (min.)	0-60
Field moisture equivalent	Not essential	Not essential	Not essential	Not essential	30 (max.)	30-120	50 (max.)	30-100	30-400
Centrifuge moisture equiv.	15 (max.)	12-25	25 (max.)	12 (max.)	Not essential	Not essential	Not essential	Not essential	Not essential
Shrinkage limit	14-20	15-25	25 (max.)	Not essential	20-30	30-120	6-14	10-30	30-120
Shrinkage ratio	1.7-1.9	1.7-1.9	1.7-1.9	None	1.5-1.7	0.7-1.5	1.7-2.0	1.7-2.0	0.3-1.4
Volume change	0-10	0-6	0-16	None	0-16	0-16	17 (min.)	17 (min.)	4-200
Lineal shrinkage	0-3	0-2	0-4	None	0-4	0-4	5 (min.)	5 (min.)	1-30
Compaction characteristics:									
Maximum dry weight, pounds per cubic foot	130 (min.)	120-130	120-130	120-130	110-120	80-100	80-110	80-110	90 (max.)
Optimum moisture, percentage of dry weight (approx.)	9	9-12	9-12	9-12	12-17	22-30	17-28	17-28	

* Percentage passing no. 200 Sieve, 0 to 10. † NP—Nonplastic.

TABLE 3. AMERICAN ASSOCIATION OF STATE HIGHWAY OFFICIALS CLASSIFICATION OF SOILS AND SOIL-AGGREGATE MIXTURES, WITH SUGGESTED SUBGROUPS

AASHO Designation M145–49

General Classification	Granular Materials (35% or Less Passing No. 200 Sieve)								Silt-Clay Materials (More than 35% Passing No. 200 Sieve)			
	A-1		A-3	A-2					A-4	A-5	A-6	A-7
Group Classification *	A-1-a	A-1-b		A-2-4	A-2-5	A-2-6	A-2-7					A-7-5, A-7-6
Sieve analysis: % passing:												
No. 10	50 max.											
No. 40	30 max.	50 max.	51 min.									
No. 200	15 max.	25 max.	10 max.	35 max.	35 max.	35 max.	35 max.		36 min.	36 min.	36 min.	36 min.
Characteristics of fraction passing no. 40:												
Liquid limit				40 max.	41 min.	40 max.	41 min.		40 max.	41 min.	40 max.	41 min.
Plasticity index	6 max.		NP	10 max.	10 max.	11 min.	11 min.		10 max.	10 max.	11 min.	11 min. †
Group index ‡	0		0	0	0	4 max.			8 max.	12 max.	16 max.	20 max.
Usual types of significant constituent materials	Stone fragments, gravel and sand		Fine sand	Silty or clayey gravel and sand					Silty soils		Clayey soils	
General rating as subgrade	Excellent to good								Fair to poor			

* *Classification procedure:* With required test data available, proceed from the left to right on above chart, and correct group will be found by process of elimination. The first group from the left into which the test data will fit is the correct classification.

† Plasticity index of A–7–5 subgroup is equal to or less than LL minus 30. Plasticity index of A–7–6 subgroup is greater than LL minus 30.

‡ See group index formula and Fig. 11 for method of calculation. Group index should be shown in parentheses after group symbol as: A–2–6(3), A–4(5), A–6(12), A–7–5(17), etc.

3. Only tests for particle size, liquid limit, plastic limit, and plasticity index are needed.[29]

Subgroups added to the A–2 classification indicate the properties of the fine material that largely determine the suitability of the soil. The old soil designation A–2 indicated a granular material of which less than 35% passed the no. 200 sieve. It told nothing about the properties of the fines, whether they were silt, clay, or colloid. The added digit which, for example, makes a designation read A–2–7, shows that the fine material is an A–7 plastic clay, and that the soil is therefore the least desirable material in the A–2 class.

The subgroups added to the A–7 classification indicate in more detail the properties of the different clay soils. Thus subgroup A–7–5 includes those materials that may be highly elastic as well as subject to considerable volume change under variations in moisture content. Similarly subgroup A–7–6 includes those materials that may be highly elastic and subject to extremely high volume change.

As an example of the workings of the AASHO classification, consider a soil which when tested shows:

Sieve analysis:	% passing no. 40	55
	% passing no. 200	30
Liquid limit		42
Plasticity index		9

The classification procedure (using Table 3) is as follows:

1. Under the heading "General Classification" it is found that the soil is a granular material, as less than 35% passes the no. 200 sieve: thus the material falls into groups A–1, A–3, or A–2.

2. Under the heading "Sieve analysis—% passing no. 40" it fails to meet the requirements for group A–1, as more than 50% passes the no. 40 sieve, but does meet those for group A–3 or A–2.

3. Under the heading "Plasticity index" it falls outside group A–3, which is nonplastic and has no plasticity index. It must then be in group A–2, under which the PI of 9 meets the demands of subgroups 4 or 5.

4. Under the heading "Liquid limit" the value of 42 finally places the sample in classification A–2–5.

A textural classification for the soil can also be obtained from Table 3. The material is a gravelly soil, as indicated by the A–2 description; the fines are of a silty nature, as indicated by the subgrouping 5. As subgrade material it is on the border between good and fair.

[29] The recommendation of the committee, however, is that "for the closest possible evaluation of materials for use under particular conditions" the other tests called for under the PRA classifications be used to provide important additional information.

An important feature of the AASHO classification is the "group index" which is based on the service performance of many soils. It permits a more precise prediction of soil behavior than is possible by soil classification alone. It is used by many highway designers to guide in determining the combined thickness of pavement and base over a given soil (see p. 344). The "group index" is defined by the empirical equation

$$\text{Group index} = 0.2a + 0.005ac + 0.01bd$$

in which a = that portion of percentage passing no. 200 sieve greater than 35% and not exceeding 75%, expressed as a positive whole number (1 to 40).

b = that portion of percentage passing no. 200 sieve greater than 15% and not exceeding 55%, expressed as a positive whole number (1 to 40).

c = that portion of the numerical liquid limit greater than 40 and not exceeding 60, expressed as a positive whole number (1 to 20).

d = that portion of the numerical plasticity index greater than 10 and not exceeding 30, expressed as a positive whole number (1 to 20).

A chart that provides for rapid solution of the group-index formula appears as Fig. 11.

Soil classification of the Office of the Chief of Engineers [30]

The U. S. Engineer Department in 1942 tentatively adopted a new system of soil designation, referred to as the airfield classification. It was developed by Arthur Casagrande, and was so designed that soils could be classified by experienced engineers after visual and manual inspection. It employs letters instead of numbers to designate the various groups. Mechanical analysis and liquid- and plastic-limit tests are the primary classification tools.

Principal symbols and soil designations are as follows:

    For coarse-grained soils:
      1. Gravels or gravelly soils, symbol G.
      2. Sands and sandy soils, symbol S.
    Subdivisions of sands or gravels are:
      (a) Well-graded, fairly clean material; symbol W.
          Thus GW signifies well-graded gravel, and SW well-graded sand.
      (b) Well-graded material with excellent clay binder (corresponding to PRA classification A–1); symbol C, in combinations GC and SC.

[30] For a detailed description see *Transactions American Society of Civil Engineers,* pp. 901–930 (1948).

(c) Poorly graded, fairly clean material; symbol P, in combinations GP and SP.

(d) Coarse materials containing fines, not covered by preceding groups; symbol F, in combinations GF and SF.

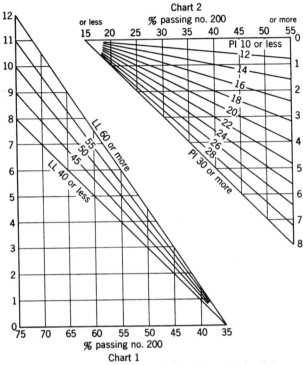

FIG. 11. Chart for determining the group index of a soil when the per cent passing the no. 200 sieve, liquid limit, and plasticity index are known. Group index = sum of readings on vertical scales of charts 1 and 2

For fine-grained soils:

1. The inorganic, silty, and very fine sandy soils; symbol M (from the Swedish terms *mo* and *mjala*, flour), used for fine-grained, nonplastic or slightly plastic soils, and designating the fractions from 0.2 mm to 0.02 mm and from 0.02 mm to 0.002 mm.
2. The inorganic clays; symbol C.
3. The organic silts and clays; symbol O.

Each of these fine-grained soils is grouped according to its liquid limit into:

(a) Fine-grained soils having liquid limits less than 50, that is, of low to medium compressibility; symbol L, in combinations ML, CL, and OL.

(b) Fine-grained soils having liquid limits greater than 50, that is, of high compressibility; symbol H, in combinations MH, CH, and OH.

Highly organic soils, usually fibrous, such as peat and swamp soils having very high compressibility are not subdivided but placed in one group; symbol Pt.

According to Casagrande, the performance of soils in these groups, and the corresponding PRA groupings, are as follows:

Airfield Classification		Value as Foundation When Not Subject to Frost Action	PRA Classification
GW	SW	Excellent	A-3
GC	SC	Excellent	A-1
GP		Excellent	A-3
SP		Good	A-3
GF		Good to excellent	A-2
SF		Fair to good	A-2
ML		Fair to poor	A-4
CL		Fair to poor	A-4, A-6, A-7
OL		Poor	A-4, A-7
MH		Poor to very poor	A-5
CH		Poor to very poor	A-6, A-7
OH		Very poor	A-7, A-8
Pt		Extremely poor	A-8

Pedological classification [31]

Soil science (pedology) is the basis for the pedological classification. Its principle is that *like soils are developed on like slopes when like materials are weathered in like fashions.* As an illustration: weathering of limestone produces a reddish silty clay soil. Where slopes and climate are alike, the depth and nature of this soil mantle are similar, regardless of geographical location.

Under the pedological classification, soils produced in like manner from the same parent rocks are grouped together, as it is assumed that they possess similar engineering properties and require the same engineering treatment. The number of samples subjected to physical tests may be reduced below that usually required, as the test results serve more as a check on pedological classification than as primary design tools. This procedure is in direct contrast to the other classification methods, which rely almost exclusively on physical tests and make little use of pedological information.

Three valuable sources of information regarding soils are geological, topographic, and agricultural soil maps, which are available for many areas of the

[31] Excellent references on this subject are *Highway Research Board Bulletins 13* (1948) and *28* (1950) titled The Appraisal of Terrain Conditions for Highway Engineering Purposes and Soil Exploration and Mapping, respectively, and Symposium on Surface and Subsurface Reconnaissance, *ASTM Special Technical Publication 122*, pp. 46–88 (1951).

country and can be obtained from various government agencies. Aerial photographs also provide important data. All this information, along with performance records of existing roads in the same or like areas, can be of great use in roadway design. Several state highway departments, among them those of Michigan, North Carolina, Virginia, Missouri, and New York, have developed engineering soil maps or manuals from these sources.

As mentioned, like soils occur under like conditions of materials, slopes, and weathering. In addition, like landforms or soil patterns are developed. Thus, such elements as surface-drainage patterns, erosion characteristics, and soil color reflect the nature of the soil. As examples: the shapes of the gullies reveal soil texture or clay-pan development; color patterns often reflect ground-water conditions; ridges with parallel axes may indicate wind-blown sands and silts. To the trained observer a study of landforms, particularly on aerial photographs, can lead to a pedological classification and to accurate prediction of the soil conditions to be encountered in a given area.[32]

DESIGN OF THE ROADWAY STRUCTURE

Causes of roadway failures

The problems of roadway design are somewhat parallel to those of structural design. A bridge must support a vehicle by transferring its load through successive members to the foundation beneath. Similarly, a roadway structure must support the vehicle load on its surface and transfer this load through successive layers of pavement, base course, and subgrade to the undisturbed soil on which it rests. Bridge structures are usually built of steel, concrete, or timber, the properties of which are reasonably predictable. Roadways, however, are built of soils whose properties vary widely, and about which much is still unknown.

To the roadway structure are applied the wheel loads of motor vehicles which may number several million over a period of years. Each time a load passes, some deflection of the surface and the underlying layers occurs. If the load is excessive, repeated applications will cause roughening and cracking that ultimately lead to complete failure. This deflection of the pavement may result from elastic deformation, from consolidation of the base and subsoils, or from a combination of elastic and plastic deformation (see Fig. 12).

[32] For more on this subject see Donald J. Belcher, The Engineering Significance of Soil Patterns, *Proceedings Highway Research Board* (1943), and the Engineering Significance of Landforms, *Highway Research Board Bulletin 13* (1948). Also Merle Parvis, Drainage Pattern Significance in Airphoto Identification of Soils and Bedrocks, *Highway Research Board Bulletin 28* (1950).

Elastic deformation occurs as the live or wheel load temporarily deforms the foundation materials and compresses the air that fills the voids of the base and subgrade. In truly elastic deflection, the surface returns to its original position after the load passes, so that permanent unevenness does not occur, even under repeated applications of load.

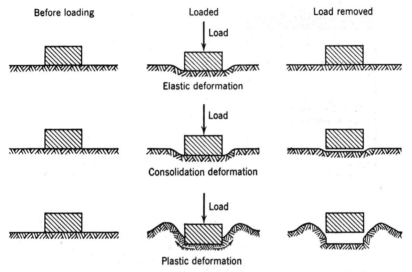

Fig. 12. Diagram illustrating soil deformation under wheel loads

Consolidation deformation occurs when the load produces large enough pressure in the pores of the soil to expel part of the air and water and thus consolidate the material. Although the consolidation that results from one application of a moving wheel load is small, the deformation is permanent. It progresses with additional load repetitions until the affected layers become consolidated. Failure may not result from this consolidation if the traffic is well distributed and the pavement settles uniformly as a whole.

Plastic deformation occurs when the fluid and air pressure in the pores of the subgrade, base material, or paving combine with forces produced by the load to displace the roadway material. Deflection resulting from plastic deformation is progressive under load repetition; it constitutes the major cause of failure of roadway surfaces. Figure 13 illustrates the usual methods of occurrence. Each is the result of a shearing-type failure accompanied by movement in the affected layers. Pavement, base, and subgrade are all susceptible.

However, the perimeter along which failure occurs has the least length if the shortcoming is in the surface layer, and becomes longer as the source of trouble moves to greater depths (see Fig. 13). Since the

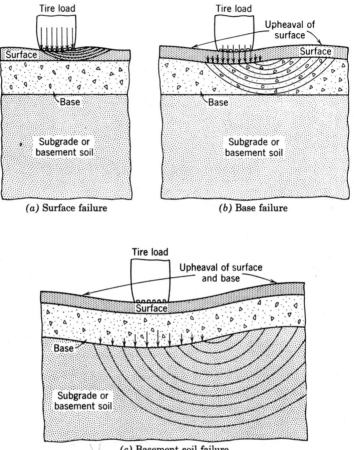

(a) Surface failure   (b) Base failure

(c) Basement soil failure

Fig. 13. Results of plastic deformation in basement soil, base, or surface course
(After F. N. Hveem)

total applied load in a given instance is constant, it follows that the unit shearing stresses which may be developed become smaller as the distance below the surface increases. This in turn indicates that the materials in successive layers downward from the surface may be progressively weaker without increased likelihood of plastic deformation and failure.

From Fig. 13 it is also apparent that failure is accompanied by downward movement under the load and a corresponding *upward* movement in adjoining areas. This in turn means that the pavement and other layers have been subjected to bending in a horizontal plane and have yielded in tension or compression or both. From this, it follows that high beam strength in pavement or base will strengthen a roadway against plastic deformation.

Principles of roadway design

As indicated, highways may be built successfully over poor soils if they are protected with sufficient cover of better materials. Roadway design, then, involves fixing the minimum safe distance from the pavement surface to the top of each layer of the roadway structure. Stated differently, it involves setting the respective thicknesses of pavement, base course, sub-base (if any), and other imported materials which must overlie the native soil. Often, any one of several combinations of materials and layer thicknesses will meet the requirements of a particular design method. Then the problem is to establish which of these is least costly in the long run. At times, variables like weather and soil-moisture conditions dictate more conservative treatment than usual. Without question, roadway design involves much more than substituting data into a formula or taking values from a design chart.

The design methods in common use are empirical and are founded largely on careful observation of past successes and failures, supplemented at times by findings from test tracks or experimental roads. Some methods rely on physical tests or soil classifications to relate past performances to the problem at hand. Layer thicknesses are found by substituting these test results in formulas or charts. As yet, theoretical analyses similar to those employed in designing with metals, concrete, and some other materials are little used in roadway design.

Roadway design

By precedent. Many highway agencies, particularly those of small cities and counties that do not have laboratory equipment or personnel, rely almost entirely on precedent in making roadway designs. The rule for residential subdivisions of a small western city furnishes an illustration: It calls for 6 in. of compacted base course from a local quarry topped by 2 in. of plant-mix bituminous surfacing. This standard design is employed for all roads, regardless of the subgrade conditions. On completion, the city assumes all responsibility for maintenance. Performance has for many years been generally satisfactory, although failures over particularly bad subgrades have caused concern and may lead to some revision in the design. For business streets and other traffic arteries, layers are thicker, but their dimensions are likewise determined by precedent.

Many satisfactory roadways have been designed by such "rule-of-thumb" methods. However, dimensions appropriate for one set of soil, moisture, climatic, and traffic conditions are not necessarily appropriate under different circumstances. Thus, rule-of-thumb design methods should be used only over small areas where like conditions exist, or where previous experience indicates that good results can be expected. Design by precedent may often be uneconomical. If a particular design proves satisfactory on all the streets or roads in an area, it is so because the design is appropriate for the worst soil condition of that area. Other sections probably are overdesigned and therefore more costly than necessary.

A 1952 survey of the design practices of the state highway departments [33] indicated that 13 of them used no physical tests or testing methods in arriving at their roadway designs. Of this group, all made soil classifications, but these were not related directly to design procedures.

Group-index method. [34] A design method based on the group index (see p. 337) is presented in simplified form as Fig. 14. From the chart can be determined the recommended thicknesses of bases and pavements to be placed over various kinds of subgrades and original grounds. For example: assume that a fill and the original ground under it are poor materials (group index of 9). Daily traffic will include 200 buses and trucks. This method recommends as a minimum design that the total thickness of pavement, base, and better materials overlying this poor soil be 15 in. This total might be made up as follows: bituminous pavement, 3 in.; granular base, 4 in.; other good material with group index of zero, 8 in. Another acceptable design could be: bituminous pavement, 1.5 in.; granular base, 5.5 or 6 in.; good material with group index of zero, 4 in.; and soil with a group index of 4, 4 or more in. There is serious doubt, however, that so

---

[33] See Report of Committee on Flexible Pavement Design, *Highway Research Board Bulletin 80* (1953).

[34] First presented in *Proceedings Highway Research Board* (1945) by D. J. Steele of the Public Roads Administration. As of 1952 some use of the group index was made by 13 state highway departments.

many thin layers would be economical. Usually, several combinations of materials and thicknesses will meet design requirements. Then the choice should be made on the basis of over-all cost.

Compaction called for by the group-index method is as follows: subgrade and top 6 in. of original ground to 95% of AASHO standard density. Sub-base and base to 100% AASHO standard.

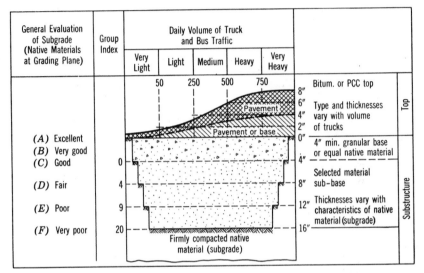

FIG. 14. Group index Design chart (Courtesy D. J. Steele)

Michigan method. The Michigan design method has been developed around the pedological classification. On the basis of "condition surveys" in progress since 1925, pavement performance has been correlated with soil types. From this a definite set of design recommendations has been developed and published in the *Field Manual of Soils Engineering*.[35] Factors influencing the design are: location of grade line with respect to natural ground surface, normal depth of groundwater table, drainage requirements, quantity of frost-heave excavation, suitability of soil for fill construction, necessity for topsoil removal, and suitability of soil for stabilization in place.

The Michigan method has been referred to as the "inverted method of design." There are standard pavement sections ranging from

---

[35] The *Field Manual of Soils Engineering* (3d edition, 368 pp., 1952) of the Michigan State Highway Department offers an excellent and detailed treatment of the highway-soils problem encountered in that state. The manual may be purchased through the Contract-Estimate Engineer's office, Lansing 13.

bituminous concrete on a 7- to 9-in. gravel base and 21-in. sub-base for heavy traffic to gravel 5 to 7 in. thick on an 18-in. sub-base for low traffic volumes. The method is directed towards providing proper foundations for these standard pavement designs.

California bearing-ratio method. This method, often referred to as the CBR, combines a load-deformation test performed in the

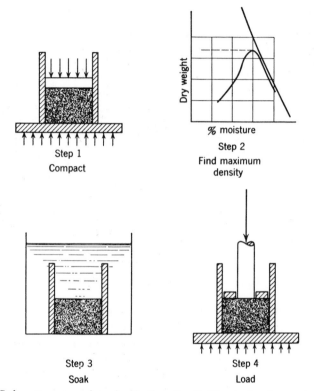

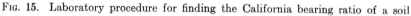

Fɪɢ. 15. Laboratory procedure for finding the California bearing ratio of a soil

laboratory with an empirical design chart to determine the thicknesses of pavement, base, and other layers. The original test was developed by the California Division of Highways.[36] The CBR procedure, modified in various ways, was, in 1952, the design method of 15 state high-

---

[36] The basic laboratory tool of the California Division of Highways is now the Hveem stabilometer (see p. 350). For a discussion of correlation between CBR and stabilometer test results, see A New Approach to Pavement Design by F. N. Hveem, *Engineering News-Record*, July 8, 1948.

way departments, although in some cases it was supplemented by other tests. It is also employed by the Corps of Engineers, U. S. Army, for airport design.[37]

The California bearing-ratio test is conducted in general as follows (see Fig. 15):

Step 1. Disturbed samples of the soil (each about 4000 grams) at different moisture contents, are compacted by a static load of 2000 lb per sq in. into cylindrical steel molds 6 in. in diameter and 8 in. high. The resulting specimen depth is about 4 in.

Step 2. The moisture-density curve is plotted, and the sample with greatest dry density is selected.

Step 3. The specimen, still in the mold, is immersed in water and soaked for 4 days to simulate saturation that may occur in service.

Step 4. A small cylindrical piston, 3 sq in. in end area, is forced into the still-confined test specimen. Load-deformation data are gathered as the specimen is penetrated. Usually the piston passes through a surcharge ring (weight 10 lb) which provides confinement for the material and simulates the effect of overlying pavement.

CBR load-deformation curves for a variety of soils are shown as Fig. 16. From such curves, or the load-deformation data itself, the California bearing ratio (CBR) is computed as follows:

$$\text{California bearing ratio} = \frac{\left\{\begin{array}{l}\text{load carried by test specimen at 0.1-in.}\\ \text{piston penetration}\end{array}\right\}}{\left\{\begin{array}{l}\text{load carried by standard crushed rock base}\\ \text{at 0.1-in. piston penetration}\end{array}\right\}}$$

Thus, the CBR states the quality of the material in terms of that of an excellent base course. As examples: The sandy-loam soil of Fig. 16 has a CBR of 0.4, whereas the CBR of adobe is only about 0.05.

Once the California bearing ratio (CBR) for each material is known, layer thicknesses are found by reference to an empirical design chart. Figure 17 is the CBR chart of the Wyoming Highway Department. It gives the total thickness of pavement, base, and other better materials that must overlie a soil with a stated CBR value. Design curve 4, the farthest to the left, would be used where traffic volume and wheel loads are small, where annual rainfall is less than 10 in., and where

[37] For a discussion of the development of the CBR method and its application to airport design, see *Transactions American Society of Civil Engineers*, pp. 453–589 (1950).

groundwater and frost action both are absent. Curve 15 represents the most adverse assumptions regarding each condition. The par-

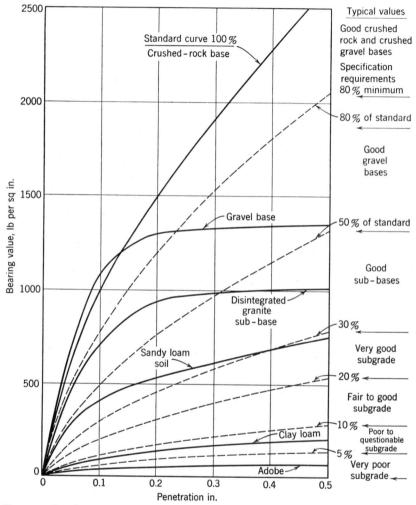

Fɪɢ. 16. Load-penetration curves for typical soils tested by the CBR method
(After O. J. Porter)

ticular curve for each design situation is selected by weighting all the above-named factors in a prescribed manner.[38]

[38] See Thickness of Flexible Pavements, *Highway Research Board Current Road Problems 8-R,* November 1949.

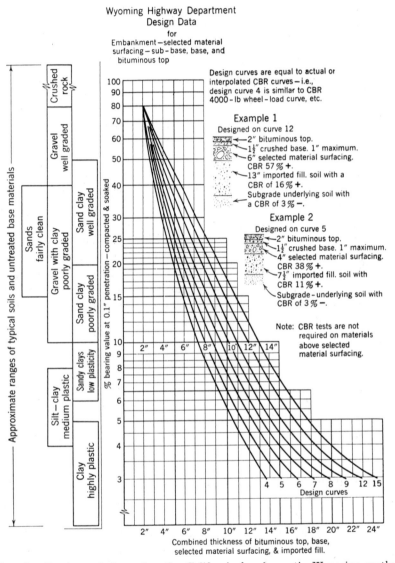

FIG. 17.   Roadway design using the California bearing ratio–Wyoming method
(Courtesy Highway Research Board)

Almost every agency that has adopted the California bearing-ratio method has made some change from the original procedure. As examples: The Corps of Engineers, U. S. Army, compacts samples with the impact of a free-falling hammer instead of a static load and has its own design chart for airport loadings. The Minnesota Department of Highways has changed compaction methods and the penetration at which significant strength is recorded. In addition it has its own design charts. Thus it must be recognized that direct comparison between CBR designs of different agencies is not possible.

Hveem stabilometer method. The Hveem stabilometer method is employed (1952) by four state highway departments. It is based on tests made in the Hveem stabilometer, a device developed originally about 1930 for the testing of bituminous mixtures. The test specimen is a short cylinder about 4 in. in diameter and $2\frac{1}{2}$ in. high, and is prepared at optimum moisture content by a tamping-foot (kneading-type) compactor. Soaking in water to simulate moisture conditions in service follows. Testing is accomplished in the stabilometer (see Fig. 3, p. 473). The specimen, enclosed in a flexible sleeve, is loaded at its ends, and the lateral pressure that develops in the confining fluid is recorded. Results of the stabilometer test are stated in terms of "resistance value," which is given by the formula

$$R = \left(1 - \frac{P_h}{P_v}\right) 100$$

where R = resistance value of the material tested.
P_v = the vertical pressure applied to the ends of the cylinder (typically 160 lb per sq in.).
P_h = the transmitted horizontal pressure as measured in the stabilometer.

Notice that the resistance value of a fluid, where P_h equals P_v, would be zero, while that of an infinitely rigid solid would equal 100.

The design chart used with the stabilometer is shown as Fig. 18. Entry is made on scale A, which is the resistance value. Scale B is a traffic index which weights the effect of wheel-load magnitude and repetition.[39] A straight line through them to scale C gives the total

[39] This traffic index represents a summation of the destructive effect of all the wheel loads to which the road will be subjected during its life. Basic data are from traffic volume and weight counts, projected into the future. In determining equivalent wheel loads passenger cars are not counted at all. Truck wheel loads are counted as follows: [Continued on next page

thickness of gravel with which the tested material must be covered. An additional step recognizes that support against plastic deformation is furnished by the beam strength of pavement and base. Measurement of this property is by the cohesiometer, which subjects the stabilometer specimen to bending around a diameter of the base. A straight line running from scale C through scale D to scale F gives total design thickness in inches, subject to the exceptions noted on the diagram.

As mentioned earlier, soils that expand during soaking should not be placed near the roadway surface. Instead, they should be covered with weight enough to prevent expansion and the absorption of excessive amounts of water. One part of the stabilometer test procedure is to measure this tendency to expand. During soaking, the specimen is kept in the steel mold. This provides lateral restraint. Vertical expansion is also prevented by means of a device that measures the expansive force exerted by the sample. For materials that develop an expansive force, a second element is introduced into the stabilometer design procedure: that of balancing the weight of the superimposed fill against the expansive pressure of the soil. Figure 19 illustrates the application of this principle to design. Curve A of this figure shows the thickness of cover needed to satisfy stabilometer requirements through a range of moisture percentages. As would be expected, an increase in moisture in the material under test reduces its strength and calls for an increase in the thickness of base and surface covering it. Curve B shows expansion pressures stated in terms of the thickness of overlying material necessary to prevent swelling. Here increases in moisture decrease the expansion pressure. For the material of Fig. 19, stabilometer and expansion requirements are both satisfied by 9 in. of cover, compacted at 11% moisture. This does not mean that the optimum moisture content is 11%. Optimum moisture content is less than that value. Rather, it means that the expansive characteristics of the soil govern the design.

Wheel Load, lb	Equivalent Wheel Loads
4500–5500	1
5500–6500	2
6500–7500	4
7500–8500	8
8500–9500	16
9500 and over	32

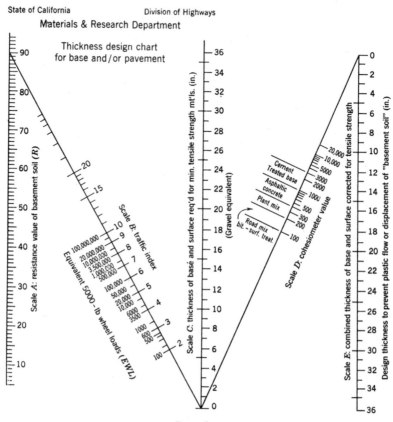

State of California   Division of Highways

Materials & Research Department

Thickness design chart for base and/or pavement

Scale A: resistance value of basement soil (R)

Equivalent 5000-lb wheel loads (EWL)

Scale B: traffic index

Scale C: thickness of base and surface req'd for min. tensile strength mt'ls. (in.)

(Gravel equivalent)

Scale D: cohesiometer value

Scale E: combined thickness of base and surface corrected for tensile strength

Design thickness to prevent plastic flow or displacement of "basement soil" (in.)

Cement Treated base

Asphaltic concrete

Plant mix

Road mix

bit.~surf. treat.

Procedure

With a straightedge intersect scale A at the value for R (as determined by the stabilometer or some other substitute method) and scale B at the traffic index for the total traffic load for the design life of the highway. The intersection of this line with scale C is the thickness of gravel required to support the load (neglecting abrasion, etc.). From this point intersect scale D at the cohesiometer value of the surface. This line will intersect scale E at the thickness of base and surface required to resist plastic flow of the basement soil.

When the thickness of the surface material is to be less than one-half that indicated on scale C, correct cohesiometer value for use on scale D as follows:

$$S = \frac{\text{pavement thickness}}{0.5 \times \text{scale } C \text{ reading}} \times c$$

where S = corrected cohesiometer value
     c = original cohesiometer value

FIG. 18. Design chart for use with the Hveem stabilometer (Courtesy F. N. Hveem)

Triaxial methods. Several agencies employ triaxial compression tests as their basic roadway-design tool. Important elements of the test device are shown in Fig. 20. The sample is encased in a flexible membrane and confined laterally by fluid enclosed in a Lucite or other container. Then load is applied vertically.

For the "open"-system triaxial test, lateral pressure is held constant by releasing fluid from the container as increased load causes the

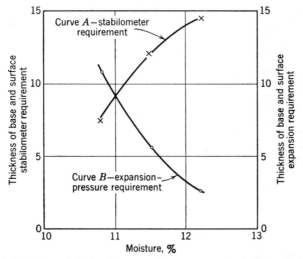

Fig. 19. Modification of design to recognize soil expansion—Hveem stabilometer method (Courtesy F. N. Hveem)

sample to expand laterally. Variables here are vertical load and vertical deformation, which when plotted give a load-deformation relationship comparable to that for steel, concrete, or other structural materials. Typical load-deformation curves are shown as Fig. 21. Test results are related to thickness of base and pavement by empirical formulas or design charts which recognize factors like traffic volume and weight, groundwater conditions, rainfall, and freezing and thawing. The Kansas Highway Department is one agency that uses "open"-system triaxial testing for design purposes.[40]

Some agencies employ the "closed"-system triaxial test. For this, all fluid is retained in the encircling container. As vertical load is

[40] See Design of Flexible Pavements Using the Triaxial Compression Test, *Highway Research Board Bulletin 8* (1947), for a detailed description of this method.

applied, the sample tends to deform laterally, which increases the pressure in the surrounding fluid. Variables are vertical load and fluid pressure. Actually, the Hveem stabilometer is a "closed"-system triaxial device, although the connotation is usually applied only to tests on tall cylinders.[41]

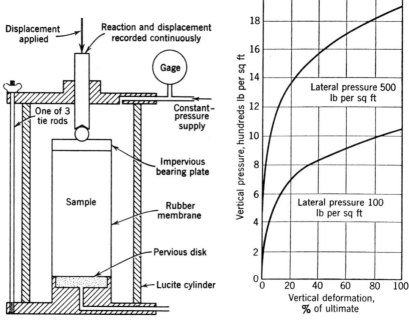

Fig. 20. Essential features of triaxial test (open system)

Fig. 21. Typical results of soil test using open triaxial device

Plate-bearing methods. Large-scale plate-bearing tests are employed for design purposes by certain highway and airport agencies. Some test large samples prepared. in the laboratory; others load the undisturbed ground or compacted fill during construction. As an example, the North Carolina Highway Department prepares in the laboratory samples of compacted base course, sub-base, and subgrade 42 in. square and 24 in. deep. Loading is through a rigid steel plate

[41] For triaxial-testing techniques as applied to bituminous-paving mixtures see p. 475. For reports on much of the basic research in triaxial testing of soils and bituminous materials see Triaxial Testing of Soils and Bituminous Materials, *American Society for Testing Materials Special Publication 106* (1951).

12 in. in diameter. Layer thickness is related to applied pressure by formula.[42]

ROADWAY DESIGN FOR UNUSUAL SOIL CONDITIONS

Among the problems in roadway design and construction are stability of fills and slopes, elasticity, volume change, compression, and permafrost. They are discussed in the following paragraphs.

Stability of fills and slopes

At times, materials in cut banks will slip downward onto the road. Again, portions of high fills slide outward and downward, often carrying portions of the roadway or shoulder along. Such failures are often spectacular and gain considerable attention although they may

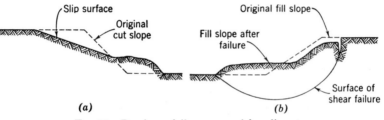

(a)   (b)

FIG. 22. Roadway failures caused by slipouts

be relatively unimportant in the over-all scheme of things. Figure 22a illustrates a common failure, in which slipping occurs along a seam of wet or weak material. Figure 22b shows settlement of a fill. Notice that the shearing surface approaches the arc of a circle and that the entire disturbed mass has rotated around the radius point. This pattern of failure is common in fills or cut slopes of nongranular materials.

Any extensive discussion of slope stability is beyond the scope of this book, and for further information the student is referred to textbooks in soil mechanics.[43] It should be emphasized, however, that many slides result from lubrication or pressures created by infiltrating water, and that sealing off or removing this water may offer the best solution.

---

[42] See Thickness of Flexible Pavements, *Highway Research Board Current Road Problems 8-R* (1949). In this same publication are a detailed description and an excellent bibliography on plate-bearing studies for airports.

[43] See also Analysis of Landslides, *Highway Research Board Bulletin 49* (1952).

Permeability

Permeability permits the passage of fluids. Coarse-grained soils like gravels and sands are highly permeable; clays and fine-grained soils are almost impermeable. In general, highly permeable soils make excellent subgrade material, as coarse-grained soils are stable whether dry or saturated. However, permeable soils may carry seepage water

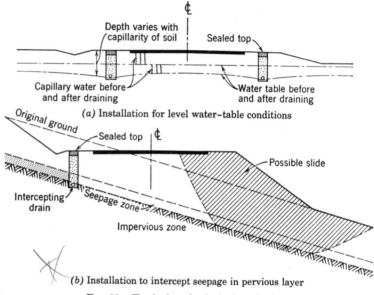

(a) Installation for level water–table conditions

(b) Installation to intercept seepage in pervious layer

FIG. 23. Typical underdrain installations

and create serious stability problems by furnishing a·source of supply for capillary moisture, by lubricating slippage surfaces, or by producing seeps in cut slopes.

Figure 23 shows two situations in which the removal of water from pervious soils may be advantageous. In Fig. 23a, the high water table would provide a source of capillary moisture which, on rising, would saturate the subgrade or cause frost heave. The installation of deep underdrains would lower the water table so that capillary moisture would not rise high enough to be troublesome. Figure 23b shows the use of an underdrain to intercept seepage water which otherwise might lubricate a slippage surface between pervious and impervious layers and cause a slipout. All subdrains need gravity outlets.[44]

[44] For a report on the subdrainage practices of the various state highway departments see Subsurface Drainage, *Highway Research Board Bulletin 45* (1951).

Subdrains are not effective in impermeable soils through which water flows very slowly, such as those classified in the *A–4* to *A–7* ranges. Neither will they remove capillary moisture already in the soil.

Engineering studies have greatly extended previous knowledge about the proper design of subdrains.[45] Some resulting recommendations are:

1. Pipe always should be used to carry away the collected water. Older "French drain" installations which contained no pipe have been unsatisfactory. Pipes of corrugated metal, concrete, or vitrified clay, perforated to permit entry of water, or unperforated concrete and vitrified clay pipe, laid with open joints, can be employed. The number, size, and location of openings into the pipe must be studied carefully to prevent excessive entrance velocity which will cause silting of the pipe.

2. Filter material with which the trench is backfilled should be finer grained than the large crushed rock formerly used. For example, if the drain is installed in a silty soil, the backfill material should be similar in grading to concrete sand.

3. The top of subdrains should be sealed with an impervious soil to prevent the entrance of surface water. Earlier practice which combined subdrains with drains for surface water by extending the filter material to the surface has proved unsatisfactory.

4. Intercepting drains (see Fig. 23*b*) to be effective must extend downward into the impervious zone.

5. Pipe must be laid with the flow line at least 48 in. below the finished grade and be carefully bedded in gravel or filter material.

Capillarity

Capillarity permits the creep of free water through the pores and fine channels of the soil. In coarse-grained materials like sand and gravel, the behavior of free water is governed almost entirely by gravity and the water will tend to seek a level as if in an open channel. As grain sizes become smaller and channel diameters decrease, the forces of surface tension influence the behavior of the water. For example, if the pores of a soil are not full of water and if free water is available, capillary forces will tend to pull free water through the

[45] See for example, *Proceedings Highway Research Board*, pp. 469–487 (1943); pp. 359–389 (1944); pp. 422–450 (1945); Investigation of Filter Requirements for Underdrains, U. S. Waterways Experiment Station, Vicksburg, Miss., *Technical Memorandum 183–1;* and *Public Roads*, February 1952, pp. 251–267.

soil until all voids are full. Such movement can take place in any direction, but upward movement usually creates the most serious problems. Capillary action is most pronounced in soils composed mainly of fine sands, silts, or silty clays, as they are fairly permeable and have channels through which moisture can pass. Yet the diameters of the openings are small enough that the capillary forces are high. Clays and colloidal soils are practically impermeable and are little subject to capillarity.

There is evidence that large amounts of water can be raised considerable distances by soils subject to capillarity. If the surface of the soil is open and this moisture evaporates as fast as it rises, no damage may result. But, if evaporation is slow or the surface is sealed by pavement or some other impervious blanket, this capillary water accumulates and saturates the subsurface layers. Many surface failures have resulted.[46]

Failure resulting from subgrade saturation. Partially compacted soils often have void space great enough that, when saturated, the moisture content of the soil mortar will be well above the plastic limit. If they are subject to capillary action and also are near groundwater or other sources of moisture, they will in time become saturated, soften, and fail.

Failures resulting from frost action.[47] Failures variously described as frost heaving, frost boils, and spring breakup often are the result of the combination of capillary action with the freezing and thawing of the ground. A simplified explanation of this phenomenon is as follows: [48]

1. When the soil temperature decreases below the freezing point, water in the larger voids freezes, but that in the capillary tubes does not, because its freezing point is lower (see Fig. 24).

2. This capillary water is drawn to the frozen particles with tremendous force.

[46] Test data show capillary rise of 45 in. in 24 hr in coarse silt with 78 to 120 in. maximum rise. A capillary flow of 2.7 cu ft per sq ft of area in 24 hr at 18 in. above groundwater also is of record.

[47] For an excellent summary of the literature and a bibliography on this subject see Frost Action in Roads and Airports, *Highway Research Board Special Report 1* (1952). A companion volume, *Special Report 2*, titled Frost Action in Soils, a Symposium, offers 40 papers by engineers engaged in study of various phases of the subject.

[48] For an early report on the subject see Steven Tabor, *Journal of Geology,* vol. XXXVIII, May–June 1930; also *Public Roads,* August 1930.

3. When this water comes in contact with the ice particles, it freezes and increases the thickness of the ice layer, thus raising the overlying material. Pressures of about 200 lb per sq in. can be developed, which far exceed the usual superimposed load.

4. Water drawn from the soil pores is replaced with moisture supplied by capillary action from the groundwater below, and that in turn is added to the growing ice lens.

5. Growth of a lens is halted and another below it begins to form when the temperature between them becomes low enough to freeze the

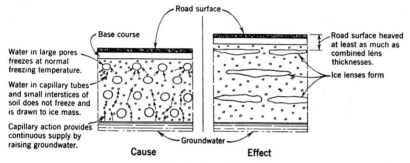

Fig. 24. Mechanics of frost heave

capillary moisture. The rate at which cooling takes place governs the number and thickness of lenses.

In the northern United States, even where the ground seldom freezes more than 2 to 3 ft below the surface, heaving or raising of the road surface by 6 in. or more is not uncommon. In one case heaving of 2 ft has been reported. Very often heaving is not uniform but occurs only in stratified layers or pockets of fine sand, silts, or silty clays. Thus a small section of the road surface will rise abruptly and create a serious accident hazard. Unfortunately, many subgrade soils whose characteristics vary abruptly occur within the frost areas of this country.

With spring thaws, the ground and ice lenses melt, and free water under the surface escapes through cracks to form "frost boils." Harmful settlement of the road surface follows. When water remains under the surface until vehicles break through, the action is described as "spring breakup."

Several remedies for frost heave have been used. Among them are:

1. Remove the soil that is subject to capillary action to below the frost line, and replace it with a granular noncapillary material.[49]

2. Install subdrains to lower the groundwater below the reach of extensive capillary action.

3. Excavate the soil to the frost line, and place an impervious seal such as an asphaltic membrane or a layer of granular, noncapillary material at this level to cut off the flow of capillary water. Then replace the original material.

Load-bearing tests conducted in several northern and eastern states have demonstrated that freezing definitely weakens subgrades and untreated bases, even though frost heave does not occur. When the roadway was frozen, supporting power matched that found during the fall months. As thawing downward from the surface began, strength fell rapidly. By the time all frost was out of the ground, supporting power had decreased by about 50%. Strength was regained slowly over a period of 3 or more months. These findings offer strong support for the practice of certain states that limits axle loads during the spring.months.[50]

Elasticity

Elasticity means that soils are springy and compressible under load. Often they will return to shape or "rebound" when the load is removed. Elasticity is a property of soils whose fines consist mainly of flat, flaky particles such as mica. It can be detected on construction work by a characteristic "rubbery" action of compression and rebound under heavy wheel loads. Under repeated manipulation and reworking of the soil, elasticity usually becomes worse until the soil loses almost all its strength. "Elastic" soils should never be placed close to the roadway surface where they will be subject to repeated wheel loads. They can, however, form the side slopes of fills of reasonable height.

Elasticity of poor soils should not be confused with the elastic behavior of good soils under load repetition. The better materials

---

[49] Casagrande states that, if less than 3% of a material is finer than 0.02 mm, frost heaving will be prevented, *Transactions American Society of Civil Engineers*, p. 917 (1948).

[50] For detailed reports on these tests see C. L. Motl, *Proceedings Highway Research Board*, pp. 273–281 (1948), *Research Report 10-D* (1950), and *Bulletin 54* (1952) of the same agency.

can be compacted to high densities, whereas the so-called "elastic" soils cannot.

Volume change

High volume change (expansion, swell) under changes in moisture content indicates soils that are generally unsatisfactory for fill construction, although at times they must be used. Also, roads sometimes must be built on such swelling ground. If this condition exists, special precautions concerning the amount of surcharge, moisture content, and the degree of compaction must be observed.[51]

Construction and service failures have occurred when concrete pavements were laid directly on expansive soils. Sometimes the newly laid concrete was damaged when the subgrade swelled as it absorbed water from the mix. In other cases, rainwater reaching the subgrade through joints or at the edges of the slabs caused differential swelling. This in turn brought curling and roughening of the pavement.

Soil compression

Soil compression reflects the tendency of some soils to decrease in volume under continued load. Pressure gradually forces the water and air from the pores and causes a decrease in soil volume. In fills over swampy materials of considerable depth, consolidation may continue for years.

Satisfactory roads have been built over compressible material by using "flexible" pavements which adjust to the settlement without damage. Enough depth of suitable base material must be provided to prevent local failures. Methods for accelerating the rate of settlement of deeper deposits have been devised (see p. 392).

Permafrost

In northern districts of Canada and in Alaska and Siberia, a frozen-soil condition known as "permafrost" presents serious problems. The ground is frozen permanently and often to great depths. During the summer the top few feet thaw from the top down, leaving a quagmire. In the winter the ground freezes solid again, with freezing progressing downward from the surface. When the first sections of roads were built through permafrost areas on the Alaska highway, conventional procedures were followed. The thick moss and other plant growth

[51] See also p. 322.

and the thawed soil below them were removed, and the fill was constructed on the frozen material. Sections so built failed almost immediately, as the blanket of relatively warm fill material furnished heat which melted the underlying ice and left the road without support. On subsequent construction, care was taken to prevent thawing of the ground. Vegetation was left in place, and often brush and other material were added to provide insulation.

SOIL SURVEYS

A preliminary soil investigation is an integral part of highway reconnaissance and preliminary location surveys. Soil conditions as well as directness of route, topography, right of way, and other factors must be weighed in fixing the position of the road. Normally, this preliminary soil study consists of visual examination coupled with a small amount of sampling and testing where the findings might influence the final decision. There will, of course, be situations where comprehensive soil study will precede selection of the final route. For example, if one proposed location crosses a marsh while the alternative remains on stable ground, careful testing, preliminary design, and cost studies might precede the final decision.

Most highway agencies make a detailed soil study along with the final location survey. Its purpose, as stated in the specifications for highway materials of the AASHO,[52] is to provide pertinent information on the following subjects:

(a) Location of the road, both vertically and horizontally.

(b) Location and selection of borrow materials for fills and subgrade treatment.

(c) Design and location of ditches, culverts, and drains.

(d) Design of the roadway section.

(e) Need for subgrade treatment and type of treatment required.

(f) Location of local sources of construction materials for base and wearing courses.

(g) Selection of the type of surface and its design.

An early phase of the soil survey is the collection and examination of all existing information. This may include the identification of soil types from geologic and agricultural soil maps, aerial photographs,

[52] See, Standard Methods of Surveying and Sampling Soils for Highway Purposes, *AASHO Designation T86–49.*

and other sources, investigation of groundwater conditions, and an examination of existing roadway cuts and other excavations. A review of the design, construction procedures, and present condition of roads that traverse the area often is extremely helpful.

Soil exploration along the road site usually is made by means of auger borings and test pits. There is no definite rule to follow except that sampling should be at frequent enough intervals to fix the boundaries of each significant soil type. Test holes always should extend a significant distance below the proposed grade line.[53] Deeper holes may be appropriate to locate bedrock, adverse ground such as peat or muck, or groundwater conditions that would influence design or construction. A complete and systematic record should be made for each hole. Its location, the nature of the ground, origin of the parent material, landform, and agricultural soil name, if known, should be recorded. Each soil layer should be described according to its thickness, texture, structure, organic content, relative moisture content, and degree of cementation. The depth of seepage zones or free water table and of bedrock should be included when they are encountered. On the basis of these reports, many agencies plot a *soil profile*, which records the test data in visual form. Such a soil profile appears as Fig. 25. It shows the location of each test hole, a soil profile along the roadway center line, and (at the top) the range of soil-profile characteristics for each distinct soil type.

The locations at which laboratory samples will be taken are found from a study of the auger borings or soil profile. Disturbed samples of earth may be obtained to a depth of about 6 ft with a hand-operated soil auger or to depths up to about 30 ft if the auger is power-driven. Specimens in hard or boulder-filled soil may be gained by digging test pits. Many highway agencies have specially trained crews and elaborate equipment for making soil surveys. Power-driven augers are common. Wash boring rigs, churn drills, and rotary drills are available for exploration to greater depths or in hard or rocky materials. Special devices have also been made for taking undisturbed samples from deep down in swamps and bogs.

Two geophysical methods are also in use for subsurface exploration. One of these, called the refraction seismic method, relies on the principle that the speed of travel of shock waves through the earth's surface is different for different materials. For example: waves travel through light, loose soils at approximately 600 ft per sec; but through dense, solid rock at speeds ap-

[53] The standard AASHO procedure suggests that this distance be at least 3 ft.

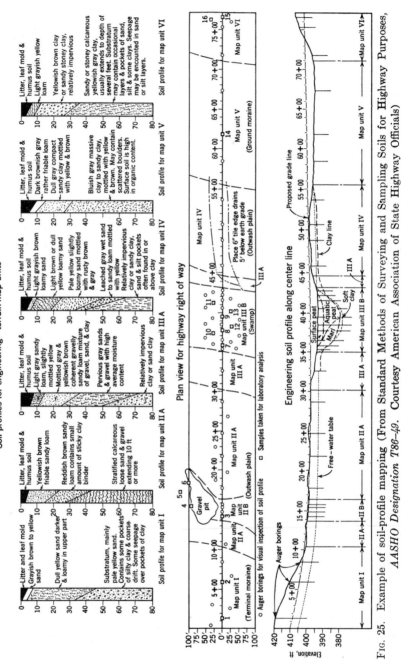

FIG. 25. Example of soil-profile mapping (From Standard Methods of Surveying and Sampling Soils for Highway Purposes, *AASHO Designation T86–49*. Courtesy American Association of State Highway Officials)

proaching 20,000 ft per sec. The test device records the time it takes for the shock from an explosive charge to reach several points at increasing distances away (see Fig. 26). If the earth's crust is of uniform composition for some depth, these time intervals are directly proportional to the distance from the point of explosion. If, on the other hand, the surface layer is underlain by a harder, denser material, the time interval to more distant points is shortened because the shock wave travels downward into the denser material, along its

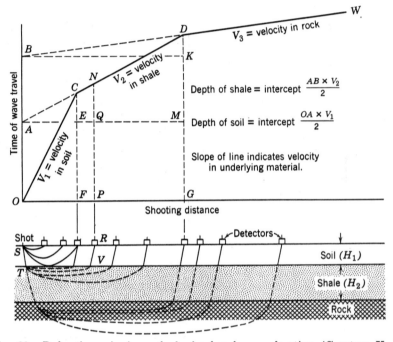

FIG. 26. Refraction seismic method of subsurface exploration (Courtesy U. S. Bureau of Public Roads)

upper margin, and up again to the recording device. By plotting time of wave travel against shooting distance the number and thicknesses of the various underlying layers and the depth to bedrock can be predicted (see Fig. 26) This test has proved particularly useful in determining the depth to rock.

· The variation in the electrical resistivity between different subsurface materials offers another method of soil exploration. Ordinary moist soils containing moderate amounts of clay and silt and some electrolytic agent have comparatively low resistance. On the other hand, sand, loose dry soils, and solid rock have relatively high resistivity. In performing the test, direct current is made to flow through the soil between two electrodes. The drop in potential is then measured, not between these supply electrodes, but between two others placed intermediately at the third points. It has been established empirically that this voltage drop measures the resistance of the entire soil layer to a depth equal to the spacing of the intermediate electrodes. The change in resistivity with depth is obtained by recording the resistivity at various electrode spacings. By comparing a plot of these findings with those for a deposit of like material that has already been exposed, layer thicknesses can be found. This method is generally quite reliable, although there have been occasions when it has not furnished completely dependable information regarding the presence of solid rock. It is particularly useful in area exploration, as when it is desired to find localized sand and gravel deposits.[54]

[54] For more information on subsurface exploration by special methods see R. W. Moore in *Public Roads,* August 1950 and *Highway Research Board Bulletin 62,* pp. 62–107 (1952). Also see *American Society for Testing Materials Special Publication 122,* pp. 89–228 (1951).

13 —————— Constructing the Roadway

INTRODUCTION

This chapter covers the building of the roadbed, from site clearing through subgrade completion. It presents accepted construction procedures and discusses methods of payment for the work. It includes the application of the principles of soil mechanics to roadbed construction.

CLEARING THE SITE

Clearing the site precedes all grading operations. If it consists merely of removing and disposing of coarse grass and small bushes and shrubs its cost is usually included in the price paid for excavation. If considerable work is called for, it is usual to pay under special items adapted to the type of operation required.

Clearing and grubbing

Clearing and grubbing frequently involves removing trees and tree stumps from the road site and disposing of the debris. Accepted procedure is to remove practically all vegetable material from the road site or from fill material, since if allowed to remain it may decay and leave voids that result in settlement.

In heavily timbered areas, clearing may involve considerable cost and require the employment of skilled men. Great care must be exercised to avoid fires, particularly when the logs, brush, and slashings are burned. Contractors may be required to employ special fire guards and to supply fire-fighting equipment. If the trees are suitable for lumber, it is common to specify that the logs be cut into merchantable lengths and be piled in designated locations. Clearing operations may considerably lengthen the time needed to complete a road. If debris can be burned only in prescribed burning seasons,

367

the progress of the entire job may be held up. Consequently, clearing operations are often set up as special winter or wet-season contracts.

Under some conditions, the removal of stumps is not required. For example, the Public Roads Administration Specifications for national forest and national park roads states:

"Where embankment is to exceed 3 feet, stumps exceeding 3 inches may be left in place if sawed one foot or less above the ground and if they are not closer than 2 feet to subgrade or slope surface. Otherwise, all stumps, roots larger than 3 inches in diameter, and matted roots shall be dug out and removed. No stumps or roots may remain closer than 18 inches to subgrade, shoulder, or slope surface. Beyond the road prism slope lines, when so ordered, stumps may be cut flush with the ground."

Clearing and grubbing is usually paid for by the acre of land cleared, at the unit price bid for "clearing and grubbing." In special circumstances, where only a few trees are to be removed, payment may be made under the heading of "Removal of Trees," at the bid unit price per tree.

Clearing for the roadway in metropolitan areas

Preparation for grading operations through built-up areas presents an entirely different problem from that found in rural locations. Houses, pavements, sidewalks, and like obstructions must be removed. Surface utilities such as telephone and power lines which parallel or cross the right of way must be relocated or adjusted to provide adequate clearance.

For depressed urban freeways, the clearing problem becomes extremely complex. Rearrangements must be made not only of surface installations and facilities but of the underground utilities as well. In the central district of a large city, utilities under a typical city street include many service pipelines and wire conduits. Often some or all of these facilities must be relocated out of the way of the improvement. Much time will be consumed in their rearrangement, and the costs will be high. To avoid similar problems in the future, many highway engineers recommend that utilities be either excluded from highway rights of way or placed in a common tunnel or conduit outside the pavement.

Methods of payment for site clearance can be quite complex. Pavement and sidewalk removal are commonly paid for at a bid price per square yard or cubic yard of material removed or on a lump-sum basis. Other items of work can be paid on a unit basis, such as a bid price per foot of pipe or conduit removed or replaced. Often much of the work must be done by the specialized crews of the utility company involved, with reimbursement for the actual expenses it incurs. At times the utility company itself must pay for the changes, as it occupies space in the right of way under an easement that requires the utility to move its facilities at no cost to the highway agency.

GRADING OPERATIONS

Grading is an all-inclusive term to describe construction operations between site clearing and paving. All excavating, hauling, spreading, and compacting activities are included.

Until 1925 or so, all grading in earth or "common" material was done with scrapers of $\frac{1}{2}$ cu yd or less capacity, pulled by horses or mules. Since then, tremendous improvements have been made in grading equipment. Now some of the very largest jobs are done by scrapers with capacities up to 50 cu yd, pulled by powerful tractors of the crawler or wheel type. Because of such improvements in techniques, the unit cost of grading work has remained largely unchanged while many other construction costs have more than doubled.

Excavation

Excavation is the process of loosening and removing earth or rock from its original position in a cut and transporting it to a fill or to a waste deposit. Selection of equipment depends on the nature of the material, how far it is to be moved (hauled), and the method of disposal.

Materials are usually described as "rock," "loose rock," or "common," with "common" signifying all material not otherwise classified. Rock, or sometimes "solid rock," nearly always must be drilled and blasted, then loaded with a power shovel into trucks or other hauling units (see Figs. 1 and 2). Blasted rock may be moved or drifted for short distances by means of a bulldozer, which is, in effect, a huge tractor-mounted blade (see Fig. 3). Loose rock includes materials like weathered or rotten rock, or earth mixed with boulders, and often is dug with power shovels without previous blasting. At times, however, further loosening by blasting may permit faster loading and decrease equipment wear, with an attendant reduction in total cost. Power shovels easily dig common excavation without blasting.

Grading procedures in "common" or earth excavation are governed by length of haul. Where material is moved less than about 200 ft or steeply downhill, drifting with a track-type or wheel-type bulldozer (see Fig. 3) is cheapest. For moderate distances, self-loading scrapers pulled by crawler tractors usually are better. For longer hauls, self-loading scrapers pulled by rubber-tired hauling units offer lower costs (see Fig. 4). For hauls of considerable length, loading with a power

Fɪɢ. 1. Drilling solid rock preparatory to blasting. Machine shown is a "wagon drill" powered by compressed air (Courtesy Joy Manufacturing Co.)

shovel into trucks or rubber-tired wagons pulled by rubber-tired tractors (see Fig. 2) may be cheaper. Stated differently, haul distances may be grouped into "zones." For each zone, one particular equipment type will do the work more cheaply than any other. Unfortunately, the boundaries of these zones cannot be clearly defined. In the first place, they will vary from job to job as soil character, terrain, grades, weather, and other factors change. Furthermore,

FIG. 2. Power shovel loading blasted rock into a dump truck (Courtesy Bucyrus-
Erie Co.)

FIG. 3. Bulldozer on highway construction drifting material from cut to fill.
Working in a shallow trench gives larger load (Courtesy Caterpillar Tractor Co.)

various manufacturers suggest zone limits that favor their equipment. Few factual data on earthmoving costs are available for general use, although many contractors have confidential records from projects that they have constructed. Some information is now being made available as the results of time studies of highway construction equipment made by the U. S. Bureau of Public Roads.[1]

Fig. 4. Rubber-mounted bulldozer loading rubber-mounted tractor scraper unit
(Courtesy LeTourneau-Westinghouse Co.)

Tractor-scraper units have been successfully employed to excavate loose rock which in earlier years was handled solely by power shovels. The change has resulted from the development of large rooters, pulled by one or more tractors, which effectively break up loose rock or hardpan.

Payment for excavation commonly is made at a bid price per cubic yard measured "in place" in the space originally occupied. This unit price includes payment for loosening and loading the material, transporting it any distance less than the "free-haul" limit,[2] and spreading

---

[1] See *Highway Research Board Correlation Service Circulars 58, 68, 84, 85, 87, 93, 94, 101, 124, 197, 205, 206,* and *221.* Also see F. B. Farrell, *Highway Research Abstracts,* November 1953, pp. 26–34.

[2] A free-haul limit of 500 ft was usual before mobile motor equipment was developed. Many agencies have now increased the free-haul distance to some higher stated value. At times an agency may set different free-haul limits for different terrains or materials.

it in the fill. Payment for light clearing and grubbing and for trimming cut and fill slopes is also included in the unit price for excavation. Sometimes embankment compaction likewise is charged against the excavation item.

The pay item for excavation usually is listed as "unclassified," which means that the contractor bids and is paid at one unit price, whether the material is solid rock, loose rock, or earth. Sometimes, however, excavation is segregated into "rock" and "common," and a separate unit price is established for each. This practice is now less prevalent than in earlier years. Throughout the Mountain and Pacific Coast States where much heavy excavation is encountered, the usual grading item on the contractor's bid sheet is "unclassified excavation." Sometimes the profile sheet indicates the estimated percentage of solid rock in cuts, but many times it does not.

There are several reasons for dropping the two classifications of "rock" and "common" in favor of the single bid item of "unclassified excavation." First are the arguments that arise between the contractor and engineer in classifying borderline material. On the job, it frequently is difficult to determine the level at which "rock" begins and "common excavation" ends. Often unexpected material appears that is neither "common" nor "solid rock." For example, even when rock excavation is defined as "ledge rock" that requires blasting, the contractor may demand and deserve payment for "rock" if he encounters a hardpan that, for economy in handling, should be blasted. Conversely, some rotten granites can be excavated economically by power shovel without blasting. If a considerably higher price is to be paid when blasting precedes excavation, the contractor and engineer may often disagree on whether or not blasting is really required. Large pockets of big boulders and slides of rock fragments are also troublesome to classify. Sometimes, in an attempt to escape such difficulties, an intermediate classification called "loose rock" is introduced, but this may increase rather than decrease the uncertainty.

Another reason for dropping the dual classification is that, with increasing use of heavy machinery, the difference in the cost of handling rock and dirt has decreased. Typical of this modern equipment are larger power shovels (1¼- to 2½-yd-capacity rather than ¾- to 1-yd), bulldozers, and heavy rooters.

At times two classifications may be helpful. If, for some reason, the road location is changed in a way that increases the percentage of solid rock, the basis of payment is established beforehand. This eliminates troublesome arguments and possible lawsuits over the adjustment of unit prices. Also, if the road location runs through terrain where only occasional well-defined ledges occur, the double classification may result in a lower total bid for the work.

Excavation, however classified, is commonly but not always measured in the original, undisturbed position. The place and method of measurement must be carefully stated in the specifications, because almost all materials change volume in movement from cut to fill. Excavated solid rock will expand so that 1 cu yd of rock in the cut will occupy 1.15 to 1.50 cu yd in the fill. If, however, the voids in the rock embankment are filled with earth or other fine material, the volume in the fill will just about equal the combined volumes in the two source locations. Excavated earth will expand beyond its original volume in the transporting vehicle, but it will shrink below the excavated volume when placed in the fill. To illustrate, 1 cu yd of earth in the cut may use 1.25 cu yd of space in the transporting vehicle, and finally occupy only 0.85 to 0.65 cu yd in the embankment, depending on its original density and the amount of compaction applied. These changes in volume are referred to as "swell" or "shrinkage."

Measurement of earthwork quantities is one of the duties of the field survey party. Cross sections perpendicular to the road center line are taken at selected stations along the road. By plotting and planimetering these sections, the area of the roadway prism at each section is found.[3] The quantity of earth between adjacent cross sections is usually computed by the "average-end-area" method, which assumes that the true volume between the sections is equal to the average of the end areas multiplied by the linear distance between them measured horizontally along the center line of the road. Usually the average-end-area method gives an answer greater than the true one. If adjacent cross sections are somewhere near the same size this difference is small; but if one area is considerably larger than the other the difference becomes appreciable. The discrepancy can be reduced by taking intermediate cross sections or by using more exact methods of computation.[4]

Slides

The side slopes of all cuts are steeper than the original ground surface. Side slopes for high fills often are made as steep as the material will stand in order to reduce the quantity of embankment. In either event slides may occur during construction or at a later date some time after the road is in service.[5] Ordinarily, it is better practice to risk some sliding or adjustment of large cut slopes than to flatten them all and thus increase the pay yardage. Areas that threaten persistent slides should be avoided if possible during location. Minor slope-adjustment slides and ledge falls that occur during construction must

[3] At times, these "end areas" can be computed directly from the field notes by the "criss-cross" method which eliminates plotting and planimetering the sections.

[4] For more on this subject, see any of the standard textbooks on route surveying.

[5] See Fig. 22, p. 355.

be removed and usually are used to widen fills or to flatten their slopes. In rough country, estimates for excavation should allow some extra quantities to provide for slides and the flattening of unstable slopes.

Payment for slides not covered under the specifications by the item "excavation" usually will be made under one or more special bid items or on a force-account basis.[6]

Some larger slides are difficult to handle and may become destructive. Any doubtful areas should be explored by test borings and examined by experienced construction engineers, geologists, and soils specialists.

Slides may result from mud flows, slope adjustments, or movement caused by underground water or by undercutting a rock strata. Less frequently coarser material such as rock talus, coarse sand or gravel, or weathered debris from above the road will threaten grading operations or the completed highway.

Many troublesome slides result when an underlying inclined surface of shale, soapstone, clay, or like material is lubricated by seepage water. During the rainy season or after hard rains or heavy snowfall, this surface may become lubricated, causing the entire mass above the slippage surface to move. Such slides can be controlled by removing all or a large portion of the material above the slippage surface or by some drainage device which keeps water from the surface of weakness. If the surface of a slip is lubricated by surface water from above the cut slope, the water may be intercepted by surface ditches farther up the slope or sometimes by oiling or otherwise waterproofing the area of penetration. If the water comes from a pervious layer at a fairly shallow depth below the surface (say, 10 ft or less), underdrains may be installed to cut the flow off higher up. If the threatening mass is too deep for these procedures, flows sometimes may be intercepted by drainage tunnels of small cross section backfilled with coarse sand over open pipe. These drains would run on a downgrade from the apex zone to a gravity outlet. The water must always be intercepted before it can lubricate the critical slip surface. On most of these wet-slope readjustment slides, barriers such as lines of piling, rock windrows, or ordinary breast or retaining walls will fail.

The California Division of Highways has developed a "hydrauger method" for stabilizing slopes [7] which has proved both cheap and effective. A special machine drills holes into the cut or fill slope on a slight upward inclination. A perforated pipe which intercepts and carries off the flow is then driven into these holes.

Slides of dry material have been checked by sturdy masonry breast walls at the foot of the slides. Some apparently threatening dry debris masses fail to move when cut into, probably because the cubical or angular-shaped rock fragments on such slopes tend to lock together. The dribbling of an occasional

---

[6] Often special work of an unusual nature or work not anticipated when the contract was awarded is paid for by "force account." Under this procedure, the contractor is paid for all labor, materials, and equipment expense incident to the work plus a predetermined percentage for overhead and profit.

[7] See *California Highways and Public Works*, January-February 1948.

loose rock or boulder down the slope onto the road often can be prevented by treating the surface with a thick cement grout, or can be intercepted by a wall or heavy fence along the inside of the road. The cost of handling bad slides obviously must be compared with the cost of alternative designs employing half-trestle or similar construction which avoids deep cuts and high fills.

Overbreak

Overbreak occurs in rock cuts when material outside the staked back-slopes becomes loosened and falls or is removed along with the intended excavation. It develops either because the cleavage surfaces of the rock lie at unfortunate angles or because of overshooting. It is largely controllable. Unavoidable overbreak, up to some fixed percentage, usually is paid at some predetermined unit price per cubic yard. If overbreak results from the contractor's carelessness or error, no payment is made.[8]

Overhaul

It is often necessary or advisable to move excavated material beyond the stipulated "free-haul" distance. This operation is called "overhaul." The unit in which overhaul is commonly computed and paid is the "station-yard." One station-yard is 1 cu yd of excavated material moved one 100-ft station. For extra long hauls a cubic-yard-mile is sometimes the unit of overhaul.

The U. S. Bureau of Public Roads defines overhaul thus:

When excavated or borrowed material is hauled as directed more than 500 feet, overhaul will be allowed on such material. The overhaul distance will be the distance between the centers of volume of the material in its original position and after placing, less 500 feet. This distance shall be measured along the shortest practicable route. The number of station-yards of overhaul shall be the product of the volume of the overhauled material, measured in its original position, in cubic yards, by the overhaul distance in feet, divided by 100.

Definitions of overhaul of other agencies are similar. Some use a longer free-haul limit, such as 1500 ft.

Where grading for a project involves overhaul, it is customary to plot a "mass diagram," which provides a convenient means for studying haul and overhaul and for computing payment. Figure 5 shows

[8] The U. S. Bureau of Public Roads will pay up to a maximum of 10% of the roadway prism within any 50-ft station if the overbreak is unavoidable. Payment then is made at the unit price bid for excavation. Some highway agencies have a special bid item for overbreak.

the profile for a short section of road with the corresponding mass diagram directly under it. Table 1 gives the earthwork quantities for a portion of the length and indicates how the ordinates of the mass diagram are computed.

The Mass Diagram

A profile has engineer's stations for its abscissa and elevation for its ordinate. The mass diagram has the same abscissa, but its ordinate represents the algebraic sum of excavation and embankment between a selected point of beginning and any station in question. Since 1 cu yd of excavation rarely occupies exactly 1 cu yd of space in the fill, either excavation or embankment quantities must be adjusted before the ordinates of the mass diagram are computed.

The adjustment to put excavation and embankment quantities on a common basis is made by employing a "shrinkage or swell factor," defined as the volume occupied in the embankment by material that occupied 1 cu yd before it was excavated. For uniform material it is convenient to apply the adjustment to the embankment quantities by *dividing* them by the shrinkage or swell factor. Then the ordinates of the mass curve are in terms of *excavated* volume. Where the shrinkage or swell factors differ considerably between cuts, the adjustments often are applied instead to the excavation quantities by *multiplying* them by the shrinkage or swell factor for each kind of material. Then embankment quantities remain in terms of measured net volumes.[9]

Shrinkage and swell are often expressed as "per cent shrinkage" or "per cent swell," which represent the per cent volume change between cut and fill. The volume occupied in the cut is always considered as unity. Thus, if 1 cu yd from the excavation swells to 1.20 cu yd in the embankment, the per cent swell equals $(1.20 - 1) \times 100$ or 20%. Again, if 1 cu yd from the excavation makes only 0.80 cu yd of embankment, per cent shrinkage equals $(1 - 0.80) \times 100$ or 20%.

Table 1 shows a typical computation for obtaining mass curve ordinates. The embankment yardages have been adjusted; thus the mass curve is in terms of excavated volumes. Figure 5 shows the mass curve as plotted from Table 1 and added like data. Notice that the mass curve does not represent the total yardage but the summation of the difference between cut and fill.

Certain characteristics of the mass curve must be understood before it can be used successfully. They are:

1. A *rising* mass curve denotes excavation at that point on the roadway; a *falling* curve denotes embankment.[10]

2. Steep slopes of the mass curve reflect heavy cuts or fills; flat slopes indicate small earthwork quantities.

[9] Where this procedure is followed, the ordinates of the mass curve must be adjusted when the pay item of overhaul is computed, since the volume of overhauled material is, by definition, measured in its original position.

[10] Where the roadway lies on a sidehill, the same cross section often shows both excavation and embankment. In such cases, a rising curve indicates an excess of excavation and a falling curve an excess of embankment.

3. Points of zero slope on the mass curve represent points where the roadway goes from cut to fill, or vice versa.[11]

4. The difference in ordinate between two points on the curve represents the net excess of excavation over embankment between those points, or conversely, the net excess of embankment over excavation.

5. If a horizontal line intersects the mass curve at two points, the excavation and embankment are in balance (equal in amount) between those points.

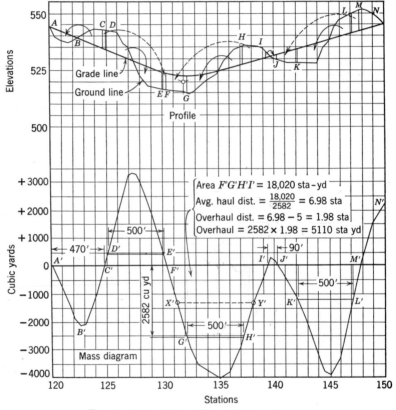

Fig. 5. A typical profile and mass diagram

Use of the mass curve to compute overhaul, based on a free-haul distance of 500 ft, is illustrated in Fig. 5. The procedure is as follows:

1. Determine all the free-haul sections. (These are sections not exceeding 500 ft in length in which the cuts just balance the fills.) This is done by

[11] These low or high points on the mass curve may not come at the exact station at which the profile goes from cut to fill. There may be a net excess of excavation or embankment at this point if the cross slope is irregular.

TABLE 1. TYPICAL COMPUTATIONS FOR A MASS DIAGRAM

Swell or Shrinkage Factor = 0.82

Station	Excavation, Cu Yd	Embankment, Cu Yd	Embankment plus Shrinkage, Cu Yd	Excess Material in Section, Cu Yd Excavation	Embankment	Mass Curve Ordinate, Cu Yd
120						0
	0	321	391	—	391	
+ 50						−391
	0	401	489	—	489	
121						−880
	0	483	589	—	589	
+ 60						−1469
	0	318	388	—	388	
122						−1857
	0	271	330	—	330	
+ 65						−2187
	205	73	89	116	—	
123						−2071
	421	0	0	421	—	
+ 50						−1650
	593	0	0	593	—	
124						−1057
	1421	0	0	1421	—	
125						+364
	1543	0	0	1543	—	
126						+1907
	832	0	0	832	—	
+ 60						+2739
	514	0	0	514	—	
127						+3253
	81	12	15	66	—	
+ 20						+3319
	125	153	187	—	62	
+ 60						+3257
	0	241	294	—	294	
128						+2963
	0	336	410	—	410	
+ 40						+2553
	0	628	766	—	766	
129						+1787
	0	1123	1370	—	1370	
130						+417
	0	1162	1417	—	1417	
131						−1000
	0	1141	1391	—	1391	
132						−2391
	0	516	630	—	630	
+ 50						−3021
	0	427	521	—	521	
133						−3542
Totals	5735	7606	9277	5506	8948	

locating horizontal lines exactly 500 ft in length whose ends lie on the mass curve. In Fig. 5 these are $D'E'$, $G'H'$, $K'L'$. Also locate any sections less than 500 ft in length within which the mass curve intersects the zero ordinate twice, as lines $A'C'$ and $I'J'$ of Fig. 5. These free-haul lines must lie either on the zero ordinate of the mass curve ($A'C'$ and $I'J'$) or inside the loops formed by the zero line and the mass curve ($D'E'$, $G'H'$, and $K'L'$). If the lines are drawn *outside* the loops, the completed earthmoving plans will include "cross haul," which will mean hauling material in one direction, followed later by moving material over it in the opposite direction. The actual movements of excavated material are indicated on the profile by arrows.

2. Determine the disposition of the remaining excavation. To illustrate, the mass curve shows that the excavation and embankment are in balance between C and F. Then cut CD should be deposited in fill EF. Similarly, cut HI makes fill FG, and cut LM makes fill JK, all as indicated by dotted arrows on Fig. 5. Any other haul plan will result in cross haul.

For this particular mass diagram, excavation within the section considered exceeds embankment by about 2200 cu yd, as shown by the ordinate of the mass curve at station 150. This material is not needed for fill and might be wasted or used on some other section of the road. In practice, the grade line probably would be raised to secure a closer balance between cut and fill. Inclusion of waste in this illustration merely serves to indicate an added problem that is often encountered.

3. Determine the haul distance. Any *area* such as $F'G'H'I'$ on the mass curve, when corrected for scale, is in station-yards, which are the units for haul and overhaul. Thus, the area $F'G'H'I'$ represents the station-yards of haul needed to move cut HI into fill FG. Similarly, areas $C'D'E'F'$ and $J'K'L'M'$ give the hauls to place cuts CD and LM in fills EF and JK, respectively.

The average haul distance is found by dividing the appropriate area on the mass curve (station-yards) by its ordinate (cubic yards of excavation).[12]

4. Compute the overhaul. The overhaul distance (see definition) is the haul distance less the free-haul distance. Overhaul, the pay item, is the product of overhaul distance and cubic yards of excavation. Typical calculations for overhaul for area $F'G'H'I'$ are shown on Fig. 5.

Mass diagrams often are more complex than that shown in this illustration. For example, if material is wasted or borrowed, the base line is shifted up or down, respectively. Again, unusual haul arrangements to provide for the placement of the more desirable materials near the finished roadway surface or to dispose of poor materials in deep fills or under the side slopes sometimes must be introduced.

Borrow and waste

In grading for a highway, "borrow" material often must be brought in to the roadway from outside the grading prism. Thus, in flat coun-

---

[12] The width of the overhaul area at mid-height (line $X'Y'$ on Fig. 5) gives a close approximation to the haul distance. The shorter solution gained by using this approximation is entirely satisfactory for many purposes.

try, it often is desirable to raise the roadway surface 4 or 5 ft above the groundwater table, or above the reach of flood waters. On prairies subject to snowfall, the wind usually will keep a slight fill free of snow. Approaches to major bridges often traverse high fills for a considerable distance. A "cushion" of soil 6 in. or more in depth is often placed on rock cuts. All such hauled-in materials are commonly classified as "borrow."

Material for fills in level country is often obtained as "side borrow" from the roadside within the limits of the right of way. In the past, poor side-borrow practices have produced many troublesome conditions. For example, where rights of way were narrow, deep ditches were left along the roadside to become an accident hazard and a trap for rainwater. Correct practice permits side borrow only when a safe and well-drained cross section can be maintained.

Much borrow today comes from large "borrow pits" located away from the road and from widened roadway sections in adjacent cuts. Designation of the source of borrow often results in a material superior to that from along the roadside. Some specifications stipulate that all borrow pits must be wholly invisible from the road; others that all pits must be neatly trimmed and dressed after the material has been removed.

Pay for borrow usually is by the cubic yard measured in the space originally occupied in the borrow pit. Occasionally, the borrow volume is determined in the completed fill. Some agencies have been paying for borrow on a weight basis, at a bid price per ton. This practice is especially common when the borrow is for "select" material for the roadway or for topsoil.

Excavated material which sometimes remains after all fills within an economical haul distance have been completed is designated as "waste." Waste is often used to widen fills or flatten fill slopes of adjacent sections. No payment other than for excavation is involved when material is wasted, except for occasional overhaul.

CONSTRUCTION OF FILLS AND EMBANKMENTS

Principles of embankment construction

Formerly many fills, whether of rock or earth, were constructed to full height at one time by "end dumping" from the transporting vehicle. In this procedure the material slid or rolled into place down the face of the progressing fill. No attempt was made to control moisture content or to secure compaction. It was anticipated that such fills would settle for some time and initial pavement, if any, was of a flexible sort that would not be damaged by differential settlement. Construction of permanent pavement over high fills often was deferred for a year or more after completion of the fill to allow settlement.

In the 1930's engineers found that superior embankments could be constructed by spreading the material in relatively thin layers and compacting it at optimum moisture content.[13] The improvement resulted largely because greater density was obtained, since this greater density resulted in higher "strength" in the soil mass and in decreased settlement and permeability. The change in construction procedures also produced greater uniformity in the material itself and in its density and moisture content. This was beneficial since any subsequent volume change in the fill would be relatively uniform. By contrast, in fills constructed by end dumping or in thick layers, material, density, and moisture content could vary greatly from one spot to another. Volume change would be nonuniform and would result in differential settlement or swell between adjacent areas.

The densities necessary for satisfactory embankments vary with such factors as soil type, fill height, and nearness to the roadway surface. Densities recommended by the AASHO committee on compaction of subgrades and embankments appear in Table 2. They are stated in terms of "relative compaction," as compared with AASHO standard compaction.[14]

Control of embankment construction

There are two basically different control procedures for assuring proper embankment density. The first is to specify the desired result, stated as the minimum acceptable value for relative compaction, and to make sure, by field density tests, that the specified density is obtained. The second procedure is to state the manner and method for constructing the embankment. In this case, layer thickness, moisture control, and the number of passes by a roller of specified type and weight are predetermined. Field control is largely a matter of carrying out the specified procedure. Actually, most highway agencies combine these approaches, but in different ways and to varying degrees.

Theoretically, control of embankment construction is not difficult,

[13] See p. 323 for an explanation of moisture-density relationships.

[14] See pp. 328–330 for the methods for measuring standard and in-place densities and for computing relative compaction.

TABLE 2. RECOMMENDED MINIMUM REQUIREMENTS FOR COMPACTION OF
EMBANKMENTS

Condition of Exposure

Class of Soil (AASHO M145–49)	Condition 1 (Not Subject to Inundation)			Condition 2 * (Subject to Periods of Inundation)		
	Height of Fill, Ft	Slope	Compaction, % of AASHO Max. Density	Height of Fill, Ft	Slope	Compaction, % of AASHO Max. Density
A–1	Not critical	1½ to 1	95+	Not critical	2 to 1	95
A–3	Not critical	1½ to 1	100+	Not critical	2 to 1	100+
A–2–4	Less than 50 ⎫	2 to 1	95+	Less than 10 ⎫	3 to 1	⎧ 95
A–2–5	Less than 50 ⎭			10 to 50 ⎭		⎩ 95 to 100
A–4	Less than 50 ⎫	2 to 1	95+	Less than 50	3 to 1	95 to 100
A–5	Less than 50 ⎭					
A–6 ⎫	Less than 50	2 to 1	90–95 †	Less than 50	3 to 1	95 to 100
A–7 ⎭						

From *Highway Research Board Bulletin 58*, 1952.

* Recommendations for condition 2 depend upon height of fills. Higher fills of the order of 35 to 50 ft should be compacted to 100%, at least for part of fills subject to periods of inundation. Unusual soils which have low resistance to shear deformation should be analyzed by soil-mechanics methods to determine permissible slopes and minimum compacted densities.

† The lower values of minimum requirements will hold only for low fills of the order of 10 to 15 ft or less and for roads not subject to inundation nor carrying large volumes of very heavy loads.

but, as a practical matter, it offers many problems. Often soil types cannot be segregated during construction as they can in the laboratory. For example, efficient equipment operation may demand that loads of unlike materials from several sources be combined in a single embankment. Under such circumstances, moisture control and density determination may prove very difficult. Again, the handling of poor materials is often troublesome. To illustrate, heavy topsoils usually are unsatisfactory as embankment material and should be placed deep in the fill or under the side slopes where they will carry little load, and construction operations must be planned accordingly. Aeration of soils that are too wet is another troublesome and expensive operation.

Field measurement of relative compaction is often a difficult task. In the first place, the test is time-consuming. This means that relatively few samples can be taken and that test-hole locations must be carefully selected to represent fairly the area tested. Then too, careful planning is necessary to prevent delays to the heavy and expensive construction equipment while the test is under way or test results must be awaited.

Current practice in embankment construction

Embankment-construction practices of the state highway departments are typical of those currently employed in highway work.[15] Every department now constructs embankments in thin compacted layers. Procedures are generally the same, but specific details are quite different. A brief summary follows.

Density requirements. Over three-fourths of the state highway departments specify that embankments for some or all projects be compacted to a stated minimum relative compaction. In 32 states the AASHO standard impact test furnishes the basis for comparison. Minimum acceptable relative compactions range from 90 to 102% of this standard.[16] California and Nevada requirements are 90% of California impact densities. Certain other states require a certain number of passes of a roller: in New Jersey a 6-in. compacted layer must be subject to 8 passes of a sheepsfoot, 5 passes of pneumatic tires, or 4 passes of a 3-wheel, 10-ton machine. Other agencies require compaction "to the satisfaction of the engineer."

Moisture control. At times, soil in its natural state in cut or borrow pit is considerably wetter than its optimum moisture content and must be dried if satisfactory compaction is to be obtained. Often this is done by aerating the material with a motor grader or traveling mixer. In other areas the soil is too dry, and water must be added by sprinkler truck or other means. In either situation, accurate control of water content is fraught with many difficulties. For example, evaporation or rainfall may alter the moisture content before compaction is completed. Again, it is not easy to maintain a relatively uniform moisture content throughout the large volumes of soil that are being processed.

Most of the highway departments stipulate that overly wet soils be aerated and that water be added to excessively dry ones. However, few agencies actually specify a permissible range in moisture. Rather, control comes by specifying the minimum acceptable density, which can only be met when moisture content is near optimum. Ohio is one exception. It specifies that moisture content must not exceed optimum

[15] See Compaction of Embankments, Subgrades, and Bases, *Highway Research Board Bulletin 58* (1952), for an authoritative statement on the principles of soil compaction and a detailed description of present-day procedures and equipment. This bulletin also reviews in detail the practices and requirements of the individual state highway departments.

[16] Some states set different minimums for sandy than for fine-grain soils. Others increase the required density near the top of the fill.

by more than 2%. For elastic soils, moisture content must be optimum or lower.

Experienced engineers, after becoming familiar with soils, can often judge moisture content quite closely by examination. General guides are that friable soils at optimum moisture content (AASHO standard) contain sufficient moisture to permit forming a strong cast by compressing the soil in the hand. For some clays, optimum moisture approximates the plastic limit, and can be judged by forming a ribbon, thread, or cube of a sample. The Proctor penetration needle is also employed by some to measure moisture content. Drying samples to constant weight offers another but slower method.[17]

Compaction. Rollers or other compaction devices increase soil density by expelling air from the voids in the soil and by forcing the soil grains into more intimate contact. Water aids as a lubricant up to the optimum moisture content. In porous soils air is easily forced out, but in heavy or tight, cohesive soils much effort is required. Because of this, heavy cohesive materials must be placed in thin layers if the air is to be expelled readily.[18]

There is a practical limit to the compaction that can be obtained with a given roller, for the added compaction obtained with repeated loads soon becomes very small. Repetitions of load are particularly effective in increasing the density of fine-grained soils but have less effect on coarse-grained materials. Frequently, then, heavier rollers or a different method rather than many load repetitions may offer a better way to produce increased densities. However, heavy rollers are not a cure-all for compaction problems. The cost and trouble of moving heavy rolling equipment over the highways from one project to another may preclude its use on small projects. More important, many fine-grained soils become plastic and troublesome when remolded by heavy rollers but can be satisfactorily compacted in thin layers with lighter equipment. With such soils, it may sometimes prove advisable to replace heavy tractor-scraper earthmoving equipment with lighter units.

[17] See *Highway Research Board Bulletin 58* (1952), pp. 38–50, for descriptions and references on the more common methods for measuring moisture content and density in the field.

[18] According to O. J. Porter, the energy required to compact heavy, cohesive soils varies as the square of the depth of layer. See the Use of Heavy Equipment for Obtaining Maximum Compaction of Soils, *American Road Builders Association Technical Bulletin 109* (1946).

Roller types include tamping or "sheepsfoot" rollers, pneumatic-tired rollers, smooth-tired rollers, and the hauling equipment itself. Vibratory and impact compactors are still under test or limited to special jobs.

Roller use among the various highway agencies is far from uniform. The 1952 survey indicated that the tamping roller was most common, being described in the specifications for embankment in 42 states. Requirements for smooth-wheeled rollers were stated in the specifications of 34 agencies and those for pneumatic rollers by 23. Past practice has been to specify a given type and weight of roller for all projects, regardless of soil type or the density to be obtained. The trend today is toward specifying the roller that best fits the requirements of the particular job. As further knowledge of roller performance is gained, this selection process will be improved.

Tamping or sheepsfoot rollers (see Fig. 6) consist of hollow metal drums to which have been attached tamping feet. One or more of these drums are mounted on an articulated frame which permits uniform load on all the feet. The drums usually are pulled by a tractor, although special self-propelled units have been used. Pressure on the feet may be increased by filling the drum with water, sand, or a high-density fluid such as a water-baroid slurry. The tamping feet first penetrate the soil and compact the bottom of the layer; then as consolidation proceeds they "walk out" until the layer is consolidated and the feet barely penetrate. Tamping rollers vary from the *light standard* which weigh 6000 to 10,000 lb for an 8-ft width to giant rollers which, when fully loaded, weigh up to 75,000 lb for a 10-ft width. Pressures on the feet vary correspondingly from 60 to 100 lb per sq in. for the light standard up to 400 to 1000 lb per sq in. for the giant rollers. Tamping rollers are widely employed, but their effectiveness in coarse-grained soils is questioned as the feet tend to tear and displace the material rather than compact it.

Pneumatic-tired rollers (see Fig. 7) also are in wide use. This type consists of two or more rubber tires mounted on an articulated frame which provides uniform load on each tire. The frame of the roller is so built that the load can be increased by placing weights on the roller body. Motive power usually is provided by a tractor. Compaction under pneumatic tires comes in part from a kneading action which is particularly effective on loose, sandy soils. Pneumatic rollers for highway work generally weigh 6 to 8 tons. For airport work, rollers weighing up to 200 tons have been used.[19]

Smooth-tired rollers, of the two-wheeled (tandem) or three-wheeled type, long have been employed to compact bases and bituminous surfaces (see Fig. 11, p. 495). Such rollers compact the soil from the top downward, whereas the tamping roller works from the bottom upward. Many engineers prefer smooth rollers for compacting fills composed of glacial till or like material in which large rocks are combined with finer material.

[19] A mammoth, two-wheeled, rubber-tired roller is reputed to have compacted a sandy subgrade on the Baltimore International Airport to a depth of 5 ft.

Hauling Equipment. Often sufficient compaction can be obtained by properly routing the heavy hauling equipment. If no other compaction is provided, strict control must be maintained to see that the entire fill is covered. Otherwise nonuniform compaction will result. Obviously this method is much the cheapest.

Fig. 6. Sheepsfoot roller pulled by a crawler tractor. Bulldozer attachment permits tractor to spread embankment material before compaction (Courtesy Caterpillar Tractor Co.)

Impact and Vibratory Compactors. Hand-operated pneumatic tampers for compacting backfill in close quarters have been in use for several years. Studies have indicated that vibratory and impact forces are effective in compacting sandy soils.

American manufacturers are now producing surface vibrators and pneumatic rollers with vibrating wheels, although as yet their use is largely experimental. In Europe a number of vibratory and impact devices are in development or use.[20]

[20] For more on compactive equipment see *Highway Research Board Bulletin 58*, pp. 25–36 and 67–84 (1952). Also see R. K. Bernhard, *Proceedings Highway Research Board*, pp. 563–592 (1952).

Thickness of soil layers. The ideal layer thickness would be that which gained the required density at the least total cost. Variables would include the cost of placing and spreading the material, correcting its moisture condition, and compacting it with a roller of the proper type and weight. Each of these costs would be different for each soil type. With so many alternatives and so many factors still unknown, wide variation in current practice should be expected and does exist. Among the state highway departments, maximum permissible layer

Fig. 7. Large rubber-mounted tractor pulling a pneumatic roller. Sprinkler unit appears in the background (Courtesy Southwest Welding and Mfg. Co.)

thickness before compaction ranges between 3 and 24 in. Twenty-four agencies set lift thickness (measured before or after compaction) at 6 in. Fourteen departments employ 8-in. lifts, measured loose. Ten agencies, most of them in the Northeast, permit layers 12 in. thick before compaction.

Depth of subgrade compaction. Present state highway practice requires that the original ground be compacted before the overlying layers are placed. In most instances, compaction is by rolling the original ground surface without provision for adding or removing moisture. A further requirement in some of the states is that the top few inches of the subgrade meet embankment density requirements. The depth to which these densities are measured generally ranges from 4 to 12 in. Two states have more exacting requirements. California specifies compaction equal to that in embankments for $2\frac{1}{2}$ ft below profile grade. New York calls for a minimum of 95% of AASHO standard density for 4 ft below the pavement crown.

A study of pavement failures reveals that many of them occur in cuts or on low fills. Often these failures result because materials of low density lie close under the pavement surface. It must be concluded that a specification that merely requires compaction of the subgrade is not enough; instead, subgrade compaction must be related to depth below the surface of the pavement. At times it may even be necessary to remove the soil and replace it in compacted layers. At locations where the grade line passes from cut to fill, the further precaution of replacing the topsoil with suitable borrow material may be warranted.

Problems in embankment construction

Much knowledge is still to be gained regarding embankment construction. It has already been indicated that the comparison of the various types and weights of compactors and their relation to layer thickness offer a fertile field for research. Among the other questions on which research is under way or is needed are the following:

Is relative compaction, which compares field density to the density obtained by different methods in the laboratory, the proper measure of field compaction? If so, are the present standards of compaction proper? At present, compaction standards for nearly all soils, good and bad, are approximately the same (see Table 2). If they represent the proper density for poor soils, do they result in overdesign for the good ones? (The offered explanation is that the added density in good soils is beneficial and can be obtained cheaply; so why not get it?)

Regarding moisture control: Do the present laboratory methods for obtaining optimum moisture indicate the field optimum-moisture content for the different compactive devices? Evidence is that they do not. How far may the percentage of moisture vary from the optimum and still allow adequate compaction? Should this variation be the same for all soils when the moisture-density curves for some have sharp, well-defined peaks and those of others are quite flat? Would it be cheaper to relax moisture control somewhat and increase the compactive effort? What about compaction on the "wet" side of optimum as against compaction on the "dry" side? Some tests have indicated that soils compacted on the "dry" side show greater supporting power after saturation than soils compacted to equal density on the "wet" side. If this is true, would it be advantageous to dry the wet soils below the optimum moisture content to secure this added strength?

Regarding temperature: All other things being equal, the compactive effort required to produce a given density decreases as the temperature increases. Does this offer any opportunity for gaining greater densities or decreasing construction costs?

Payment for embankment construction

Methods of payment for embankment construction vary. Some states specify that the price per cubic yard of excavation or of borrow shall include all charges for compaction, for water as needed, or for aerating the soil. Others pay separately a bid price for installing a water supply, plus the bid price per 1000 gal of water, as needed. Still others pay for rolling, either at a bid price per hour of rolling with an acceptable roller or at a bid price per cubic yard of material. None of the states pays for aeration or other drying unless by special provision on individual contracts.

EMBANKMENTS THROUGH MARSHY AREAS

Highways sometimes must pass through swampy or marshy areas where the mucks and peats encountered will not provide stable support for the fills and pavements. Here conventional fill construction is unsatisfactory and special procedures are necessary. These include the removal and replacement of unsuitable material, various methods for its displacement, the surcharge method, and the vertical sand drain method.

Removal and replacement method

The removal and replacement method is suitable where the unstable material is shallow. It calls for removal to the level of the underlying stable material before fill construction is begun. Sometimes, after excavation, the road site lies below water, but many such installations have been completed satisfactorily. On a project through tidal lands along San Francisco Bay, excavation was performed with floating clamshell dredges. The succeeding hydraulic dredge fill was of sand from the bay bottom, transported up to 5 miles through the discharge pipeline.

Displacement methods

Many fills have been built over marshes by displacing the unsuitable muck with better material. Displacement may be caused by the weight of the fill alone or by this weight supplemented by explosives or water jetting. Satisfactory fills constructed in 80 ft of unstable material are on record, although success at this depth was under extremely favorable conditions. For shallow fills through mucks up to about 10 or 12 ft deep, the fill material is sometimes piled onto the muck and displaces it sidewise. Again, a trench about the width of the embankment may be blasted out and immediately backfilled with stable embankment material. The blast throws part of the muck out of the trench, and an added amount is liquefied so that it is easily displaced.

Where the muck is deeper, the "underfill" method is often employed. A trench is blasted and a large portion of the fill material placed. Explosive charges, set off in the underlying muck, force it from under the embankment, which settles into place. A refinement of the underfill method is the relief method. After the fill material is placed, relief ditches are blasted along the sides of the fill to make displacement of the underlying muck easier. In this way, the explosive charge can be reduced and disruption to the fill minimized.[21]

Surcharge method

The instability of peats and mucks results largely from their extremely high moisture content, often 100% of their dry weight.[22] If a sufficient portion of this moisture can be displaced and the soil grains forced into more intimate contact, the supporting power may become adequate.

The surcharge method is begun by laying a working table of fill material over the muck to support construction equipment. The fill then is built in compacted layers until its height, allowing for settlement, approximates final grade. A surcharge of uncompacted fill material is then placed. This added weight accelerates the flow of water from the muck and speeds up consolidation. Care must be exercised in order that loads do not exceed the shearing strength of the muck; otherwise it will be displaced, and disastrous settlement of the fill will result. After a period of consolidation, the surcharge material is removed for other purposes, and base course and temporary pavement are placed.

The surcharge method is employed for low fills over shallow muck up to 12 or 15 ft in depth. It may not provide for complete consolidation during the construction period, but it does obtain most of it. If the muck is of fairly uniform consistency and moisture content, subsequent slow settlement will be fairly uniform, and the road surface will develop only minor roughness. However, large differential settlement is possible where subsurface conditions vary greatly. After

[21] For more on displacement methods see the *Field Manual of Soils Engineering,* Michigan State Highway Department, pp. 102–109. Also see M. N. Sinacori, W. P. Hofmann, and A. H. Emery, *Proceedings Highway Research Board,* pp. 601–621 (1952).

[22] At 100% moisture content a cubic foot of muck contains only 45 lb of soil.

several years have passed and consolidation is largely completed, a permanent pavement can be placed.

Vertical sand drain method [23]

Vertical sand drains provide rapid consolidation of deep layers of muck. They were first employed in 1934 by the California Division of Highways and by 1948 had been used by this agency on 22 projects.

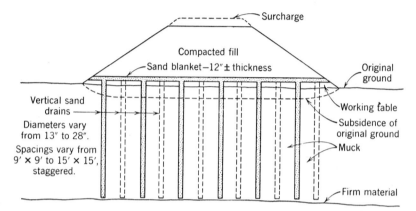

Fig. 8. Typical vertical sand drain installation

Many others in the United States and abroad have also made successful installations. An outstanding example is the New Jersey Turnpike where the combined length of sand drains underlying the 113-mile road is 947 miles.

Sand drains are vertical columns of sand that penetrate the muck almost to solid material. Across their tops is a horizontal sand blanket extending through the side slopes of the fill (see Fig. 8). Under the pressure induced by fill and surcharge, subsurface water flows up the drains and out of the fill. Rapid consolidation of the muck results.

It has been proved that, other things being equal, the time required to force water from a fine-grained soil varies about as the square of the distance the water must travel. Without sand drains, this distance is at least half of the fill width; with them, it is nearer 5 ft. Furthermore, most mucks have greater permeability in a horizontal than in a

[23] See O. J. Porter in *Proceedings Highway Research Board,* part 2, pp. 129–141 (1938), and (with L. C. Urquhart) in *Civil Engineering,* January 1952, pp. 51–55. Also see T. E. Stanton, *California Highways and Public Works,* March, April 1948, pp. 16–19.

vertical direction, and the drains provide an easy means for the vertical movement of water. It has been estimated that sand drains produce the same consolidation in a hundredth of the time. Stated differently, 50 years' settlement is gained during a 6-month construction season. Figure 9 gives time-settlement data on two installations on the New Jersey Turnpike. In both, almost all settlement was obtained in less than 14 months.

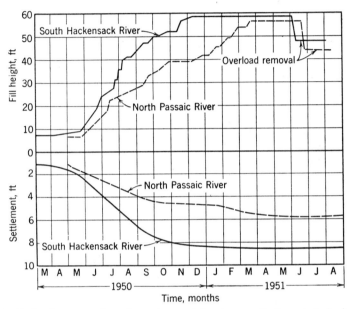

Fig. 9. Embankment and settlement record for two vertical sand drain installations on the New Jersey Turnpike (Courtesy *Civil Engineering*)

Sand drain construction begins with the placing of a working table of fill material (see Fig. 8). Special equipment as described below operates from this table to install the vertical columns of sand. Placing of the sand blanket, compacted fill, and surcharge is done by conventional methods.

As fill and surcharge are placed over the sand drains, internal pressures develop in the muck, and, if these become too great, the muck will be displaced from under the fill. It is possible to measure these pressures by gages connected to well points driven to proper depths. When the gage readings approach the predetermined shearing strength of the muck, filling is halted and not resumed until the pressure has fallen to a safe level.

Brief descriptions of four ingenious methods for installing the vertical sand columns follow:

Rotary-drill method. Vertical holes are drilled with a rotary bucket similar to a soil auger and immediately backfilled with sand. If the underlying material is particularly unstable, it tends to squeeze in and fill the holes, although this action sometimes can be controlled by filling the hole with water. Depths of 70 ft have been reached with the rotary drill.

Rotary-jet method. The holes are drilled by a high-speed rotary jet, and the cuttings are washed to the surface by the water. This method is unsatisfactory in materials that will not stand.

Driven-mandrel method. A hollow steel tube with a hinged bottom is driven down by a pile driver. The bottom is closed during driving to keep the mandrel empty. After the driven tube has been filled with sand, it is slowly withdrawn, and the sand flows out through the bottom and fills the hole. Often compressed air is charged into the top of the tube to force the sand to flow more rapidly. Drains 100 ft deep have been installed in this manner. The driven-mandrel method is more widely used than any other. However, it is unsatisfactory in tenacious soils which prevent withdrawal of the mandrel, or where the jarring action of the pile driver will damage adjacent structures.

Jetted-mandrel method. Water jets in the base of the mandrel open the ground for it. Sand is placed as the mandrel is withdrawn. Both "closed-end" and "double-walled" types of jetted mandrels have been successful.

14 — Gravel and Crushed Rock Roads— Stabilized Roads

INTRODUCTION

Roadway fills are constructed of material from adjacent cuts or nearby borrow pits. On these fills are placed the base courses and wearing surfaces on which vehicles travel (see Fig. 1, p. 309). The nature, thickness, and composition of these upper layers will vary widely with the volume and character of traffic, the cost and availability of materials, and the opinions of roadway designers. Common to all is the fact that they are composed largely of soil, sand, and rock. Often a small percentage of bituminous material, cement, or a salt may be added to the surface or even to the underlying layers, but the bulk always comes from the earth's crust, usually from some location fairly near the project under construction. No other material presently available can compete with these on a cost and service basis.

Materials in bases and wearing surfaces must be of higher quality than those suitable for the subgrade, as greater demands are placed on them. This higher quality is obtained by careful selection of the source material and (usually) by special processing like crushing or screening. Sometimes materials from two or more sources are combined to secure a better product.

Over the United States, with its wide variety of materials, climates, and service needs, many satisfactory methods and processes for producing good road surfaces have been developed. At one extreme is the earth road, constructed by shaping the native soil to the cross section of the finished road. At the other are found high-type concrete and bituminous pavements separated from the subgrade by a considerable thickness of relatively expensive and carefully selected base course. It is the highway engineer's responsibility to decide which of the many possible choices best meets the requirement of lowest over-all cost for each job.

In the United States (1951), some 1.1 million miles of the 1.7 million miles of improved rural roads have surfaces of untreated soil mixtures, often called "gravel" roads (see Fig. 1). In addition, another 580,000 miles are graded and drained but unsurfaced and they present the same problems. The bulk of these mileages are under the jurisdiction of local rural road agencies. However, 170,000 miles of state-administered highways also fall under these classifications, and so the problem

Fig. 1.   An excellent untreated gravel surface

is not entirely a local one. Urban areas have some 80,000 miles of streets surfaced with untreated soil mixtures.

This chapter describes the design and construction of road surfaces from soils or other natural material and also deals briefly with certain methods for stabilizing these natural materials.

ROAD SURFACES OF UNTREATED SOIL MIXTURES

General requirements

For roads of low traffic volume, surfaces of untreated soil mixtures described as gravel or crushed rock give excellent service. They consist largely of stone pebbles or crushed-rock particles combined with clay, lime, iron oxide, or other fine material in sufficient amount to bond the coarse particles together. Many locally occurring materials such as blast-furnace slag, limerock, shells, caliche, chert, iron ore, and volcanic cinders have also been satisfactory.

Requisites of road surfaces of untreated soil mixtures, as given by E. A. Willis of the Bureau of Public Roads are: [1]

First, stability: that is, they must support the superimposed loads without detrimental deformation. Second, they must stand the abrasive action of traffic. Third, they should shed a large portion of the rain which falls on the surface since a large amount of water penetrating the surface might cause loss of stability in the wearing course or softening of the subgrade. Finally, they should possess capillary properties in amount sufficient to replace moisture lost by surface evaporation and thus maintain the desirable damp condition in which the particles are bound together by thin moisture films. An added requirement is that the surface course must be of low cost, as funds for the improvement of low-traffic roads are limited. This, in turn, limits the sources of materials to the immediate locality, because of high costs involved in transporting them any great distance.

The proportions of almost all satisfactory untreated soil surfaces are found to conform to a set of simple rules first set forth for sand-clay roads by Dr. C. N. Strahan,[2] as follows:

(a) Enough clay present to cement the sand and silt in dry or low moisture condition; but not so much clay that its expansion by water will dislocate the seating and imbedment bond of the granular particles, vis., the surface should maintain a constant volume.

(b) A liberal amount of coarse sand grains to furnish an adequate seating or bearing bond, not materially affected by water content.

(c) Only moderate amounts of silt and very fine sand. A superabundance of silt, very fine sand, and especially clay tends to reduce percolation after rains and to hold larger amounts of water in the surface whereby the liquid limits of the fine ingredients are more rapidly approached and the stability of the surface more rapidly weakened.

(d) When coarse material (retained on the No. 10 sieve) is present or is added to a good soil mortar in appreciable amount (10 per cent or more) the hardness and durability of the surface is increased until the full gravel type of surface is reached.

Further criteria established by later research are:

1. Control of grading is essential to insure stability of granular mixtures containing soil binders. Limits on the percentages passing the no. 40 and no. 200 sieves offer a suitable check on the part passing the no. 10 sieve.

2. Control of the plasticity index is essential when the final mixture contains more than 40% passing the no. 10 sieve. Road-surface ma-

[1] *Proceedings Highway Research Board*, part II, pp. 206–208 (1938).
[2] See *Public Roads*, September 1929, pp. 117–136.

terials with a low but measurable plasticity index are to be preferred to absolutely nonplastic ones, and decidedly superior to those having appreciably higher plasticity index values.

The quantity and character of the clay is very important, as it serves as both a binder and a moisture regulator. In dry weather the moisture film on the clay particles binds the entire mass together. In wet weather the first rain that falls on the surface causes the clay to expand and close the pores, thereby preventing water from entering and softening the material. Traffic over the wet surface merely creates a thin layer of nonslippery mud which rebinds when drying. The effect of excessive amounts of highly expansive clays is, when wet, to swell and unseat the coarser materials layer by layer, thus weakening the road.

Where no underlying source of capillary moisture is present, long dry periods without rainfall result in deterioration of untreated surfaces. When the moisture film around the clay particles disappears, the binding power of the clay also disappears, and the surface disintegrates under traffic.

The usual specifications for untreated road surfaces are so written that the important properties mentioned above are prescribed. They include statements to control grading of the material, the plasticity of its fines, and the strength of the aggregate particles.

Typical of permissible gradings are Type I, gradings C and D, and Type II, gradings E and F, of the AASHO (see Table 1). Notice

TABLE 1. GRADING REQUIREMENTS FOR SOIL-AGGREGATE MATERIALS

AASHO Designation M147–49

Percentage by Weight Passing Square Mesh Sieves

Sieve Designation	Type I				Type II	
	Grading A	Grading B	Grading C	Grading D	Grading E	Grading F
2-in.	100	100	.....	......	......	......
1-in.	.....	.....	100	100	100	100
⅜-in.	30–65	40–75	50–85	60–100	......	......
No. 10	15–40	20–45	25–50	30–65	40–100	55–100
No. 40	8–20	10–25	12–30	15–40	20–50	30–70
No. 200	2–8	3–10	4–12	5–15	6–20	8–25

that, though a wide variety of materials is acceptable, the limits assure a fairly uniform distribution of particle size from coarse to fine. The

AASHO specifications include an added general requirement with a like purpose: it is that the fraction passing the no. 200 sieve shall not be greater than two-thirds of the fraction passing the no. 40 sieve.

Some plasticity is desirable in untreated surface courses. The AASHO specifications call for a maximum liquid limit of 35 and a plasticity index range from 4 to 9 for soil-aggregate surface courses that are to be maintained for several years without bituminous-surface treatment or other impervious surfacing. They also set minimum limits of 8% passing the no. 200 sieve for surface courses of grading types C, D, and E.

Regarding strength and soundness of aggregates, the AASHO specifications read as follows: "Coarse aggregates (retained on No. 10 sieve) shall consist of hard, durable particles or fragments of stone, gravel, or slag. Materials that break up when alternately frozen and thawed or wet and dried shall not be used. Fine aggregate (passing No. 10 sieve) shall consist of natural or crushed sand and fine mineral particles passing the No. 200 sieve. The composite soil-aggregate mixture shall be free from vegetable matter and lumps or balls of clay."

Specifications for untreated surface courses vary considerably among agencies, although some of the state highway departments now use those of the AASHO, as outlined above. Many agencies stipulate that all the large or oversize material in the gravel pit be crushed. In this way they include all the tougher, harder stones, and also gain the angular shapes and rough surfaces so important to stability. A few highway departments require physical testing beyond that called for by the AASHO specifications. Typical provisions are that the coarse aggregate be subjected to the Los Angeles rattler test (see p. 467), and that the loss on this test not exceed 50%; that the California bearing ratio (CBR) be at least 80; and that the expansion of a compacted sample during soaking not exceed 1%.

The principal problems in connection with large volumes of motor traffic on roads with untreated surfaces have been the prevention of dust and "corrugations" and the annual wearing away of materials from the surface. There is serious doubt that such roads are economical when traffic exceeds 400 to 500 vehicles per day.

Grading and draining untreated surfacings

For much modern road construction, untreated or "dry-gravel" surfaces are employed temporarily as a "stage-construction"[3] surfacing.

[3] "Stage construction" is a step-by-step improvement of a roadway structure

This idea applies particularly where traffic must be carried economically for long distances until a more durable type of surface can be financed. Consequently, high design standards for grade and alinement of the roadbed are demanded at the outset. In the past, because of limited funds, wearing surfaces have sometimes been too narrow; in fact, some one-way gravel roads only 10 ft wide have been built. Two-way roads with a surface width of 16 or 18 ft have also been constructed. Present-day standards for secondary roads,[4] many of which are gravel-surfaced, call for minimum roadbed widths, including shoulders, of 20 to 26 ft, depending on traffic volume. Good practice dictates that the gravel surface course as well as any underlying base courses be carried across the full roadway width.[5]

Distribution of traffic over the full width of gravel surfaces is very desirable to preserve the stability of the material and to distribute the wear. To this end, the tendency has been toward wide surfaces and lower crowns. A cross slope as low as $\frac{1}{4}$ in. to the foot is now sometimes built, particularly if the material is sufficiently stable that such a low crown will shed water. It may be necessary on grades of 5% or more to increase the crown to $\frac{3}{8}$ or possibly $\frac{1}{2}$ in. to the foot in order that rainwater may be carried quickly to the side ditches. If such high crowns are employed, they must be reduced before any kind of bituminous surface is applied.

Roads with untreated surfaces should be designed and constructed with suitable superelevation on curves and with widened traveled way wherever the curvature is sharp or the visibility limited. In fact,

as the expenditures are justified by the demands of increased traffic. To illustrate, stage 1 might be an earth surface; stage 2, untreated gravel; stage 3, bituminous-surface treatment over the gravel; stage 4, some higher-type pavement.

[4] *Design Standards*, AASHO, March 1949.

[5] In the past the so-called "trench" and "feather-edged" cross sections for surfaces have been widely used. In the former, the base or surface courses extended only to the shoulders. The shoulders themselves were constructed of ordinary fill material. Thus, the surface or base materials lay in a trench. Many failures resulted because of instability of the shoulders and the entrapment of subsurface moisture. These failures led to the gradual abandonment of the method.

Feather-edge construction involves placing a variable thickness of surfacing. At center line, the surfacing is made quite thick, whereas at the edges it "feathers" out to a thin layer. For roads carrying very little traffic so that vehicles generally travel in the center of the road, this method is satisfactory. Where vehicles must continuously use the full roadway width, the thin "feather-edge" soon fails.

gravel roads frequently require all the refinements in design and construction demanded by the more expensive surface types.

Material for untreated surfacings

It is difficult to specify the best material for a given service and condition. A governing element is the relative economy of each possible type of surface. Consequently, local deposits ordinarily must be used. In general, bank or glacial gravel is better than river gravel which is frequently loose and sandy. Desirable qualities for the gravel are that it shall consolidate sufficiently by rolling or traffic, remain stable, and not wear excessively or "pit" under traffic. Gravel found cemented together in the bank usually is excellent. The more angular and rough-surfaced particles the gravel contains the better. Crushed gravel is therefore desirable, and some state specifications set a minimum percentage of crushed fragments.[6] Any pit of otherwise suitable gravel with 20% or more oversized material justifies crushing. The final superficial layer of material of 1 in. or less in thickness, however, need not stay tightly bonded. In fact, a thin "floating" layer of small pebbles is often desirable (see Fig. 1).

It is now universally recognized that large pebbles or large crushed pieces in the gravel are not permissible. Many miles of gravel roads are in use in which gravel retained on 2-in. or even on 1-in. screens ruins the road surface. Surface or top-course gravel should be fine and usually should pass a 1-in.-square opening. If the top course is at least 3 in. thick when compacted, the base course may contain larger material, say material passing a $1\frac{1}{2}$-in. opening—especially if the gravel "packs" readily and there is no danger of the base material becoming in any way mixed with the top. There are, of course, successful variations of this standard.

The best grading of the gravel below the maximum size is a matter of less certainty. There are various favorable gradings, depending on the kind of gravel and the nature of the fines or material passing the $\frac{1}{4}$-in. mesh screen. It is commonly held that for the top course about 25 to 50% of material must pass the 10-mesh screen. Extremes in specifications allow between 3 and 25% of the material to be clay and silt passing the 200-mesh screen. However, excess clay, loam, or other binder may cause the surface to pack hard and form a crust which pits.

[6] There are exceptions to this rule. The fresh-broken surfaces of some rocks, such as quartz, are slick and smooth, and their use results in low stability. On the other hand, some rounded stream pebbles have rough surfaces and serve very well.

Gravel that consists of clean pebbles without any fines is very difficult to consolidate. On the other hand, the "fines" which quickly bring a gravel surface to a tight consolidated condition make the dust that goes off first under traffic. The best test of the binding quality of gravel is its use on the road. A sample section is of immense value in deciding on the proper source for the material.

Construction of untreated surfacing

The best roads demand a base course extending across the full width of the roadbed and a thoroughly rolled subgrade. The untreated surfacing then is usually placed not less than 8 in. in loose depth,[7] frequently in two courses and sometimes in three. All courses are consolidated separately. Any lower course should be laid somewhat in advance of the following course. Dumping of any surfacing material in piles directly on the subgrade or on the bottom course is prohibited. Material for each course is distributed from moving dump trucks, spreader boxes, or self-powered spreading machines (see for example Fig. 3, p. 441). Good practice also permits distribution in one or two windrows and then the spreading of the material with a blade grader.

Rolling the surfacing after placement is standard practice, but rolling without sprinkling is scarcely worth while except in climates where there is intermittent rain or where the material itself has a considerable percentage of moisture. Watering is frequently available at moderate cost and is a great help in hastening the consolidation of the road. In such cases, water should invariably be used. Rolling commonly is done with a smooth-wheeled roller weighing not less than 8 tons. It begins at the edges or sides and progresses toward the center, with each passage lapping the rear wheel track a half-width. However, pneumatic rollers are permitted or required by some agencies. Rolling, with watering and blading if needed, should continue until the rolled course or layer is thoroughly consolidated.

Although power rolling with alternate watering is preferable, it is not indispensable. When rolling is omitted, it is good practice to extend the successive layers of surfacing material away from the source of supply and to insist that the hauling vehicles spread their tracking entirely across the full roadbed width and not in ruts. Repeated light dragging or blading will then in time obliterate ruts and consolidate the layers of gravel. Heavy motor trucks thus afford an excellent substitute for rolling. It is better to use a light drag or light blade

---

[7] On compaction these materials usually shrink between 20 and 25%. Thus an 8 in. loose layer will be approximately 6 in. thick after compaction.

and not to attempt to fill the ruts continually but rather gradually to obliterate them and to allow consolidation of the spread gravel to develop from the bottom upward. A relatively thick layer is favorable for such final consolidation from the bottom upward, but no courses should exceed 6 in. loose measure. When traffic has brought about partial consolidation or has compacted the base and part of the top, it frequently is beneficial both to traffic and to the surface itself to blade or scrape off temporarily the remaining loose layer into a side windrow. Then at favorable opportunities after rains the windrowed material should be "floated" or "drifted" back gradually and traffic allowed to consolidate it progressively.

Some of the best untreated-soil surfaces have been obtained by a thorough blading of the entire layer of gravel back and forth across the road to mix the materials thoroughly into a uniform condition, with the fines well distributed.

Payment for untreated-soil surfacing

Untreated-soil surfacings are paid for in a number of ways. The most common bases are tons or cubic yards of material furnished in place on the road. The methods described in the specifications of the Bureau of Public Roads for national-forest and national-park road construction are typical. They are essentially as follows:

The type and grading of base- and/or top-course material to be paid for and the units of measure shall be as called for in the bid schedule, i.e., either tons weighed on scales furnished by the contractor or cubic yards loose measured in the vehicle at the point of delivery, except that selected borrow-base or top-course material shall be measured in original position by the method of average end areas.

These quantities of materials, including any filler blended on the road, placed, bonded, and accepted in the corresponding completed course, or placed in authorized stockpiles, shall be paid for at the contract unit prices, which prices and payment shall constitute full payment for furnishing, hauling and placing, mixing, blading and rolling, conditioning roadway, including shoulders and gutters; for construction, repair, and obliteration of access roads and cleanup of pits and quarries; for handling and disposal of unsuitable materials encountered in quarry or pit operations, and cleaning and leveling of stockpile sites; for furnishing and sealing of scales and weigh house and for all labor, equipment, tools, and incidentals necessary to complete the item; except that the clearing and stripping of designated pits and quarries and required w̧atering may be measured and paid for under separate items desig-nated, respectively, as "clearing," "borrow," and "watering."

Surfaces of fine-crushed rock or gravel

About 1920 a surface of fine-crushed stone was initiated in Oregon and Washington. It was found that crushed stone or crushed gravel passing an inch screen bonded well and could be obtained cheaply, particularly in the Columbia River Basin country. Material from basaltic talus slopes was par-ticularly favorable. Base course of broken stone passing a 1½-in. circular opening was commonly used. Sometimes the top course was required to pass a ¾-in. circular opening.

The prevailing general intent was to use available local material. For mass production of the fine-crushed material, a combination of primary and sec-ondary crushing plants was generally required, with some form of disk or roll crusher for the secondary unit. Greater care was taken progressively in the producing-plant setups, especially in the use of concrete foundations for the various mechanical units. The "processing" of the fine material back and forth across the road by heavy blade graders was especially favorable in pro-ducing a uniform mixture.

With the advent of processing with liquid bituminous materials, beginning about 1927 in the Far West, the fine-crushed-rock or fine-crushed-gravel roads became even more important. Gravel pits with considerable oversize were utilized to good advantage. As the bituminous or "oil" processing developed, the grading specifications tended to permit a larger fraction of the fine material passing the ¼-in. screen. About 1928 the Bureau of Public Roads specifica-tions stipulated that binder material passing the ¼-in. opening should not exceed 35%, of which 40% should be retained on a no. 30 sieve, and 15 to 35% should pass a no. 200 sieve.

There is no essential difference between the methods of constructing fine-crushed-rock or fine-crushed-gravel roads and the methods employed on other untreated-soil roads. Unless the top-course material is 3 in. or more in thickness, it is well not to permit any fraction of larger size in the bottom-course material than in the top. Otherwise, any subsequent bituminous road-mixing construction or "oil" processing of the top 2½ in. may bring up larger pieces into the top course.

There is no question that angular crushed hard stone and crushed gravel are wearing on rubber-tired vehicles, especially during the consolidation stage of the surfacing. Because of the presence of considerable fines on the road, another objection is the dust that is usually present in the thin floating surface layer. In some cases transverse corrugations are likely to develop. All these objections are eliminated by the present practice of quickly surface-treating or mixing with bituminous material in some form. In fact, with travel exceeding about 400 vehicles per day, unless in areas of sufficient intermittent rainfall, the "dry" fine-crushed roads are of doubtful economy, in spite of their excel-lence and low first cost. In some dry areas suitable clay binder has been used with success, but it must always be introduced very sparingly, particularly if there is to be any subsequent treatment with bituminous material.

The cost of these road surfaces of fine-crushed material does not much exceed the cost of good soil surfaces. It will depend, of course, largely on the thickness and width of the road surface and on the availability of local materials. Payment for them is by the methods already indicated.

Locally occurring surfacing materials

Several materials of local occurrence serve as excellent surfacing for low-traffic roads. In general, the same types of cross sections, thicknesses, and construction and maintenance procedures as for untreated-soil surfaces are used. As a rule, special specifications must be written for them.

Blast-furnace slag. In areas where slag is available as a by-product of the production of metals, it is widely employed as a road-surfacing or base-course material. In some cases, coarse aggregates and binder are both produced from the slag; in others, slag for the coarse particles is combined with binder from other sources. Ofter a macadam-type [8] construction is advantageous.

Limerock (marl). In some of the Southeast, Gulf Coast, and Mississippi Valley states there are deposits of a soft limerock which has served as a base and road surface. As a surface course it has certain objectionable qualities such as a white, glaring surface under sunlight and a tendency to dust under traffic and to soften in continued rainy weather. When well-drained, it gives good service if protected by a bituminous surface treatment.

Shells. Deposits of oyster, clam and similar shells occur along the eastern and Gulf coasts. These shells, usually obtained by dredging, are used as a surfacing for lightly traveled roads. The mud that is dredged with the shells serves as binder. When traffic is heavy, the surface must be protected by a bituminous treatment or stabilized with Portland cement.

Caliche. In parts of Texas, New Mexico, and Arizona occurs a calcium formation consisting of sands and gravels cemented together by coats of calcium carbonate. This chemical was carried in solution by groundwater and remained when the water evaporated. In most cases caliche is essentially soft limestone with varying percentages of clay. It is widely used on low-traffic roads as a surface material, often as a substitute for gravel.

Chert. Chert gravels, found in some quantity in the southeastern United States, consist of mixtures of coarse chert particles and fine material from the dust of fracture and clay. They have given satisfactory service as surface courses; but, when they were used as base courses, numerous failures resulted because of excessive amounts of active binder. There is strong indication that their behavior can be greatly improved by the addition of basic material such as hydrated lime or basic slag.[9]

Iron ore. In some of the southern states low-grade iron ore serves for road surfacing in a manner similar to gravel.

Volcanic cinders. Volcanic cinders occur widely throughout the southwestern United States, and long have been employed successfully as a surface for lightly traveled roads. Experience has indicated that they can also be used successfully as base-course material for a thin bituminous surface treatment on more heavily traveled roads. Careful selection is required.[10]

[8] See p. 434.

[9] See E. A. Willis and P. C. Smith, *Public Roads*, June 1940, pp. 65–68.

[10] See E. A. Willis, Henry Aaron, and R. C. Lindberg, *Public Roads*, October 1942, pp. 125–135.

Maintenance of soil-surfaced roads [11]

In general, maintenance is by a combination of motor blade patrol and supplementary or extra gangs with motorized equipment. The extra gangs supply new gravel and do heavy blade-grading and scarifying. Late fall and early spring maintenance operations are especially important in areas where the winters are severe. Frequently it is necessary at the earliest possible moment in the spring to use a heavy blade grader to smooth out defects that have developed during the winter. The extra gang often is called upon to scarify roads that have large-size gravel protruding. If the road has become deeply rutted or pitted it is necessary to scarify at least to the depth of the deepest holes and remove oversize gravel by blade or by hand raking. Such oversize material should be removed completely; otherwise it may be dragged back into the surface by the patrol maintenance. Heavy blading in the spring should cover the entire width of the road, including ditches, and the first trips may be made with the blade set nearly at right angles to the axis of the road. It may be necessary to supply additional surfacing material to fill ruts and replace material worn away. This should all pass the 1-in. screen, preferably the ¾-in. screen, and should be relatively clean. Excess binder in new material will tend to cause crusts and pits to form. The new application should be not less than the yearly loss by traffic, which amounts to a thickness of half an inch to an inch over the road's surface. The patrol may also supply gravel from stockpiles. When the extra-gang operations are complete, the road should be in good shape for economical patrol maintenance for the remainder of the season. In the late fall, the entire road should be given a thorough conditioning to insure that it starts the winter as smooth as possible and with the drainage system working perfectly.

There are various types of equipment for maintaining the surface of gravel and like roads. Probably the most common is the power grader (see Fig. 2). This machine not only blades the road surface but also cleans and shapes side slopes and gutter ditches. It has the further advantage of high travel speed when moving from one work location to another. At times blade graders pulled by tractors are used, particularly for heavy work. Sometimes a detachable blade for surface maintenance is fastened to the undercarriage of a heavy truck. The road drag (or road planer) has done much duty in surface main-

[11] See *A Policy on Maintenance of Roadway Surfaces*, AASHO, January 1948, pp. 7–18.

tenance. It is a heavy frame of timber or steel to which are fastened one or more hardened-steel cutting edges. This is pulled along the road by a truck or light tractor and smooths the surface by cutting off high spots and filling in holes and corrugations. A dump-truck, drag combination is particularly advantageous, as the truck may be freed for hauling gravel and like purposes.

FIG. 2.   Motor grader blading a rough gravel road surface (Courtesy Galion Iron Works and Mfg. Co.)

The most effective maintenance is done immediately after a rain. Then the surface is soft and can be cut with the blade or drag. The loosened material fills holes and corrugations and is fixed in place by the moisture, coupled with the compactive action of traffic.

An important rule is to maintain the crown. Otherwise water will stand, and soak and soften the road surface. Furthermore, the standing water is troublesome to motorists.

A frequent adverse condition is the transverse corrugation of the gravel or fine-crush surface. This "washboard" effect is associated usually with higher volumes of motor traffic, but may appear when the count is as low as 100 vehicles per day. The transverse shallow waves tend to average about 30 in. from crest to crest and not to exceed 1½ in. in depth from crest to trough. Sometimes they reach entirely across, and in cases noted they are at an angle of less than 90 degrees with the road axis. Washboarding increases with traffic. Frequent planing and dragging is the necessary treatment. If corrugations are prevented from becoming pronounced, they usually can be eliminated by effective patrol maintenance. Otherwise, the extra gang may have to apply heavy blading after a rain. In any event constant vigilance is necessary. Above a certain volume of travel, however, surface treatment with bituminous material is the only complete correction.

If a light mulch with a sufficient percentage of angular particles is constantly kept moving by blading or dragging, corrugations in general do not tend to develop rapidly. In fact, the use of a thin coat of loose material is one of the most effective elements developed by modern gravel-road maintenance. It must, however, be kept constantly moving to be effective, and, when greater travel develops, the patrol may have to be shortened and the weight of equipment increased. It is a mistake to think that blading or dragging the gravel road is of no benefit during dry weather.

One of the most serious defects of the "dry" gravel road is the annoying and dangerous dust that increases with traffic. Only bituminous surface treatment or some other form of surfacing effectively cures this ill.

The winter use of gravel roads is hard on the surface, particularly when the road becomes covered with ice and automobiles with chains travel in a single rut. In general, however, snow removal helps the subsequent maintenance during the summer.

STABILIZED ROAD SURFACES

Sand-clay roads

Since about 1932, the collective term "stabilized road" has become significant. It now denotes a class of bases or road surfaces built with controlled mixtures of local soil and mineral materials with or without the addition of such commercial additives as calcium chloride, bitumen, or Portland cement. It thus includes sand-clay roads.

Essentially, a sand-clay road is a favorable mixture of clay, silt, fine and coarse sand, and preferably some fine gravel. It is built thicker than most road surfaces, usually 8 or more inches in finished depth. Sand-clay mixtures also make an excellent base for certain types of pavement.

Successful practice with sand-clay construction must be based on the principles previously laid down for untreated-surface courses. Furthermore, such roads are economical only in areas where suitable sources of sand and clay are available locally. They originally developed in the South Atlantic States but in later years have been built in some of the middle western and western states, particularly Nebraska, Kansas, and Wyoming.

Early development of the sand-clay road. Observations in the South Atlantic States during the light traffic of the period of 1900–10 showed that road surfaces of "topsoil," "gray soil," "gray grit," "black tobacco soil," "upland soil," and "rotten granite" were usually successful. These materials often were natural deposits of sand and clay that occurred on slight knolls adjacent to the road, particularly in cultivated fields. Deposits evidenced aeration, water leaching, and oxidization. Such material usually was in a thin gray layer not exceeding a foot in thickness but occasionally occurred outside of cultivated fields and in deeper layers. In the beginning the best guide to the selection of material was a service test on the roads. Roads were built by simply hauling the soil onto the roadbed and depositing a thick layer which consolidated and cured under traffic. Later these roads were successfully dragged.

Early studies made on the quality of the material showed that sand was frequently disintegrated quartzite, and the clay decomposed mineral feldspar or leached-out feldspar. Water-deposited or sedimentary clays were found to be firmer and more plastic as determined by the sticky or doughlike quality in the presence of water. Some clays were sufficiently plastic that balls made of them would cohere when immersed. Clays falling to pieces in water were called "slaking clays" and were considered less satisfactory. It was recognized that the clay binder should just about fill the voids in the sand, but usually no precise measurement of the voids was made. It was further observed that excess clay deformed the roads and that insufficient clay caused raveling. Much puddling was considered necessary, and conditions for puddling were found favorable after a long rain.

When the subgrade was clay, it was covered with a few inches of sand and plowed and disk-harrowed, preferably when moist. When the subgrade was sand, an even layer of dry clay was spread, beginning next to the clay pit so that hauling broke up the clay lumps. Another layer of sand was added; then usually it was considered necessary to plow and harrow. Advantage was taken of rains, and sand or clay was added as conditions developed.[12]

Such early roads were very cheap. When labor in the South could be had for $1 per day, and teams for $3, and the average haul did not exceed a mile, a 12-ft-wide sand-clay road 6 in. deep, consolidated, could be built for about $600 per mile. Sometimes roads were built

Fig. 3. Hauling topsoil to an early demonstration road in Yanceyville, N. C. (Courtesy, U. S. Bureau of Public Roads)

for as low as $300 per mile. Figure 3 illustrates the construction practices employed on these early roads.

Modern sand-clay roads. In areas where gravel or crushed stone is expensive, and especially where labor is cheap, the modern sand-clay road for traffic up to about 500 vehicles is relatively economical and gives good service. Following the work of Dr. C. M. Strahan from 1922 to 1927 in Georgia in cooperation with Bureau of Public Roads, specifications have been developed very carefully. It has been found

[12] See particularly W. L. Spoon, Sand-Clay and Burnt-Clay Roads, *Farmers' Bulletin 311*, U. S. Department of Agriculture, December 1907; Sand-Clay and Earth Roads in the Middle West, *Circular 91* (1910); and Descriptive Catalog of the Road Models of the Office of Public Roads, *Office of Public Roads Bulletin 47* (1913).

also that the well-built sand-clay road as a first stage of construction or as a subgrade for superior surfaces may be an important element in highway construction in some areas.

A favorable grain-size distribution for sand-clay mixtures [13] is grading F of Table 1. The plasticity requirements set forth for untreated soil mixtures (see p. 399) also apply to materials for sand-clay road surfaces.

Improvement has been made in thin natural deposits of topsoils by first plowing and thoroughly mixing them before they are hauled. Any subsurface deposits found in pits are also most thoroughly harrowed after transfer to the roadbed. More recently there have been not only improvements in details of mixing, but also better methods of packing or consolidating the slab from the bottom upward by the abundant use of water and by taking quick advantage of rain.

Topsoil will compact to about two-thirds of its loose depth. A 12-in. layer of loose topsoil will thus consolidate to about 8 in. Since the consolidation occurs from the bottom upward, traffic, after the mixing is complete, is ordinarily beneficial. Rolling with a three-wheel power roller is not of special benefit. Any rolling should be done with a sheepsfoot roller in order to pack the lower layers first. Green slabs that have become muddy and thoroughly puddled during rain show ultimately greater strength when packed, but they will require considerable machining and reshaping until finally set.

Sand-clay roads are now built with a crown of $\frac{3}{8}$ to $\frac{1}{4}$ in. per ft, and sometimes with even less crown if they are very wide. The shoulder should preferably be built with a thin sand-clay mixture. In fact, a sand-clay surface from out to out of the graded width of the roadbed will more effectively drain the surface, distribute traffic, and prevent the admixture of inferior material by maintenance operations.

Granular stabilized roads

In many areas of the United States there occur in separate deposits coarse aggregates, sands, and binder soils. These, when properly combined and processed, make excellent base courses as well as road-surface materials for low-traffic roads. As with gravel, crushed-rock, or sand-clay surfacing in other localities, this type developed because it offered the most economical solution to the road-surfacing problem.

[13] See *AASHO Designation M61–42* in the 1947 edition of *Highway Materials* for a somewhat different specification which covers mixtures containing some particles retained on the no. 10 sieve.

No sharp line can be drawn between granular stabilized roads and gravel or crushed-rock roads. All must follow the same principles of controlled grading and quality of fines if they are to perform satisfactorily. Stabilization usually implies that the source materials come from two or more locations and must be mixed before placing.

Complete and thorough mixing of the component materials is essential. During the first few years that stabilization was employed, it was customary to dump the various materials in layers on the subgrade. They were then pulverized with harrows and other soil pulverizers, and mixed with blade graders. After mixing, they were spread by the blades and consolidated by traffic. In this manner, many excellent roads were and still are built. Often, however, results were not uniform. In one spot the surface when wet would displace or become slick because of too much binder, while nearby it would ravel because of an excess of gravel. Investigation revealed that accurate control was lacking in spreading the component materials, in mixing, or in both operations. As a result, over the years, refinements in proportioning, mixing, and spreading methods have developed until, at present, procedures and controls as elaborate as those for bituminous pavements are often employed. Figure 4 shows a diagrammatic sketch of a continuous-type stationary plant, complete with provisions for adding water and calcium chloride (if desired). Batch-type mixers and traveling mixing plants are also in common use.

Along with refinements in the methods for proportioning and mixing have come refinements in placing and compacting procedures. Plant-mixed materials are commonly placed with a mechanical spreader of the type used for bituminous construction (see Fig. 10, page 494), as closer depth control and smoother surfaces can be maintained in this way than by blade spreading. Compacting may be done with pneumatic-tired or tamping rollers followed by smooth-wheeled rollers, or by smooth-wheeled rollers alone. Some agencies permit the placing of the full stabilized course in one layer; others limit the depth of each compacted layer to 3 in.

Stabilized roads, unless protected by a bituminous cover, must be laid with high crowns. Some authorities recommend that the cross slope be ½ in. per ft to provide quick removal of surface water. Crowns as flat as 0.24 in. per ft showed excessive pitting of the road surface from traffic action in wet weather.[14] It is further recommended that the cross slope be uniform rather than parabolic or circular. The crowns

[14] Fred Burggraf, *Proceedings Highway Research Board*, part 2, p. 237 (1938).

recommended for unprotected surfaces are excessive for bituminous surfaces. If after a short curing period the stabilized material is to be covered with a wearing surface, crowns suitable for bituminous pavements should be adopted initially.

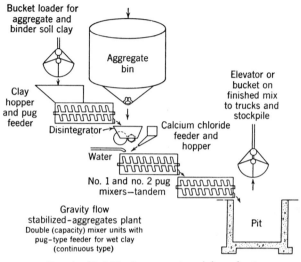

F<small>IG</small>. 4.   Stabilized aggregate mixing plant

Treatment with calcium chloride [15]

Calcium chloride ($CaCl_2$) is a white, deliquescent, and hygroscopic salt. Deliquescence is the ability of a material to absorb moisture from the air and thus to dissolve and become liquid. Hygroscopicity is the ability to absorb and retain moisture without necessarily becoming liquid. These two properties make calcium chloride useful as a dust palliative for soil-bound road surfaces. With material of proper gradation and plasticity, it serves as a stabilizing agent. Some agencies permit the use of calcium–magnesium chloride instead of calcium chloride.

Calcium chloride does not occur naturally except in solution in salt brines and mineral springs. The most important sources are natural brines and as by-products from the manufacture of ammonia or am-

[15] For a detailed presentation of the properties and uses of calcium chloride, see Uses of Calcium Chloride in Granular Stabilization of Roads, *Highway Research Board Report 2-F* (1945). For a statement on later research and development see H. F. Clemmer, Report of Committee on Soils-Calcium-Chloride Roads, *Highway Research Board Abstracts,* June 1952.

monium carbonate, carbon dioxide from marble, potassium chlorate, and sodium carbonate by the Solvay process. The chemical was considered as a waste product, difficult to dispose of, until research led to its use in several varied fields.

In dry weather, calcium chloride in or on the road surface results in a higher moisture content in the materials than if they were untreated. Two factors are responsible: First, because of higher vapor pressure, evaporation of water from a calcium chloride solution occurs at a slower rate than if the water were untreated. Second, because of its deliquescent properties, the calcium chloride will replace lost moisture at night or under other favorable humidity conditions. It follows, then, that, in areas of fairly high relative humidity, calcium chloride will act as a dust palliative since it will hold moisture to bind the road surface together whereas without it the road would be dusty and ravel badly.

Calcium chloride as a dust palliative was recognized by Byrne in 1907 in his book on highway construction. The usual application is about 2 lb per sq yd per year. About 1 lb is placed in the summer when the moisture from the spring rains is still in the road, and two applications of ½ lb each are made later in the season. After a road has been maintained for a year or so with calcium chloride, the total yearly amount may drop to 1½ lb or even as low as 1 lb per sq yd. Best results are obtained if, immediately after a rain, the surface is bladed and patched and then the chemical is distributed in flake form. Mechanical spreaders give more uniform distribution. If application is made just before a rain, a great part of the calcium chloride may be washed off the road and lost.

The mixing of calcium chloride into surface and base-course materials began about 1932 when it was discovered that it not only acted as a dust palliative but also had a beneficial effect on stability. As previously mentioned, it aids in maintaining a moisture film to bind the particles together. Furthermore, this moisture film has greater cohesion than water alone, because calcium chloride solutions have greater surface tension than water. There is also some evidence that the addition of calcium chloride may produce "base exchange,"[16] and at times improve the stability of the road by changing the chemical properties of the clay particles.

In areas of high relative humidity, a loose-gravel road surface may

[16] "Base exchange" or "ion exchange" is defined as the substitution of a base for another base or for hydrogen in a soil.

be tightened with calcium chloride by blade-mixing the loose float and dust with the chemical and spreading this mixture over the road surface. Precautions concerning the proportions of gravel and dust and proper weather and moisture conditions must be observed if results are to be satisfactory. If it is desired to stabilize a previously placed surface course, the common procedure is to scarify and pulverize the material, add and mix in about ½ lb of calcium chloride per square yard per inch of depth, and lay this mixture with a blade. For this operation to be successful, ample moisture must be present, and for stabilization in dry weather large quantities of water must be added. Where water is quite expensive, it may be advantageous to dry-mix the aggregates and binder with flake calcium chloride, windrow the mixture to the side of the road, and wait for a rain before final mixing, spreading, and compacting. Road-mixing operations for new surfaces are conducted in a similar manner.

Plant mixing of calcium chloride stabilized materials has many advantages. Not only is greater uniformity obtained, but delays from unfavorable weather and interruptions to traffic are held to a minimum. The mixture, at proper moisture content, is hauled to the road, placed, and compacted at once.

Compaction to high density is important for calcium chloride stabilization just as in other cases. Conventional rollers are normally used. Numerous tests have indicated that these mixtures are much more easily compacted than untreated ones. The explanation is that calcium chloride increases the surface tension, viscosity, and lubricating properties of water.

Maintenance of calcium chloride treated surfaces consists of blading and patching. Blading should be done immediately after a rain or even commenced near the end of the rain. Calcium chloride migrates through the soil and during a dry spell tends to concentrate near the surface so that blading during that time is likely to cause loss of the chemical. Under ordinary conditions, much less blading is required than for the untreated material. Moisture is maintained by light applications of calcium chloride whenever the surface begins to show signs of drying or dusting. Patching is normally necessary only during long dry spells. Scattered pits that develop can be patched with a mixture containing equal weights of graded aggregate under ½ in. in size and stable sand-clay, 6 to 10% of water, and calcium chloride at the rate of 100 to 150 lb per cu yd.

When properly maintained, calcium chloride treated surfaces have longer lives and lower blading costs than untreated surfaces.[17]

Treatment with sodium chloride

Sodium chloride (common salt) is also employed for stabilization of road surfaces.[18]   Like calcium chloride, sodium chloride controls the moisture content of graded mixtures and thereby effects a decrease in volume change and an increase in density and stability.   Calcium chloride has its effect through electrolytic and deliquescent properties and sodium chloride through electrolytic and crystalline properties. Generally, surfaces treated with sodium chloride are harder, with a drier appearance and slightly more dust, for in dry weather the sodium chloride forms fine crystals which give a hard crust of salt and aggregate.   Construction and maintenance methods for sodium chloride stabilization closely parallel those for the calcium chloride treatment. Sodium chloride may be applied as either rocksalt or brine; quantities used are comparable.

[17] See, for example, E. M. Baylard, *Proceedings Highway Research Board,* pp. 336–348 (1952).

[18] For a more detailed description of sodium chloride stabilization, see *Report of Subcommittee on Treatment with Sodium Chloride,* Highway Research Board (1936).

15 ——————————— Base Courses

INTRODUCTION

A base course is the layer immediately under the wearing surface (see Fig. 1, p. 309). This definition applies whether the wearing surface is bituminous or cement concrete 8 or more inches thick or is but a thin bituminous surface treatment. Because the base course lies close under the pavement surface, it is subject to severe loading. It follows that the materials in a base course must be of extremely high quality and construction must be carefully done.

Until about 1940 base courses almost always consisted solely of mineral aggregates. The most common type, called "granular base course," was a mixture of soil particles ranging in size from coarse to fine. Processing involved crushing oversize particles and screening where necessary to secure the desired grading. "Macadam"-type bases involving successive layers of crushed rock bound with rock dust were also employed. Since about 1940 "treated bases" composed of mineral aggregates and additives to make them stronger or more resistant to moisture have become increasingly common. Among the treating agents are bituminous binders, Portland cement, and certain chemicals including calcium chloride and lime.

For clarity of presentation this chapter subdivides base courses into granular and treated types. Macadam bases are discussed in Chapter 16.

GRANULAR BASE COURSES

General requirements

The requirements of a satisfactory soil-aggregate surface have previously been given as stability, resistance to abrasion, resistance to penetration of water, and capillary properties to replace moisture lost by surface evaporation.[1] Upon the addition of a wearing surface, these

[1] See p. 397.

417

requirements change. The first, stability, which is the ability to transfer wheel loads to the underlying layers without permanent deformation, is still absolutely necessary. The second, resistance to abrasion, disappears as the wearing surface now performs this function. Importance of the third and fourth requirements, concerned with moisture penetration and capillary action, are dependent on the type of wearing surface to be used.

Suppose, for example, that a soil-aggregate base course is to be protected by an open-mix pavement through which water may penetrate freely. The soil-aggregate combination then must contain enough clay to seal its surface against the penetration of this water in order that the base will remain stable in wet weather. On the other hand, capillary moisture offers no great problem, as in dry weather it can evaporate freely through the open pavement. Thus, a base course under an open pavement should react to moisture much like a good soil-aggregate surface course does. If, on the other hand, the wearing surface is impervious to water or water vapor, a lower clay content is advisable. In this case, surface moisture cannot penetrate to the base course and presents no problem. However, if capillary moisture [2] is present, its evaporation is prevented, so that in time both base and underlying subgrade become saturated. If either material, when saturated, becomes plastic as the result of high clay content, inadequate compaction, or other cause, failure will occur.

The changes in service characteristics between surfaces and bases are of particular importance when stage construction of a road over a period of years is planned, for then a material that meets service requirements of both surface and base must be selected. Likewise, when a wearing surface is to be placed on an existing soil-aggregate road, careful consideration must be given to the characteristics of the existent surface course and subgrade when the choice of pavement type is made.

Specifications for granular base course

Base courses must be of higher quality than the underlying "basement" soils. Typical of the many different specifications for base courses are those established by the American Association of State Highway Officials (*AASHO Designation M147–49*). Grading requirements for six different types are given in Table 1, page 398. Four of

---

[2] This moisture may be supplied from underlying groundwater, from nearby puddles or ditches, or may enter through unprotected shoulders or fill slopes.

these are also suitable for soil-aggregate surface courses. Strength and soundness standards are also the same (see p. 399). The provisions covering plasticity characteristics are different, however. For base courses, the maximum liquid limit is set at 25, and the maximum plasticity index at 6; for surface courses to be used for several years without surface treatment, the maximum liquid limit is 35 and the plasticity-index range is 4 and 9. As lower values of liquid limit and plasticity index indicate lower clay content, this change in the specification reflects the difference in service requirements discussed in previous paragraphs.

Agencies other than the AASHO have somewhat different specifications for base courses. In general, grading requirements are about the same, but physical tests other than for plasticity index may be used to control the properties of the soil mortar. For example, one specification requires that the California bearing ratio (CBR) for base courses be not less than 80 and that expansion when a compacted sample is soaked not exceed 1%. As another illustration, the California Division of Highways sets a minimum resistance value (Hveem stabilometer) of 75 or 80, and a minimum "sand equivalent" of approximately 30 for its untreated rock base.

No attempt will be made here to set out requirements for certain local base-course materials such as caliche, gypsum, cinders, or limerock. They vary greatly from the normal materials described above in specific gravity, absorption, or grading so that appropriate limits based on local experience must be set for each.

Under some conditions two layers of base course, one of higher type than the other, may be used to good advantage and will result in a lower over-all cost. The lower course may be designated by such names as "sub-base," or "select material." To illustrate, in areas subject to frost action a sub-base of free-draining, granular material containing little fines passing the no. 200 sieve may be placed between the subgrade and usual base course in order to block the upward movement of capillary moisture. In other cases, a material not suited for use directly under the pavement but cheaper than the usual base course may be interposed between base course and subgrade.

The problems to be met in producing base courses from unprocessed materials are the same as those for producing surface courses. Sometimes they may be loaded at the pit and placed on the road without any processing whatsoever. At the other extreme, if close control is demanded, crushing, separating into various sizes, proportioning by weight, and recombining, along with a controlled amount of water, may be specified.

The thickness of base-course layers is controlled by the character of the underlying subgrade over which it distributes the wheel loads delivered from above. Several design methods have been presented in Chapter 12 on pages 343 to 355. Minimum thickness, which is commonly [3] between 4 and 6 in., is controlled by the limitations of common construction procedures. Sometimes special considerations such as frost action may control the base-course depth. For example, some northern states employ sand and gravel sub-base thicknesses roughly one-half the depth of frost penetration.

Procedures for compacting base courses are the same as those for subgrades. Generally this includes observation of moisture-density relationships and compaction to some predetermined relative compaction. Controls are set quite closely, as the demands on the base course are higher than on the underlying layers. However, procedures vary considerably between highway agencies, just as they do for embankment compaction.[4]

Payment for granular base course

Payment for base courses is usually made on a unit basis at a bid price per cubic yard or per ton, with payment by weight gaining increasing favor. This price may include water and/or rolling, or these may be paid for under separate bid items. Some organizations pay for bases at a bid price per completed square yard of a specified thickness or include payment for the base in the price per square yard of completed pavement.

TREATED BASE COURSES

Soil-aggregate base-course materials are sometimes combined with bituminous material or cement to produce treated base courses. Again, materials like clean sands or even clays which alone would be unsatisfactory as bases may furnish the soil portions of these mixtures. Cal-

---

[3] Some agencies use a "select material" 4 in. or more in thickness in which the maximum-size particle may be set at 1½ to 2 in. Over this is placed a thin layer, possibly 2 in., of "base course" with a ¾- to 1-in. top size. This latter material, free from large particles, is more easily finished to close tolerances than a material containing coarser aggregate.

[4] For details of state highway department practices see *Highway Research Board Bulletin 58* (1952).

cium chloride or lime are also employed on occasion to treat base-course materials. These treatments are adopted when, in the judgment of the roadway designer, a satisfactory result can be obtained at a lower over-all cost. Some of the methods that have been successful are discussed in the succeeding paragraphs.

Soil-bitumen base courses

The term "soil–bitumen" is usually applied to a product resulting when cohesive soils are waterproofed by means of a bituminous admixture. As a rule cohesive soils have satisfactory bearing capacity at low moisture content but lose strength when the moisture content becomes high. By incorporating a bituminous waterproofing agent with the soil, it is possible to maintain the low moisture condition and an adequate load-carrying capacity in the base. To give satisfactory results, soil-bitumen mixtures must be laid on properly compacted and drained subgrades.

The bulletin, Soil Bituminous Roads, of the Highway Research Board,[5] gives an excellent and extensive discussion of several types of bituminous stabilized base courses. It states that best results with bituminous stabilization have been achieved using soils conforming to the following grain-size distribution:

Passing no. 4 sieve	More than 50%
Passing no. 40 sieve	35 to 100%
Passing no. 200 sieve	Not more than 50% nor less than 10%

Stated differently, these limits signify that soil-bitumen bases can be constructed successfully using aggregate combinations with gradings between those for stabilized bases and those for combinations of fine sands, silts, and clays. Whatever the soil grading, liquid limits less than 40 and plasticity indices smaller than 18 are to be preferred.

Various bituminous binders have been used successfully.[6] Petroleum asphalts of the rapid-curing, medium-curing, and slow-curing types; road tars in the grades RT–3 to RT–6; and emulsified asphalts have proved satisfactory on different projects. Selection of the general type of binder will depend on which is economically available and on the previous experience of those supervising the work. Because a great

[5] Highway Research Board Current Road Problems 12 (1946).

[6] See pp. 445–466 for a detailed discussion of the properties of bituminous binders.

variety of climates and soil conditions exist in the United States and Canada, a single recommendation cannot be made. It can be stated that the bitumen selected must be so constituted that it will readily mix with the soil. The amount of binder normally ranges between 4 and 7% of the dry weight of the soil, with the lower percentages applying when the aggregate contains greater amounts of sand, gravel, crushed stone, or other large particles. The percentage of binder also depends on the chemical composition of the clay minerals, with larger amounts needed if they are high in silica and smaller amounts if they are high in iron or aluminum compounds. For any given soil, however, the combined volume of bitumen and water must not exceed the pore space of the soil system at the desired compacted density. If it does so the mixture will lack stability even though its resistance to deterioration under the influence of water is comparatively high.

Soil-bitumen roads are now in the developmental stage, and procedures are far from standardized. Indicative of this are the large number of design methods employed by various highway agencies, at least 16 in all.[7]

Soil-bitumen base courses are usually laid in thickness of 4 to 8 in. Processing may be done either on the road with blade graders or traveling mixers or at a stationary plant.[8] Aggregates may consist of the natural soils from the roadbed with or without granular admixtures or may be imported from some other local source. Bitumen and water are added separately. If processing is done on the road, distributor trucks are used; otherwise the liquids are added at the plant. In any event, careful control must be exercised to keep the liquid content near the optimum. Soil-bitumen bases must be well compacted if high stability is to be attained, and a minimum density requirement of 95% of AASHO standard is common. Sheepsfoot and pneumatic-tired rollers have both been used satisfactorily. When possible, moisture content during compaction should be held on the dry side of optimum to assure higher strengths. This is particularly true when weather conditions make it advisable to seal the surface soon after compaction has been completed.

The surface of a soil-bitumen mix is usually friable and, under traffic, will scuff and develop unevenness. In time, potholes may form. Unprotected mixes will soften if water stands on the surface. For these

[7] See F. W. Reagel, *Symposium on Soil Test Methods,* American Society for Testing Materials (1943).

[8] See pp. 501–511 for a more detailed description of these methods.

reasons a water-tight and abrasion-resisting wearing surface should be provided.

Sand-bitumen base courses.[9]

Sand-bitumen base courses consist of loose sand from beach, dune, pit, or river cemented with bituminous materials. As already mentioned, sand-clay mixtures have long been used as road surfaces and for base courses. In more recent years, bitumens, consisting of cutback asphalts, emulsified asphalts, or tars have often been substituted for the clay binder to produce excellent base courses for highways and airports. Sand-bitumen bases have had particular application in the southern and Gulf states where deposits of clean sand are often available within reasonable distances.

Sands, to be suitable for sand-bitumen bases, must be relatively clean. Grading is not critical, but the sand must be stable; that is, the surface properties and grain shape must be such that they will resist displacement under load.[10] If the sand is not satisfactory, it may be blended with sharp angular particles like crushed aggregates, stone or slag screenings, stone dust, loess, or other substantially non-cohesive mineral matter to produce a stable mixture.

Bituminous binders commonly employed are tars (grades RT–6 to RT–10), rapid-curing asphalts (grades RC–1 to RC–3), or slow-setting emulsified asphalts. The percentage of binder, by weight, ranges from 4 to 10 for tars and cutbacks and from 5 to 10 for emulsified asphalts.

Sand-asphalt mixtures to be successful must be laid on a properly prepared and compacted subgrade. Combination of the sand with the binder has been achieved by "mix-in-place" methods using cultivators, harrows and blades, by employing traveling mixing plants, and at a central mixing plant. Which method is selected depends on the peculiarities of the job. For the "mix-in-place" method, successive applications of bituminous material, each ½ gal per sq yd or less, are spread over the sand by distributor truck. This binder is usually heated before spreading, with the application temperature dependent on type and weather conditions. Each application is mixed in before the next is placed. Before final spreading, the mixture is

---

[9] See footnote, p. 421, for reference.

[10] The Hubbard-Field stability test (see *Asphalt Institute Research Series 1*) and the Florida bearing-value test (see *Proceedings Association of Asphalt Paving Technologists*, 1943) are commonly used to determine stability of sands for sand-bitumen mixes.

tested to see that enough volatiles have evaporated from the binder to insure stability of the completed base. Compaction is done with pneumatic-tired or smooth-wheeled rollers.

Sand-bituminous surfaces should be protected from the abrasive action of traffic. This is often accomplished by applying a seal coat of bituminous binder covered with coarse sand or stone or slag chips. If traffic is heavy, a higher-type bituminous surfacing may be warranted.

Waterproofed stabilized bases [11]

In some areas engineers have employed bituminous materials to waterproof the usual stabilized base courses. It is well established that the strength of a stabilized mixture decreases as its moisture content increases. It follows that, if a base can be placed at low moisture content and subsequent moisture penetration can be prevented, the base will maintain high strength.

The grading of the soil components of a waterproofed stabilized base are about the same as those for granular bases (see Table 1, p. 398). However, the plasticity index of the soil mortar may be higher than the maximum of 6 commonly set for ordinary bases because water in detrimental quantities is kept from the clay binder. Maximum plasticity-index values of 10 to 15 appear reasonably safe, although the lower is to be preferred. Waterproofing is accomplished by mixing a light bituminous material such as RT–4 tar or RC–0 or RC–1 asphalt with the base-course material. Plant mixing in a pug mill is the common procedure. The usual amount is 1 to 2% by weight of bituminous material, although 2 to 3% is recommended if the base contains more than 13% passing the no. 200 sieve. Water is added to bring the mixture close to optimum moisture content. Placing and compacting are done in the usual manner. Before the base is placed, the subgrade should be carefully compacted. In addition, its surface should be covered with a prime coat of MC–0, RT–2 to RT–4, or emulsified asphalt. This prime coat is blotted with sand. The seal thus provided protects the subgrade during construction of the base and also prevents saturation of the base by capillary moisture from below. After the base has been placed and compacted, it must be protected from abrasion and moisture penetration from above by a seal coat or bituminous wearing surface.

[11] See footnote, p. 421, for reference.

Soil-cement bases [12]

Base courses of soils, stabilized with Portland cement and protected by a bituminous-surface treatment, serve as pavements for lightly traveled roads or streets. For major thoroughfares, soil-cement mixtures may replace the usual base course as a support for asphaltic plant mix or Portland-cement-concrete pavement. This base is of particular value under concrete pavements subject to joint pumping or slab distortions, a condition that often occurs if the subgrade is fine grained.

Soil–cement is an intimate mixture of soil and Portland cement, compacted at optimum moisture content and cured to hydrate the cement. It forms a strong, stable base that has little susceptibility to changes in moisture or temperature. Six inches is the common depth although thinner layers are sometimes used.

The surface of a soil-cement base is friable. It must be protected from the weather and from direct contact with the tires of motor vehicles or it will scuff and pit. A bituminous surface treatment offers sufficient protection for low volumes of light traffic. Otherwise, the function of soil–cement is that of a base course, covered by a suitable pavement.

Design of soil-cement mixtures. Satisfactory soil-cement mixtures have been produced with a wide range of soils, all of which, however, fall into three general subdivisions, as follows: (1) sandy and gravelly soils containing 10 to 35% combined silt and clay; (2) sandy soils, deficient in fines, such as beach sands, glacial sands, and wind-blown sand; (3) silty and clayey soils. Soil gradings for a major portion of the projects constructed in the United States have fallen within the following limits:

Sieve Designation	Percentage Passing, by Weight
3 in.	100
No. 4	55–100
No. 40	15–100
No. 200	0–50

[12] Many excellent articles and pamphlets are available on this subject. The Portland Cement Association has issued a number of publications which are technically authoritative. Other references include M. D. Catton, *Proceedings Highway Research Board*, pp. 821–855 (1940), and Committee Report on Soil-Cement Stabilization, *American Road Builders Association Technical Bulletin 137* (1948). See also the standard specifications of many of the state highway departments or other road-building agencies.

The liquid limit has usually been below 40 and the plasticity index not greater than 18.

Cement contents for properly designed mixtures vary from 7 to 16% by volume. This relationship is between loose cement volume (using a 94-lb sack of cement as 1 cu ft) and compacted soil-cement volume. Sandy and gravelly soils require the lower amounts whereas silty and clayey soils call for the higher percentages. The quantity of cement needed for the stabilization of heavy clays is even higher, but it is extremely doubtful whether their treatment is feasible from a cost standpoint. By weight, cement content ranges from 5 to 18% of that of the dry aggregate.

Dry densities for soil–cements compacted by the AASHO standard method range from 135 lb per cu ft for well-graded gravel down to 90 lb per cu ft for silty or clayey soils. Optimum moisture contents range from 6 or 7% upward. The recommended field density is about 95% AASHO standard.

The minimum desirable cement content for a soil-cement mixture is controlled by laboratory tests for maximum density and optimum moisture content,[13] wetting and drying,[14] and freezing and thawing.[15] The procedure for determining maximum density and optimum moisture content is the same as the AASHO standard method for determining the compaction and density of soils as already outlined. For the other tests, samples at optimum moisture and maximum density are moist cured for 7 days and then subjected to either 12 cycles of wetting and drying or 12 cycles of freezing and thawing. After each cycle the samples are brushed on all surfaces with two firm strokes of a wire brush. The quality of the soil-cement mixture is measured by its ability to resist the abrasive and disintegrating action to which it is subjected. This is expressed as "per cent loss" by weight.

To determine the cement content to be used with a particular soil, samples containing various percentages of cement are tested as outlined above.[16] Percentages of loss permitted in either test are as follows:

[13] Moisture Density Relations of Soil-Cement Mixtures, *AASHO Designation T134–45, ASTM Designation D558–44.*

[14] Wetting-and-Drying Test of Compacted Soil-Cement Mixtures, *AASHO Designation T135–45, ASTM Designation D559–44.*

[15] Freezing-and-Thawing Test of Compacted Soil-Cement Mixtures, *AASHO Designation T136–45, ASTM Designation D560–44.*

[16] For a shorter method of determining the percentage of cement to employ with sandy soils see J. A. Leadabrand and L. T. Norling, *Highway Research Board Bulletin 69* (1953).

AASHO Soil Classification M145–49	Maximum % Loss in Test
A–1–a, A–1–b, A–3, A–2–4, A–2–5	14
A–2–6, A–2–7, A–4, A–5	10
A–6, A–7–5, A–7–6	7

Some highway agencies now cement-treat the granular base courses placed under heavy-duty bituminous and Portland-cement-concrete pavements. This upgrades the granular base by increasing its strength and decreasing the effects of moisture change. The cement content is usually lower than for soil-cement mixtures, commonly ranging from 4 to 7% of the weight of the dry aggregate. The California Division of Highways cement-treats high-type granular bases under heavy-duty bituminous pavements as a means of increasing the strength and effective depth of the base course. Cement content may fall as low as 1 to 2% by weight. This agency also cement-treats the top 4 in. of carefully selected subgrade material underlying Portland-cement-concrete pavements. In this instance the purpose is to stop erosion under the pavement slab caused by pumping at joints and cracks.

Construction of soil-cement bases. Construction of soil-cement bases involves spreading, compacting, and curing an intimate mixture of soil, cement, and water on a prepared subgrade. Where the soil is to be imported, as for cement-treated granular base, "plant mixing" in a continuous or batch-type mixer has certain advantages. In particular, closer control can be held over proportioning and mixing, and the possibility of damage to the mix or interruption to construction by bad weather is minimized. On the other hand, when the soil is already in place on the road or when a mixing plant is not readily available, processing on the road, called "road mixing," may be more satisfactory. Figure 1 illustrates the "train-processing" method, where mixing is accomplished with a number of pieces of equipment operating in sequence. Figure 2 shows one of several machines that pick up soil and cement from a windrow, add water to them, and discharge the mixed product ready for spreading and compacting. Compaction and curing procedures are outlined below.

The construction of soil-cement bases, regardless of the method selected, includes some or all of the steps involved in constructing a soil-cement base from the existing road surface. These steps are briefly as follows:

Leveling the Roadway. The roadway must be shaped to line and grade before processing is commenced. Otherwise the completed surface must be uneven or the thickness of the soil–cement must vary.

Preparation of Roadway for Processing

First, the roadway section is graded to line and grade required in completed section. All such grading must be completed before pulverizing and processing operations start.

Outside edges of roadway to be pulverized are defined with guide stakes in the same manner as for processing. A short section is then loosened and pulverized to 5½" depth with road rooter, scarifier on motor grader, disk harrows, rotary speed mixers, springtooth cultivators, gang plows, etc., as needed. Should soil be dry and hard, it may be made mellow for rapid pulverizing by repeated water applications which are permitted to soak into the soil. After soil characteristics are learned pulverizing may be completed on some soils as part of mixing operations after cement is added.

Usually on the day before cement is spread, sufficient water is applied on section to be processed and partially mixed in so that 3 to 6 water applications per 10' width during processing operations will fulfill water requirements. The section is then leveled for cement spread and processing.

Note: For 18' to 22' roadways use same train arrangement being sure on 22' width to obtain coverage with mixing equipment.

Mixing Train Units

Unit No.	No. Req'd.	Width	Description of Unit	Motive Power
1	1	4'-8"	Gang plow, heavy duty, 4-14" bottoms (omit coulters).	Tractor, crawler type. Min. 35 DBHP
2	1	4'-8"	Gang plow, heavy duty, 4-14" bottoms (omit coulters).	Tractor, crawler type. Min. 35 DBHP
3	1	12'	Motor grader 12' moldboard	Self-powered
4(1)	1	8'	Cultivator, heavy duty, springtooth, 12" spacing. Fitted with 4" double-pointed chisels.	Tractor, crawler type. Min. 35 DBHP
5	1	8'	Cultivator, heavy duty, springtooth, 12" spacing. Fitted with 4" double-pointed chisels.	Tractor, crawler type. Min. 35 DBHP
6(2)	2	10'	Pressure distributor, 1000 gal capacity	Self-powered
7(1)	1	6'	Rotary speed mixer, self-powered, trailer mounted	Tractor, crawler type. Min. 35 DBHP
8	1	6'	Rotary speed mixer, self-powered, trailer mounted	Tractor, crawler type. Min. 35 DBHP
9(1)			Cultivator-Unit No. 4 or rotary speed mixer-Unit No. 7	

Routing of Mixing Trains

First round trip (see sketch). Use cultivators (units 4 and 5) and rotary speed mixers (units 7 and 8) only. These machines, otherwise, to maintain same relative position each passage.

Second round trip. Add plows (units 1 and 2) and distributor (unit 6). Use entire train as shown. All machines to maintain same relative positions. Generally desirable to add about ¼ of required water on outbound and ¼ on inbound passages. On outbound passage, motor grader (unit 3) will define pavement edge line by cutting V-shaped trench to depth of subgrade; and on inbound passage to blade in any loose cement wasted outside the edge line. *This unit to be used on outer edges only—not along center line. Intermediate round trip or trips.* If, at this stage it is determined that remaining water requirements cannot be supplied in one final round trip, remove plows (units 1 and 2) and rotary speed mixers (units 7 and 8) and make intermediate round trip or trips with distributor (unit 6) followed immediately by cultivators only (units 4 and 5) until deficiency is supplied.

Final round trip. Use entire train as shown. Add remaining water requirements. On outbound passage, motor grader (unit 3) will blade in any loose soil-cement wasted outside the edge line and on inbound passage will define edge by cutting V-shaped trench to depth of subgrade. Mixing train then moves to next train lane. Sheepsfoot roller compaction train and finishing operations follow. There should be no traffic intervening.

(1) Unit 9, cultivator (unit 4) or rotary speed mixer (unit 7) concentrate for short periods on cross mixing adjacent to previous day's run. Hand shovelers supplement mixing adjacent to headers to keep ends even, to remove any raw soil and return mixed soil-cement to section.

(2) When necessary, second distributor (filled) should be available to replace (unit 6) on inbound passage. Spray bars should be of the full width of train lane. On long water hauls additional distributor or water supply trucks may be needed.

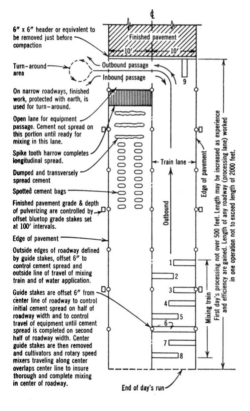

6" x 6" header or equivalent to be removed just before compaction

Finished pavement
10'   10'

Turn-around area

Outbound passage
Inbound passage

On narrow roadways, finished work, protected with earth, is used for turn-around.

Open lane for equipment passage. Cement not spread on this portion until ready for mixing in this lane.

Spike tooth harrow completes longitudinal spread.

Dumped and transversely spread cement

Spotted cement bags

Finished pavement grade & depth of pulverizing are controlled by offset bluetop grade stakes set at 100' intervals.

Edge of pavement

Outside edges of roadway defined by guide stakes, offset 6" to control cement spread and outside line of travel of mixing train and of water application.

Guide stakes are offset 6" from center line of roadway to control initial cement spread on half of roadway width and to control travel of equipment until cement spread is completed on second half of roadway width. Center guide stakes are then removed and cultivators and rotary speed mixers traveling along center overlaps center line to insure thorough and complete mixing in center of roadway.

Train lane
Outbound
Edge of pavement
Mixing train

First day's processing not over 500 feet. Length may be increased as experience and efficiency are gained. Length of any roadway (processing lane) worked in one operation not to exceed length of 2000 feet.

End of day's run

Substitutions

It is inevitable that units of equipment available will vary with different jobs. However, it is recommended that even though substitutions or omissions are necessary, the pattern of the train and order of its movements be followed as closely as possible.

FIG. 1. Soil-cement "train processing" for a 20-ft roadway. Two train lanes, each 10 ft wide (Courtesy Portland Cement Association)

Pulverizing the Soil. The soil must be thoroughly pulverized to insure an intimate mixture between soil and cement. Great care must be exercised to loosen only the desired depth, as variations will substantially alter the proportions of the mix. Pulverizing offers no serious problem with gravelly or sandy soils. With clays, it may create serious difficulties since these soils cannot be broken up when too wet or too dry. The problems of careful moisture

Fig. 2. Single-pass soil stabilizing machine processing soil-cement (Courtesy Harnischfeger Corporation)

control, plus the fact that large percentages of cement are needed to stabilize clays, usually make cement stabilization of such materials unattractive.

Spreading the Cement. Uniform distribution of cement may be obtained in several ways. If hand-labor methods are used, the cement in sacks is carefully spaced along the roadway and spread by hand. In some instances, mechanical spreaders, attached directly to a bulk cement truck, distribute the cement entirely by mechanical means. Procedures between these extremes have often been employed.

Dry-Mixing Cement and Soil. Soil and cement are dry mixed before water is added. If water and cement are added at the same time, the cement will ball up, and intimate mixing will be impossible. Some moisture in the soil makes dry mixing easier. Completion of dry mixing is indicated by a uniform color of the material.

Damp Mixing. If the mixing-train method is employed, water is added to the dry soil-cement mixture by introducing a distributor truck to the mixing train. Application is in increments of ½ to 1 gal per sq yd until optimum moisture content (plus an allowance for evaporation during processing) is reached. If a traveling mixer is used, all the water is added at once. Optimum moisture content is determined by moisture-density tests like those used for soils. Soil-cement mixtures at optimum moisture are not mushy or muddy like freshly mixed concrete, but rather are just damp enough to moisten the hands; they can be packed in the hands to form a tight cast that can be handled considerably without breaking. Too much moisture must be avoided, as mixes that are too wet cannot be properly compacted.

Compacting. Soil–cements are normally first compacted with sheepsfoot rollers, beginning at the edges and working toward the center. Very sandy soils which cannot be compacted with a sheepsfoot are processed by pneumatic-tired rollers instead. Compaction of the top 1 or 2 in. is by pneumatic-tired roller, preceded by a shaping with a blade grader. After this, the surface is usually dragged with a nail drag to remove surface compaction planes and rolled with a smooth wheel roller. If a tight surface is desired, the final operation consists of sprinkling lightly, followed by compaction with a pneumatic-tired roller.

Curing. Evaporation of moisture from the completed soil–cement must be prevented until hydration of the cement is complete. A protective cover of earth or straw, kept moist, is often employed, with 7 days as the common curing period. A covering of moisture-proof paper or a bituminous seal to prevent loss of moisture already in the mixture is also satisfactory.[17]

Calcium chloride treated base courses

Calcium chloride, up to 3% by weight, is sometimes employed as a stabilizing agent for base courses.[18] It assists in the compactive process, making it possible to obtain greater densities and greater strengths with normal compactive effort or to get usual densities with greatly decreased rolling. Construction methods are like those outlined earlier for calcium chloride stabilized surface courses.

Lime-treated base courses [19]

Lime as a stabilizing agent was used by the Romans in constructing the Appian Way. It has also been employed for many years in India

[17] For detailed reports on the various methods of curing soil cements and on their effectiveness see *Highway Research Board Bulletin 8-F* (1949), and A. W. Maner, *Proceedings Highway Research Board*, pp. 541–558 (1952).

[18] Report of Committee on Calcium Chloride Soil Stabilization, *American Road Builders Association Technical Bulletin 127* (1948).

[19] See particularly *American Road Builders Association Bulletin 147* (1948); A. M. Johnson, *Proceedings Highway Research Board*, pp. 496–507 (1948); M. G. Spangler and O. H. Patel in the 1949 *Proceedings*, pp. 561–566; L. J. Minnick and R. H. Miller, in the 1952 *Proceedings*, pp. 511–528; E. M. Whitehurst and

.and China. Since World War II it has been applied successfully in the United States as a means for reducing the shrinkage and plasticity index of soils having clay or caliche binders. For example, on a particular Texas project, the addition of 2.5 to 3% of waste lime produced a base course with a plasticity index averaging 8 from an untreated material having a plasticity index of 15 to 20.

Lime is usually introduced in slaked form. On some projects it has been employed in combination with fly ash. On one project, bulk quicklime was substituted for hydrated lime as an economy measure.

Other soil-stabilization methods

Research, in part for the Armed Forces of the United States, has developed several other soil-stabilization processes that may hold promise for the future. Among the stabilizing agents are sodium silicate, chrome–lignin (a waste product from the sulfite pulp process), Plasmofalt (a combination of molasses and fuel oil), calcium acrylate, and aniline–furfural.[20]

E. J. Yoder, pp. 529–540 of the same volume; and L. J. Minnick and W. F. Meyers, *Highway Research Board Bulletin 69* (1953). Also see *Texas Engineering Experimental Station Bulletin 124* (1951).

[20] See *Proceedings Soil Stabilization Conference,* Massachusetts Institute of Technology (1952).

16 — Macadam Surfaces—Macadam Bases

INTRODUCTION

The term "macadam" originally designated a road surface or base in which clean broken or crushed ledge stone was mechanically locked by rolling and bonded by stone screenings which were worked into the voids and "set" with water. With the beginning of the use of bituminous material, the term "plain macadam," or "ordinary macadam," and more frequently "waterbound macadam" was employed to distinguish the original type from "bituminous macadam" in which the binder was a bituminous material. The original macadam was for 100 years the highest type of road surface known. Although it is no longer built in the United States as a road surface without the addition of at least some bituminous material, the details of macadam construction not only are historically interesting but also are fundamental for a number of road-surface types. So-called "bituminous macadam," or "penetration macadam," is essentially a stone macadam with a bituminous material introduced as a binder; and waterbound macadam is widely employed in some areas as a base course.

Macadam roads developed originally in France and England and are named after John Louden MacAdam.[1] MacAdam deserves great credit for the work he did; but, when MacAdam was only 21 years of age, Tresaguet[2] was presenting in France to the Assembly of Bridges and Highways a report that was in fact a treatise on road construction.

[1] John Louden MacAdam, 1756–1836, was a famous Scottish road builder and engineer. Probably his greatest contribution was the development of the road-surface type that bears his name.

[2] Pierre-Marie Jerome Tresaguet, 1716–96, great French engineer, improved the methods for construction and maintenance of stone roads. He made it possible for Napoleon to build the great system of French highways and may be called the father of modern road building. Tresaguet preceded both Telford and MacAdam.

Tresaguet improved the drainage, crowned the grade and the stone foundation, and reduced the depth of broken stone to 10 in. Some 30 years later, Telford,[3] in Scotland, constructed roads like those developed by Tresaguet. His foundation course was of stones of 3-in. minimum thickness, 5-in. breadth, and 7-in. height (see Fig. 1), with a broken-stone wearing surface 4 to 7 in. thick. He used a flat subgrade and obtained a slight crown with stones of varying height.

FIG. 1. Laying telford foundations in Mercer County, Pa., 1911

MacAdam omitted the Telford foundation of large stones and introduced small, broken stones not exceeding 1 in. in diameter, on the contention that they should lock together because of their angularity. He developed the function of the wearing course of broken stone and demonstrated the adequacy of well-drained earth subgrades when covered with proper surfaces. His road surfaces were never more than 10 in. thick and had crowns of 3 in. for roads 30 ft. wide. Consolidation was by traffic traveling the road, but continued raking kept the surface smooth until it had set.

The invention of the stone crusher in 1858 by Blake[4] greatly advanced macadam construction. Almost simultaneously came the invention of the steam roller in France, first used on the Bois de Boulogne

[3] Thomas Telford, 1757–1834, a Scot, born in Dumfriesshire and buried in Westminster Abbey, founded the Institution of Civil Engineers and was president of it until he died.

[4] Eli Whitney Blake of New Haven, Conn., 1795–1886. His crusher was used by Hartford, Conn., in 1859.

in 1860. The first roller in England was employed in Hyde Park 6 years later. In 1867 Aveling and Porter made their first steam roller, a machine of 30 tons, and one was imported into the United States the next year. However, horse-drawn rollers were employed for many more years.

Before 1893 macadam roads in America were usually built relatively thick, and surfaces less than 8 in. in depth were rare. When it became fully apparent that macadam was essentially a thoroughly waterproof wearing surface, thinner roads were built and more attention was paid to the subgrade. A depth of 6 in. after rolling became standard.

Two macadam roads in this country of historical interest are the Valley Pike, a toll road in the Shenandoah Valley of Virginia, built by General Crozier, and the old Cumberland Road [5] or National Turnpike from Baltimore through Cumberland, Md., to Steubenville and points west.

MACADAM SURFACES [6]

Subgrade and foundation

Ordinary macadam was built on earth subgrades, which were carefully excavated by hand after the road had been rough graded. This subgrade developed in the form of a shallow vertical-edged trench between 3-ft earth shoulders. It was thoroughly rolled, and all soft spots were removed and replaced by sound material. This trenched subgrade frequently required drains through the shoulders. When rolled to an unyielding condition by a 10-ton or heavier roller, the subgrade was ready for the broken stone of the macadam course. The rolling was carried well out to the inside edge of the shoulders. Only thorough preparation of the subgrade prevented sagging (particularly at the edges) and low spots in the finished road surface. The "trench" subgrade, however, was hard to drain and weak at the edges. For all modern surfacings it is being rapidly discarded in favor of a full-width foundation course between the outside shoulder edges.

Where soft or boggy ground was encountered it was formerly quite common to build telford foundations for macadam surfaces, a modification of Tresaguet's method (see Fig. 1). A full-width crude pavement of large stones set upright on their thickest edges, with their longest diameter across the road, was constructed. These stones were

[5] Albert Gallatin seems to have suggested this road, for which Congress first appropriated $30,000 in an act signed by President Jefferson on March 29, 1806.

[6] For a more detailed treatment of this subject see L. I. Hewes, *American Highway Practice*, John Wiley & Sons, vol. I, pp. 291–315 (1942).

usually about 10 to 15 in. long, 4 to 6 in. wide, and 6 to 10 in. deep. They were hand-placed in an excavated and crowned trench, then smaller stones were driven into the top voids by mauls, and the whole surface was trued by breaking the projecting points. Finally, the telford foundation was rolled. In setting telford it was not uncommon first to place a layer of 2 or 3 in. of good gravel over any soft material encountered to prevent mud squeezing up into the telford and weakening it. It was essential that each stone of a telford course be set on its own bed and not leaned against the preceding stone.

Material for macadam roads

The first scientific development of the necessary qualities for good broken stone was in France. Beginning in 1878, standard stone tests were applied in the laboratory of Ponts et Chausées in France. French practices were adopted and somewhat elaborated in America.[7] The tests were to determine hardness, toughness, and binding power of various rocks. A test for the cementing value of the broken-stone dust was introduced by Page, who also devised a supplemental test for toughness by the Page impact machine.[8]

It was quite common to classify rock in two large groups: (1) the traps and (2) all others. Since hardness and toughness of rock generally are associated, it gradually became standard practice to rate stone for macadam and other surfaces according to the *per cent of wear*, determined by the Deval test.[9] This was reported by the French as the coefficient of wear which was found by dividing 40 by the per cent of wear. Thus a stone with a wear of 5% had a French coefficient of 8. All the various trap rocks commonly show low percentage of wear. The testing of broken stone for wear by the Los Angeles rattler test [10] is now becoming a standard practice that probably will supersede testing in the old standard Deval abrasion machine.

The trap-rock group includes andesite, basalt, diabase, diorite, gabbro, and rhyolite; all are of igneous origin, are denser and more finely grained than granite, and have an interlocking crystalline structure yielding high toughness, a percentage of wear running from about

---

[7] The first American testing laboratory was established in 1893 by the Lawrence Scientific School of Harvard University, in charge of Logan Waller Page, afterward first director of the U. S. Bureau of Public Roads. The Bureau of Public Roads has tested stone since 1905.

[8] *AASHO Designation T5–35.*

[9] For the Deval abrasion test see description and reference, p. 467.

[10] For the Los Angeles abrasion test see description and reference, p. 467.

2 to 4, a corresponding French coefficient of about 20 to 10, and a hardness [11] of 13 to 20. Next in order of suitability may be rated certain types of granite, limestone, and dolomite, and a few harder sandstones. Clean bank gravel or crushed gravel has also been employed to some extent for the base stone of macadam roads.

Screenings for macadam construction were crushed stone fragments, usually ranging in size from half-inch to dust. *AASHO Designation M77–49* in the standard specifications for highway materials is typical of modern specifications for stone, slag, and screenings for waterbound macadam.

Constructing the base course

On good rolled subgrades, the base usually was about 4 in. thick after thorough rolling. Clean stone sized from $2\frac{1}{2}$ to $1\frac{1}{4}$ in. was standard, but crusher run sometimes was used. To avoid unevenness, broken stone was not dumped into piles on the road, since it would thus retain a core of finer sizes. Instead, it was dropped onto steel or wooden dumping boards, usually about 6 ft by 3 ft, which necessitated the complete rehandling by shovelers. Before any rolling was undertaken, the base course was inspected thoroughly for low and high spots and for segregated or dirty stone, and the spread stone was shifted considerably by shovels and rakes in order to true the surface. To produce a 4-in. compacted layer, it usually was necessary to place nearly 6 in. of loose stone, as these grades of broken stone shrank about one-third during rolling.

Rolling was done by a power roller weighing not less than 10 tons or sometimes by a roller weighing not less than 300 to 350 lb per in. width of the roller tread.[12] Rolling began at the outer edge with the rear wheel overlapping the shoulder. When the broken stone became firm, the roller was shifted to the opposite side of the road and the operation repeated. After both edges were rolled moderately firm, the roller was gradually moved toward the center until the entire base or lower course was thoroughly compacted. Sometimes during rolling depressions formed, and these were brought to true section and grade by the addition of more base stone.

[11] Coefficient of hardness $= 20 - \frac{1}{3}w$ where w is loss in weight in grams of the standard core 25 mm in diameter after 1000 revolutions of a steel disk against it with the abrasive action of quartz sand.

[12] Rollers formerly had the rear wheels "coned" more nearly to fit the road crown. This coning has been discontinued.

Originally filler was seldom employed to choke or restrain the base stone. However, it is now almost universal practice to fill the base with stone screenings just before the final rolling, as described below in the discussion of wearing-course construction. By such a procedure the base is made much more solid.

Second, upper, or wearing course

After the base was thoroughly compacted, the earth shoulders were usually rebuilt to line. Later, wooden forms, gaged to the compacted thickness of the top course, were used. It was good practice to have the base course a foot wider than the top course in order to insure solid support for the edges of the finished road. The stone for the top course usually was sized from $1\frac{1}{4}$ to $\frac{1}{2}$ in. and was scrupulously clean. It was deposited and rolled as was the base, but usually to a tighter consolidation. The rolling was expected to produce a true surface. It was judged by eye until later the 10-ft straightedge was introduced. Spreader blocks and stretched strings also served as thickness gages. Depressions or high spots were eliminated by moving the rolled stone or by additional stone. The top course was spread to about 3 in. loose depth on the 4-in. compacted base. Usually it was possible, especially with trap rock, to roll a very solid, locked layer of top course. No travel whatever was permitted on the stone. Consequently it was necessary to work toward the stone supply.

Applying the binder course

When the surface course had been thoroughly rolled and the surface corrected, the stone screenings or stone dust, usually called the binder, was applied. These screenings were the product of the crusher which passed the half-inch screen. Seldom was the binder separated into sizes, but a more satisfactory result was obtained when the coarser particles were introduced first into the interstices of the top course. Never under any condition was the binder dumped upon the top-course stone. It was spread either directly from carts by hand or from piles deposited along the shoulders (see Fig. 2). The best practice demanded the introduction of the binder by thin successive spreads. The coarser particles at the bottom of the roadside piles of screenings were first thrown into the road by a lateral motion in casting from the shovels, and disappeared forthwith upon rolling. The roller was worked continuously as the screenings were spread. Workmen applied successive thin layers by lateral casting until the screenings began to appear in the top surface. In this way the larger particles found their way to the bottom of the top course, and the smaller particles wedged into the subsequently reduced voids. The use of brooms to distribute the dry screenings was very effective in producing uniform results. Only when the voids began to fill with screenings was it time to sprinkle.

The best type of sprinkler was one with a direct vertical discharge in a fan- or cone-shaped spray that drove the fine material downward

Fig. 2. Spreading stone screenings in three coats on a macadam road

into the voids. When sprinkling began, alternate applications of binder and rolling continued until a batter of stone dust and water began to flood ahead of the roller wheels. If dry screenings were first well worked in, there was very little danger of softening the subgrade by excessive sprinkling. During hot weather, it was sometimes necessary to await rain for the final rolling, as sprinklers could not supply enough water to keep the surface continuously wet.

It was very important to use only enough screenings to fill the voids and leave a film over the top course. Any depressions that appeared were evidence of defects in the spreading of the top-course stone and could not be corrected with screenings only. Such depressions were immediately rebuilt with top-size stone, and a thorough patch with the application of screenings to fill the voids was completed. Much depended on the skill of the roller operator and on continuous rolling.

With good stone it was possible to produce a final surface that was completely waterproof and that would ring under horses' hoofs when the road was dry. Frequently when macadam roads were opened to traffic the calks on the horses' shoes would loosen the surface to some extent, and it was necessary to keep the roller and sprinkler operating to smooth out such temporary raveling. The appearance of raveling was frequently alarming to inexperienced road makers, but in almost every instance where the work has been thoroughly done the raveling was only temporary, and the road became solid and tight almost immediately.

Maintenance of waterbound macadam

Before the development of automobile traffic, macadam was considered the best pavement for rural highways. In Massachusetts, for instance, 95% of the state highways were macadam. With increasing numbers of automobiles, it was seen that even the best macadam roads would not withstand their action. The roads raveled rapidly and in the worst instances became during a single season merely a pile of loose stones. It was thought at first that the rubber tires produced a "suction" which pulled out the fines from the top-course stones, but later it was found that the tractive effort of the rear wheels, combined with the partial vacuum under the vehicle itself, largely accounted for the destructive effect of the motor vehicle. The rapidly moving vehicle raised any loosened binder which was then blown off the surface altogether, thus robbing the top course. The thrust backward on the individual stones by the rear wheels and the thrust forward under the front wheels formed an effective loosening process which soon completely disintegrated the top. Macadam roads built to withstand automobile traffic must therefore be covered with a bituminous seal.

Many miles of old waterbound macadam are still rendering excellent service as base courses under bituminous blankets or bituminous seal coats. Their biggest defects are narrow widths and excessive crowns.

MACADAM BASE COURSES

The combination of tightly keyed coarse aggregate with the bond produced by stone chips and dust creates a base course equally as good as other untreated bases. Thus the decision whether or not to use macadam bases becomes an economic one. In areas where aggregates must be quarried and crushed or where slag is readily available, macadam bases can compete favorably. However, where suitable graded materials are at hand in streambeds or other deposits, dense-graded granular bases will undoubtedly be cheaper. Among the macadam bases there are the alternatives of "waterbound," employing a binder of stone chips and dust, and "bituminous" or "penetration," with the binder a bituminous product.[13]

Macadam base construction follows the procedures previously outlined for macadam surfaces. The marked difference lies in the degree of mechanization. Earlier construction techniques employed large numbers of workmen and relatively little equipment. Today macadam construction is highly mechanized.

Materials for macadam bases

Crushed stone for macadam bases must be strong and tough to resist breaking during rolling. The trap rocks and certain types of granite, limestone, dolomite, and sandstone are the most suitable. Where available, slag of proper toughness is also satisfactory. *AASHO Designation M75–49*, a typical specification for aggregate for macadam base, sets the maximum percentage of wear under the Los Angeles rattler test at 50 for both stone and slag; but indicates that tougher material is to be preferred. For crushed stone only, there is the added requirement that the loss under five alterations of the sodium sulfate soundness test [14] be no greater than 12%. Typical aggregate gradings for coarse aggregate for macadam base courses are offered in Table 1. The larger sizes are employed with thicker base layers.

Screenings of crushed stone or slag are employed for binder materials. The AASHO specification states that "screenings shall be the No. 4 to 0 size, well graded from coarse to fine and free from dirt or other foreign material." Grading is passing $\frac{3}{8}$-in. sieve 100%, passing no. 4 sieve 85 to 100%, passing no. 200 sieve 10 to 30%.

Constructing macadam bases

Macadam base courses generally are 6 to 8 in. in total thickness, constructed in two layers.[15] The first course is laid on an insulating

---

[13] Original plans for the New Jersey Turnpike specified waterbound macadam base course because preliminary estimates indicated it was cheaper. After the contracts were awarded, the contractors were permitted to substitute a bituminous macadam base at a somewhat lower unit price. See *Civil Engineering*, January 1952, p. 76.

[14] These tests are outlined on p. 467.

[15] Some agencies employ a single-course macadam base 3 to 4 in. thick.

TABLE 1.   GRADING FOR CRUSHED-STONE AND CRUSHED-SLAG AGGREGATES
FOR WATERBOUND- AND BITUMINOUS-MACADAM BASE COURSES

AASHO Designation M75–49

Class of Aggregate AASHO Standard Size Size Range, In.	No. 1 3½ to 1½	No. 2 2½ to 1½	No. 3 2 to 1
Passing 4-in. sieve, %	100		
Passing 3½-in. sieve, %	90–100		
Passing 3-in. sieve, %		100	
Passing 2½-in. sieve, %	25–60	90–100	100
Passing 2-in. sieve, %		35–70	95–100
Passing 1½-in. sieve, %	0–15	0–15	35–70
Passing 1-in. sieve, %			0–15
Passing ¾-in. sieve, %	0–5	0–5	
Passing ½-in. sieve, %			0–5

blanket of dry stone screenings, intended to prevent subgrade material from working into the base course.   Different blanket thicknesses are employed by the several highway agencies, with the range between 1

FIG. 3.   Machines spreading aggregate for a macadam base course (Courtesy Jaeger Machine Co.)

and 3 in.   Some specify that the blanket shall be rolled; others state that it shall not.   The crushed stone or slag of specified grading is spread to proper depth on this cushion.   Machine spreading is usual (see Fig. 3).   Sometimes the roadway edges are defined by side forms of steel or timber; [16] again the stone is laid against a previously pre-

[16] See p. 573 for further discussion of side forms.

pared bank of earth or gravel (see Fig. 3). The placed stone is then consolidated and keyed together by rolling with a smooth-wheel roller, usually of the 3-wheel type weighing 10 tons or more. The shoulders are rolled first to lock the stone firmly at the edges, and then rolling gradually progresses toward the center. Vibrotampers to supplement or replace rollers offer considerable promise.

For waterbound bases, each layer is bound with stone screenings applied gradually over the surface. Dry rolling continues to prevent caking or bridging on the surface. Successive applications of screenings are halted only when the interstices in the coarse aggregate are filled. Sweeping with mechanical or hand brooms is an important aid to proper spreading. Finishing involves sprinkling the surface with water until it is saturated, followed immediately by rolling. Screenings are added as required. Sprinkling, sweeping, and rolling continue until a grout has been formed that will fill all the voids and form a wave before the roller wheels.

For bituminous macadam, the rolled coarse aggregate is sprayed with a bituminous binder. Details of this operation are like those for bituminous macadam pavement given on pages 512 to 519.

Succeeding layers of base are laid directly on the one or ones already completed and by repetition of the procedure already outlined. If the base is of the waterbound type, subsequent hauling operations must be kept off the surface. On the other hand, a bituminous-bound base is not injured by such use.

17 ——————— Bituminous Pavements

INTRODUCTION

Bituminous pavements consist of combinations of mineral aggregates with bituminous binders. Under this broad heading are included a multitude of pavement types, ranging from inexpensive surface treatments ¼ in. or less thick to asphaltic concretes, which are sometimes comparable in cost and dimension to Portland-cement-concrete pavements.

The layman refers to all bituminous surfaces as *blacktop*, because of their appearance. Much unwarranted criticism has resulted from this connotation, as failures of the cheapest temporary pavements have been construed by the uninformed to mean that all bituminous pavements are unsatisfactory. On the other hand, such a diversity of names has grown up among highway engineers that the person who tries to distinguish among them often becomes bewildered. F. N. Hveem, materials and research engineer, California Division of Highways, has stated the problem well, as follows:

Mixtures of these two simple ingredients, rock particles and asphalt, have masqueraded under a number of names, such as Asphalt Macadam, Asphaltic Concrete, Sheet Asphalt, Topeka Mix, Mastic; proprietary, process, or trade names such as Tarvia, Warrenite, Bitulithic, Willite, Ameisite, Durite, Permatite, National Paving; and type names, such as plant mix, road mix, armor coat, retreads, penetration, inverted penetration, multiple lift, oil mat, and so on. This is by no means a complete list, but represents some of the most commonly used. These various names and terms do serve a purpose in identifying certain types of mixtures or methods of construction, but tend to make the engineer forget that virtually all bituminous pavements consist of nothing but mineral aggregate and asphalt.

The subject of bituminous pavements is further complicated for the student because there are many right answers; that is, there are many combinations of aggregates and binders that will make good pavements, even under restrictive local conditions. This idea is alien to much of

443

the engineer's earlier training which has been devoted to solving problems having but one correct solution.

If good service is to be received from bituminous pavement, it must, for its full life, retain the following qualities: freedom from cracking or raveling; resistance to weather, including the effects of surface water, heat, cold, and oxidation; resistance to internal moisture, particularly to water vapor; tight, impermeable surface, or porous surface (if either is needed for continued stability of underlying base or subgrade); smooth riding and nonskid surface. The design of a pavement that will meet all these demands for a considerable number of years is an exacting task. It requires careful selection and control of materials and close supervision of each step of construction. Proper design and construction of subgrade and base course are a "must"; otherwise pavement failure is a foregone conclusion.

Pavements meeting all the requirements outlined above have been produced by six distinctly different construction processes as follows: [1]

1. Heat a viscous bituminous binder to make it fluid; then, in a plant, mix it with heated aggregate. Place and compact the mixture while it is still hot.

2. Use a fluid bituminous binder. Mix it with aggregates at normal temperatures. Mixing may be done in a plant (plant mix) or on the prepared roadway base (road mix). Spread and compact the mixture at normal temperatures.

3. Add a solvent such as naphtha or kerosene to a viscous bituminous binder to make it fluid. Mix the fluid with aggregate at normal temperatures by either plant-mix or road-mix methods. Spread and compact at normal temperatures before the solvent evaporates.

4. Use a fluid emulsion of viscous bituminous binder in water. Mix it with aggregates at normal temperatures by either plant-mix or road-mix methods. Spread and compact at normal temperatures before the emulsion breaks down into its components.

5. Spread and compact clean crushed aggregate as for waterbound macadam. Over it spray heated, dissolved, or emulsified bituminous binder which penetrates open areas of the rock and binds the aggregate together. This is commonly called the *penetration* method.

6. Spread a bituminous binder over the roadway surface; then cover it with properly selected aggregate. This is commonly called the *inverted-penetration* method.

---

[1] This breakdown deliberately oversimplifies current American practice, which introduces many variations within the processes here outlined. A combination of some heat with partial liquefaction of the binder is particularly common.

Not all the listed methods will serve on roads carrying large volumes of heavy vehicles; neither can those that are most costly be used economically on roads of low-traffic volume. Availability of suitable aggregate is often a controlling factor. Personal preference and experience of the engineer in charge will play a large part in the final choice of method and of the details of that method.[2]

In this text, pavements are classed as dense-graded mixes, open mixes, penetration types, and inverted-penetration types. This approach makes for an orderly presentation of design and laboratory procedures. Bituminous pavements have been helpfully subdivided in a different manner into intermediate surfacings and higher-type surfacings.[3] Intermediate surfacings are those that use liquid asphalts and tars as the binding agent and might be termed "low-cost" pavements. They include temporary dustlayers, prime coats, protective coats, surface treatments, seal coats which are usually laid by the inverted-penetration method, and the cheaper dense-graded pavements constructed by either the road-mix or plant-mix method. The term "higher type surfacings" designates pavements of greater first cost which include dense-graded mixes like sheet asphalt and asphaltic concrete and penetration types such as penetration macadam.

The remainder of this chapter presents, in a limited way, details of current bituminous-pavement practice in the United States. It is suggested that the student, when reading it, keep firmly in mind the previously mentioned qualities of successful pavements and the common procedures used to construct them. If he does so, the need for each of the many materials and the purposes of the many tests will become apparent; the subject will become an integrated whole rather than a mass of unrelated details.

BINDERS FOR BITUMINOUS PAVEMENTS

Bituminous binders for road-building purposes are viscous liquids. Consistencies at normal temperatures range from something slightly thicker than water to hard and brittle materials that will shatter under a hammer blow; but even the hardest of them will flow if subjected to

---

[2] Flexible-Pavement Design, *Highway Research Board Bulletin 80* (1953), presents an excellent summary of the current practice of the various state highway departments. Many of the statistics on American practice used in this chapter were taken from this bulletin.

[3] Low-type surfacings, needed to complete this classification, would include gravel, crushed rock, and stabilized roads.

long, continuous loading. This plastic characteristic of all bituminous binders has led some writers to designate all bituminous pavements as *flexible* pavements.

Regardless of the type of pavement in which they are used, bituminous binders must be in liquid form when combined with the aggregates. This fluid state may be produced either by using a liquid material or by making harder asphalts liquid by heating, by dissolving in solvents, or by emulsifying in water.

In completed pavements, the action of the binders depends greatly on the aggregates with which they are combined. If pavements are of the "open" type, consisting entirely of coarse particles held together by bituminous materials, these binders in themselves must resist the abrasive and suction forces produced by vehicular traffic. The cohesive strength required to perform this function is gained by using a tenacious, heavy binder. On the other hand, if the aggregates contain fine particles, cohesion is developed by surface tension in the thin bituminous films surrounding these fines, just as water films develop cohesive forces in fine-grained soils. For mixes containing fines, then, fairly thin bituminous liquids may be employed successfully as binder.

Sources of bituminous binders

All bituminous binders are hydrocarbons, which are combinations of hydrogen and carbon. The lighter and more volatile members of this hydrocarbon family include natural or manufactured gas, gasoline, kerosene, and Diesel oil. Heavier combinations provide lubricating oils and paving materials. Some of the hydrocarbons employed in paving occur naturally, but most of them are by-products from the manufacture of gas, liquid fuels and lubricants, or coal gas and coke. Principal sources of bituminous materials for pavements are listed in the paragraphs that follow.

Native asphalts. Native asphalts from Trinidad Island off the northeast coast of Venezuela, Bermudez and Maracaibo, Venezuela, and Cuba, softened with viscous petroleum fluxes, were once extensively employed as binders for asphaltic surfaces. Fluxed Trinidad asphalt was used in the United States as early as 1875, on Pennsylvania Avenue in Washington. Later, fluxed Bermudez was widely employed. Only a little asphalt came to the United States from Maracaibo or Cuba. The Trinidad Lake asphalt when ready for fluxing contains approximately 40% organic and inorganic insoluble matter, whereas that from Bermudez has about 6% insoluble matter. With the development of petroleum asphalts, native asphalts have become unimportant. The

Bermudez Lake has not produced since 1933, and the importation from Trinidad in 1949 was only 5000 tons.

Rock asphalts. Rock asphalts are natural deposits of limestone or sandstone impregnated with bituminous material. In Paris in 1854 Meriam, a Swiss engineer, laid a surface with material from the Vale de Travers mine in the canyon of Neuchâtel, Switzerland. It was a bitumen-impregnated limestone which compacted under traffic. In 1876 sections of Pennsylvania Avenue in Washington were paved with it.

Rock asphalts occur in various parts of the United States, especially in Alabama, Kentucky, Oklahoma, Texas, Utah, and California. They have generally made extremely durable and stable road surfaces, but high transportation costs have limited applications to the general areas of occurrence. The percentage of bitumen varies widely between deposits, 4.5 and 18% representing the extremes. Often the rock asphalt as mined must be processed by adding mineral aggregate, asphaltic binder, or both.

Petroleum asphaltic materials. Petroleum asphalts were first used in the United States for road treatment in 1894, when crude petroleum from the Summerland wells was sprinkled on earth roads in Santa Barbara County, Calif. Production of paving materials from California and Mexican crude petroleums followed. Asphaltic paving materials now come from domestic crudes originating in Kentucky, Ohio, Michigan, Illinois, Mid-Continent, Gulf-Coastal, Rocky Mountain, and California fields. Foreign sources include Mexico, Venezuela, and Colombia. Production of paving-type asphalts totaled 10.5 million tons in 1952.

A flow chart for a typical refinery producing fuels, lubricating oils, and paving materials is diagrammed in Fig. 1. The several classes of paving materials and their characteristics are discussed in succeeding paragraphs.

Slow-curing (*SC*) road oils are petroleum distillates with the volatile, light fractions largely removed. Slow-curing oils harden or "set" very slowly and are employed where nearly the same consistency of binder is desired both at the time of processing and after a curing period has elapsed. The consistencies of slow-curing oils at normal temperatures range from light liquid (SC–0) to semisolid (SC–6); application temperatures vary from normal daytime air temperatures to 325° F. Table 1, which is typical of current practice, gives for slow-curing oils and other bituminous materials the range of application temperatures permitted by the Ohio Department of Highways.

✳ *Asphaltic cements* (*AC*) are semisolid hydrocarbons remaining after lubricating oils as well as fuel oils have been removed from petroleum.

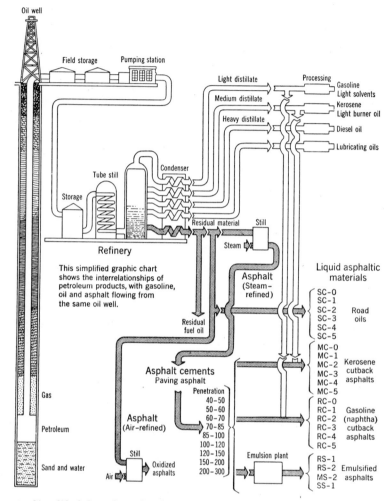

FIG. 1. Simplified flow chart showing recovery and refining of petroleum asphaltic materials (Courtesy The Asphalt Institute)

They may be thought of as an extension of the slow-curing road oil series into a more viscous range.[4] The consistencies of asphaltic

---

[4] SC–6 and 200–300 penetration asphaltic cements are used for comparable purposes.

TABLE 1. TEMPERATURES AT WHICH VARIOUS BITUMINOUS MATERIALS
SHALL BE APPLIED

| Material | | Temperature, °F | | |
Description	Designation	Correct for Average Conditions	Min.	Max.
Asphalt cement	60–70, 70–80, 85–100	250–325	225	350
Asphalt cement	150–200, 200–300	250–275	225	325
Asphalt waterproofing primer	Primer A *	50–80	40	100
Rapid-curing liquid asphalt	RC–0 & RC–1 *	75–125	50	150
Rapid-curing liquid asphalt	RC–2 & RC–3 *	100–150	75	175
Rapid-curing liquid asphalt	RC–4 & RC–5 *	175–225	150	250
Medium-curing liquid asphalt	MC–0 & MC–1 *	75–125	50	175
Medium-curing liquid asphalt	MC–2 & MC–3 *	150–200	125	225
Medium-curing liquid asphalt	MC–4 & MC–5 *	200–250	175	275
Slow-curing liquid asphalt	SC–0 & SC–1 *	75–125	50	175
Slow-curing liquid asphalt	SC–2 & SC–3	175–225	150	250
Slow-curing liquid asphalt	SC–4, SC–5, SC–6	225–325	200	375
Asphalt emulsion	RS, MS, SS, WPE	60–120	50	150
Brick filler	F–1	400–475	375	500
Brick filler	F–2	475–500	450	525
Waterproofing asphalt	WPA	300–350	275	375
Powdered asphalt	Pwd. A			
Tar waterproofing primer	Primer T	50–80	40	100
Light tar	RT–1, RT–2, RT–3	80–120	60	140
Medium tar	RT–4, RT–5, RT–6	125–150	100	200
Heavy tar	RT–7, RT–8, RT–9	185–225	175	250
High-carbon tar	RT–10, RT–11, RT–12	185–225	175	250
Tar cutback	RTCB–5, RTCB–6 *	80–120	60	120
Waterproofing pitch	WPP	250–350	200	375

From *Construction and Material Specifications*, Ohio Department of Highways,
January 1, 1949.
* These materials contain flammable volatile constituents and extreme care must
be used in handling and heating.

cements are given in terms of *penetration,* the distance that a standard needle penetrates a sample under known conditions of loading,
time, and temperature. The softest grade commonly employed for
paving is 200–300 penetration, the hardest 30–40 penetration. Acceptable limits for intermediate grades differ among highway agencies,
but those shown in Tables 1 and 3 are representative. All asphaltic
cements are so viscous that both aggregate and binder must be heated
before mixing and placing of pavements can be accomplished. Table 1
shows common working temperatures.

Medium-curing (MC) cutback asphalts are asphaltic cements fluxed or cut back to greater fluidity by mixing with distillates of the kerosene or light Diesel-oil type that evaporate at a relatively slow rate. Medium-curing products have good wetting properties that permit satisfactory coating of fine-graded and dusty aggregates. They are employed when greater fluidity is desired at the time of processing than after the finished road has cured for a while.

The consistencies of medium-curing oils range from light liquid (MC–0) almost to semisolid (MC–5); application temperatures from 100 to 225° F (see Table 1). Fluidity of the various grades is controlled by the amount of solvent; MC–0 may contain as much diluent as 50% by volume and MC–5 as much as 18%. Consistency of the binder after the solvent evaporates depends on the asphaltic cement originally chosen, which is generally of 85–100 penetration. Penetration of the residue from distillation, a measure of the hardness of the asphalt in actual service, is somewhat higher.

Rapid-curing (RC) cutback asphalts are asphaltic cements cut back with a petroleum distillate like gasoline or naphtha, solvents that evaporate rapidly. Rapid-curing products are employed when a quick change from the liquid state of application back to the original asphaltic cement is desired.

Grades range from RC–0 to RC–5; consistencies, application temperatures, per cents of solvent, and penetration of the original asphaltic cement closely follow those for comparable designations of the MC series. Penetration of the residue after distillation approximates that of the original asphalt.

Emulsified asphalts are mixtures in which minute globules of asphalt are dispersed in water or in an aqueous solution by means of an emulsifier.[5] Emulsions offer the asphalt in liquid form for application or mixing at normal temperatures. When they break down and the water evaporates, the paving asphalt remains. Products with fast, medium, and slow breaking times make emulsions suitable for a variety of purposes; in many situations either emulsions or cutbacks will be satisfactory. Emulsions are superior with wet aggregates as the water medium carries the asphalt into intimate contact with the particle surfaces.

[5] Various processes for the production of emulsions have been patented, and many of the products are marketed under proprietary names such as Bitumuls, Bitucote, and Colas. Emulsifying agents include the soap of fatty and resinous acids, glue, and gelatin.

Designations for emulsified asphalts are not uniform among the various road agencies, although the specified properties are comparable. The Asphalt Institute classifies them as "rapid setting" (RS), "medium setting" (MS), and "slow setting" (SS), with one or more subheads under each to designate the viscosity of the emulsion or the penetration of the suspended asphalt.

All emulsions are liquid in form and are applied at normal or only slightly elevated temperatures. Asphalt content is approximately 55 to 65% by weight. Asphaltic cement of 150–200 penetration is the basis for all emulsified asphalts except type SS–2, in which a harder grade is employed. When frozen, ordinary emulsions will break down so that they must be protected if extreme cold is expected. Special emulsions which are not damaged by freezing are available.

Blown or oxidized asphalts result when air is blown through heated asphaltic materials. They have higher softening points than normally refined asphalts of comparable penetration, which makes them suitable for roofing and similar applications. Highway uses are limited largely to the waterproofing of structures and filling of joints in concrete pavements.

Road tars. Tars are a by-product of the destructive distillation of coal. In 1867 a tar-aggregate mixture was laid in Prospect Park, Brooklyn. Soon thereafter similar installations were made in other locations. However, the early mixtures required a month or more to harden, and in addition there were numerous failures. With modification of production methods, adequate specifications, and more efficient testing, these difficulties were overcome, and at present tars are widely employed in the East, Middle West, and South.

Tars are produced by the gashouse, coke-oven, or water-gas methods. The American Society for Testing Materials makes the following designations:

Gashouse coal tar: coal tar produced in gashouse retorts in the manufacture of illuminating gas from bituminous coal.

Coke-oven tar: coal tar produced in by-product coke ovens in the manufacture of coke from bituminous coal.

Water-gas tar: tar produced by cracking oil vapors at high temperatures in the manufacture of carbureted water–gas.

Tars are affected by the character of the oil or coal and by the methods and temperatures involved in their production. As with petroleum asphalts, tars are supplied in a number of forms from light liquid to semisolid and as cutbacks, so that they fit a wide range of construction methods.

Classifications for road tars are not uniform among road agencies. The AASHO classification, used by many, includes 14 grades: RT–1 to RT–12, and RTCB–5 and RTCB–6. RT–1 is a light oil suitable for application at normal temperatures. As the number designations become larger the tars become more viscous until RT–12 can be used only at elevated temperatures (see Table 1). The grades RT–1 to RT–6 are usually manufactured by fluxing heavier tars with suitable lighter oils or tars. RTCB–5 and RTCB–6 are tars cut back with a quick-evaporating solvent for low-temperature application and quick setting.

Bitumen-Rubber Mixtures. An experimental pavement bound with a bitumen-rubber mixture was laid in Holland in 1929. Unfortunately data are not available by which it can be judged. The first use of this binder in the United States was made in 1947 when an experimental section was laid in Akron, Ohio. The pavement was conventional, except that finely divided rubber amounting to 5 to 7½% of the bitumen by weight was included. Since that time experimental roads have been laid by (among others) the state highway departments of Virginia, Ohio, Texas, Massachusetts, California, and Colorado, and the cities of New York and Baltimore. On the Massachusetts project, rubber added was 10% of the bitumen content in the base and 15% of bitumen content in the surface.

It is reported that adding rubber decreases the ductility and flow of the paving mix, raises the temperature of the softening point, and lowers that of the cracking point. Skidding tests in Virginia show relatively little improvement from the additive on newly laid pavements. On 6-month-old pavements, however, the stopping distance had decreased, particularly at higher speeds. At 40 mph stopping distance on plain pavement was 101.2 ft and on that with rubber additive [6] was 87.5 ft.

These experimental roads have been in service for such a short time that as yet no conclusive evidence has been gained regarding their relative merits or economy.

Specifications and tests for bituminous binders

The consistency, quality, and certain other properties of bituminous binders must be carefully controlled if successful pavements are to be constructed with them; and specifications and tests to furnish this control have been developed. Typical specifications for the more common types are given in Tables 2 to 7, inclusive. These tables are taken largely from standards of the American Association of State

[6] See Shelburne and Sheppe, Road Surface Properties, *Highway Research Board Bulletin 27* (1950). See also *American Road Builders Association Technical Bulletin 194* (1953).

Highway Officials and the Asphalt Institute. The specifications of many highway agencies will differ from them in some particulars, and where exact data are required reference should be made to the specifications of the agency in question. The appropriate AASHO or ASTM test numbers appear in the tables.

Tests for consistency. A bituminous binder must have the expected consistency both at the time of processing and after completion and curing of the pavement. For this reason, two tests for consistency are made, one on the material as supplied and another on the residue from one of the distillation tests or the test for loss on heating. If the material complies with the first of these, the user is assured that its consistency will be right at the time of processing; if it complies with the second, it will be satisfactory after curing or deposition, when the solvents or suspending agents have evaporated. Different testing methods and temperatures are employed for liquid, semisolid, and relatively solid materials or residues, and also for different binders. The tests for consistency specified in Tables 2 to 7 are Furol viscosity, Engler viscosity, float test, penetration, and softening point. All these tests are comparative; they merely assure the engineer that the binder tested will have properties similar to those of another binder that has already served successfully. Careful control of testing temperatures is imperative, as the consistencies of bituminous materials change rapidly with variations in temperature. For example, in SC, MC, or RC materials, a temperature decrease of roughly 20° F changes the consistency to that of the next higher grade of the series.

The Furol viscosity test is the control of consistency for liquid petroleum asphalts (SC, MC, and RC series) and of emulsified asphalts (see Tables 2, 4, 5, and 6). The Saybolt-Furol viscosimeter is a special cylindrical vessel approximately 1.2 in. in diameter and 5 in. high, enclosed in an oil bath. The outlet tube in the base is about 0.12 in. in diameter and ½ in. long. The viscosity is defined as the time in seconds required for 60 ml of the oil to flow by gravity from the completely filled cylinder. Testing temperature is carefully controlled by regulated heating of the oil bath and, in order to make testing times reasonable, is different for oils of different fluidity. Tests conducted at 140° F on slow-curing products give times ranging roughly between 15 sec for an acceptable SC–0 to 10,000 sec (2.8 hr) for an acceptable SC–6.

The Engler specific viscosity test is the control for consistency of liquid-tar products, RT–1 to RT–6 and RTCB–5 and RTCB–6 (see Table 7). The Engler viscometer is a shallow cylindrical vessel of unspecified dimension equipped with a slightly tapered outlet tube about 0.11 in. in diameter and 0.8 in. long. The vessel and outlet fit into a brass jacket filled with water or cottonseed oil. Controlled heat is applied to the jacket. The vessel is cali-

TABLE 2. SPECIFICATIONS FOR SLOW-CURING LIQUID ASPHALTIC MATERIALS *

Specification designation	ASTM Method	AASHO Test	SC-0	SC-1	SC-2	SC-3	SC-4	SC-5	SC-6
General requirements			The material shall be free from water.						
Flash point (Cleveland open cup), °F	D92	T48	150+	150+	175+	200+	225+	250+	275+
Furol viscosity at 77° F, sec	D88	T72	75-150	....	....	....	....	....	....
Furol viscosity at 122° F, sec			......	75-150	......	......	......	......	......
Furol viscosity at 140° F, sec			......	......	100-200	250-500	......	......	......
Furol viscosity at 180° F, sec			......	......	......	......	125-250	300-600	......
Furol viscosity at 210° F, sec			......	......	......	......	......	......	250-500 †
Water, %	D95	T55	0.5-	0.5-	....	....	....	....	....
Distillation									
Total distillate to 680° F	D402	T78	15-40	10-30	5-25	2-15	10-	5-	2-
Float test on residue at 122° F, sec	D139	T50	15-100	20-100	25-100	50-125	60-150	75-200	150-350
Asphalt residue of 100 penetration, %	D243	T56	40+	50+	60+	70+	75+	80+	90+
Ductility asphalt residue at 77° F	D113	T51	100+	100+	100+	100+	100+	100+	100+
Solubility in carbon tetrachloride, %	D4 ‡	T44 ‡	99.5+	99.5+	99.5+	99.5+	99.5+	99.5+	99.5+
Spot test §		T102	....	....	....	....	....	....	....

* The requirements given in this table are those of *AASHO Designation M141-49*, but the table has been rearranged and the test numbers added. The table also corresponds to the specifications of the Asphalt Institute, except that the SC-6 grade has been added.

† Approximate penetrations for SC-6 range from 200 to 350.

‡ Carbon tetrachloride used in place of carbon disulfide, method 1.

§ Many highway agencies specify that slow-curing asphalts show a negative reaction to the spot test. This requirement is not a part of the Asphalt Institute specifications.

TABLE 3. SPECIFICATIONS FOR ASPHALT CEMENTS PREPARED FROM PETROLEUM *

Specifications of			Asphalt Institute			AASHO Designation M-20	
Characteristics	ASTM Method	AASHO Test					
General requirements	.....	.....	The asphalt shall be prepared by the refining of petroleum. It shall be uniform in character and shall not foam when heated to 350° F.			The asphalt shall be homogeneous and free from water and shall not foam when heated to 347° F.	
Flash point (Cleveland open cup), °F	D92	T48	450+	425+	350+	347+	
Penetration, 77° F, 100 g, 5 sec	D5	T49	Penetration Grades			Penetration Grades	
			40–50 50–60 60–70 70–85 85–100	100–120 120–150 150–200	200–300	30–40 40–50 50–60 60–70 70–85	85–100 100–120 120–150 150–200
Loss on heating 325° F, 5 hr, %	D6	T47	1−	2−	2−	1−	1−
Penetration after loss on heating 77° F, 100 g, 5 sec, % of original	D5	T49	70+	70+	60+	75+	65+
Ductility							
At 77° F, cm	D113	T51	100+	60+	.....	†	100+
At 60° F, cm	D113	T51	.....	.....	60+	.....	.....
Solubility in carbon tetrachloride, %	D4	T44	99.5	99.5	99.5	.....	.....
Solubility in carbon disulfide, %	D4	T44	.....	.....	.....	99.5	99.5
Proportion of bitumen soluble in carbon tetrachloride, %	D165	T45	.....	.....	.....	99.0	99.0
Spot test (when specified) with ‡		T102					
Standard naphtha solvent						Negative—all grades	
Naphtha xylene solvent,—— % xylene						Negative—all grades	
Heptane xylene solvent, —— % xylene						Negative—all grades	

* AASHO specifications for Trinidad lake asphalts, *Designation M22-42*, cover the same grades given for petroleum asphalts, and in general are comparable. In addition, specifications for lake asphalts include ranges for per cent inorganic matter, softening point, and specific gravity.

† Not less than numerical value of penetration.

‡ The use of the spot test is optional under AASHO standards. When specified, the engineer shall indicate whether the standard naphtha solvent, the naphtha xylene solvent, or the heptane xylene solvent will be used in determining compliance with the requirement, and also, in the case of the xylene solvents, the percentage of xylene to be used.

TABLE 4. SPECIFICATIONS FOR MEDIUM-CURING LIQUID ASPHALTIC MATERIALS

AASHO Designation M82-42

Specification designation			MC-0	MC-1	MC-2	MC-3	MC-4	MC-5
General requirements	ASTM Method	AASHO Test	The material shall be free from water.					
Flash point (open tag), °F		T79	100+	100+	150+	150+	150+	150+
Furol viscosity at 77° F, sec	D88	T72	75–150	......	....	....	....	....
Furol viscosity at 122° F, sec			......	75–150	....	....	....	....
Furol viscosity at 140° F, sec			......	......	100–200	250–500	....	....
Furol viscosity at 180° F, sec			......	......	....	....	125–250	300–600
Distillation								
Distillate (% of total distillate to 680° F)								
To 437° F	D402	T78	25–	20–	10–	5–	0	0
To 500° F			40–70	25–65	15–55	5–40	30–	20–
To 600° F			75–93	70–90	60–87	55–85	40–80	20–75
Residue from distillation to 680° F, volume %, by difference			50+	60+	67+	73+	78+	82+
Tests on residue from distillation								
Penetration 77° F, 100 g, 5 sec	D5	T49	120–300	120–300	120–300	120–300	120–300	120–300
Solubility in carbon tetrachloride, %	D4 *	T44 *	99.5+	99.5+	99.5+	99.5+	99.5+	99.5+
Ductility at 77° F for residues of less than 200 penetration	D113	T51	100+	100+	100+	100+	100+	100+
Ductility at 60° F for residues of 200–300 penetration	D113	T51	100+	100+	100+	100+	100+	100+
Spot test (when specified) with †		T102						
Standard naphtha solvent			Negative—all grades					
Naphtha xylene solvent,—— % xylene			Negative—all grades					
Heptane xylene solvent, —— % xylene			Negative—all grades					

* Except that carbon tetrachloride shall be used instead of carbon disulfide as solvent, method 1.

† The use of the spot test is optional. When it is specified, the engineer shall indicate whether the standard naphtha solvent, the naphtha xylene solvent, or the heptane xylene solvent will be used in determining compliance with the requirements and also, in the case of the xylene solvents, the percentage of xylene to be used.

brated at 25° C by filling it with water and measuring the time in seconds needed for the passage under gravity of 50 cc. Bituminous materials are tested in a like manner at a specified temperature. Engler specific viscosity, a dimensionless number, is the quotient resulting when the flow time of the bituminous material at specified temperatures is divided by the flow time of water at 25° C. The nearly constant ratio of 4 to 1 exists between Furol and Engler viscosities when the tests are conducted at the same temperatures, so that the Furol test would be satisfactory for testing tars.

The float test is for heavier tars, RT-7 to RT-12, and the residues that result when slow-curing asphaltic oils are distilled (see Tables 7 and 2). The specimen for the test is a small tapered plug of bitumen about 0.9 in. long with top diameter about 0.4 in. and bottom diameter about 0.5 in. This plug is molded into a brass collar which is threaded to fit into the bottom of a small aluminum dish. In testing, plug and dish are floated in ice water at 5° C for 15 min to assure thorough chilling of the samples; then the assembly is placed in a water bath held at the specified test temperature until the water breaks through the plug and into the dish. Results are given as the time in seconds, measured from the placing of the assembly in the bath until the water breaks through. The time is shorter for soft materials than for hard ones.

The penetration test is to determine the consistency of asphalt cements and of the residues after distillation of medium- and rapid-curing asphaltic oils and of emulsions (see Tables 3, 4, 5, and 6). A standard needle penetrates the sample vertically under known conditions of loading, time, and temperature. The needle, made of a steel rod 1.00 to 1.02 mm in diameter, is pointed at a taper between 8° 40' and 9° 40'. The pointed end is then blunted to a truncated cone, with the diameter of the smaller base 0.14 to 0.16 mm. The finished needle must be hardened and highly polished, as small irregularities will greatly affect results. Load, time, and temperature of test are normally 100 grams, 5 sec and 77° F, respectively. Units of penetration are in hundredths of a centimeter. Increased values for penetration indicate softer asphalts. In contrast, higher numerical results for the viscosity or float tests indicate harder asphalts.

*The softening-point test—ring and ball method—*is the control for consistency of lake asphalts and of the residue of tars after distillation (see Table 7). This test is fixed and arbitrary, as bituminous materials have no definite softening point but gradually change from a brittle and exceedingly thick and slow-flowing material to a softer and less viscous liquid. A brass ring ⅝ in. in diameter and ¼ in. thick is filled with a melted sample of the material to be tested and is suspended in a glass beaker with its base 1 in. above the bottom of the beaker. A solid steel ball ⅜ in. in diameter is also placed in the beaker. The beaker is partially filled with water at 41° F, after which the water's temperature is maintained at the same level for 15 min. The ball is then placed in the center of the upper surface of the bitumen in the ring, and heat is applied in such a manner that the temperature of the water is raised 9° F each minute. The softening point is the temperature of the water at the instant that the softened bituminous material, pushed downward by the ball, touches the bottom of the vessel.

TABLE 5. SPECIFICATIONS FOR RAPID-CURING LIQUID ASPHALTIC MATERIALS

AASHO Designation M81-42

Specification designation			RC-0	RC-1	RC-2	RC-3	RC-4	RC-5
General requirements	ASTM Method	AASHO Test	The material shall be free from water.					
Flash point (open tag), °F		T79	......	......	80+	80+	80+	80+
Furol viscosity at 77° F, sec			75-150	......	....	....	....	......
Furol viscosity at 122° F, sec	D88	T72	......	75-150	....	....	....	......
Furol viscosity at 140° F, sec			......	......	100-200	250-500	....	......
Furol viscosity at 180° F, sec			......	......	....	....	125-250	300-600
Distillation								
Distillate (% of total distillate to 680° F)								
To 374° F	D402	T78	15+	10+	....	....	....	....
To 437° F			55+	50+	40+	25+	8+	....
To 500° F			75+	70+	65+	55+	40+	25+
To 600° F			90+	88+	87+	83+	80+	70+
Residue from distillation to 680° F, volume %, by difference			50+	60+	67+	73+	78+	82+
Tests on residue from distillation								
Penetration 77° F, 100 g, 5 sec	D5	T49	80-120	80-120	80-120	80-120	80-120	80-120
Ductility 77° F	D113	T51	100+	100+	100+	100+	100+	100+
Solubility in carbon tetrachloride, %	D4 *	T44 *	99.5+	99.5+	99.5+	99.5+	99.5+	99.5+
Spot test (when specified) with †		T102						
Standard naphtha solvent			Negative—all grades					
Naphtha xylene solvent,—— % xylene			Negative—all grades					
Heptane xylene solvent, —— % xylene			Negative—all grades					

* Except that carbon tetrachloride shall be used instead of carbon disulfide as solvent, method 1.

† The use of the spot test is optional. When it is specified, the engineer shall indicate whether the standard naphtha solvent, the naphtha xylene solvent, or the heptane xylene solvent will be used in determining compliance with the requirements and also, in the case of the xylene solvents, the percentage of xylene to be used.

Test for ductility. A ductile material is one that will elongate (be led out) when subjected to tension, as contrasted to a brittle material that will break rather than stretch. Almost all specifications for bituminous binders set minimum values for ductility. For asphaltic cements these apply to the original material, and for liquid and semiliquid materials they apply to the residue after distillation. The test provides assurance that the binder in the completed road will be ductile

TABLE 6. SPECIFICATIONS FOR EMULSIFIED ASPHALTS *

Specification designation	ASTM Method	AASHO Test	Quick Setting		Medium Setting				Slow Setting	
			RS-1	RS-2	MS-1	MS-2	MS-3	MS-4	SS-1	SS-2 *
Description and principal uses			Low viscosity for surface treatment and bituminous macadam	High viscosity for surface treatment and bituminous macadam	For retread mixes with coarse aggregate	For plant mixes with coarse aggregate	For plant mix and general maintenance patching with coarse aggregate	Resistant to freezing (same uses as MS-3)	For fine-aggregate mixes. Soft asphalt	For fine-aggregate mixes. Hard asphalt
Tests on emulsion										
Furol viscosity at 77° F, sec		T59	20-100	.....	20-100	100+	.....	.....	20-100	20-100
Furol viscosity at 122° F, sec			.....	50-300	.....	.....	.....	.....	.....	.....
Residue by distillation, %			55+	60+	55+	60+	65+	65+	57+	55+
Settlement, 5 days			3-	3-	.....	.....	.....	.....	1.0-‡	1.0-
Demulsibility, 50 ml, 0.1 N, CaCl$_2$, %			30-90	60+	5-	5-	.....	.....	.....	.....
Demulsibility, 35 ml, 0.02 N, CaCl$_2$, %			.....	.....	45-†	45-†	.....	.....	.....	.....
Sieve test, %			0.10-	0.10-	0.10-	0.10-	0.10-	0.10-	0.05-	0.10-
Miscibility with water			.....	.....	Pass	Pass	Pass	Pass	.....	Pass
Stone-coating test			.....	.....	Pass	Pass	Pass	Pass	.....	.....
Freezing test			.....	.....	.....	.....	.....	Pass	.....	.....
Modified miscibility, %			.....	.....	.....	.....	.....	.....	4.5	.....
Cement-mixing test, %			.....	.....	.....	.....	.....	.....	2.0-	2.0-
Tests on residue										
Penetration, 77° F, 100 g, 5 sec	D5	T40	100-200	100-200	100-200	100-200	100-200	100-200	100-200	40-90
Solubility in carbon disulfide	D165	T58								
Petroleum asphalts, %			97.5+	97.5+	97.5+	97.5+	97.5+	97.5+	97.5+	97.5+
Native asphalts, %			95.0+	95.0+	95.0+	95.0+	95.0+	95.0+	95.0+	95.0+
Ash, %			2.0-	2.0-	2.0-	2.0-	2.0-	2.0-	2.0-	2.0-
Ductility at 77° F	D113	T51	40+	40+	40+	40+	40+	40+	40+	40+

* Based on *AASHO Designation M140-49*, except that the AASHO specifications do not include SS-2 grade. Specifications for it are those of the Asphalt Institute.
† This limit is for ordinary use. If it is desired to set more restrictive specifications, based on climatic conditions, the following are suggested: for hot dry climates 0-5%, for mild climates 5-30%, for cool damp climates 20-45%.
‡ Asphalt Institute specification. Not prescribed by AASHO.

TABLE 7. SPECIFICATIONS FOR ROAD TARS

AASHO Designation M52-42

Grades	ASTM Method	AASHO Test	RT-1	RT-2	RT-3	RT-4	RT-5	RT-6	RT-7	RT-8	RT-9	RT-10	RT-11	RT-12	RTCB-5	RTCB-6
Consistency																
Eng. sp. visc. at 40° C		T54	5-8	8-13	13-22	22-35	......	......	......	......	......	......	......	......	......	......
Eng. sp. visc. at 50° C			......	......	......	......	17-26	26-40	......	......	......	......	......	......	17-26	26-40
Float test at 32° C			......	......	......	......	......	......	50-80	80-120	120-200	......	......	......	......	......
Float test at 50° C			......	......	......	......	......	......	......	......	......	75-100	100-150	150-220	......	......
Sp. gr. at 25 C/25° C		T43	1.08+	1.08+	1.09+	1.09+	1.10+	1.10+	1.12+	1.14+	1.14+	1.15+	1.16+	1.16+	1.09+	1.09+
Total bitumen, % by wt.		T44	88+	88+	88+	88+	83+	83+	78+	78+	78+	75+	75+	75+	80+	80+
Water, % by volume		T110	2.0-	2.0-	2.0-	2.0-	1.5-	1.5-	1.0-	0.0	0.0	0.0	0.0	0.0	1.0-	1.0-
Total distillates, % by wt.	D20	T52														
To 170° C			......	......	......	......	......	......	......	......	......	......	......	......	2.0-8.0	2.0-8.0
To 200° C			7.0-	7.0-	7.0-	5.0-	5.0-	5.0-	3.0-	1.0-	1.0-	1.0-	1.0-	1.0-	5.0+	5.0+
To 235° C			......	......	......	......	......	......	......	......	......	......	......	......	8.0-18.0	8.0-18.0
To 270° C			35.0-	35.0-	30.0-	30.0-	25.0-	25.0-	20.0-	15.0-	15.0-	10.0-	10.0-	10.0-	35.0-	35.0-
To 300° C			45.0-	45.0-	40.0-	40.0-	35.0-	35.0-	30.0-	25.0-	25.0-	20.0-	20.0-	20.0-	......	......
Softening point of residue, °C	D36	T53	30-60	30-60	35-65	35-65	35-70	35-70	35-70	35-70	35-70	40-70	40-70	40-70	40-70	40-70
Sulfonation index (when specified) on distillate	D872	T108														
To 300° C			8-	7-	6-	6-	5-	5-	......	......	......	......	......	......	......	......
300° C to 355° C			1.5-	1.5-	1.5-	1.5-	1.5-	1.5-	......	......	......	......	......	......	......	......
Typical uses and suggested temperatures for application *			Prime coat 60 to 125° F		Prime coat and surface treatment 80 to 150° F		Surface treatment and road-mix 80 to 150° F		Surface treatment, premix, and seal coat 150 to 225° F		Surface treatment, road-mix, and seal coat		Surface treatment, premix, seal coat, penetration, and crack filler 175 to 250° F			Surface treatment, road-mix, and premix. When low-temperature application and quick setting are desired 60 to 120° F	

+ Sign indicates that value shown is the minimum allowable.

- Sign indicates that value shown is the maximum allowable.

* For the guidance of the user and not a part of the specification.

rather than brittle, so that the pavement surface will distort rather than crack under the effects of load or settlement.

The material to be tested is heated and poured into a special mold which produces a specimen with a thickness of about 0.4 in., a width varying from 0.8 in. at the ends to 0.4 in. at the center, and a length between grips of about 1.7 in. This specimen is placed in a special tension machine which pulls the ends apart horizontally at designated speed. Testing is conducted under water of controlled temperature. Usual test speed is 5 cm per min; usual test temperature is 77° F. Resulting ductility is given as the distance in centimeters that the specimen stretches before breaking; a ductility of 100, which is common, indicates that the specimen stretched to something over 20 times its original length.

Tests for solubility or for per cent bitumen. Bitumen, the active cementing portion of bituminous binders, is, by definition, soluble in carbon disulfide. By specifying some minimum per cent of solubility the purchaser avoids accepting materials unduly adulterated with sand, dirt, or other impurities.

Petroleum products are almost pure bitumen, usually more than 99.5% soluble in carbon disulfide. Lake asphalts have relatively high percentages of inorganic matter.[7] Tars contain some organic matter commonly designated as "free carbon," the amount varying with the source of coal and production conditions.

Carbon disulfide is flammable, and carbon tetrachloride is often used in lieu of it to determine the solubility of bituminous materials. However, carbon disulfide must be employed to determine total bitumen.

Distillation tests. Bituminous materials of the same consistency may have widely different characteristics. For example, a liquid slow-curing oil may have the same viscosity as a rapid-curing oil made up of hard asphalt cut back with gasoline. The difference can be determined, however, by ascertaining the percentages distilled off at each of several temperatures and by measuring the consistency of the residue. Reference to Table 2, for slow-curing, nonvolatile oils, shows that a relatively small percentage is distilled away to 680° F, and the residue is quite soft, as shown by the float-test values. Table 4, for medium-curing oils, shows the kerosene distilling off and a residue of paving-grade asphalt. Table 5, for rapid-curing oils, shows parallel values except that the light-gasoline solvent distils away at a lower tempera-

[7] AASHO specification M22 sets the total bitumen in asphaltic cement produced from Trinidad asphalts between 68 and 74% for 30–40 penetration grade and between 77.6 and 83.6% for 150–200 penetration grade. Bitumen content of intermediate grades lie between these limits.

ture. A modification of the distillation test determines the percentage
of water in a bituminous material.

For asphaltic cements the "loss-on-heating" test replaces the more
complex distillation test, as its purpose is to reveal readily volatile
material and to give assurance that the binder will not harden unduly
when heated for application or mixing (see Table 3).

Flash point. Bituminous materials are flammable, and the lighter
vapors, when mixed with air, create explosive mixtures. If the processing temperature is so high that vapors are driven off, suitable precaution to eliminate fire hazards must be taken. The flash point is
the temperature at which a bituminous material, during heating, will
evolve vapors that will temporarily ignite or flash when a small flame
is brought in contact with them. Comparison of working temperatures
(see Table 1) with specified flash points for the various types of binders
indicates that often fire or explosion is a real hazard. This is particularly true with the heavier grades of RC and MC cutbacks which have
low flash points but require fairly high processing temperatures.

To make the test, the material is heated in an open cup, and at
intervals a small flame is applied near its surface. For cutback products of low flash point, the Tagliabue open-cup test is used; for those
of higher flash point, the Cleveland open-cup test is specified.

Tests for homogeneity of petroleum asphalts. Petroleum asphalts
that have been overheated during refining, that are the residuals of the
"cracking" process, or that have been air-blown at high temperatures
contain small carbon flecks and are classed as "heterogeneous." Normal
steam-refined or native asphalts and slightly oxidized residuals from
asphaltic-based crude oils do not contain these flecks and are classed
as "homogeneous." The heterogeneous or cracked asphalts have been
viewed with disfavor by many highway engineers on the grounds that
they weather badly,[8] and their use is prohibited by a number of
agencies. This is accomplished by ruling out those asphalts that show
a positive reaction to the Oliensis spot test or one of its modifications.

[8] There is some doubt whether cracked asphalts are inferior for road-building
purposes, particularly when the amount of cracking is limited. Conclusions
drawn from Bureau of Public Roads tests were that the positive reaction to
the spot test does not definitely indicate that the product will weather badly
and that identification tests restricting material to limited sources or processes
of manufacture cannot predict weather-resisting properties with accuracy. However, it has been established that cracked asphalts become hard and brittle more
rapidly than uncracked ones. See J. T. Pauls and J. Y. Welborn, *Public Roads*,
August 1953, pp. 187–202.

For the Oliensis spot test using the standard naphtha solvent, a drop of a mixture of the asphalt and naphtha is placed on a filter paper and the uniformity of the resulting spot observed. If the entire spot is uniform in color on the first test and on a repetition after the mixture stands for 24 hr, the tested asphalt is said to be homogeneous, and the test result is reported as negative. If the center of the spot is black, surrounded by a lighter-colored ring, the asphalt is classed as heterogeneous, and the test result reported as positive.

Some California uncracked asphalts and high-sulfur crudes reacted positively to the spot test using the standard naphtha solvent. Through research it was found that, if a solvent, in part heptane and in part xylene, were used, some measure of the degree of heterogeneity could be obtained. If the spot test showed negative when the solvent contained no xylene (a heptane-xylene equivalent of zero), the asphalt was clearly homogeneous. Severely cracked residuals showed negative results as the percentage of xylene in the solvent approached 100 (a heptane-xylene equivalent of nearly 100). A change from a negative result in the spot test at some intermediate heptane-xylene equivalent to a positive result at a slightly higher one served to indicate the extent of cracking. Based on these and other findings, a number of highway agencies in the western states have modified the spot test to control the amount of cracked material by specifying that the heptane-xylene equivalent be 35 or less. In this way they permit the inclusion of some cracked products, but limit the amount.

Special tests for emulsified asphalts. Tests previously described serve to measure the asphalt content and consistency of emulsions and the consistency, solubility, and ductility of the suspended asphalt. Others are needed, however, to assure suitable behavior of the emulsion as a carrying agent for the asphalt; for, if it breaks down in an improper manner, construction will not be successful.

Test for Settlement. If, after an emulsion has been in storage for some time, the percentage of asphalt at various levels in the container is considerably different, serious difficulty will be encountered in controlling the asphalt content of the finished pavement. To test for settlement a sample is permitted to stand for 5 days, after which the percentage of asphalt at the top and at the bottom of the container is determined by distillation. Settlement is defined as the numerical difference in percentages of asphalt in the two samples.

Test for Demulsibility. The speed with which an emulsion breaks down into its components is extremely important. To illustrate, if the binder for a pavement were a slow-setting emulsion and the emulsion broke down before mixing and placing were completed, the asphalt-aggregate mixture would become hard and unworkable and be a total loss. To test demulsibility, calcium chloride solution is added to the emulsion to accelerate its breaking down into asphalt and water. If the emulsion breaks, the asphalt will solidify and adhere to the vessel while the water and calcium chloride solution may be poured off. Demulsibility, which is stated as a percentage, is the ratio between the weight of asphalt separated from a sample by the demulsibility test and that obtained by distilling a sample of equal weight. For testing rapid-setting emulsions, 35 cc of $0.02 N$ calcium chloride solution is added to 100 grams of emulsified asphalt. The specifications (see Table 6) require that a minimum of 60% of the emulsion break down. In this case it is important that the emulsion break. For testing medium- and slow-setting emulsions, more of a stronger calcium chloride solution is used (50 cc of 0.1 N solution with 100 grams of emulsified asphalt). A maximum value for demulsibility is set, as here it is essential that the emulsions be resistant to breaking.

Sieve Test. The emulsion is poured through a 20-mesh sieve to be sure it contains no lumps of separated asphalt or other material which might clog up distributing equipment.

Miscibility Test. It is often desirable to dilute emulsified asphalts with water, and this dilution must be accomplished without the emulsion breaking down. For this test, 50 ml of emulsion is added to 150 ml of distilled water. The sample is satisfactory if after 2 hr there has been no appreciable coagulation of the asphalt contained in the emulsion.

For slow-setting emulsions, a "modified miscibility test" is prescribed. As before, 50 ml of emulsion is diluted with 150 ml of water. After stirring, the mixture is permitted to stand for 2 hr. Then samples taken from three levels in the container are placed in an oven at 163° C for 2 hr to drive off the water. Weighing before and after permits calculation of the percentage of asphalt residue at each level. Results are reported as the maximum numerical difference in percentage of asphalt content between any two of the three levels.

Freezing Test. A sample is exposed to 0° F for 12 hr, after which it is permitted to thaw at laboratory temperature. In all, three cycles of freezing and thawing are run. Samples that fail the freezing test will be separated into distinct layers which cannot be rendered homogeneous by stirring. Samples that remain homogeneous or can be made so by stirring pass the test and are reported as "homogeneous."

Stone-Coating and Cement-Mixing Tests. For most uses of medium- and slow-setting emulsions, it is important that the asphalt remain in suspension in the water after contact with the aggregate; otherwise mixing cannot be accomplished. For medium-setting emulsions the stone-coating test is used; emulsified asphalt is mixed with a standard washed coarse aggregate. By observation it is determined whether or not the rock has been satisfactorily coated or if the emulsion broke before mixing was completed. For slow-setting emulsions the cement-mixing test is employed. One hundred milliliters is mixed for one minute with 50 grams of high early-strength cement. After this, 150 ml of distilled water is added and the mixing continued for 3 more minutes. This mixture is then poured through a no. 14 sieve. Any material retained is dried at 163° C and weighed. The weight in grams of dried material retained is reported as the percentage emulsion broken. A maximum of 2% is allowed.

Test for sulfonation index for tars. Four divisions of hydrocarbons are present in tars and petroleum products. They are: (1) the paraffinic or saturated straight-chain group, (2) the naphthenic or cyclic saturated compounds, (3) the olefinic or unsaturated straight-chain group, and (4) the aromatics, which are the derivatives and homologs of benzene. Investigation has shown that often high percentages of paraffinic hydrocarbons were present when distress in tar roads occurred. Typical failures were that priming materials did not set up or that residual tars became greasy and failed to hold the cover stone.[9] However, it was possible to devise a test to detect paraffinic materials and prevent their use in pavements. This test, which is called the sulfonation index, is based on the wide differences in reactivity of these hydrocarbon divisions when mixed with sulfuric acid; paraffinic and naphthenic compounds are not attacked appreciably whereas the others are oxidized or converted into sulfonic acids. Although the AASHO specifications (see Table 7) indicate that the test is applied only to tar grades RT–1 to RT–6, many agencies set up like controls on all grades of tar.

Sulfuric acid (37 N H_2SO_4) is added to a sample of the distillate that was taken at a specified temperature or in a given temperature range. After repeated shaking to mix the liquids intimately, the sample is centrifuged, which separates the oils which were not acted upon by the acid. The sulfonation index is the milliliters of unsulfonated residue per 100 grams of tar.

Discussion of specifications and tests for bituminous binders. The specifications and tests just discussed are used to make sure that bituminous binders for pavements will give satisfactory results. Considerable evidence has accumulated that the performances of some binders which wholly meet present specifications are not acceptable. It may be anticipated that, as evidence accumulates, some of the old tests will be discarded and new ones substituted. This must not be done indiscriminately, as such changes may be far-reaching in their effects on deliveries, production processes, and costs. Typical criticisms of the present tests are the following: [10]

1. The present specifications, in excluding poor materials, also exclude many good ones.

2. Tests conducted on bituminous materials alone do not truly reflect their performance in service, as the thick test specimens do not react the same as the thin films which actually occur in pavements.

3. None of the present tests measures the rate at which binders will harden and age during mixing and under exposure to service conditions.

[9] See The Sulfonation Index Test for Tars, *Public Roads,* January, February, March 1943, pp. 141–154.

[10] For excellent discussions of this subject, see *Proceedings Association of Asphalt Paving Technologists.* Many articles appear in the magazine *Public Roads.* Also the Highway Research Board has prepared an annotated bibliography (*Bibliography 9, 1951*) titled Resistance of Bituminous Materials to Deterioration Caused by Physical and Chemical Changes.

Accelerated tests for oxidation, aging, and weathering are proposed to eliminate those binders that will age too rapidly.[11]

MINERAL AGGREGATES FOR BITUMINOUS PAVEMENTS [12]

Mineral aggregates constitute 88 to 96% of a pavement by weight, or something more than 75% by volume. The most common materials are broken stone or slag, crushed or uncrushed gravel, and sand. At times a finely divided mineral filler is also employed. Because of the large quantities involved, the cost of transporting mineral aggregates long distances is prohibitive, and they are usually obtained from relatively nearby sources. Over the country, commonly used aggregates differ widely in particle-size distribution and other characteristics; as a result, pavement types may also differ widely. In all cases, control over certain characteristics of the aggregates is imperative for satisfactory pavements; for this purpose specifications and tests have been developed.

Specifications and tests for mineral aggregates

General requirements. Certain general requirements should be met by all mineral aggregates for pavements. Those given by the AASHO for Dense-Graded Bituminous Road-Mix and Plant-Mix Surface Course (*AASHO Designation M62–49*) are representative:

Aggregates shall be of uniform quality, crushed to size as necessary, and shall be composed of sound, tough, durable pebbles or fragments of rock or slag with or without sand or other inert finely divided mineral aggregate. All material shall be free from clay balls, vegetable matter and other deleterious substances, and an excess of flat or elongated pieces. Slag shall be air-cooled blast-furnace slag of reasonably uniform density and quality. Excess of fine material shall be wasted before crushing.

Tests for particle size. For "dense-graded" pavements, particle sizes of the aggregate range from coarse to dust; for "open" pavements, one or more layers of coarse rock of uniform size are used; and, for sheet asphalt, carefully graded sand and mineral dust are employed. Although the particle sizes and size distribution vary between pavement types, control is necessary for every type and is obtained by

[11] See J. T. Pauls and J. Y. Welborn, *Public Roads*, August 1953, pp. 187–202, for a description and evaluation of three such tests.

[12] See Bibliography on Mineral Aggregates Annotated, *Highway Research Board Bibliography 6*, for a listing and summary of literature on this subject.

screening the material through standard sieves.   Particle sizes for the common pavement types will be discussed in later pages.

Tests for strength and soundness.   As mentioned above in the general requirements, aggregates should be sound, tough, and durable.[13] Common tests for strength are the Los Angeles abrasion test, the Deval test, and in one instance the wet-shot rattler test.   For soundness there are the sodium sulfate and freezing and thawing tests.

Los Angeles Rattler Test (AASHO Designation [14] *T96–49; ASTM Designation C131–49)*.   This test is conducted in a hollow steel cylinder closed at both ends.   The cylinder is 28 in. inside diameter and 20 in. long and contains a steel shelf which projects radially inward 3½ in.   It is mounted with its axis horizontal on stub shafts attached at the ends.   A 5000-gram selected sample of coarse aggregate is charged into the cylinder along with a prescribed number and size of cast-iron spheres, and the cylinder then is rotated for 500 (or 1000) revolutions at a speed of 30 to 33 revolutions per minute.   After testing, the sample is sieved on a no. 12 sieve, and that portion which passes through is discarded.   The loss (percentage of wear) is the difference between the original and final weights of the test sample expressed as a percentage of the original weight.

Deval Test for Abrasion (AASHO Designations T3–35 and T4–35).   The test machine consists of a closed iron cylinder about 8 in. in diameter and 13 in. in length mounted with its axis at an angle of 30 degrees to a horizontal shaft.   In the Deval test 5 kg of selected coarse aggregate along with six cast-iron spheres 1.875 in. in diameter are placed in the cylinder and rotated 10,000 times at a speed of 30 to 33 revolutions per minute.   After testing, the sample is sieved on a no. 12 sieve, and that portion which passes through is discarded.   The loss (percentage of wear) is the difference between the original and final weights of the test sample, expressed as a percentage of the original weight.

The California Division of Highways uses a wet-shot rattler test which differs from the Deval test in that enough water is added to the cylinder to cover the sample and abrasive charge.

Soundness of Aggregates by Use of Sodium Sulfate or Magnesium Sulfate (AASHO Designation T104–46; ASTM Designation C88–46T).   This test subjects dried and sized samples of aggregate to immersion in a saturated solution of sodium or magnesium sulfate, followed by draining and oven drying. The liquid penetrates the interstices of the individual particles and, on drying, creates pressures which cause splitting, crumbling, cracking, or flaking of the surface.   Usually, several immersion-drying cycles are run.   After washing and drying, the sample is examined visually and also sieved again to determine the change in particle size.   Results are reported as "percentage loss," which is measured as the percentage by weight which passes a sieve on which the particles were originally retained.

[13] Fairly soft coarse aggregates have been used successfully on occasion in dense-graded plant mixes, but only under controlled conditions.

[14] See *Highway Materials,* part II, *Tests,* AASHO (1950).

Soundness of Aggregates by Freezing and Thawing (AASHO Designation T103-42). This test has the same purpose as the sodium sulfate test and is conducted in a comparable way. Samples are frozen for 2 hr, then thawed for ½ hr. The number of cycles is not specified in the standard test, but is large. The State Highway Commission of Indiana uses 50 cycles. Results are reported as the findings of visual examination and as "percentage loss" as defined above. In its statement on the scope of the freezing and thawing test, the AASHO standard method states, "Because of the limited amount of information concerning the significance of the test results and because of the lack of information as to the uniformity of tests made in different laboratories, the test method should not be used as an arbitrary basis of rejection; it should be used only to furnish information to indicate whether or not the materials require further investigation as to their soundness."

Requirements under the tests for strength and soundness vary from state to state, and with pavement type. By 1953, 35 states employed the Los Angeles rattler test, and the number seemed on the increase. Most severe requirement is that the coefficient of wear be not greater than 20 for stone and 30 for gravel, but excellent aggregates are available, so that the requirement causes no difficulty. The AASHO specifications set limits of 40 to 50 depending on pavement type, although they recommend that tougher rock be obtained if possible. Some states use the Deval test. Typical are the New York specifications which set the maximum percentage of wear at 4.0 to 8.0, depending on use. California sets maximum percentage of wear of the combined mineral aggregate, measured by the wet-shot rattler test, at 50 for the usual plant-mix surfacings, but at 37 for open-graded pavements.

The AASHO specifications for most pavement aggregates, other than those for dense-graded mixes, include the soundness test. This test is required by relatively few highway agencies. Some require it for aggregates for macadam pavements but not for dense-graded mixes.

Tests for aggregate-bitumen affinity and for swell. If a pavement is to be strong and durable, the binder must adhere firmly to the aggregate particles. If the binder separates or "strips" from the aggregate, the pavement will soon disintegrate under traffic. Furthermore, the paving mixture must retain constant volume. If it swells, interlock and internal friction are destroyed and stability is lost.

Moisture is the chief cause of stripping and swelling. Some aggregates, which are classed as *hydrophilic*, have greater surface affinity for water than for bitumen,[15] and, in service, water gradually replaces the bitumen in contact with the aggregate. In a pavement mixture containing fines susceptible to expansion when wet, stripping is accom-

---

[15] The opposite designation is *hydrophobic* which, interpreted literally, means "fear of water."

panied by swelling of the pavement mass. Wherever stripping or swelling occurs, pavement deterioration is to be expected.[16]

Testing procedures for stripping and swelling of aggregates are not uniform between agencies. For dense-graded mixes, some groups, including the AASHO, use the swell test (*AASHO Designation T101*) or the swell test coupled with a specified maximum value of 6 or less for the plasticity index. The California Division of Highways adds a water-asphalt preferential test for testing mineral fillers. For open-graded mixes containing only coarse aggregates, a film-stripping test is common. Many highway agencies use no tests at all for stripping or swelling, probably because experience has shown that the available aggregates are not affected.

For the swell test, samples of aggregate and bituminous binder are mixed, at elevated temperatures if necessary. After curing, the sample is tamped into a cylindrical steel mold; final compaction is by static pressure of 2000 lb per sq in. The sample is then submerged in water for 24 hr, after which its expansion is measured.

Two test methods are available: Method *A* uses the bituminous binder selected for the paving and a compacted test specimen 4 in. in diameter and approximately 4.3 in. high; method *B* uses a standard SC–2 binder and a compacted test specimen 4 in. in diameter and about 1¾ in. high. A typical specification, that of the AASHO for aggregates for dense-graded bituminous road and plant-mix surfaces (*Designation M62*), limits swell to 0.030 in. maximum for method *A* and to 0.062 in. for method *B*.

For the water-asphalt preferential test of the California Division of Highways, samples of filler dust and SC–2 oil are mixed, after which water is added and the whole stirred for 5 min with an electric stirrer. Materials are satisfactory if the filler remains coated with asphalt; they are unsatisfactory if dust and oil separate.

The stripping test for coarse aggregate of the California Division of Highways evaluates either aggregate or bituminous material. The aggregate, which is washed only if washing is to be employed on construction, is uniformly coated with the binder at a temperature comparable to that employed during construction. Water is added and the whole agitated in a shaking machine at room temperature for 15 min. The surface area from which the binder has been stripped is then observed. Aggregates for open-graded mixes are rejected if the stripped area exceeds 25% of the total.

Engineers of the Bureau of Public Roads have developed an immersion-compression test.[17] Duplicate sets of molded compression-test cylinders of

---

[16] Antistripping additives for bituminous materials are available and have often been effective. To date, however, none has been completely proved. When positive control of stripping is accomplished, many aggregates now considered unsuited for bituminous pavements will become acceptable.

[17] See *Public Roads*, July, August, September 1945 and December 1948. See also *Designations D1074–49T* and *D1075–49T*, *Book of ASTM Standards*, part **3 (1949)**.

bituminous-surfacing mixture are tested, one set dry and the other after immersion in water. Differences in strength serve to measure the effect of stripping that results from water action.

DENSE-GRADED BITUMINOUS PAVEMENTS

A large percentage of the more important roads in the United States are surfaced with dense-graded bituminous pavements. They consist of aggregates graded from coarse to dust intimately mixed with bituminous binder before being placed.

Stability of dense-graded bituminous pavements

Dense-graded pavements have all been placed in one general group because the same design principle controls: materials and proportioning must give a stable mixture which will not shove or distort under traffic. Figure 13, page 342, indicates how failure of a bituminous mix occurs over adequate support: a shearing action along one or more surfaces permits material to flow from under the load. Before this shearing failure can occur, three resisting elements must be overcome: namely, the friction between aggregate particles which might be called the sliding resistance, the cohesion or stickiness introduced by the bituminous binder, and the inertia of the pavement mass.

Research has indicated that frictional resistance provides the most important element of stability and that this frictional resistance is largely dependent on aggregate qualities. Granular materials, without binder, can distort under load only if the particles slide over each other or become displaced in some other way. Resistance to sliding, like static friction in mechanics, depends largely on the total load normal to the direction of motion and on the angle of sliding friction between particle surfaces. It is largely independent of the rate at which load is applied and the size of the loaded area. From this it can be concluded that aggregates with rough surfaces will offer greater resistance to displacement than those with smooth surfaces. Sharp angular particles will be more resistant to displacement than rounded ones. Upon the introduction of a lubricant, either bituminous material or water, the basic characteristics of static friction remain, but frictional resistance is reduced by the separation and lubrication of the surfaces, with added lubricant causing added reduction. Too much lubricant will lower frictional resistance to such a level that instability of the mix will result (see Fig. 2). In these lubricated mixtures, friction is further affected by the degree and method of compaction because of their influence on the proximity and arrangement of particles.

Addition of bituminous binders to granular materials provides cohesion or liquid friction, which also increases stability. This cohesive strength is relatively independent of normal pressure, but varies almost

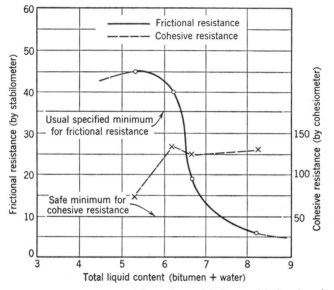

FIG. 2. Influence of percentage of bituminous binder on frictional and cohesive components of stability of a typical dense-graded bituminous paving mixture (Courtesy F. N. Hveem)

directly with the surface area of the mineral particles and the viscosity of the binder, as controlled by selection or temperature. Liquid friction offers great resistance to loads of short duration but practically none to static loads. Cohesive strength increases with bituminous content until the particles are well covered with a film of binder, after which it changes little (see Fig. 2). It increases also with greater roughness of particle surfaces. From these ideas it follows that cohesive resistance of a mixture may be increased by an addition of fine material such as mineral filler and by the use of more viscous binders; on the other hand, high temperatures and slow rates of loading cause large decreases.

One authority has estimated that the passage of a heavy truck tire over a pavement sets some 30 tons of materials in motion. From this it could be concluded that inertia forces offer great resistance to pavement distortion. However, under static loading, which represents the worst condition, the force required to overcome the inertia of even this mass is negligible. Consequently inertia resistance is usually ignored in testing procedures.

Testing for stability. The factors most commonly considered in evaluating stability are type and percentage of binder, amount and type of mineral filler, aggregate frictional characteristics, and aggregate grain-size distribution. In many cases this evaluation consists merely of following experience gained over a period of years; in others test procedures ranging from simple to elaborate are used.[18] A partial list of the basic test procedures proposed or used over the years includes single shear; punching shear; torsion; cone bearing; beam strength; tensile strength; extrusion; direct compression; penetration by rod, ball, or roller; the stabilometer; and open and closed triaxial devices. With this diversity of testing procedures go disagreements concerning the properties to be measured and the efficacy of the various testing procedures. It is beyond the scope of this work to present these arguments. Rather, four of the methods in common use are described briefly in the following pages.

Hubbard-Field Stability Test.[19] This test, which is widely employed, can be classed as an extrusion test. A cylindrical briquette of compacted paving mixture or a core specimen from an existing pavement is heated to 140° F and placed in a close-fitting cylindrical mold. The bottom of this mold is fitted with a standard circular orifice of smaller diameter than the mold proper (see Fig. 3a). Load is applied to the top of the specimen at the rate of 1 in. each 25 sec, and the maximum load developed in forcing the mixture through the orifice is recorded as the stability. For sheet asphalts or sand asphalts, the specimen is 2 in. in diameter and 1 in. high; acceptable stability for heavy traffic is 2000 lb or more. For asphaltic concrete or other heated mixes containing large aggregate, the briquette is 6 in. in diameter by 2 in. high; acceptable stability for heavy traffic is 3500 lb or more. Six-inch specimens made with liquid or semiliquid asphalts are tested at room temperatures, and a lower range of stability values is considered acceptable. The 2-in. laboratory specimens are compacted at mixing temperature.

Variables evaluated by the Hubbard-Field test are per cent of binder, per cent of mineral filler, and aggregate gradation. Its most common design use is to determine the percentages of binder and mineral filler. The testing temperature of 140° F was adopted as the highest to be expected in a pavement in service.

[18] *Highway Research Board Bulletin 80* (1953) indicates that 29 state highway departments employ some form of stability tests for bituminous mixtures.

[19] See *Asphalt Institute Research Series 1,* for a complete description of this test.

Stability as determined by the Hubbard-Field test actually measures some combination of friction and cohesion but does not express them separately. High stability values may be obtained by using too little binder or one that is too hard. Such mixes, in service, may crack badly. Also, mixes showing high stabilities may be made by combining hard asphalts with aggregates of poor frictional characteristics. Under static loads, pavements so constructed will shove and distort.

Marshall Test.[20]   This test has been adopted by the Corps of Engineers, U. S. Army, for designing asphaltic-concrete pavements for airports. It has also been adopted by several state highway departments. A cylindrical specimen, 4 in. in diameter and 2½ in. long and of controlled proportions, is compacted by impact methods. The specimen at 140° F is placed in the collarlike testing device which offers no confinement at the ends and is loaded at a speed of 2 in. per min (see Fig. 3b). Stability is measured as the maximum load applied in deforming the specimen; flow value is the deformation of the sample at the instant of maximum load.

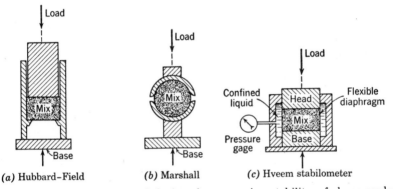

(a) Hubbard–Field   (b) Marshall   (c) Hveem stabilometer

Fig. 3.   Schematic drawings of devices for measuring stability of dense-graded bituminous mixtures

Criteria set for acceptable mixes for airport loadings (15,000- to 37,000-lb wheel loads) are: stability 500 lb minimum, flow 0.20 in. maximum, per cent voids in total mix 3 to 5, per cent voids filled with asphalt 75 to 85. Asphalt content is set at that which gives maximum stability values.

Like the Hubbard-Field test, the Marshall test measures frictional and cohesive resistance in combination.

Hveem Stabilometer.[21]   This device (see Fig. 3c) has been used by the

[20] Results of the Corps of Engineers' study, reported as *Investigation of the Design and Control of Asphalt Paving Mixtures* (3 vols.), are available from the director, Waterways Experiment Station, Vicksburg, Miss. For a summary of these see Symposium on Asphalt Paving Mixtures, *Highway Research Board Research ·Report 7-B* (1949).

[21] Articles concerning the stabilometer by F. N. Hveem and others appear as follows: *Proceedings Highway Research Board*, part II, pp. 15–54 (1934); pp. 100–123 (1946); pp. 455–466 (1947); and pp. 101–136 (1948). See also *Texas*

California Division of Highways for bituminous-pavement design since 1930, and is presently employed by several other agencies. Specimens are short cylinders of compacted paving mixtures of 4 in. diameter and 2½ in. height. Load is applied vertically to the ends of the cylinder, and the horizontal pressure developed in the fluid confining the sides of the specimen is recorded (see Fig. 3c). For bituminous paving mixtures, results are stated in terms of "relative stability" rather than as "resistance value" as is done with soil-aggregate mixtures. Relative stability is expressed by the empirical formula

$$\text{Relative stability} = \frac{22.2}{\dfrac{P_h D_2}{P_v - P_h} + 0.222}$$

where P_v = vertical pressure, typically 400 psi.

P_h = horizontal pressure in pounds per square inch, taken at the instant P_v is recorded.

D_2 = the volume of liquid that must be displaced to change the horizontal pressure from 5 to 100 psi. This factor corrects for the different degrees of smoothness or roughness in the exterior surface of the test specimens.

Values of relative stability greater than 35 are considered entirely satisfactory. Mixes bound by fluid oils usually give trouble at values lower than 30; bituminous concretes bound with asphaltic cements may be satisfactory with results as low as 25.

Compaction for stabilometer specimens is accomplished by a special tamping shoe or kneading compactor which applies many repetitions of load as the material is placed in the mold.[22] This method was adopted because stabilometer tests on laboratory samples so compacted and those of the same mix cored from completed pavements gave comparable results. Like correlation was not found between field samples and those compacted in the laboratory by static or impact methods.

The stabilometer test is so conducted that it measures the frictional resistance of the mix. The sample is at 140° F; load is applied slowly, at 0.05 in. per min. Thus the binder and any water present serve as lubricants but develop little cohesive resistance. The stabilometer may be used either to determine the per cent of binder to employ with an acceptable aggregate or to evaluate the frictional characteristics of different aggregates.

Along with the stabilometer was developed the *cohesiometer*. The same briquette is transferred from the stabilometer to the cohesiometer, which, by bending it around a diameter of the base, subjects the specimen to tension under controlled temperature and rate of application of load. Results are expressed on an arbitrary scale: A zero value indicates no tensile strength; mixes made of very hard asphalts develop values as high as 700. Mixes showing cohesiometer values lower than 50 will ravel and fray under traffic. Extremely high results may indicate binder so hard that cracking of the finished pavement will result.

Engineering Experiment Station Bulletin 126 (1952) and the several issues of *Proceedings Association of Asphalt Technologists.*

[22] See also p. 329.

Triaxial Tests for Bituminous Mixtures. A description of the triaxial test as applied to soils appears on page 353. There are similar tests to measure the stability of dense-graded bituminous mixtures. For example, the Kansas Highway Department and the Canadian Department of Transport use the "open system." [23]

West Coast engineers of the Asphalt Institute and allied oil companies have devised a "closed-system" triaxial device for designing dense-graded bituminous mixtures.[24] A tall sample is employed (4 in. in diameter by 8 in. in height) to eliminate the effects of arching of the aggregates at the ends of the specimen. The fluid is confined so that lateral pressure increases as vertical load increases. Only one sample of each mix is run. Figure 4a shows the plotted results of a typical test run on an asphaltic-concrete mix and the method and formulas to convert these results into values for the angle of internal friction and unit cohesion. Figure 4b is the design chart which shows whether or not a particular asphaltic concrete is stable enough to carry unlimited traffic without distress. For stable mixes, plotted values of unit cohesion against angle of internal friction must lie in the unshaded area in the upper right-hand section. Instability, as indicated by the shaded portion of the diagram, may result from the lack of internal friction (area *A*), the lack of sufficient cohesion (area *B*), or both (area *C*). Limiting minimum values of unit cohesion and angle of friction for bituminous pavements carrying moderate to heavy traffic are indicated by the dashed line; those for light traffic by the dotted line.

Samples are compacted by a kneading device like that for preparing stabilometer samples. Load is applied by increments; after each application, load and lateral pressure readings are delayed until they become stabilized. This procedure gives the equivalent of static loading and also eliminates the influence of temperature on cohesive strength.

Asphalt content of dense-graded bituminous mixes

Stability requirements for dense-graded bituminous mixes dictate the maximum safe percentage of binder for each mix. If the amount goes above this level, the mix will be unstable because lubrication has too greatly reduced friction between particles. Mixes that are too rich are unsatisfactory also because the kneading of traffic drives the ag-

[23] See Design of Flexible Pavements Using the Triaxial Compression Test, *Highway Research Board Bulletin 8* (1947), and N. W. McLeod, *Proceedings Highway Research Board*, pp. 107–159 (1949). For a description of an improved triaxial test cell see C. A. Carpenter, J. F. Goode, and R. A. Peck, *Public Roads*, August 1951, pp. 173–179.

[24] See V. A. Endersby, The Mechanics of Granular and Granular-Plastic Materials with Special Reference to Bituminous Road Materials and Subsoils, *Proceedings ASTM*, vol. 40 (1940); and V. R. Smith, Triaxial Stability Method for Flexible Pavement Design, *Proceedings Association of Asphalt Paving Technologists*, vol. 18 (1949). Comprehensive discussions dealing with all the more common forms of triaxial testing as applied to bituminous materials and to soils appear in *ASTM Special Technical Publication 106* (1951).

gregate down and brings the binder to the top. The resulting surface, when wet, becomes very slick and therefore unsafe. There is a minimum safe percentage of binder also. Below it, the mix will not be properly cemented and will ravel under traffic. Good pavements can and have been built with bituminous percentages at all values between the limits outlined. However, the majority of engineers (but not all)

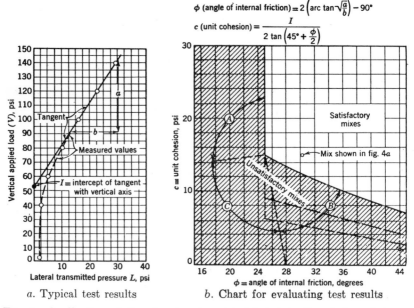

ϕ (angle of internal friction) $= 2\left(\text{arc tan}\sqrt{\frac{a}{b}}\right) - 90°$

c (unit cohesion) $= \dfrac{I}{2 \tan\left(45° + \frac{\phi}{2}\right)}$

a. Typical test results

b. Chart for evaluating test results

FIG. 4. Application of the closed-system triaxial test to the design of dense-graded bituminous paving mixtures (Courtesy The Asphalt Institute)

are of the opinion that bituminous content slightly below that at which stability decreases rapidly (possibly around 6% for the mix of Fig. 2) gives the best and longest-lasting pavement. The principal reason is that thicker films of bituminous materials better resist oxidation and the effects of sunlight and other deteriorating forces that cause the binder to harden. Thus, cracking and breaking up are postponed.[25] Also, if the aggregate tends to absorb the bitumen as some do, the extra binder provides a reserve which gives added pavement life. Good judgment dictates that in general the percentage of binder be held

[25] There is mounting evidence that bituminous pavements begin to crack up when the penetration of the binder (as extracted from the failed pavement) drops as low as 30.

somewhat below the upper limit established by stability requirements. Proportioning identical with that of the design mix cannot be reproduced in construction even with the most careful control, and a little extra binder or small decrease in fines or dust would change the mix from stable to unstable.

Dry aggregates are highly desirable. Water serves as a lubricant, just as bitumen does, so that any appreciable amount of water may produce instability. It is common to require that aggregates contain no more than 1% moisture when combined with the binder.

If stability tests are not employed, the percentage of bituminous binder must be established in some other way. Further, as most stability tests are too complex for field purposes, some less elaborate method of control must be used to provide for day-to-day variation.[26] Methods range from reliance on experience with no testing at all to procedures that carefully measure the surface and absorptive characteristics of the aggregate. A few of the more common ones are outlined in succeeding paragraphs. It is fortunate that for the most part the spread between too little and too much binder is relatively wide so that comparatively few unstable mixes result even with somewhat crude controls. However, it would be dangerous to attempt to set the percentage of binder close to either limit using such methods.

Bituminous Content Based on Particle-Size Distribution. A given volume of small particles of a given shape and roughness has a greater surface area than the same volume of larger particles of like characteristics. It might then be reasoned that, as the number of fine particles increases, the amount of bituminous binder needed to coat these surfaces also increases. Based on this concept, formulas expressing percentage of bitumen in terms of grain-size distribution were developed. Such formulas were of little use with the carefully controlled gradings of early-day pavements. However, the advent of road mix, which employed the old road metal or other material of widely varying grading as mineral aggregate, made the problem of the percentage of binder a serious one. The first formula for determining the "oil" content was offered in 1927 by C. L. McKesson and W. N. Frickstad. This formula was

$$P = 0.015a + 0.03b + 0.17c$$

where, by weight, P is the per cent of oil required, and a, b, and c are, respectively, the percentages of material retained on the no. 10 sieve, passing the no. 10 sieve and retained on the no. 200 sieve, and passing the no. 200 sieve. This formula has since been held to give too lean a mixture and has been modified considerably. In 1935 the formula used in California, with the above notation, was as follows:

[26] For data on a proposed field stability test see Chu and Spangler, *Proceedings Highway Research Board,* p. 159 (1949).

$$P = 0.02a + 0.045b + 0.18c$$

with the stipulation that, for coarse mixtures, in which less than 50% pass the no. 4 sieve and only 4 to 5% pass the no. 200 sieve, the coefficient c be increased to 0.20, and, for fine mixtures, all of which pass the no. 4 sieve, this coefficient be reduced to 0.15. A number of like formulas were developed by New Mexico, Nebraska, Wyoming, and other states.

The use of these formulas has been confined mainly to cheap road-mix and plant-mix projects classed as intermediate-type surfaces. At times they have proved unsatisfactory, as when the mineral aggregate contained large amounts of blow sand or other hard, slick, fine material. Under these conditions, the percentage of oil called for by the formula gave a mix so rich that under traffic free oil came to the surface to streak vehicles traveling the roads. Such mixes were often unstable also. Experienced engineers checked formula results by rubbing unmixed samples between the hands and observing the relative ease of coating the particles. In all instances, careful observation of completed sections was made as a further check.[27]

Bituminous Content Determined by Surface-Area Methods. Engineers of the California Division of Highways have developed the surface-area method for determining the percentage of binder. The grain-size distribution is determined by sieve analysis and elutriation. Total surface area per pound of aggregate is then computed by multiplying the percentage of aggregate in each of several size groupings by its appropriate surface-area constant and taking the sum of the products. Table 8 shows these computations for a sample sized

TABLE 8. COMPUTATION FOR SURFACE AREA OF AGGREGATE FOR DENSE-GRADE BITUMINOUS PAVEMENTS

Sieve No.		Fraction between Sieves	Surface-Area Constants	Surface-Area Fractions
Pass.	Ret.			
270 *	...	0.04	300	12.00
200	270	0.08	200	16.00
100	200	0.01	120	1.20
50	100	0.07	60	4.20
30	50	0.13	30	3.90
16	30	0.13	16	2.08
8	16	0.09	8	0.72
4	8	0.17	4	0.68
⅜ in.	4	0.13	2	0.26
¾ in.	⅜ in.	0.15	1	0.15
Totals		1.00		41.19

* Silt in suspension.

[27] Some asphalt technologists maintain that, although these methods have merit for determining the minimum limit to the amount of binder, they are of no value in setting the oil content at which stability is lost. They state that, once the particles are thoroughly coated, added binder causes no further change in appearance.

on 10 selected sieves. Surface-area constants also have been developed for grain-size distributions measured by 7, 6, 4 and 3 sieves.[28] Once the surface area of the aggregate is known, the proper amount of oil is determined by using Fig. 5. For an aggregate of grading like that of Table 8 (surface area 41.19 sq ft per lb of aggregate) and of average surface roughness (curve 4 of Fig. 5)

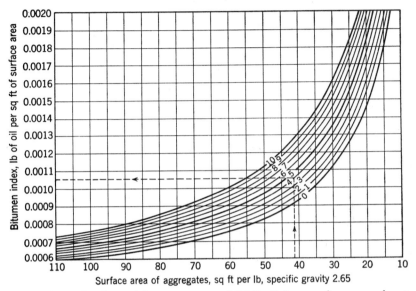

FIG. 5. Chart for determining percentage of SC-2 oil from surface area of combined aggregate (Courtesy F. N. Hveem)

Procedure

1. Find surface area of sample on lower margin.
2. Follow the line upward to one of the curves.
3. Then to left margin indicating bitumen index, i.e. pound of oil per square foot of surface area.
4. Multiply surface area of sample by the indicated bitumen index.
5. Result will give pounds of oil per pound of aggregate.

Note

Numbers 0–10 on curves relate to surface factors. Lower numbers apply to smooth, hard particles. Higher numbers indicate increasing roughness.

Values are for aggregates of 2.65 sp. gr. For other specific gravities calculate thus:

$$\text{Oil ratio} = \frac{2.65}{\text{actual sp. gr.}} \times \text{surface area} \times \text{bitumen index}$$

[28] See F. N. Hveem, The Centrifuge Kerosene Equivalent as Used in Establishing the Oil Content of Dense-Graded Mixes, *California Highways and Public Works*, October 1946.

the bitumen index is 0.00104 lb of oil per square foot of surface area. The oil ratio, or pounds of oil per pound of aggregate is 0.00104 × 41.19 = 0.043, or 4.3%. If binders more viscous than SC–2 oils are used more bitumen is gen-

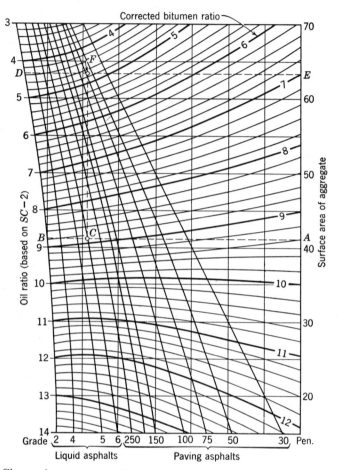

Fig. 6. Change in percentage of oil with change in consistency of binder—for dense-graded bituminous mixtures (Courtesy F. N. Hveem)

erally needed, as films are of greater thickness. Further increases in bitumen must be made if the aggregates are absorptive. The experience of the California Division of Highways is shown in Fig. 6. The dotted lines on the chart illustrate its application for the combination of SC–6 oil with the aggregate just discussed: Beginning with the surface-area scale to the right, draw a horizontal line through the proper value, in this case line AB at a height of 41.19. This intersects the slanting line for SC–6 at point C. Through point C draw a vertical line, and extend it upward (or downward) until it intersects at F a horizontal line *DE*, representing the oil ratio for SC–2 of 4.3% as already determined. The corrected bitumen ratio for an SC–6 or other oil of like viscosity is 4.7%, as read from the curved lines of generally horizontal direction.

In the earlier applications of the surface-area method, surface-roughness factors were evaluated for each aggregate source by means of the stabilometer. Adjustments in the oil ratio for variations in grading were then made in the field, using the chart shown here as Fig. 5. Recently, however, the *Centrifuge kerosene equivalent* (CKE) has been developed.[29] This test is designed to measure surface area, surface roughness, and absorption of binder in a single operation. A sample of aggregate passing the no. 4 sieve is saturated in kerosene after which it is centrifuged for 2 min at 400 times gravity in an inexpensive portable centrifuge. The weight of kerosene retained, expressed as a percentage of the weight of aggregate, is the CKE. Design charts have been developed giving the oil ratio in terms of the CKE and per cent of aggregate passing the no. 4 sieve. Conversions can also be made between CKE and surface-area methods so that they may be used together.

ASPHALTIC- OR BITUMINOUS-CONCRETE PAVEMENTS

The term "asphaltic concrete" denotes a type of road surface made of hot, graded, coarse mineral aggregates and fines premixed with hot asphalt. "Bituminous concrete" is a more general term which includes both asphaltic concrete and similar mixtures made with refined tar. The coarse aggregate is generally crushed stone, crushed slag, or crushed gravel, to which is added sand or sand and filler. By contrast, sheet asphalt involves the use of sand and filler only.

Bituminous concrete is the highest and most expensive type of premixed bituminous pavement and is suitable for the most heavily traveled roads. It is mixed and laid at high temperatures, around 325° F, and requires a heavy binder. The penetration grades of binder generally are 50–60, 60–70, 70–80, and 85–100. Mineral aggregates are of high quality and are proportioned within tight limits. Specifications for mixing, placing, final density, and accuracy of surface finish provide close control over all phases of construction. Formerly, asphaltic concrete was not advocated for steep grades because of a tendency to develop a smooth surface texture under traffic and so to become slippery when wet. Developments in producing the mixture and in laying and finishing it have much improved the quality, so that this objection no longer holds against properly designed mixes. Bituminous concrete has the important advantage that traffic may use it immediately after construction.

[29] See *ibid.*

History of asphaltic concrete

Sheet asphalt was quite commonly used before asphaltic concrete was developed, and some engineers still prefer it. Some of the early pavement mixtures in Washington, D. C., however, were essentially asphaltic concrete. In addition, there are in early reports of the state highway authorities of New York, Rhode Island, and New Jersey records of the construction of road surfaces with mixtures of tar or asphalt and broken stone. Hamilton, Ontario, used a refined tar and stone mix as early as 1880. Toronto and Ottawa built similar pavements in the years 1900–06.

In 1903 a patent (no. 727,505) was issued to F. J. Warren of Massachusetts for a paving mixture of graded aggregate and bituminous materials. It covered, by 13 claims, the construction of dense paving mixtures in which the mineral aggregate consisted of several grades so combined as to produce in the aggregate itself "inherent stability" and a minimum of 21% voids, which were filled with bituminous material.[30] Asphaltic concrete, known under the Warren patent as "bitulithic" pavement, produced an excellent, dense, waterproof road surface of splendid wearing qualities.[31] "Warrenite" was a proprietary name given under the Warren patents to certain less rigidly defined mixtures which frequently used gravel aggregate and sand instead of graded crushed rock and permitted proportioning of the various sizes of aggregate by volume instead of by weight.

The Warren patents had a marked influence on the design of asphaltic-concrete mixtures because certain favorable gradings of coarse aggregate could be employed only in these proprietary mixes. For a number of years the use of aggregates larger than ½ in. for other dense mixtures practically ceased, although open mixes consisting of coarse aggregates without smaller material were developed. A typical grading for such mixtures ranged from 2 to ½ or ¼ in., which resulted in a pavement that was not dense.

In 1910, by court decision, it was held that certain asphaltic-concrete paving mixtures laid in Topeka and Emporia, Kans., did not infringe on the Warren patent. The essential element of this "Topeka mix" was a fraction, usually about 20%, of mineral aggregate passing the ½-in. sieve but retained on the no. 10 sieve, whereas the Warren patent used stone 2 in. or more in size. A "modified Topeka" mix, intended to

---

[30] For added details of the Warren patent see Hewes, *American Highway Practice,* John Wiley & Sons, vol. 2, pp. 89–97 (1942).

[31] See the Oregon specification of 1917 in Table 10 for an example of the grading of this proprietary mix.

improve that allowed by the court decree, was also developed. It was essentially a sheet asphalt to which about one-third of small crushed stone passing the ½-in. sieve and retained on the no. 10 sieve was added.

The Warren patent expired in 1920, but its effect is still reflected in present-day practice. Many of the mixes developed to circumvent it are still in use as they proved satisfactory in service. Mixes that do not include large aggregate are common, despite the fact that large stones contribute markedly to stability.

Materials for bituminous concrete

Asphaltic cements, largely from petroleum sources, are usually specified as the binder for bituminous concrete. In earlier practice, the harder grades, such as 30–40 or 40–50 penetrations, were commonly used. More recent studies have shown that there is advantage to using softer grades, in that weathering and oxidizing are slowed, which results in less cracking. In addition, the softer grades of asphalt require less heating, resulting in some economy in plant operation. In current practice 60–70 and 85–100 penetration asphalts are common (see Tables 9 and 10). Under some circumstances tars of the heaviest grades are also employed. Percentages of binder by weight for typical mixes are shown in Tables 9 and 10.

Coarse aggregate [32] is generally broken stone or crushed gravel, although uncrushed gravel has sometimes been used. For stability, rough aggregate surfaces are essential, and angular shape is desirable. Crushing the proper stone or gravel produces both. Some specifications exclude uncrushed material entirely by stating that coarse aggregate be made from large stones (about 2 in. minimum size) recrushed to meet grading requirements. Others specify that samples present some minimum number of fresh surfaces produced by crushing. To illustrate, the Indiana Highway Commission requires that for asphaltic-concrete base courses 65% of the coarse aggregate particles show two crushed surfaces; for surface courses the percentage is increased to 85. Some use partially crushed material; the Ohio Department of Highways requires that coarse aggregate contain at least 40% of fractured pieces. Considerable strength and toughness is desirable and usually specified (see p. 468), although softer aggregates which would be

---

[32] Coarse aggregates are defined by many agencies as those retained on the no. 10 sieve. Others set the division at the no. 4 sieve. Actually this break point is of little practical significance.

entirely unsuited for open mixes or macadams have been employed successfully.

Fine aggregates are the particles ranging in size from the no. 10 or no. 4 sieve downward, and consist of sand or stone screenings or a combination of the two.[33] It is usually specified that they be free from large amounts of dirt or organic matter and range in size from coarse to fine. Individual particles are to be clean, uncoated, hard, and moderately sharp. In general, no specific tests (except for grading) are set out to secure these conditions.

Some agencies use mineral filler as a separate ingredient of bituminous concrete; others do not. Some require it in surface courses but not in the underlying base, binder, or leveling layers. (The data of Tables 9 and 10 are representative of current practice.) Acceptable mineral fillers include finely powdered limestone, Portland cement, or other artificially or naturally powdered mineral dust. It is common to insure its fineness by specification; typical is that of the Georgia Highway Department of 100% passing the no. 50 sieve, a minimum of 90% passing the no. 100 sieve, and 65% passing the no. 200 sieve. Some agencies permit diatomaceous earth and like materials as mineral filler; others exclude them. If these fillers, which have low specific gravities, are allowed, proportions by weight must be adjusted downward; otherwise too much of them will be included.[34]

Aggregate grading for bituminous concrete

Many different aggregate gradings have given excellent bituminous-concrete pavements. However, the shape of the curve of per cent passing against sieve opening will conform in a general way to that plotted in Fig. 7. Chief variables between mixes are maximum size of aggregate and per cent passing the no. 200 sieve. Maximum aggregate size is controlled by the thickness of the pavement layer and rarely exceeds 75% of that value, but is often much less. Surface courses commonly have smaller maximum sizes than underlying layers. Per cent passing the 200-mesh sieve is usually higher for surface courses than for the lower layers, as the added fines make for easier manipulating and finishing and give a more impervious surface, but at greater cost.

[33] A few agencies exclude stream sands and permit only products resulting from crushing rock or gravel. Research has indicated that angularity in the fine aggregate greatly increases stability. See W. H. Campen and J. R. Smith, *Proceedings Association of Asphalt Technologists,* vol. 17 (1948).

[34] For a report of the effect of fillers of trap-rock dust and fly ash on the water-resisting properties of bituminous concrete see C. A. Carpenter, *Public Roads,* December 1952, pp. 101–110.

On Fig. 7 are also indicated the problems that may arise if grading departs too far from that of the usual asphaltic concrete.[35] Gradings that plot outside the dotted lines of the figure present the problems indicated. Of particular importance is the danger of instability resulting from the inclusion of excess fines.

Two methods for stating the desired aggregate gradings for bitumi-

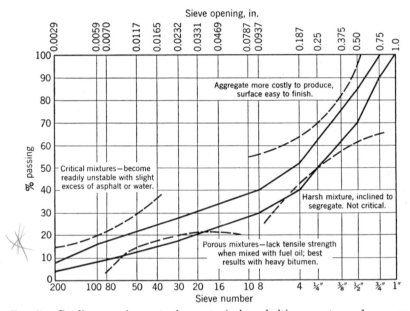

FIG. 7.   Grading requirements for a typical asphaltic-concrete surface course
(After T. E. Stanton, Jr. and F. N. Hveem)

nous concrete are in use. One (see Table 9) specifies limits to the percentages by weight smaller than given sieve sizes; the other (see Table 10) specifies limiting percentages of material within given size ranges. By either method, consistent gradings can be obtained. From a study of these tables, which present only a part of the gradings used by nine highway agencies, the student can begin to realize the diversity of practice in the United States.[36]

[35] This information was presented by T. E. Stanton, Jr. and F. N. Hveem in *Proceedings Highway Research Board*, part II (1934).

[36] In recent years the Bureau of Standards has proposed that a few standard gradings for aggregates be specified by all agencies. These have been published by the AASHO as Standard Specifications for Standard Sizes of Coarse Aggregate, *AASHO Designation M43–49*. To date the adoption of these standards has proceeded slowly.

486   Bituminous Pavements

Preparation of bituminous-concrete mixtures

Elaborate, expensive "hot plants" are required to prepare bituminous-concrete mixtures. An over-all view of such a plant is shown as

TABLE 9. TYPICAL EXAMPLES OF PROPORTIONING FOR ASPHALTIC CONCRETE

By Per Cent Passing

	Per Cent by Weight Passing Sieves									
Sieve Openings for Aggregates	Asphalt Institute Surface Course		Calif. Div. of Hwys. (1949)			Georgia Hwy. Dept.			Penn. Dept. of Hwys.	
	1 In. Max.	¾ In. Max.	Base Course	Leveling Course	Surface Course, Type A	Binder Course, Type A	Surface Course, Type C	Surface Course, Type E	Binder Course	Wearing Course
2½ in.			100							
2 in.			90–100							
1½ in.						100	100			
1¼ in.				100						
1 in.	100		70–95	90–100	100	95–100	95–100		100	
¾ in.	95–100	100			90–100				90–100	
½ in.	75–90	95–100	48–62	60–80	70–85	45–80	50–75	100	55–80	100
⅜ in.								95–100		80–100
No. 4	45–60	60–80	28–48	32–43	40–52	25–40	35–50		30–50	45–70
No. 8			23–33	26–36	30–40				20–40	30–55
No. 10	35–47	40–55						50–80		
No. 16						10–25	20–35	35–50		
No. 20									10–25	20–40
No. 30			17–25	19–27	18–28					
No. 40	23–33	25–35								
No. 50							10–20	15–35	2–15	5–25
No. 80	16–24	18–27								
No. 100			6–14	7–15	8–16	0–10	7–10	10–15	0–10	2–12
No. 200	6–12	8–15	1–4	1–5	4–8	0–5	3–7	5–10	0–5	2–5
Filler, % by wt.	*	*	None	None	3–5 †	None	*	*	None	*
Asphalt, % by wt.	6–8	6–8.5	4.5–5	4.5–5.5	5–6.5	4.5–7	5.5–9	6–10	5–7.5 ‡	6–9 ‡
Penetration	50–60 to 85–100		60–70 to 120–150				85–100			

* Filler specified, but included in percentages shown.
† This filler is included in the gradings shown above.
‡ These percentages are for stone aggregate. They increase to 6–9 and 7–10 for binder and wearing courses if slag is used.

Fig. 8, and schematic drawings of batch and continuous types as Fig. 9. In the vicinity of all large cities where the demand for paving materials

TABLE 10. TYPICAL EXAMPLES OF PROPORTIONING FOR ASPHALTIC-CONCRETE
SURFACE COURSES

By Percentages Passing and Retained

Sieve Openings for Aggregate		Percentages by Weight							
		Oregon, 1917 (Bitulithic)	Missouri		New York	Ohio		Washington	
Passing	Retained		Type B	Type D	Type 1A	Type A	Type C	Class A	Class C
1½ in.	½ in.	36–50							
1 in.								100	
1 in.	¾ in.					0–5			
1 in.	½ in.				0–5			25–50	
¾ in.			100	100					
¾ in.	½ in.		0–5	0–5		5–20			
⅝ in.									100
⅝ in.	½ in.								0–10
½ in.	⅜ in.					7–30	0–7		
½ in.	¼ in.	12–20	7–17	24–40	12–30			15–30	30–50
⅜ in.	No. 4					10–35	25–45		
¼ in.	⅛ in.				25–45				
¼ in.	No. 10	8–12	8–19	28–44				5–20	20–40
No. 4	No. 6					0–10	0–15		
No. 6	No. 50					20–45	20–45		
⅛ in.	No. 20				15–32				
No. 10								25–35	20–35
No. 10	No. 40		9–21	10–22				20–50 †	20–50 †
No. 10	No. 200	24–32							
No. 20	No. 80				6–16				
No. 40	No. 80		11–24	3–14				20–50 †	20–50 †
No. 50	No. 200					3–15	3–15	15–35 †	15–35 †
No. 80					3–10				
No. 80	No. 200		9–21	3–14					
No. 200		4–7	6–15	2–7		0–5	0–5	6–18 †	6–18 †
Total retained on no. 6						50–60	40–55		
Filler, % by wt.			*	*				1.0–2.0	1.0–2.0
Asphalt, % by wt.		6–9.5	6–9	3.5–8	5.5–7.5	5–9.5	6–10	4.5–6	4.5–7
Penetration			60–70	60–70		85–100	85–100		

* Filler specified, but included in percentages shown.
† That portion of aggregate passing the no. 10 sieve is considered separately as 100% in determining these limits.

is continuous, permanent installations which serve the respective metropolitan areas are found.[37]   For individual projects in rural areas a portable plant, moved to the site over railroad or highway, will probably be set up.

Bituminous materials are usually transported from refinery to "hot plant" in steam-coil-heated tankcars of 6500 to 10,000 gal capacity.[38]

Fig. 8.   A modern batch-type hot plant. Pug mill has 4000-lb capacity per batch. Exhaust from dust collector passes through wet tube dust washer (Courtesy Madsen Iron Works)

Binders are loaded at elevated temperatures; however, temperature loss in transit is about 15 to 25° F per day, depending on atmospheric conditions.   At times, therefore, it may be necessary to reheat the car before the material is unloaded.   At the plant, storage normally is in

[37] The Municipal Asphalt Plant of the Borough of Manhattan, built at a cost of $900,000 for structures and equipment, is one of the most elaborate. It is described in detail by L. Csanyi in *Transactions American Society of Civil Engineers*, pp. 1–25 (1950).

[38] Bituminous binders are sometimes moved by tank truck also. Small quantities are sometimes shipped in barrels or light steel drums. In some foreign countries, all binders are transported in the latter manner.

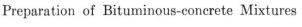

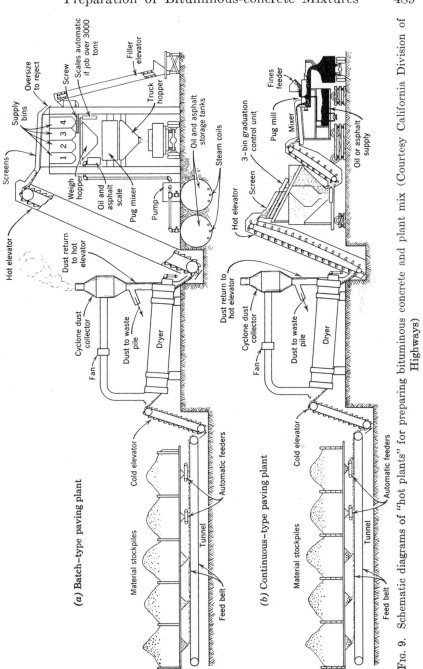

(a) Batch-type paving plant

(b) Continuous-type paving plant

Fig. 9. Schematic diagrams of "hot plants" for preparing bituminous concrete and plant mix (Courtesy California Division of Highways)

large underground tanks. These tanks often have capacity equal to that of several tankcars in order that plant operation will not be halted by delivery failures. Heating is accomplished by steam coils or, in some newer installations, by electric heating elements. Heated binder is forced from the storage tanks to the mixing platform by positive action pumps or by air pressure. Provision is made for recirculation through return pipes to prevent cooling or solidification overnight or during shutdowns.

For the installation diagrammed in Fig. 9a, coarse and fine aggregates are delivered to the plant by railroad car or truck and unloaded into stockpiles or storage bins. Materials, in the approximate proportions needed, are drawn from storage onto a belt which leads to the cold elevator. This delivers the combined aggregate into the drier, in which the aggregate falls repeatedly through hot gases until any moisture is driven off and the aggregate reaches mixing temperature (usually 300 to 325° F). The hot, combined aggregates then go up the hot elevator to the top of the mixing plant, where they are separated into several (usually four) sizes on shaking or rotary screens. Temporary "hot storage" is provided in bins located directly below the screens. For batch mixing, the prescribed amount of each of the hot aggregates is successively drawn from the bins into a "weigh box" located just below the "hot-storage" bins. Proportioned aggregates fall from the weigh box into the mixer, which is known as a "pug mill." Pairs of blades revolving in opposite directions throw the material upward between them and also knead it against the walls of the mixer. Commonly the dry aggregates and filler, which are introduced separately to the pug mill, are mixed dry for a short period, after which a weighed amount of binder is added uniformly across the width of the mixer. Mixing then continues until the binder is distributed throughout the mass and all aggregates are coated. Mixed materials are released through a gate in the bottom of the mixer into a waiting truck or into a truck hopper which holds one or more batches and permits continued mixer operation even though a truck is not immediately on hand to receive each batch.

It has been shown previously that a considerable variety of gradings have produced satisfactory bituminous-concrete pavements. Once a mix has been decided upon, however, each batch should be of like proportions and temperature; otherwise the resulting pavement may have a poor and uneven surface. To insure uniformity, many specifications prescribe within close limits the plant that will be acceptable, and, in addition, rigidly control each step of the heating, proportioning, and mixing process. Other specifications are not so precise, but give the engineer authority to regulate closely all phases of the process.

Uniform feeding of materials through the plant is of utmost importance, and premixing or controlled proportioning is often specified to produce this result. If the proper relative amounts of coarse and fine aggregate are fed through together, the temperature of the heated aggregate can be held nearly constant. Furthermore, the hot screens will be uniformly effective in separating the material to the various sizes. If, however, the feed consists largely of sand for a time, and then is largely coarse aggregate, some of the aggregate will be too cold and that which follows it too hot. If it is too cold, improper mixing and placing may result; if too hot, the binder may be seriously damaged.[39] Also, heavily loaded screens do not operate so effectively as lightly loaded ones, so that considerable variation in the aggregate grading of the final mix results.

The drier consists of a long hollow steel cylinder lined with firebrick and containing projecting radial fins. The inlet end is set slightly higher than the outlet. Heat is supplied by a jet of flame, fed by steam- or air-vaporized oil, coal dust, or gas, which is directed into the lower end of the drier. As the cylinder rotates, the aggregate is carried to the top by the fins, from where it falls downward and a little toward the outlet. By the time the aggregates have traveled the length of the drier, they are free of moisture and heated to the required temperature. Drier capacity is greatly reduced and heating costs are increased if aggregates are wet, so that both greater capacity and operating economy result from protecting aggregate supplies from rain.

In older hot plants, a smokestack was used to create a draft through the drier. This draft carried with it much of the fine dust introduced with the aggregate, which not only wasted the dust but also created a public nuisance in settled areas. Often these lost fines were replaced by expensive mineral filler. Most modern plants are equipped with a blower to produce the draft and a dust collector or "cyclone" which traps the fine particles and returns them to the heated aggregates below the drier. At times, the exhaust gas from the cyclone is washed to remove the last traces of dust.

The older plants were normally equipped with revolving circular screens for separating the hot aggregates into different sizes, but flat, shaking screens are employed in newer plants because much greater quantities of aggregate can be handled by screens occupying the same space. Screen sizes are sometimes left to the option of the contractor; again, they may be specified. To illustrate,

[39] The trend toward softer binders for bituminous pavements in order to prevent cracking and rapid aging has already been discussed. Many tests have shown that asphalts mixed with overheated aggregates harden and become brittle in the short mixing period. One authority estimates that the penetration is decreased by one-half during a 30-sec mixing period. It follows that any advantage gained by the use of softer asphalt may be lost at the mixing plant by lack of control over aggregate temperatures. Most engineers favor holding aggregate temperatures at the lowest level consistent with proper mixing and placing. Overheating of the binder in the storage tanks is not so serious, because the liquid is in bulk rather than in thin films; no air is present, and oxidation cannot take place.

the California Division of Highways requires that the plant be equipped with screens having square openings measuring, respectively, 1 in., ⅝ in., ⁵⁄₁₆ in., and 6 mesh made of 16-gage wire. Material passes into four bins, three for coarse aggregate and one for sand.

Batching aggregates into the weigh box is done carefully; some specifications require that weights even for 4000-lb batches be correct to 10 lb. Actual proportioning is often done by a weighman employed by the contractor. Many engineers have thought that this procedure did not provide proper control over the contractor's operations, as proportions could be altered without permission. Some agencies now require automatic devices which remove control of proportioning from the weighman. It is common practice as a check on the grading of aggregates to take samples of the mix from the transporting vehicle or completed pavement and, after extracting the binder, to make a sieve analysis of the aggregate.

Pug-mill mixers range in capacity from ¾ to 6 tons. Mixing procedures are not uniform among agencies. Some require that aggregate and filler be mixed dry for about 15 sec and that this process be followed by addition of the binder and a wet mixing period of 30 sec. Others specify about the same total mixing time but do not require dry mixing. In other instances, the specifications merely require complete coating of the aggregate and leave mixing time to the discretion of the engineer. Research has indicated that completed batches often are not uniform in composition, and the need for further refinements in the mixing procedure is indicated.

Many specifications permit "continuous" mixers (see Fig. 9b) as well as the "batch" mixers already described. Materials are proportioned by volume through specially calibrated devices which are correlated with the meter that measures and supplies the binder. Materials flow continuously through the mixer and are discharged in a steady stream. Properly controlled continuous plants can produce mixtures of very uniform grading and binder content.

Placing bituminous-concrete mixtures

Hot bituminous-concrete mixtures are usually transported from plant to roadway in dump trucks. If the weather is cool or the haul distance long, the load may be covered with canvas to prevent loss of heat. Most agencies prohibit placing bituminous concrete in wet or cold weather. It is common to prescribe minimum air temperatures (ranging from 30 to 60° for the various state highway departments) at which work may be carried out. During World War II much satisfactory pavement was placed under wet and cold conditions, but engineers generally are not in favor of extending this practice into normal operations.

Methods for placing asphaltic concrete have changed as new equipment has been developed. Originally the hot mix was dumped on wood or sheet-metal platforms from which it was moved and placed by hand shoveling. Leveling of the uncompacted mixture was done by skilled "rakers," many of whom displayed almost uncanny ability to produce a smooth, true surface. Some agencies permitted dumping the mix on the prepared base layers. Later it was common to deposit the mix in a movable hopper called a "spreader box" which was drawn along on the base by the truck as it unloaded. In cases where no curb or gutter had been placed, pavement edges and finished grades were defined by side forms of wood or steel similar to these used for concrete pavement (see p. 573).

In 1928, after several years of progressive development, the use of mechanical spreading machines operating on the side forms was begun.[40] These self-powered machines consisted of two moving screeds which pushed excess material ahead and leveled and partially compacted the mix. Sometimes raking elements were interposed between front and rear screeds. By careful alinement of the headers, a smooth surface was assured. These machines were similar in many ways to the finishing machines still used for Portland-cement-concrete pavements (see Fig. 16, p. 582). With these developments, the need for shovelers and rakers disappeared, except for placing occasional small, irregular, or warped areas. Daily output increased and prices per ton of mix decreased.[41]

In recent years several self-propelled finishing machines which operate directly on the base or other underlying layers have been marketed (see Fig. 10). Since they make side forms unnecessary, substantial savings result. Their use for placing bituminous concrete is now permitted by many highway agencies. These machines consist essentially of a hopper into which the truck dumps its load and a strike-off bar for spreading the mixture to uniform thickness. Some of the machines also have a tamping bar which partially consolidates the pavement. The machines are mounted on long skids or tracks in order that the finished pavement will not reflect short undulations or bumps in the surface on which the machine travels. Adjusting devices permit quick change in the depth of material placed, so that layers of varying depth, often needed to level old surfaces, may be laid rapidly. Small areas or extremely warped surfaces still must be placed and raked by hand methods.

[40] See Hewes, *American Highway Practice*, vol. II, pp. 108–113, for added information on this development.

[41] In 1924 the 8-hr output of a plant averaged 244 tons. This increased to 574 tons in 1928, with corresponding reduction in cost per ton. The breaking of the placing bottleneck immediately required larger mixing plants. Batch boxes of 1500 to 2000 lb have been replaced with boxes ranging in size up to 12,000 lb.

Fig. 10. Self-contained bituminous spreader and finishing machine (Courtesy Barber-Greene Co.)

Rolling and finishing bituminous concrete

Stability of bituminous mixtures increases as density of the mixture increases, since intergrain friction is greater when the particles are forced into closer proximity. To make sure that adequate compaction is obtained, most agencies specify that some minimum amount of rolling equipment be available. Requirements are far from uniform. A 1947 survey by the American Road Builders Association reports the following:

Four states allow a hot-mix bituminous concrete to be rolled with 5-ton rollers. One state employs a 5-ton roller initially but requires 8- to 10-ton rollers for finishing. Still another state requires three types of rollers—a 5-ton tandem plus a 10-ton three-wheel, plus an 8- to 10-ton tandem for finishing. Thirty-three states require 8-ton weight or more. Six states use rollers as heavy as 12 tons, and one state uses a 14½-ton roller. . . . More and more states are specifying rollers by weight per inch of width per roll rather than total weight. . . . As a matter of fact there is no trend, rhyme, nor reason in the present specifications for rollers.

The number of rollers to be provided is usually dependent on the tonnage laid. Ohio, for example, requires that one roller be provided for each 30 tons of material placed per hour or for each 500 sq yd when the depth of course is such that 30 tons of material is spread over an area exceeding 500 sq yd.

The depth of layer that can be placed in a single lift is usually specified. Rarely may thicknesses over 2½ in. be placed at once; rather, two courses must be placed and compacted separately.

Rolling of hot bituminous concrete is commenced as soon as the spread mixture will sustain the roller without excessive displacement or checking and is continued until roller marks are no longer perceptible on the surface. It is usual to require that the edges of the newly placed

Fig. 11.   Tandem and 3-wheeled rollers compacting bituminous concrete (Courtesy Buffalo-Springfield Roller Co.)

material be rolled first, after which rolling progresses toward the center; this provision is of particular importance when mixes are laid without side forms. Some agencies require rolling only along the length of the roadway; others also require "cross rolling" or "diagonal rolling." Figure 11 shows a typical rolling operation in progress. In this process, roller wheels are kept moist to prevent the hot mix from adhering to them.

A three-axle-type roller has been developed which has been accepted favorably by many engineers. Wheels on all three axles can be locked into a single plane, or the center wheel can be fixed in higher or lower positions. With such a machine, high spots normally difficult to correct can often be ironed out by applying greater than normal pressures through the center wheel.

Checks to determine the density of completed pavements are the

exception rather than the rule. California, one of the few states that
specifies minimum density, requires that completed pavements show a
unit weight of 95% of that obtained in a standard laboratory specimen
compacted by means of their special tamping foot. Most agencies rely
on a specified amount of rolling to produce the desired compaction.

The surface of a properly compacted bituminous concrete is highly
resistant to permeation by water. In many cases where seal coats are
applied, the intention is to provide a lighter color or to improve the
nonskid qualities. On occasion, where it is desired to discourage the
use of a given paved area, a coarse aggregate seal which creates a
rumble unpleasant to the vehicle occupants is applied.

With reasonable care roadway surfaces of bituminous concrete can
be finished to a high degree of smoothness. This is reflected in the
requirements of the various state highway departments. The most
rigid specification permits only $\frac{1}{8}$ in. variation from a 16-ft straightedge; however, variation greater than $\frac{1}{8}$ in. from a 10-ft straightedge
is often prohibited.

Typical designs for bituminous-concrete pavements

Some bituminous-concrete pavements having a total thickness of
only 2 in. are successfully carrying large volumes of heavy traffic.
Such· surfaces are supported by adequate bases. In other instances,
total pavement thickness has been as great as 12 in. In more recent
years, particularly in the West, there has been a growing tendency
toward thin pavements placed over carefully prepared base courses of
adequate strength. These designs are predicated on the idea that the
function of the pavement is merely to protect the base from weather
and the abrasive action of traffic. Eastern practice in general favors
thick pavements which function both as pavement and base course.
Typical sections of bituminous-concrete pavements carrying very heavy
traffic are shown as Fig. 12. These sections serve to illustrate the wide
variations in practice in the United States. In comparing them, the
student must realize that subgrade differences may account in a large
measure for the differences in combined thicknesses of pavements and
bases.

Other bituminous-concrete pavements

The bulk of the bituminous-concrete pavements laid in the United States
are hot laid. However, some highway agencies use or permit the substitution
of cold-laid mixes, hard-asphalt mixes, and certain proprietary mixes.

Cold-laid asphaltic concrete [42] consists of coarse and fine aggregate, asphaltic cement, a naphtha liquefier, and hydrated lime. The plant is similar to that

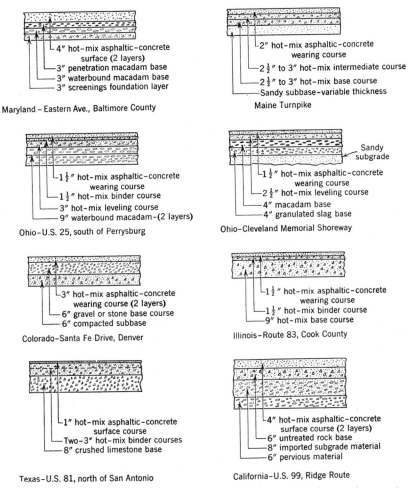

L4″ hot-mix asphaltic-concrete
   surface (2 layers)
L3″ penetration macadam base
L3″ waterbound macadam base
L3″ screenings foundation layer

Maryland - Eastern Ave., Baltimore County

L2″ hot-mix asphaltic-concrete
   wearing course
L2½″ to 3″ hot-mix intermediate course
L2½″ to 3″ hot-mix base course
Sandy subbase-variable thickness

Maine Turnpike

L1½″ hot-mix asphaltic-concrete
   wearing course
L1½″ hot-mix binder course
L3″ hot-mix leveling course
9″ waterbound macadam-(2 layers)

Ohio-U.S. 25, south of Perrysburg

Sandy subgrade

L1½″ hot-mix asphaltic-concrete
   wearing course
L2½″ hot-mix leveling course
L4″ macadam base
4″ granulated slag base

Ohio-Cleveland Memorial Shoreway

L3″ hot-mix asphaltic-concrete
   wearing course (2 layers)
L6″ gravel or stone base course
6″ compacted subbase

Colorado-Santa Fe Drive, Denver

L1½″ hot-mix asphaltic-concrete
   wearing course
L1½″ hot-mix binder course
9″ hot-mix base course

Illinois-Route 83, Cook County

L1″ hot-mix asphaltic-concrete
   surface course
LTwo-3″ hot-mix binder courses
8″ crushed limestone base

Texas-U.S. 81, north of San Antonio

L4″ hot-mix asphaltic-concrete
   surface course (2 layers)
L6″ untreated rock base
L8″ imported subgrade material
6″ pervious material

California-U.S. 99, Ridge Route

Fig. 12. Typical asphaltic concrete pavement installations for roads carrying large volumes of heavy traffic (Data collected by The Asphalt Institute)

for hot-laid mix, but includes a cooling unit between drier and mixer. The dried and cooled aggregate is separated into at least two sizes, and the coarse material is fed into the mixer and sprayed with naphtha. The asphalt is then

[42] This description is based on the 1952 specifications of the Illinois Division of Highways and is typical.

introduced, and mixing is continued. Fine aggregate and lime are successively added. Sufficient liquefier (roughly 5 to 20% of the asphaltic-cement content) is used to permit coating of the cool aggregate with the hot asphalt and to make the mix workable at laying temperatures. Hydrated lime (between 0.5 and 1.0% of total mix weight) serves the dual purpose of improving the coating properties of the binder and accelerating setting of the mix. The mix is spread and rolled as for hot-laid mix. No traffic is permitted on it until sufficient hardening has occurred.

Some agencies use ordinary asphaltic cement plus a hard, powdered asphalt softened by a fluxing oil as the binder for asphaltic concrete. Mixing and placing is commonly at air temperatures.

In addition to the processes already mentioned, certain patented mixes or processes are sometimes employed. For example, the 1947 specifications of the state of New York permit as equal alternates to ordinary hot-laid bituminous concrete the patented steam-dispersion, Laykold, and Colprovia heated processes. Cold-laid mixes are also acceptable under these specifications.

SHEET ASPHALT

Sheet asphalt, a mixture of sand, filler, and asphaltic cement, was used extensively as a surface course on city streets before the beginning of the present century. It makes a comparatively noiseless, pleasing, relatively smooth, and easily cleaned street surfacing. Little sheet asphalt has been placed on rural roads because it is too expensive to compete with other serviceable types. For this reason it is not included in the specifications of the majority of the state highway departments.

Sheet asphalt is seldom laid on grades steeper than 5% because under an extremely hot sun it has a slight tendency to flow and because it may become slippery on steeper grades when soiled and slightly wet.

Through the years much study has been devoted to such problems as the grading of sands for sheet asphalts, the percentage and kind of filler to use, and the determination of proper type and amount of asphaltic cement, but space limitations prevent their discussion here.[43] Stability of a sheet-asphalt mixture offers one of the most serious problems. As indicated previously, any mixture containing a high percentage of fines becomes unstable with only a small excess of asphalt. Sheet asphalt falls within this category.

[43] See Hewes, *American Highway Practice*, vol. II, Chapter II, for an extensive discussion and bibliography.

Proportioning sheet asphalts

Opinions regarding the proportioning of sheet asphalt have differed from place to place and time to time. In 1905, Richardson [44] indicated that filler, including the dust in sand and in the Trinidad asphalt, should constitute about 13% of the aggregate weight. Canadian practice at Montreal used increasing amounts of filler until in 1924 their requirements were that 20% of the mineral particles pass the 200-mesh sieve. Skidmore [45] in 1929 found that the voids in the sand-filler mixture were reduced as the percentage of filler was increased up to about 35. Stability increased with additions of filler to this 35% point and even beyond. To the present time, however, proportioning aggregates for sheet asphalts is done largely by precedent.

Binders for sheet asphalt are paving-grade petroleum or lake asphalts. Penetrations specified vary from about 30 to 70, but usually provide for harder binder in warmer climates and heavier traffic. Percentage of binder ranges between 9 and 12 and is determined by precedent, by the pat-stain test, or by the percentage of voids in the aggregate.

Typical of the proportioning for modern sheet asphalts is that given in the 1952 specifications of the Illinois Division of Highways:

	Per Cent
Passing no. 10 sieve	95–100
Passing no. 10, retained on no. 40 sieve	10–40
Passing no. 40, retained on no. 80 sieve	20–45
Passing no. 80, retained on no. 200 sieve	15–30
Passing no. 200 sieve	10–20
Bitumen, by weight of total aggregate	9–11

Mixing and placing

Sheet-asphalt mixtures are commonly prepared in a stationary or portable "hot plant" similar to that used for asphaltic concrete (see p. 486). The sand is heated in the drier and elevated to the storage bin from which it is fed to a pug-mill mixer. If coarse and fine sands are to be blended, the combination is made before drying. The hot sand may be screened to remove oversize material, but no attempt is made to divide it into fine and coarse sizes, as screens small enough to make such a division are not effective. However, plants to produce both sheet asphalt and asphaltic concrete for the binder course must be equipped with screens and storage bins for hot coarse aggregate. Filler

[44] Clifford Richardson, *The Modern Asphalt Pavement,* John Wiley & Sons.

[45] Hugh Skidmore, Fine Aggregate in Bituminous Mixtures, *Roads and Streets,* vol. 69, no. 10, October 1929.

normally is added without heating. Mixing methods and problems are the same as for asphaltic-concrete mixtures containing coarse aggregate. Sheet asphalt is laid only as the surface layer over a prepared base, and is commonly about 1½ in. thick. Spreading and compacting is done by methods already described for asphaltic concrete.

Undercourses for sheet-asphalt surfaces

Sheet asphalt is usually laid over an asphaltic-concrete "binder" course about 1½ in. thick. Originally the binder course consisted of screened broken stone from 1¼ in. down, mixed with coal-tar paving cement, although asphalt soon replaced tar in the majority of cases. Often the aggregate was low in screenings which resulted in a fairly open mix. Stability was improved by adding fines, and this denser mix, containing about 25% of fines, came to be known as "close binder."

Modern practice provides a binder course about 1½ in. thick composed of clean, tough, durable broken stone mixed with clean, sharp sand. Filler is usually omitted. Between 4 and 7.5% of paving asphalt like that of the sheet asphalt serves as binder. (See Table 9 for typical specifications.)

The binder course is mixed, placed, and compacted like other asphaltic concrete. Some specifications limit placing of binder course to the amount that can be covered with surface course on the same day; others place no such limitation. Some engineers prefer to lay top course in the afternoon on the morning run of binder, thus allowing an interval for cooling. At times, all traffic over the uncovered binder course is prohibited, and planking is required for hauling in the top course. In other cases, a moderate amount of traffic is allowed, providing the surface does not become dirty.

In a few instances, particularly where the pavement is laid on a Portland-cement-concrete base, the binder course is omitted and a "paint" coat of fluxed asphalt substituted.

The sheet-asphalt top and binder course must be laid on an adequate base and well-drained subgrade. Frequently this base course is 6 in. of relatively lean cement concrete laid without expansion joints. Not only is the lean concrete cheaper than a richer mix, but it is also held to have the advantage that contraction cracks which are reflected in the asphaltic top are narrower. The surface finish of the concrete should be uniform so that the covering layers can be of constant thickness; it should be slightly roughened in order that the binder course will engage with it and thus avoid displacement. Sometimes a paint coat of tar or asphalt is applied to the concrete base before the binder course is laid.

Many agencies employ an asphaltic concrete base, sometimes called "black base," under the sheet asphalt top and binder courses. Advantages are that duplication of construction machinery is avoided, and that there is no delay while the concrete cures. A typical grading for black base appears in the California specifications shown in Table 9.

Old gravel or macadam are frequently used as a base for sheet asphalt. New broken-stone or crushed-gravel bases are, of course, permissible. They should be constructed by the methods outlined in Chapters 15 and 16.

ROAD-MIX PAVEMENTS

Until about 1926, sheet asphalt and bituminous concrete were the only types of dense-graded bituminous mixtures in common use. Because of their high first cost, application was restricted to city streets or heavily traveled rural roads as was also true of pavements of Portland-cement concrete. Surface treatments (see p. 522) were also employed. None of these, however, filled the need for a cheap, dustless, and relatively permanent surface for the many miles of road carrying moderate volumes of traffic. Road mix was the first step toward filling this need. During the period between 1926 to 1929 its success, particularly in the Far West, was phenomenal. Road-mix methods are still widely used, especially on less heavily traveled state and county roads, and for processing patching material for maintenance operations.[46]

Any operation that incorporates liquid asphalts or tars with aggregates as an intimate mixture and is conducted on the roadway is designated as "road mix." Synonymous terms are "oil mix" and "mixed in place." Aggregates for the first road-mix projects were the dry-gravel

[46] In 1915, J. S. Bright, the county engineer of San Bernardino County, Calif., mixed light oil and desert sand, using plows and disk harrows, and, with several gallons of oil per square yard of surface, produced a solid roadbed several inches thick. This roadbed was serviceable for years. The "Wisconsin method" of surface treatment, described in 1924, involved mixing about 1½ in. of the road surface with ⅔ gal per sq yd of tar and was another step toward road mix. R. H. Baldock, in Oregon, also experimented independently with blade-mixing asphaltic oil into gravel road tops on the upper Columbia River Highway. In the fall of 1926 in the Imperial Valley, Calif., road mix was used in lieu of surface treatment; and in the spring of 1927 about 40 miles of fine-crushed gravel between Victorville and Barstow in the California desert was successfully treated. The method was forthwith extensively adopted.

or fine-crushed material already in place as the road surface. The top
2 or 3 in. of this surface was loosened and pulverized, using scarifiers
and tooth harrows, after which it was bladed back and forth across
the road to produce uniformity. A total of about 1½ to 2½ gal of
asphaltic oil per square yard (at 100° F or hotter) was then applied

FIG. 13. Motor grader processing road mix (Courtesy J. D. Adams Manufacturing Co.)

in successive increments by pressure distributors [47] and each application turned under by spring tooth or disk harrows. After all the oil
had been added, the mixture was "processed" by motorized blade
graders (see Fig. 13). This operation involved blading the mixture
back and forth across the road until it became homogenous and of
uniform color. The motor grader traveled fast enough (usually about
4 mph) that the material rolled rather than slid in front of the blade.
After processing, the mix was spread to uniform thickness and cross
section by a blade grader operated by a particularly skillful bladesman
called a "laydown man." Sometimes the completed surface was rolled,

[47] For a more detailed description of the pressure distributor, see p. 512.

at times only the edges were rolled, but in many cases compaction was left to the vehicles using the road. It was common practice to apply a seal coat to the completed surface to prevent the intrusion of surface moisture. Often this operation was postponed until a curing period of several weeks after laying had transpired.

Many variations to the original road-mix process have been developed. One of the most important was to import mineral aggregate

FIG. 14. Single-pass mixer processing road mix (Courtesy Pettibone Wood Co.)

from local gravel pits instead of using the loosened material from the existing road surface. In this manner it was possible to control more closely its quality and grading, particularly the percentage of dust. Furthermore, a constant amount of mineral aggregate per unit of roadway length was assured, which resulted in a more uniform oil content and fewer "fat" and "lean" spots in the completed roadway.

Road-mix processing is now often performed by a single machine which picks up the aggregate from the roadway and adds and mixes in the oil in specified amount (see Fig. 14). Spreading of the processed mix is commonly done with blade graders.

Both dense-graded and open-mix aggregates have been successfully road-mixed. Materials high in fines and without fines and with or without coarse aggregate have been employed. Sometimes roadside pits, even without screening, offer suitable materials. At times, no processing other than the rejection of oversize or of excess fines is needed. Angular, broken particles which produce added stability are to be preferred, but crushing to produce them adds to the cost and is avoided unless it is necessary to produce the desired grading. A typical specification for mineral aggregates for road mix, which reflects the wide range of acceptable aggregate gradings, is that of the Arizona Highway Department: 100% passing the 1-in. sieve, 50 to 65% passing the no. 3 sieve, and 3 to 12% passing the no. 200 sieve. Further requirements are that the swell shall not exceed 0.06 in. by test method B (see p. 469) and the plasticity index shall be 5 or less.

Oils for road mix must remain fluid at normal temperatures until mixing and placing is accomplished. For combination with aggregates containing high percentages of fines, slow-curing oils like SC–2 or SC–3 are a common choice. Cohesive strength is provided by the oil film surrounding the many fine particles. For aggregates containing smaller amounts of dust, medium-curing cutbacks like MC–2 or MC–3 are generally preferred, with the heavy residual asphalt supplying most of the cohesive strength. For clean sand or coarse open-graded aggregates, medium-curing oils, ranging from MC–2 to MC–5, and rapid-curing oils, grades RC–2 and RC–3, provide a heavy binder after curing. Slow-setting (SS–2) emulsified asphalts and liquid tars, grades RT–6 and RT–7, have also been used successfully for road mix. Other grades have served well in some instances (see Fig. 15), but the choice is usually as indicated above. Selection of binder type (for example SC vs. MC) normally is controlled by the kind of aggregates found in local deposits, for, if aggregates are transported any great distance, the low-cost advantage of road mix is lost. Choice of grade (as SC–2 vs. SC–3) depends largely on the air temperature at which mixing is accomplished, the lighter grades being used in cooler climates. In general, engineers prefer the heaviest grade that can be successfully processed. About 4% of oil, by weight, is commonly required, although this percentage varies with aggregate characteristics (see pp. 475 to 481).

Road mixes, like other pavements, must be placed on a good, sound roadbed of width somewhat greater than the pavement itself. Satisfactory results cannot be obtained over yielding subgrades or those that become unstable when the evaporation of capillary moisture is prevented by the moisture-proof bituminous blanket. Further, the roadbed must be carefully leveled and consolidated before road-mix operations are begun; otherwise variations in the thickness of the bituminous blanket or undulations in the finished surface must result. Maintaining constant surface thickness is particularly troublesome on superelevated curves.

When the mixing operation is performed with motor graders, care must be taken to avoid gouging into the base. It is common, after partial mixing, first to lay a "sole" or "tread" about ½ to 1 in. thick upon which the remaining material is further mixed. Some agencies apply a prime coat of light oil (SC–0 to SC–2 or MC–0 to MC–2) to the base before mixing, which provides a "floor" upon which mixing is performed. Roughly ¼ gal of oil per square yard is employed, the amount depending on how tightly the surface is bonded.

During the rainy season, in the late fall, or in areas subject to thundershowers, processing by road-mix methods is done under a serious handicap. Mixing in the rain soon soaks the spread-out materials; therefore, if it begins to rain, the mix must quickly be pushed into a windrow. All operations are then suspended until the materials are again dried. This is sometimes hastened by spreading and blading the mixture in good sunlight. If wet mixtures are laid down, they will probably be unstable. This is commonly controlled by a specification which states that no "laydown" may be commenced if the moisture content of the mixture exceeds some maximum such as 1 or 1.5% by weight.

PLANT-MIX PAVEMENTS

The term "plant mix" could well designate any bituminous surface for which the materials had been mixed in a plant rather than on the road. However, as the term is commonly used, asphaltic concrete and sheet asphalt are excluded, and "plant mix" generally denotes the cheaper and less rigidly controlled products. The plant-mix designation is more prevalent in the West than in the Middle West, East, or South.

Plant mixing of local aggregates with binder began soon after road mixing. At first all but the mixing phase of the road-mix process was more or less duplicated; but, by mixing the materials at a plant and placing them as soon as they were delivered to the road, many of the delays to road mix caused by inclement weather were avoided. Somewhat closer control of grading also was possible. Often these early plants consisted only of a semiportable pug mill and the appurtenant scales, elevators, storage bins, and tanks. Provision was soon made to dry the aggregates. Some of the later plants had hot screens, several storage bins, and weigh boxes so that proportioning could be

Material	Rapid Curing RC					
Grade	0	1	2	3	4	5
Dust palliative						
Priming						
Tightly bonded surfaces						
Loosely bonded fine-grained surfaces						
Loosely bonded coarse-grained surfaces						
Surface treatment, seal & color coats						
With or without light sand cover	X					
Coarse sand cover	X	X				
Clean ¼″ aggregate cover		X				
Clean ½″ aggregate cover			X			
Clean ⅝″ aggregate cover				X		
Clean ¾″ aggregate cover					X	X
Graded gravel aggregate cover						
Gravel mulch						
Mixed in place						
Open-graded aggregate						
Sand			X	X		
Max. diam. 1″, high % pass no. 10 sieve						
Macadam aggregate			X	X		
Dense-graded aggregate						
High % pass no. 200 sieve						
Max. diam. 1″, med. pass no. 200 sieve						
Fine soil						
Modified penetration						X
Cold patch						
Open-graded aggregate			X	X		
Dense-graded aggregate						
Tack coat			X	X	X	
Plant mix						
Cold laid						
Sand			X	X		
Open-graded, high % pass no. 10 sieve				X		
Macadam aggregate				X	X	
Precoating to be followed with soft AC						
Dense graded, high % pass no. 200 sieve						
Dense graded, low % pass no. 200 sieve				X		
Hot laid						
Sand						
Dense graded					X	X
Asphalt macadam, penetration method						
Hot mix, asphaltic concrete						
Stone-filled sheet asphalt						
Sheet asphalt, binder and surface courses						
Grout filler for stone block						

FIG. 15. Principal uses of asphaltic materials

Notes: SC-6 slow-curing oil, not shown in table, is employed for same purposes ployed for surface treatment and modified penetration. MS-4 emulsified asphalt,

Medium Curing MC						Slow Curing SC						Emulsified AS.						Asphalt Cements AC							
0	1	2	3	4	5	0	1	2	3	4	5	RS 1	MS 1	MS 2	MS 3	SS 1	SS 2	50-60	60-70	70-85	85-100	100-120	120-150	150-200	200-300
						X	X																		
X						X																			
	X					X																			
		X					X																		
		X																							
		X																							
															X										
															X									X	X
				X																				X	X
		X	X						X																
		X						X																	
		X	X																						
			X	X										X											
			X	X																					
		X						X	X																
		X	X					X																	
		X															X								
												X													
			X												X										
		X						X																	
												X													
		X														X									
				X	X																				
X																					X				
			X						X																
			X						X																
																					X	X			
				X	X							X	X												X
																					X	X	X		
																			X	X	X	X	X	X	
																		X	X	X	X				
																		X	X	X	X				
																		X	X	X					

for pavements (Courtesy The Asphalt Institute)

as 200–300 asphalt cement. RS-2 emulsified asphalt, not shown in table, is em-
not shown in table, is substituted for MS-3 where freezing may occur

accurately controlled. Soon the range of binders was extended to include more viscous grades which could be mixed only with hot aggregates. At present, many agencies require that plants producing "plant-mix" materials must contain most of the equipment found in asphaltic-concrete plants. Others, however, may specify only that provision be made for drying, separation into two sizes, proper proportioning, and mixing at the plant.

No definite line of demarkation can be drawn between asphaltic concrete and high-type plant mixes. In general, differences might be summarized as follows:

Binders for asphaltic concretes are paving-grade asphalts, usually of penetrations less than 100; softer binders are often employed for plant mixes. Often cutbacks or emulsions are used. It follows that plant mixes are mixed and placed at temperatures lower than the 300° F common for asphaltic concretes.

Coarse aggregates for asphaltic concrete must be produced by crushing. Uncrushed gravels of proper surface characteristics are often used for plant mixes.

Tolerances in aggregate grading are set closely for asphaltic concrete. Greater variation in grading is permitted for plant mixes. (Comparisons of Tables 9 and 11 indicate this clearly.)

Asphaltic-concrete surface courses commonly contain mineral filler; plant-mix surface courses do not.

The cost of producing plant-mix materials increases each time some additional refinement is introduced and as controls over grading and other characteristics are tightened. However, by introducing these refinements and controls the engineer gains added assurance that the completed surface will give satisfactory service. In general, the specifications of agencies that are responsible for large mileages of lightly traveled roads, but that have limited funds, are much less stringent than those of agencies whose roads carry large volumes of heavy traffic. Of course, previous successes and failures have great influence on present-day practice. Illustrative of this is the current use, by some agencies, of high-type plant mixes on roads carrying large volumes of heavy traffic. A few years ago the choice would have been among asphaltic concrete, sheet asphalt, and Portland-cement concrete.

A wide variety of asphaltic binders works successfully in plant mixes, as shown by Fig. 15. Tars of grades RT–7 to RT–9 also serve well. The choice is largely controlled by aggregate grading and mixing and placing temperature. For "cold-laid" mixes, binders are the same as for road mix, although slightly more viscous grades may be employed.

For "hot-laid" plant mixes, heavier binders are usually selected. With cutbacks, maximum temperatures are often controlled by the fire and explosion hazard. Typical aggregate gradings and percentages of binder for plant-mix surfacings are given in Table 11. An examination of those for dense-graded mixes shows that many different gradings have proved acceptable. It is of more importance that, once the proportions have been set, variations between batches be controlled. Comparison of the two Asphalt Institute specifications shows that the grading requirements are less severe for the cheap "cold-laid" mix than for the more costly "hot-laid" one.

Open-graded plant mixes, as shown by Table 11, contain little fine

TABLE 11. TYPICAL EXAMPLES OF PROPORTIONING FOR PLANT-MIX SURFACINGS

By Per Cent Passing

Sieve Opening for Aggregates	Per Cent by Weight Passing Sieves											
	Asphalt Institute		Ariz. Hwy. Dept.*	Calif. Division of Hwys.			Public Roads Administration, National Forest and Park Roads †				AASHO (1949) †
	Dense Graded		Dense Graded	Dense Graded (Type C)		Open Mix	Dense Graded ‡		Open Mix		Dense Graded ‡
	Hot Laid	Cold Laid					Grading A	Grading E	Pri-mary	Choker §	
1 in.	100	100	100	100			100	100	100		100
¾ in.	75–90			95–100	100		75–100	85–100	90–100		85–100
½ in.					95–100	100					
⅜ in.				67–85	80–95	90–100			20–55		
No. 3			50–65								
No. 4	50–70	50–70		50–65	57–78	30–50	30–45	60–95	0–10	100	45–65
No. 8						15–32			0–5	85–100	
No. 10	35–50	35–60					20–35	45–80			30–50
No. 16						0–15					
No. 30				18–28	21–34						
No. 40	20–30										
No. 200	0–8	0–14	3–12	3–8	4–9	0–3	2–7	5–15	0–2		5–10
Binder, % by wt.	4–6	4–6					3.5–7	3.5–7	3–5		

* Plasticity index restricted to 5 or less.
† During any 8-hr run, maximum variation permitted (from average), passing no. 4, 5%; no. 10, 5%; no. 200, 2%.
‡ Plasticity index restricted to 6 or less.
§ Crushed product only.

aggregate or dust. For stability they depend on friction and inter-locking of the aggregates, as do penetration macadam pavements (see p. 511). They differ from macadam in that aggregates and binder are combined by mixing rather than penetration methods, and that they are often laid as one course, whereas macadams are constructed by a series of operations performed on the road. Open mixes are used where it is desirable that moisture pass upward from base or subgrade or where sand or other cheap fine aggregate is not available. By proper sealing, the surface may be made watertight and the base protected from surface moisture.

Recently the California Division of Highways has employed a 1-in. layer of open-mix surface course (see Table 11) as a retread over old bituminous or concrete pavement. This mix, sometimes referred to as "popcorn," leaves a nonskid and relatively noiseless surface.[48] Experience to date indicates that, compared with dense mixes, this open mix better resists the extension of cracks from the old pavement upward to the surface.

Plant-mix surfaces over untreated bases are laid in compacted thicknesses ranging from $1\frac{1}{2}$ to 4 in. The deeper ones, over about $2\frac{1}{2}$ in., are placed and compacted in two layers. Spreading [49] in most cases is by a finishing machine like that shown in Fig. 10. This assures a smooth, uniform surface comparable to that obtained for asphaltic concrete and much superior to that sometimes obtained by blade spreading. Compaction is usually done with smooth-wheeled tandem or three-wheel rollers, although pneumatic rollers are permitted (or required) by some agencies. As with asphaltic concretes, rolling requirements are far from standardized.

Bituminous prime coats are often applied to the base before plant mix is laid. This serves not only to bind any loose particles of base but also to act as a bond between base and surface layer and to deter rising moisture from penetrating the pavement. Many agencies do not use prime coats, and many excellent installations have been made without them.

Some agencies use seal coats over newly laid plant mixes; others do

[48] See R. M. Gillis, *Asphalt Forum*, Asphalt Institute, vol. XI, no. 1 (1948).

[49] For "cold-laid" or other mixes for which the binder is a lighter-class cut-back, aeration before laying may be needed to permit the evaporation of some of the solvent. In these cases, the mix is spread along the roadway in a windrow and then bladed back and forth across the roadway by a power grader. After aeration, the mix is laid with the grader. Mixes made with emulsified asphalts are often treated in a similar manner.

not. Selected types vary widely. Sealing over mixes made with slow-curing products can be done almost at once; but, over cutbacks, the operation must be delayed until most of the solvent has evaporated.

PENETRATION MACADAM

Penetration or bituminous macadam is a high-type pavement consisting of successive layers of progressively smaller, clean, sharp, angular stones. Each layer is consolidated and keyed by rolling, after which it is sprayed with bituminous binder. Bituminous macadam represents the adaptation of the waterbound macadam surface (see Chapter 16) to the motor vehicle. This surface or penetration course is usually 2 to 3 in. in compacted thickness. The term "oil macadam" is employed frequently instead of penetration macadam, and the term "asphalt macadam" is not uncommon. This type of surface is laid on a base of varying thickness, depending on local conditions, but it must be sound and unyielding. There frequently is also a sub-base or foundation course, particularly in areas subject to heavy winter freezing.

The present method of constructing penetration or bituminous macadam in the United States has developed gradually since about 1907. The general penetration method was originally used by Massachusetts, New York, and Ohio, and to some extent by New Jersey. Later it was adopted in Rhode Island and other New England States and in California, and now it is used also by Pennsylvania, Louisiana, Georgia, Oregon, and Texas, among others. In 1951, some 36,000 miles of state-administered roads were of bituminous penetration types. Roughly 80% of this mileage was supported on rigid, as contrasted with nonrigid, bases.

Bituminous macadam contains a large percentage of voids, particularly in the lower part of the layer. If in time the base on which it is placed softens, the pounding of traffic will force base and surface together, and the pavement will distort and become rough. In addition, the interlock which holds the individual stones together may be disrupted. For this reason, a permanent, unyielding, and well-drained base is absolutely necessary with macadam construction.

Expensive equipment is required to produce the mineral part of macadam pavements, since all aggregates must be crushed and then screened to size. Furthermore, durable macadams of good riding qualities can be produced only with skilled and experienced workmen. For these reasons, the use of macadams is not prevalent in areas where aggregates suitable for dense-graded mixes are available at reasonable cost. Macadam construction during cold weather is difficult. Often specifications state that no binder shall be spread if the air temperature is less than 60° F or some comparable figure. In areas where winters are severe, the construction season may be restricted to the warmer months. Intervals without rain should be long enough that relatively dry aggregates can be provided and a lift completed and sealed without interruption.

Materials for penetration macadam

The binder for bituminous macadam must in itself be cohesive enough to hold the aggregate mass tightly together and to resist abrasion by traffic. For this purpose, asphaltic cements, penetrations 85–100, 100–120, and 120–150, are recommended by the Asphalt Institute (see Fig. 15). Harder binders, like 60–70 penetration, are permitted by some specifications; likewise softer material, such as 200–300 penetration grade or SC–6 road oil, is sometimes stipulated. These binders, heated to produce fluidity, are sprayed over the aggregate, and the particles are coated before the binder hardens. Tars, grades RT–10 to RT–12, are used in a similar manner. Rapid-setting emulsions which break on contact with the aggregate likewise are suitable. In some instances rapid-curing cutbacks, grades RC–3 and heavier, have been employed successfully.

The type and amount of binder are greatly influenced by the source. To illustrate, California asphalts, widely used in the western states, are more sensitive to heat and are relatively sticky compared with those from other fields. Because of these properties, smaller amounts and softer grades are appropriate. Approximate amounts of binder for a typical three-application bituminous-macadam pavement are given in Table 12.

Almost always binders for bituminous macadams are sprayed over the aggregates by pressure-distributor trucks, although in the past hand-pouring methods were common. The modern pressure distributor (see Fig. 16) consists of a truck-mounted tank fitted with a spray bar which, through special nozzles, spreads the binder over a prescribed width of roadway. The liquid is subjected to pressure by a power pump, usually of the gear or gravity type. The pump sometimes is powered by the truck motor, although drive by an auxiliary engine is preferable as it offers better pressure control. There is a return pipe to the tank from the spray bar; flow through it is controlled by an adjustable relief valve which maintains constant pressure on the nozzles.

Recirculation also keeps the hot binder in the spray bar and nozzles from cooling and solidifying between spreads. For a given binder at a given temperature, the rate of application will depend on the nozzle opening, pressure, and truck speed. With good equipment and skilled operators, quantities very close to those specified can be spread.[50]

FIG. 16.   Pressure distributor applying binder during bituminous macadam construction (Courtesy E. D. Etnyre Co.)

Distributors with capacities ranging from 400 to 2000 gal are available on truck or semitrailer mountings. Spray bars covering a width of 20 ft are often provided. On some units the tanks and appurtenances are insulated; on others they are not. Some have provisions for heating the load. Controls on the spray bar often permit application through part or all of the nozzles, as needed for the particular spread. Thus, in special cases, shoulders, or half or partial widths can be covered. Often an auxiliary spray is provided for touch-

[50] The actual amount of binder delivered to an area has been checked by spreading strips of paper or special pans over a surface to be sprayed by a distributor truck, and then determining the amount of binder deposited on them. In many cases this test has indicated that, although the proper distribution was obtained for an entire load, considerable variation occurred between individual sections along the length and width of the area. Careful checking on the performance of distributor trucks before using them seems to be indicated.

ing up lean or white streaks caused by clogged or slow-flowing nozzles. Some specifications require a trough arrangement that can be swung under the spray bar to check the application suddenly or to prevent dripping.

Nozzles may be either the cone or slotted type, and are available in various aperture sizes. They must be of proper design and kept scrupulously clean; otherwise coverage by individual sprays will be uneven, or the adjacent sprays will overlay and leave wet streaks. To assure uniform coverage, the distributor truck should be traveling at prescribed speed before the nozzles are

TABLE 12. SEQUENCE OF PLACING OPERATIONS AND AMOUNTS OF MATERIAL REQUIRED FOR THREE-APPLICATION BITUMINOUS-MACADAM PAVEMENT *

Sequence of Operations	Bituminous Material, Gal per Sq Yd	Aggregate Lb per Sq Yd		
		Coarse	Key	Chips
First spreading		270		
First application	1.50			
Second spreading			30	
Second application	0.50			
Third spreading			25	
Third application	0.30			
Fourth spreading				15
Supplemental stockpile				10
Total	2.30	350		

* Class D, type D-2, of the Public Roads Administration. From specifications for Construction of Roads and Bridges in National Forests and National Parks. Specifications of many other agencies are comparable.

opened. At the junctions of succeeding spreads, a double application or none at all may result. This is often prevented by covering the last few feet of the completed section with a temporary cover of building paper or sand on which spraying is started.

Modern bituminous macadams tend to be one-stone thick; that is, the maximum size of coarse aggregate approximates the thickness of the completed pavement. This provides stability, because the larger stones engage the base course and the surface has no tendency to "roll" or "wave." If the stone is soft, a somewhat larger maximum size may be specified to offset the effect of breakage under rolling. Individual particles should tend to be cubical in shape. "Pencil" or "slab" shapes are undesirable. The variation in size of stone for each course is small. Grading should be uniform within these limits, however. Table 13, which is typical of current practice, shows that most of the coarse aggregate is sized between 3 and 1½ in., and key aggregate between 1 in. and no. 4 sieve size. The smallest stone in the coarse aggregate is ½ in. larger than the largest stone in the key aggregate.

Aggregates for macadams should be strong and tough, as excessive crushing under the roller will spoil the interlock between individual stones. Also, the finer crushed particles tend to close the surface so that penetration by the binder is retarded and "fat" spots in the completed pavement result. Typical requirements for hardness and toughness are: Bureau of Public Roads and California Division of Highways,

TABLE 13. REQUIREMENTS FOR GRADING OF AGGREGATE FOR THREE-APPLICATION BITUMINOUS-MACADAM PAVEMENT *

Percentage by Weight Passing Square Mesh Sieves

Sieve Designation	Coarse Aggregate	Key Aggregate	Chips
3 in.	100		
2½ in.	90–100		
2 in.	35–70		
1½ in.	0–15		
1 in.		100	
¾ in.		90–100	
½ in.			100
⅜ in.		20–55	90–100
No. 4		0–10	10–30
No. 8		0–5	0–8

* Class *D*, type *D*–2, Public Roads Administration. Specifications for National Forest and Park roads.

per cent of wear (Los Angeles rattler test) not greater than 40 after 500 revolutions; Georgia Highway Department, not greater than 45. New York specifies a maximum percentage of loss by the Deval test [51] of 5.7.

Aggregate surfaces must be clean so that excellent coating by the binder can be obtained. Some agencies specify that dirty aggregates

[51] Many agencies in their specifications for per cent of wear or loss do not distinguish between macadam aggregates and aggregates for asphaltic concrete. This does not mean, however, that any aggregate suitable for asphaltic concrete is satisfactory for macadam also. The coarse aggregate in asphaltic concrete is partially protected during rolling by the matrix of fine aggregate and binder in which it is embedded. Macadam aggregate, on the other hand, has no such protection but is directly subjected to the roller wheel.

In many areas deposits of satisfactory trap rock or any stone of comparable qualities do not occur. Consequently it frequently will be necessary to use inferior stone to avoid excessive cost. A good surface can be made with hard limestone and also with the tougher granites. If the weaker stones are used. great care is necessary in rolling.

be washed before use. At times aggregates are treated either by plant mixing or spraying on the road with some liquid designed to improve coating properties. These products, which are patented, are commonly called "facilitating agents" or "mobile oil."

Constructing penetration macadam

The sequence of operations for constructing a three-application bituminous-macadam pavement is shown in Table 12. For some simpler macadams, one application, rather than two, of keystone is made which also eliminates one application of bituminous material. For others more elaborate procedures may be used, including the "choking" of the coarse aggregates with a finer stone before the binder is spread.[52] In every instance stability is gained by interlocking the coarse aggregate by rolling before the application of binder. Subsequent courses of smaller stone are "keyed" into the surface voids of the coarser aggregate by rolling and serve further to lock the stones into a unified mass.

Placing and compacting coarse aggregate. Spreading of coarse aggregates is commonly done with mechanical stone spreaders. Figure 3, page 441, shows such a device. Paving machines like those in Fig. 10, page 494, are often employed. Before the advent of such equipment it was usually stipulated that the broken stone be shoveled into place from dumping boards or from piles deposited along the roadside. The loose layer should have such depth that, after rolling, no large areas exceed one stone in thickness. Smoothness of the completed surface depends largely on uniform size distribution of these coarse stones, and close inspection is a necessity. Often, because of unevenness in piling up the broken stone in the bins at railroad sidings or at the crushing plant, large and small stones will be segregated in the truck loads brought to the job. Consequently, pockets of the finer sizes may occur. These should be removed and the stone redistributed by interchange until the surface and voids look uniform. Otherwise, uneven penetration and "fat" spots or low areas will occur in the finished surface.

Many agencies require that side forms of depth equal to the compacted thickness be employed for macadam construction. Otherwise, the loose depth is controlled by tight guide lines stretched between pins set about 25 ft apart. For hand spreading, cubical gage blocks of edge dimensions equal to the thickness of the loose layer are often used. If side forms are omitted, shoulders of good earth or better material are necessary to offer lateral restraint against displacement under the roller.

Rolling the coarse aggregate. The power roller should weigh at least 10 tons, and heavier rollers are advantageous with hard stone. It is impera-

[52] As an illustration, the 1941 specifications of the Public Roads Administration include a four-application macadam pavement bound with emulsified asphalt, which is constructed in this manner.

tive that the first trips of the roller be along the edges. If there are no side forms, the shoulders should be lapped about one-half the width of the rear wheel of a three-wheel roller. Successive trips should similarly overlap as the roller progresses toward the center of the road. Roller speed should not be excessive, and some specifications set a limit like 100 ft per min to provide control. Adequate rolling is fundamental as the pieces must be locked tightly. Properly rolled stone will not creep under the roller nor displace nor rut under the heavy distributor truck. Harder stones will require considerable rolling,

Fig. 17. Stages in bituminous macadam construction. Left side complete except for final cover coat of chips or pea stone. Right side is ready for the first pour. Note that neither keystone nor pea stone is carried out to the edge of the poured portion, in order to avoid a fat streak and ridge from the lapping of the bituminous material and the extra stone

softer ones less. Cracking of the stone will warn of any excess. During and after rolling, all vehicles except the pressure distributor should be prohibited as any displacement of the stone injures the mechanical bond. If any rectification of the broken-stone layer is required during rolling, the disturbed areas must be rerolled and again locked before binder is poured.

After rolling, the surface should be tested longitudinally with a 10-ft (or longer) straightedge. Variations greater than ¼ to ⅜ in. must be corrected. The smoothness of this course determines the smoothness of the surface, as corrections cannot be made in subsequent layers. Expense and trouble is saved by checking the surface during the early stages of rolling, since correction is less difficult at this time. Figure 17 shows a completed coarse aggregate layer, ready for treatment with bituminous material.

First application of bituminous material. This operation must be faultlessly organized, as application of the proper amount of binder at a temperature that gives proper penetration is necessary for good results. Spreading is preferably done on warm summer days when the stone is thoroughly dry.[53] Just before the operation is begun, the surface should be carefully inspected and all leaves and other foreign material removed. Sometimes the drive wheels of the loaded distributor may tend to displace the stone, in which event the truck should be towed by a roller.

The amount of binder is sufficient to coat the stones, but is far less than the quantity that would be needed to fill the voids (see center section of Fig. 17).

Placing Keystone. Immediately after the first application of bituminous material, and preferably while it is still warm and soft, the intermediate-sized stone, designated as keystone, chips, splinters, or pea stone is spread.[54] Distribution is preferably made from a backing truck, often through a spreader box which gives uniform apportionment. If this is not possible, the keystone is spread from roadside stockpiles by expert shovelers. If distributed in this manner, the material should be cast parallel to the axis of the road, not across it. Often sweeping of the keystone, either with brooms attached to rollers or with hand brooms, is specified to assure a more uniform application. Enough stone is spread nearly to fill the voids in the large aggregate. Rolling follows immediately after spreading and evening of the stone. Cross rolling as well as longitudinal rolling is sometimes specified. Small amounts of key aggregate may be added as rolling progresses, if they are needed to assure filling all voids. Opinions differ as to whether or not the voids in the coarse aggregate should be entirely filled. Some engineers prefer that the coarse aggregate project slightly to carry the heavy traffic. Others like the keystone to be visible in the final mosaic pattern.

Small or flaky chips or screenings for keystone are to be avoided since they choke the larger voids and prevent the penetration of later applications of binder into all voids and pockets. The resulting uncoated materials may "shove" and form corrugations under traffic. The previously mentioned ½-in. gap in size between coarse aggregate and keystone has proved to be favorable.

Second application of bituminous material. After the keystone has been locked in place by rolling, the surface is broomed clean of loose stone, and a second application of bituminous material is made. This coats the keystone and binds it firmly to the coarse aggregate. The appearance of the surface after the keystone has been compacted and sprayed is shown on the left side of Fig. 17.

Third application of stone and bituminous binder. For three-application bituminous-macadam pavement (like that of Table 12), a second course of keystone is spread over the still warm binder and keyed into place by rolling. Binder is then spread to tie this aggregate in place. For two-application macadams, this sequence of stone and binder is omitted entirely.

Application of chips. While the binder covering the final keystone course is still warm, the surface is covered with stone chips and rolled to lock them

[53] See the section on construction with emulsified asphalt for an exception to this rule.

[54] Most specifications state that keystone shall be applied immediately after the bituminous material is spread, and while the binder is still warm. Some agencies, however, require a 24-hr delay between these operations to permit complete penetration of the binder.

tightly in place. Brooming to assure uniform coverage is commonly required. As soon as rolling is completed and the binder has set, the roadway is ready for traffic.

The surface produced in this manner is watertight and skid-resistant. Since the upper surfaces of the chips are uncoated with binder, the surface is light in color and has excellent light-reflecting properties which greatly improve visibility at night.

The procedure outlined above is not followed by all organizations. Some open the road to traffic after the second application of binder. Only enough chips are applied to cover the binder and prevent its adhering to the roller or to vehicle wheels. Some time later, usually within 4 weeks, a final application of binder and chips is made. Regardless of construction method, a tight seal for macadam pavements is a necessity. If surface water penetrates to the underlying base and softens it, trouble is sure to develop.

Penetration macadams bound with emulsified asphalts

The rapid-setting emulsified asphalts employed for macadams penetrate more freely than heated asphaltic cements or tars. They are applied at only slightly elevated temperatures, and their fluidity is little affected by cooling on contact with the aggregates. Deep and complete penetration and coating can be obtained. With emulsified asphalt as a binder, it is common to "choke" the coarse aggregate with small stones to reduce its voids before the first application of binder. Otherwise part will flow through the aggregate onto the base. Introduction of the "choke" stone in turn decreases the quantity of residual asphalt needed for binder. However, since emulsified asphalts are about 40% water, the quantity actually applied will not decrease accordingly.

Emulsified asphalts will coat wet aggregate as well as dry, and are less affected by cold aggregate. Thus they can be successfully used in cold, damp weather which would preclude construction with hot asphalts or tars. Even with emulsified asphalts, however, warm sunny weather is most favorable for the construction of macadam.

INVERTED-PENETRATION PAVEMENTS

Penetration methods of construction involve placing the aggregate first and then spraying the binder over it. *Inverted penetration* reverses the process; binder is first sprayed over the prepared surface and then covered or blotted with aggregate.[55]

Inverted-penetration methods are commonly subdivided on the basis of the purpose to be accomplished. The main subdivisions are: dust palliatives for dust control; prime coats or tack coats for treating surfaces on which a new wearing-course pavement is to be constructed; surface treatments and armor coats for providing temporary protection

[55] To simplify presentation, some processes which usually involve only the application of binder have been classed as inverted penetrations.

for untreated mineral surfaces; and seal coats for protecting, leveling, or otherwise improving existing pavements.

Dust palliatives

Wind and air disturbances caused by motor vehicles sometimes stir up dust and fine sand from the shoulders or adjacent areas along the roadway. This creates an accident hazard by limiting sight distance and causes a generally annoying condition for motorists. Wind also often erodes cut or fill slopes of sandy materials containing little binding soil. Treatment to control these conditions consists of a small application (about 0.2 gal per sq yd) of a light, slow-curing oil (usually SC–0 or SC–1). This oil penetrates the surface for a depth of about ½ in. and provides a film which surrounds the individual particles and binds them together. Slow-curing oils are selected because they remain soft for long periods of time. Cutbacks or emulsions are usually unsatisfactory, as they are made with harder asphalts. These, on setting, would produce a brittle surface that would soon crack up and disintegrate.[56] Sometimes a light application of sand is spread after the oil is placed; again it may be used only to blot up excess oil in sections where penetration is poor.

The oil, heated to around 175° F, is spread with a distributor truck or with a hand spray in less accessible areas. Treatment should be made in warm, calm weather. If the soil is slightly moist, penetration is improved.

Prime coats

Often, before the placing of a bituminous pavement over a base of earth, gravel, or waterbound macadam, the surface is "primed" by spraying on an initial application of bituminous material. The intent is to plug capillary voids in order to halt the upward movement of water and to coat and bind dust and loose mineral particles, thus hardening and toughening the surface. Adhesion between the base and the surface course is also improved. Where traffic must use half the roadway during construction, the prime coat also serves to protect the base before the placing of pavement. If paving is by road-mix methods, the prime coat provides a table on which mixing may be done.

The lighter, medium-curing cutback oils are generally chosen for prime coats. They are fluid enough to penetrate into the base but leave

---

[56] Slow-setting emulsified asphalts, diluted in 4 to 9 parts of water, have been employed successfully. Used crankcase oil from motor vehicles makes an excellent dust palliative for treating small areas.

a viscous asphalt in the pores of the treated surface. MC–0, which is most fluid, is recommended for tight surfaces; heavier grades may be employed for looser surfaces. The lighter slow-curing or rapid-curing oils are sometimes specified.[57] Slow-setting emulsified asphalts and light tars, grades RT–1 to RT–3, also have been successful. The quantity of binder to be applied depends on the tightness of the surface being primed. As little as 0.3 or as much as 0.8 gal per sq yd may be needed.

Before the prime coat is placed, the surface should be shaped, moistened, and rolled to make it solid and uniform. Variations in surface texture will result in nonuniform penetration and will leave wet and dry spots. If, when the binder is applied, the base is slightly moist, better penetration will result. The oil is spread by pressure-distributor truck at prescribed temperature (see Table 1, p. 449). After application, traffic should be detoured until the surface is no longer sticky and will not be picked up by traffic. If this cannot be done, a blotter course of sand must be applied.

Tack coats (bituminous paint binders)

Often old bituminous or concrete pavements are resurfaced with a bituminous blanket of plant mix, asphaltic concrete, sheet asphalt, or bituminous macadam. Under these circumstances it is common to precede actual resurfacing with a tack coat to bond or "tack" the old and new layers together thoroughly.

For tack coats, the binder should penetrate and soften the surface of an old bituminous mix or firmly attach itself to a concrete surface. It must also be cohesive enough to bind old and new layers tightly together. Rapid-curing cutbacks, grades RC–1 to RC–3, and rapid-setting emulsions are commonly specified. Some specifications include slow-breaking emulsions and fairly heavy tars, grades RT–8 and RT–9. The usual rate of application ranges between 0.05 to 0.15 gal per sq yd of surface. Application temperatures are fitted to the product (see Table 1). Tack coats are usually applied soon before the resurfacing is laid. Traffic must be kept from them.

---

[57] Some authorities declare that slow-curing oils are less effective in blocking capillary moisture and should be used only where moisture is not present. Rapid-curing oils should be permitted only on very open surfaces; otherwise they may harden before penetration has been accomplished.

Surface treatment—armor coats

. The term "surface treatment" ordinarily designates a thin bituminous surface of binder covered by mineral aggregates, applied to an earth, gravel, or waterbound macadam surface. On lightly traveled roads, substantial bases protected by surface treatment provide a relatively permanent, cheap pavement which solves the problems of dust control, formation of corrugations, and loss of surfacing materials created by the abrasive action of vehicle tires. For highways carrying heavy traffic, surface treatments can serve only temporarily because they lack the strength of more expensive pavements. They are often employed by agencies whose funds are limited as a temporary pavement and protection for the base material. Their use for a period before permanent pavement is placed allows easy correction of weaknesses in base or drainage.

Surface treatments were first employed about 1907 to prevent ravel and wear and to control dust on waterbound macadam roads. By 1914, in Maine, gravel surfaces were being similarly protected. By 1920 bituminous surface treatment of gravel and fine-crush surfaces had become general. In the 1920's surface treatments were also applied to sand-clay and stabilized-soil roads.[58]

Because surface treatments are thin, a firm bond between them and the aggregate courses which they protect is essential. It is common, therefore, after shaping the surface, to apply prime coats, just as in constructing many other pavements.

The surface treatment proper, which follows the prime coat, may be as thin as $\frac{1}{4}$ in., or as thick as 1 in. Usually the thinner types (sometimes called "one-shot" types) consist of about 0.20 to 0.40 gal per sq yd of fairly heavy liquid bituminous material covered with 10 to 25 lb of clean stone screenings or fine-screened gravel, slag, or equivalent material that is free of dust. Grading generally ranges between the $\frac{3}{8}$-in. and no. 10 sizes. Various procedures and quantities of material are employed. Larger cover material, with maximum sizes up to $\frac{1}{2}$ or $\frac{5}{8}$ in. will usually require 35 to 40 lb per sq. yd. The choice of liquid bituminous binder will be governed somewhat by the maximum size of the cover material. Thus, if the cover is wholly of sand, lighter oils of the SC group or equivalent tars will be sufficiently viscous to hold the particles in place, although SC–6 or light RC or MC oils are often used. For binding coarser aggregates, a more co-

---

[58] For further data and for references on early surface treatments, see Hewes, *American Highway Practice,* John Wiley & Sons, vol. 1, pp. 376–386 (1942).

hesive binder is needed, and the choice is confined to the heavier-grade cutbacks, heavy oils like SC–6, a high-penetration asphaltic cement, a rapid-setting emulsion, or a heavier-grade tar.

Bituminous material is spread at the proper application temperature (see Table 1) from a pressure-distributor truck. Cover materials are ordinarily spread from dump trucks, usually through a spreading device which assures the prescribed distribution (see Fig. 18). In order to avoid picking up the uncovered bituminous material, it is common to

Fig. 18. Spreading cover material for bituminous-surface treatment. (Note that the truck is backing)

spread from a backing truck, so that the tires roll on the freshly applied screenings. Light brooming with drag brooms follows to assure uniform distribution of screenings. Light rolling with pneumatic-tired or smooth-wheeled rollers to set the screenings firmly usually follows the brooming.

Surface treatments should be applied during good sunny weather when there is no wind and when the surface is dry and clean. The chances of failure are high if construction is attempted during cold or wet weather. In very hot weather, however, the roadway-surface temperature may rise as high as 150° F. Then the aggregates will tend to absorb even heavy liquid asphalts and may not leave enough on the surface to tie down the intended cover coat. Under such conditions the liquid application should be increased.

Surface treatments applied in two or more lifts are designated by such terms as "armor coats" and "double (or triple) surface treatments." For two-course treatments cover material for the first lift often has a maximum size of ¾ to 1 in.; for three-course treatments the maximum size commonly is 1 to 1¼ in. Maximum size of the aggregate for each subsequent lift is reduced. Binder is spread before each application of screenings, and each course is broomed and rolled. Such multiple-lift surface treatments resemble macadams in that strength is gained through interlocking the coarser aggregate by rolling and by keying it with subsequent applications of smaller stone.

In some specifications, blade mixing is stipulated after each application of binder and cover aggregate and before rolling.

Seal coats and retreads

Applications of binder to pavement surfaces, followed by cover aggregates, are designated as "seal coats" or "retreads." In many specifications and other presentations no distinction is made between seal coats and surface treatments, as the materials and construction processes and problems are almost identical.[59]

Seal coats will serve one or more of six distinct purposes, as follows: [60]

1. To seal the road surface against the entrance of moisture or air.

2. To develop a nonskid texture where the existing road surface is dangerously smooth and slippery.

3. To apply a fresh coat of asphalt which will enliven an existing dry or weathered surface and thus improve wear resistance.

4. To reinforce and build up an inadequate pavement section.

5. To provide a demarkation for traffic guidance between shoulder sections and traffic lanes.

6. To improve luminosity or visibility at night.

Cracking which results from failure of the base or waves caused by instability in the pavement itself cannot be corrected by applying a seal coat.

Many binders, the same ones used for surface treatments, have been

[59] Figure 15, showing the principal use of asphaltic-paving materials, illustrates this point.

[60] From a paper by C. V. Kiefer, Uses and Abuses of Seal Coats, presented to Second Nevada Asphalt Forum and published in the *Crushed Stone Journal*, June 1949. For another excellent and detailed article on the design and construction of seal coats see Hveem, Lovering, and Sherman, The Design of Seal Coats and Surface Treatments, *California Highways and Public Works*, July–August 1949.

successfully applied as seal coats.[61] For single-treatment seal coats, the most common aggregate consists of clean stone chips or gravel distributed in size from ½ in. to the no. 8 sieve. (The grading for chips for macadam of Table 13 is typical.) Aggregates in this size range are small enough that the resulting seal is watertight and relatively noiseless, but the particles are large enough to provide a nonskid surface. For the center lane of three-lane roads or in other situations where general use is to be discouraged, larger aggregates are often specified, since seal coats constructed from them produce a disagreeable rumble in motor vehicles. Where a light-colored surface is desired, nearly white aggregates, placed carefully to prevent coating with binder, are selected. Sand or other fine, graded aggregates are not widely employed for sealing highway surfaces as the nonskid properties are not as good. They are much used for sealing airport runways. Such cover materials must be placed very carefully to obtain uniform depth and to prevent the formation of ripples.

Seal coats should be constructed during favorable weather. A recent survey in the western states indicated that, for the projects included, between 85 and 90% of the satisfactory seal coats were placed during June and July and that 60% of those placed after October 1 were failures.

For the ½-in. maximum-size cover aggregate, the amount of binder to be applied may vary between 0.15 and 0.30 gal per sq yd, depending on the surface treated and on the shape, grading, roughness, and porosity of the cover material. If a prime coat is omitted, the quantity of binder must be raised to allow for penetration into the old surface. Then, in addition, aggregates should be embedded for about 0.5 to 0.7 of the thickness of the seal coat, which approximates the average least dimension of the aggregate. About 20 to 30 lb per sq yd of cover aggregate is needed, including an allowance for that lost by whipping off the road. Quantities are, of course, reduced if smaller aggregate is specified.[62]

[61] Kiefer expresses the opinion that of all asphaltic products RC-4 most nearly fits the common seal-coat situations. Practice of the California Division of Highways revolves generally around the SC-6 grade, sometimes cut back with naphtha or kerosene to produce consistencies like RC-5 or MC-5. These special cutbacks have a base asphalt of about 200–300 penetration as against the 85–100 penetration base stock of ordinary RC-5 and MC-5.

[62] Nomographs from which the quantities of binder and aggregate for different seal coats can be determined may be found in the article in *California Highways and Public Works* for July–August 1949, previously referred to. Space limitations prevent their presentation here.

Multiple-lift seal coats, sometimes referred to as retreads, are at times specified. Design and construction closely follow the procedures already set out for armor coats. Seal coats of hot plant-mixed binder and chips, or binder and sand, are also used at times. These are spread over a hot plant-mix or asphaltic-concrete surface course after the first rolling and are incorporated into that surface by subsequent compaction.

PAYMENT FOR BITUMINOUS PAVEMENTS

Payment for materials, equipment, labor, overhead, and profit for contract construction of bituminous pavement is either at a bid price per unit of completed pavement surface or per unit of material supplied. A number of highway agencies pay for all types by the square yard of completed surface; some incorporate charges for subgrade preparation, base, and pavement in a single item. Payment per unit of material varies from agency to agency and also with pavement type.

On a weight basis, plant mixes are usually paid for by the ton of paving mixture, including charges for hauling, placing, and compacting. Some agencies, however, pay under two items: mixed material at a bid price per ton *plus* binder at a unit price per ton or per gallon.[63] Payment under the two items makes it possible for the engineer to change the percentage of binder to fit variations in aggregate without penalizing or overpaying the contractor. Some agencies pay for rolling separately, by the hour.

Prices for road-mix, penetration-macadam, and inverted-penetration construction (if paid on a weight basis) are normally set in two items: aggregates at a price per ton, and binder at a price per ton or per gallon. These prices include all charges for hauling, processing, and compacting. Separate items for each class of aggregate are provided at times. Sometimes separate payment for preparation of the underlying surface or for processing, in the case of road mix, is made.

[63] Weights per unit volume vary with grade. For example, a ton of SC-0 at 60° F contains about 257 gal, whereas a ton of SC-6 at the same temperature contains only 239 gal. Volume-weight relationships also change with temperature; a gallon of SC-6 at 300° F weighs 8% less than at 60° F. If payment is by the gallon, the specifications will then include specific-gravity and temperature-conversion tables from which measured quantities are converted into pay quantities.

18 ——————— Portland-Cement-Concrete Pavements

INTRODUCTION

Portland-cement-concrete or "concrete" pavement consists of a relatively rich mixture of Portland cement, sand, and coarse aggregate laid as a single course. When properly designed and constructed, it has long life and relatively low maintenance cost. It is seldom slippery even when wet, unless covered with mud, ice, or oil. In 1951, some 87,000 miles of state-administered roads and streets had surfaces of Portland-cement concrete.

There is record of a short section of concrete road base outside London in 1828 and of a concrete foundation course for sheet asphalt in Paris in 1858. Concrete was once used as a base in New York in 1888. In Bellefontaine, Ohio, in 1892 a concrete street was constructed in two courses and marked in squares like a sidewalk. In 1909 concrete pavements began to emerge from the trial period, when Wayne County, Mich., paved Woodward Avenue which leads from Detroit. In that year 4 miles of such pavements were laid. By 1912 there were a number of sections in Milwaukee County, Wis., and the State Highway Department of California had adopted it as a standard paving. In that year use increased greatly and 250 miles were constructed. In 1913 this figure was doubled, and in 1914 some 1500 to 1800 miles were placed.

At the beginning of World War I (1914) concrete pavement was still in a transitional stage. The California Highway Department was building a 4-in. concrete "base" 15 ft wide. In 1915 the tone of a government bulletin was cautious. In 1917 Pennsylvania standardized on the alternatives of 5-in. slabs or slabs 5 in. thick at the edge and 7 in. at the center on flat subgrades. Precast slabs were tried at Casper, Wyo., in 1920 and in California at Suisun in 1922.

Maricopa County, Ariz., in 1918, under an $8 million bond issue,

527

built an extensive mileage of thickened-edge pavements, much of which is still rendering good service. Test tracks at Bates, Ill., and at Pittsburg, Calif., in 1920–22 thoroughly tested this and other concrete-pavement designs. Since the early 1920's, Portland-cement concrete has been accepted as one of the high-type pavements.

No other pavement type has received such study as Portland-cement concrete. Perhaps no other single use of cement has advanced the knowledge of its properties or the art of its manufacture as has road building. Since 1910 many hundreds of thousands of dollars have been devoted to research and comparable sums applied to the construction of experimental cement-concrete test roads, tracks, and slabs. From the crude, relatively weak, rough-finished roads, some of which actually rutted under traffic, there have now developed first-class concrete pavements built under rigid inspection to carefully drawn specifications. Many problems of design and maintenance still remain unsolved, however. On some research is now in progress and other studies will surely be undertaken.

It is beyond the scope of this book to explore fully all phases of concrete pavement design, construction, and maintenance. The following pages represent a summary of past and current practice and of research on the subject.[1]

DESIGN OF CONCRETE PAVEMENTS

The behavior of concrete pavement slabs is controlled by the properties of the concrete of which it is cast and those of the underlying subgrades and base courses. Concrete will withstand relatively high compressive stresses, but has little tensile strength. Because of its low tensile strength, flexural or beam strength of the slabs is also low. Concrete, like other materials, expands or contracts as its temperature increases or decreases. Like wood, it expands on wetting and contracts on drying. It also shrinks soon after placing as the mortar hardens and the cement hydrates. Under some conditions its volume increases with age. Because of these properties, and because concrete pavements are exposed to the elements, they change length with time of day, with the seasons, and with variations in the weather. In addition, daily and

[1] The Report of the Committee on Concrete Pavement Design, *American Road Builders Association Technical Bulletin 163* (1949) gives a detailed report on design and construction practices of the individual state highway departments. Statements on current practice appearing on the following pages are largely based on this bulletin.

seasonal temperature and moisture difference between tops and bottoms of slabs introduce a tendency to warp and curl. Further complications arise because the bases supporting the slabs yield when loads are imposed and recover, at least partially, when they are removed. These and other unmentioned complications make theoretical determination of the stresses in concrete pavement slabs extremely difficult.

Flexural stresses in concrete pavements

Westergaard, beginning in 1925,[2] published a series of articles on the theoretical analysis of concrete pavement slabs that has been largely accepted as fundamental. Modifications of his formulas have been suggested by various investigators but the basic considerations remain unchanged.[3] One set of formulas gives the theoretical flexural stresses produced in slabs of uniform thickness by loads placed at three critical locations as follows (see Fig. 1):

1. Load applied close to the rectangular corner of a large slab. Such a condition exists at the intersection of the pavement edge with a transverse joint if no provision is made to transfer a portion of the load across the joint to the adjoining slab.

2. Load applied to the interior of a large slab at a considerable distance from its edges.

3. Load applied at the edge of the slab at a considerable distance from any corner.

Another set of formulas gives theoretical stresses created at the same three positions by temperature differences between tops and bottoms of slabs. During the day, temperature at the surface is higher than in the elements below it, and the slab edges curl downward in relation to the central section. This tendency, which is resisted by the weight of the slab, creates flexural stresses: tension at the bottom and compression at the top. At night, temperature gradient is reversed, so that the direction of temperature warping and the sense of temperature warping stresses will be reversed.

Differences in moisture content between tops and bottoms of slabs

[2] See *Proceedings Highway Research Board,* part 1 (1925), and *Public Roads,* April 1926.

[3] See E. F. Kelley, Application of the Results of Research to the Structural Design of Concrete Pavements, *Public Roads,* July and August 1939; Teller and Sutherland, The Structural Design of Concrete Pavements, *Public Roads,* April, May, June 1943; and *Concrete Pavement Design,* Portland Cement Association (1951).

also cause warping and flexural stresses, but these are usually omitted from theoretical analysis. Kelley has stated that "During hot summer days, when moisture and temperature differentials are both a maximum, the curvature caused by one is in the opposite direction to that caused by the other and such stress as may be produced by moisture serves to reduce rather than to increase the stress due to temperature warping. . . . To ignore moisture warping appears to add some factor

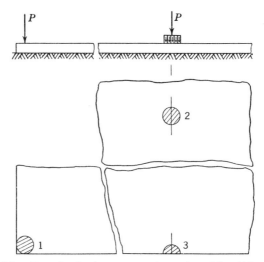

Fɪɢ. 1.   Critical locations for loads on concrete paving slabs (After Westergaard)

of safety of unknown magnitude and importance." These conclusions are supported by the findings of others.

Theoretical flexural stresses produced by loads and by restrained temperature warping, computed for slabs of uniform thickness by formulas 1 to 7, given later, are shown in Fig. 2. Slab width is 10 ft, or about that of a single traffic lane. Variables are thickness and length of pavement slab. Average values for load and impact, concrete properties, and temperature gradient have been assumed and are stated on the figure. The supporting subgrade would be rated as relatively weak.

The ultimate flexural strength of paving concrete ordinarily ranges between 600 and 700 lb per sq in. for static loading conditions. Under repeated or fatigue loadings, however, failure occurs at much lower stresses. For pavements, which are often subjected to many million load repetitions, this fatigue strength is about 55% of the static strength. Safe working stresses, even without any large safety factor, cannot then exceed 300 to 350 lb per sq. in.

A number of the fundamentals of concrete-pavement design can be explained from the data presented in Fig. 2. Among the most important are:

1. Cracking caused by flexural stresses is almost inevitable in slabs of any great length. Figures 2b and 2c show conclusively that combined stresses at slab edges and interiors, for lengths of 30 feet, far exceed the fatigue strength of plain concrete. This applies for all reasonable slab thicknesses since reduced load stresses gained by increasing slab thickness are largely offset by increased temperature stresses.

2. For constant loads on slabs of reasonable lengths, load stresses and total stresses decrease as slab thickness increases. Corollary to this, as wheel loads increase, slab thickness must increase if the unit stress is to remain within safe limits. Over the years pavement thickness has increased from 5 or 6 in. to 8 or 9 in., and sometimes to 12 in.

3. For the stated conditions of single isolated slabs of uniform thickness, the maximum unit stresses occur at the corners or edges of the slabs rather than in the interiors. If there is an abutting slab, it is common in current design to reduce these edge and corner stresses by installing load-transfer devices which provide support for the loaded section. Stress reduction at free edges has often been gained by thickening the pavement near its edge, although this practice is less common than in former years.

Formulas for flexural stresses in concrete pavement slabs of uniform thickness

The formulas for flexural stresses in concrete pavements on which Fig. 2 is based are those of Westergaard, as modified by the Bureau of Public Roads on the basis of its full-scale tests of pavement slabs.[4] The formulas, some of which are empirical and based on test results, are as follows:

Edge loading, when the edges of the slab are warped upward at night (empirical equation):

$$\sigma_e = \frac{0.572P}{h^2} \left[4 \log_{10} \left(\frac{l}{b} \right) + \log_{10} b \right] \tag{1}$$

Edge loading, when the slab is unwarped or when the edge of the slab is warped downward in daytime (Westergaard equation, based on $\mu = 0.15$):

$$\sigma_e = \frac{0.572P}{h^2} \left[4 \log_{10} \left(\frac{l}{b} \right) + 0.359 \right] \tag{2}$$

[4] For equations for load stresses under airport loadings, see Westergaard, *Transactions American Society of Civil Engineers*, pp. 425–444 (1948).

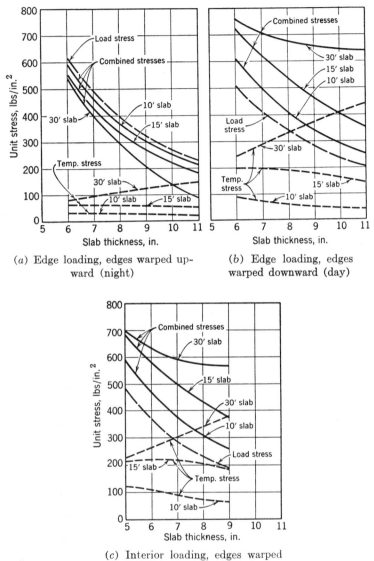

(a) Edge loading, edges warped upward (night)

(b) Edge loading, edges
warped downward (day)

(c) Interior loading, edges warped
downward (day)

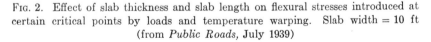

FIG. 2.   Effect of slab thickness and slab length on flexural stresses introduced at
certain critical points by loads and temperature warping.   Slab width = 10 ft
(from *Public Roads,* July 1939)

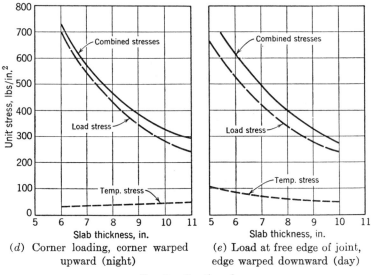

(d) Corner loading, corner warped upward (night)

(e) Load at free edge of joint, edge warped downward (day)

Fig. 2. *Continued*

Assumed Conditions

Static wheel load in dual, high-pressure tires = 8000 lb. Including impact, load = 11,800 lb.

Radius of area of load contact (a) = 7.8 in. Modulus of elasticity of concrete (E) = 5,000,000 lb per sq in.

Poisson's ratio for concrete (μ) = 0.15. Coefficient of expansion for concrete (e) = 0.000005 per degrees Fahrenheit.

Temperature difference in degrees Fahrenheit between top and bottom of slab— day, $-3°$ F per in. thickness.

Temperature difference in degrees Fahrenheit between top and bottom of slab— night, $+1°$ F per in. thickness.

Coefficient of subgrade reaction (k) = 100 lb per cu in.

Interior loading (Westergaard equation, based on $\mu = 0.15$):

$$\sigma_i = \frac{0.316P}{h^2}\left[4\log_{10}\left(\frac{l}{b}\right) + 1.069\right]_{\text{.}} \tag{3}$$

Corner loading (empirical equation):

$$\sigma_c = \frac{3P}{h^2}\left[1 - \left(\frac{a\sqrt{2}}{l}\right)^{1.2}\right] \tag{4}$$

Warping stress along the edge of a slab:[5]

$$\sigma_{xe} = \frac{C_x Eet}{2} \tag{5}$$

Warping stresses in the interior of a slab:

$$\sigma_x = \frac{Eet}{2}\left(\frac{C_x + \mu C_y}{1 - \mu^2}\right) \tag{6}$$

$$\sigma_y = \frac{Eet}{2}\left(\frac{C_y + \mu C_x}{1 - \mu^2}\right) \tag{7}$$

Symbols in these formulas are defined as follows:

σ_e = maximum load-produced tensile stress in the bottom of the slab directly under the load P at the edge, and in a direction parallel to the edge, stated in pounds per square inch.

σ_i = maximum load-produced tensile stress in the interior of the slab stated in pounds per square inch. This occurs in the bottom of the slab directly under the load.

σ_c = maximum load-produced tensile stress resulting from a load at the corner of the slab. This occurs at the top of the slab, in a direction parallel to the bisector of the corner angle.

σ_{xe} = maximum temperature-warping stress at the edge of the slab in the direction of slab length, stated in pounds per square inch.

σ_x = maximum temperature-warping stress in the interior of the slab in the direction of slab length.

σ_y = maximum temperature-warping stress in the interior of the slab in the direction of slab width stated in pounds per square inch.

P = load in pounds, including an allowance for impact.

h = thickness of slab in inches.

l = radius of relative stiffness, which measures the stiffness of the slab in relation to that of the subgrade. It is expressed by the equation

$$l = \sqrt[4]{\frac{Eh^3}{12(1 - \mu^2)k}}$$

[5] Equations 5, 6, and 7 were developed by Royall D. Bradbury from procedures indicated by Westergaard.

E = modulus of elasticity of concrete in pounds per square inch.

μ = Poisson's ratio for concrete.

k = the subgrade modulus, or resistance of subgrade to deformation, expressed in pounds per cubic inch.

b = radius of equivalent distribution of pressure, expressed in inches. This factor recognizes the influence of slab thickness on tensile stress directly under an applied load. It is expressed by the equations

$$b = \sqrt{1.6a^2 + h^2} - 0.675h \quad \text{when} \quad a < 1.724h \qquad (8a)$$

or

$$b = a \qquad\qquad\qquad \text{when} \quad a > 1.724h \qquad (8b)$$

a = radius of area of load contact, in inches. This area is assumed as circular in the case of corner and interior loads and semicircular for edge loads.

C_x and C_y = coefficients that relate slab length and the relative stiffness of slab and subgrade to temperature-warping stresses. Values of C_x and C_y are given in Fig. 3.

e = thermal coefficient of expansion and contraction of concrete per degree Fahrenheit.

t = difference in temperature between top and bottom of slab in degrees Fahrenheit.

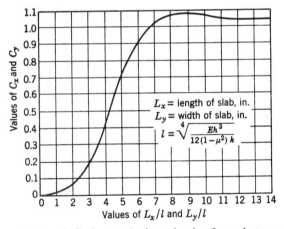

L_x = length of slab, in.
L_y = width of slab, in.
$$l = \sqrt[4]{\frac{Eh^3}{12(1-\mu^2)k}}$$

Values of L_x/l and L_y/l

Fig. 3. Values of C_x and C_y for use in formulas for flexural stresses in concrete pavements.

It is impossible to assign firm values to such terms as load, concrete and subgrade properties, and temperature variation since they change with place and situation. The following paragraphs, based on the Bureau of Public Roads study, serve to illustrate some of the complexities.

Load and impact (P). Permissible wheel loads differ widely. Many states limit axle loads to 18,000 lb, which in turn limits wheel loads to 9000 lb. Some states permit much greater loads: for example, several eastern and midwestern states permit axle loads of 22,400 lb, or wheel loads of 11,200 lb. Until about 1951, New Jersey permitted axle loads of 34,000 on large dual tires. In addition, the influence of impact varies with speed, condition of pavement surface, weight of vehicle, and tire pressure. In one group of tests conducted on reasonably smooth pavements, multipliers to convert static load to total load including impact ranged from 2.05 down to 1.24. Of particular interest was the finding that 8000-lb wheel loads on high-pressure tires developed a vertical reaction of 11,800 lb while 9,000-lb wheel loads on low-pressure tires produced only 10,000 lb vertical reaction. Whether or not static and impact loads produce the same relative stresses in the concrete remains an unsettled question.

Modulus of elasticity of concrete (E). A summary of many tests indicates that the modulus of elasticity of concrete of the character generally used in pavements is roughly 1000 times its compressive strength and ranges from 3 million to 6 million lb per sq in. Values will usually be higher than 4,500,000. The modulus varies not only with strength, but also with age, moisture state, stress condition, and other factors. In design, 5 million lb per sq in. is ordinarily used. Assuming a higher modulus makes the design more conservative, since warping stress increases directly with modulus of elasticity.

Poisson's ratio for concrete (μ). For concrete, no definite relationship exists between Poisson's ratio and strength. Based on the results of many tests, it has been determined that the range to be expected lies between 0.10 and 0.20. The average figure of 0.15 is usually adopted for design purposes. The maximum error introduced by variation between this average and the stated limits is 4.3% for interior stresses and 2.5% for edge stresses. Corner stresses are little affected.

Coefficient of subgrade reaction (k). This coefficient expresses the stiffness of the subgrade and is stated in terms of load in pounds per square inch per inch of deflection. It is assumed that the subgrade reaction at any point is proportional to the deflection. Subgrade reaction is assumed to be constant under the entire pavement slab, although limited research offers evidence to the contrary.

Values of k range from about 50 lb per cu in. for very poor subgrades such as clays of the A–7 Public Roads classification up to about 300 for good materials. They may be 700 or over for extremely good soils. The test method involves loading the prepared subgrade through a rigid steel plate 30 in. in diameter. Loads and deformations are recorded. Maximum loading on the plate may approach 30 tons which makes provision of the downward force difficult. This is commonly accomplished by transferring the upward reaction of the test device to the frames of heavily loaded trucks placed some distance on either side of the bearing plate. At times heavy anchors may be set into the ground to provide the downward reaction.[6]

The Portland Cement Association offers data correlating k values with soils

---

[6] For descriptions of this test see Middlebrook and Bertram, *Proceedings Highway Research Board*, pp. 170–171 (1942), and *Concrete Pavement Design*, Portland Cement Association, pp. 67–69 (1951).

classifications of the Public Roads Administration, American Association of State Highway Officials, and Corps of Engineers, and with the California bearing-ratio test.[7] The Public Roads Administration also has methods for simplifying the determination of k values.[8]

Reasonable variations in the values for the coefficient of subgrade reaction do not have serious effects on stresses. Kelley states that ". . . stresses computed on the basis of $k = 300$ may be too low by as much as 25 percent if the modulus happens to have a value of 50. On the other hand, stresses computed on the asumption that $k = 100$ will be too low by less than 10 percent if k happens to equal 50." He recommends a value of 100 lb per cu in. for general use. The trend toward placing a layer of selected base course under concrete pavements further minimizes the effect of variations in the value of k.

Thermal coefficient of expansion (e). For concretes like those for pavements, values for the thermal coefficient of expansion range from 0.000004 to 0.000007 per degree Fahrenheit. The highest coefficients have been found with siliceous aggregates and the lower values with granite, limestone, or diabase aggregates. Unless test data are available, a coefficient of 0.000005 is ordinarily used. It is important to note that warping stresses vary directly with this coefficient. Thus warping stresses will be higher in slabs made of concretes with high coefficients of expansion.

Temperature gradient from top to bottom of slab. Observations of temperature differences between tops and bottoms of slabs made at Arlington showed variation nearly proportional to depth of slab. Temperature differences in daytime, particularly in summer after the sun had heated the upper surface, ranged up to 4° F per in. of depth. At night, after cooling, the surface temperature was below that of the bottom by as much as 1.5° per in. of depth. Recommended values for design computations, as shown in Fig. 2, are 3° F per in. of depth in the daytime and 1° F per in. of depth at night.

Direct tensile and compressive stresses in concrete pavement slabs

Changes in temperature and moisture content not only create warping and flexural stresses, but also cause over-all lengthening and shortening of slabs. If slabs were perfectly free to move, these volume changes would take place without creating stresses. However, the subgrades on which pavements rest offer considerable resistance to horizontal movement. Thus, the tendency for slabs to shorten because of temperature drop or drying creates tensile stresses, whereas the tendency to lengthen from temperature rise or increased moisture creates compressive stresses.

Tensile stresses in unreinforced slabs vary more or less directly with the daily temperature drop, the distance between joints, and the coefficient of subgrade resistance, which is the average coefficient of fric-

---

[7] See *Concrete Pavement Design,* Portland Cement Association, pp. 8–11 (1951).

[8] See Teller and Sutherland, *Public Roads,* April, May, June 1943.

tion between the slab and its supporting subgrade. Kelley reports [9] that stresses slightly larger than 100 lb per sq in. may be expected for the average temperature drop of 40° F, a slab length of 100 ft, and an average coefficient of subgrade resistance of slightly over 2. Stresses are proportionally lower for shorter slabs. He concludes that, for unreinforced pavements provided with transverse joints at reasonable intervals, crack formation unless at early ages generally cannot be attributed to direct tensile stresses. Rather it must be assigned to the warping stresses mentioned earlier. Tensile stresses resulting from decreased moisture content are ignored in design as they usually are opposite in sense and partly compensatory for those caused by temperature change.

The length of an unconfined concrete slab will increase if its temperature rises or its moisture content increases. If this expansion is in part or wholly restrained, compressive stresses are created. Such stresses, considered alone, are much below the compressive strength of the concrete. In combination with other factors, however, they may lead to "blowups," in which short sections of slab abruptly buckle upward. This problem is discussed further under the subject of joints.

Effects of edge support on the design of concrete pavements

When load is applied near the edge or corner of a concrete slab, the slab deflects downward. If the slab is isolated or free from connection with its neighbors, the load is carried by the cantilever action of the slab plus the support of the underlying subgrade or base course. However, when adjacent slabs are interconnected in some manner, the edges of both deflect downward together, and the load is distributed between them. It is common practice in concrete pavement design to provide for load transfer between adjacent slabs to gain this stress reduction

[9] Kelley states that tensile stresses are dependent, not on seasonal temperature change, but on the temperature drop that occurs during one single period of continuously falling temperature or, at most, during a relatively few cycles of temperature change in which the minimum temperatures are decreasing. Based on a 3-year observation period, the maximum 24-hr difference in air temperatures recorded in 22 cities in the United States was 60° F, at Denver, Colo. Temperature variation was smallest in Miami, Fla., where the maximum change was 27° F. Changes in slab temperatures would be less than these values. The coefficient of subgrade resistance varies with subgrade type, amount of slab displacement, and slab thickness. Typical values are 0.34 for loam subgrade and a movement of 0.001 in.; 2.18 for a 3-in. crushed stone subgrade and a displacement of 0.05 in., and 3.5 for a slab only 2 in. thick supported on silt-loam soil and displaced 0.10 in.

or to permit a decrease in pavement thickness. There are many methods for providing for load transfer (see the discussion of joints), but much is yet to be learned regarding their effectiveness.

Effects of thickened edge on the design of concrete pavement

When a load is applied very near an unsupported pavement edge, the flexural stress in a slab of uniform thickness is higher than that resulting when the load is applied at other points. If the depth is set to keep

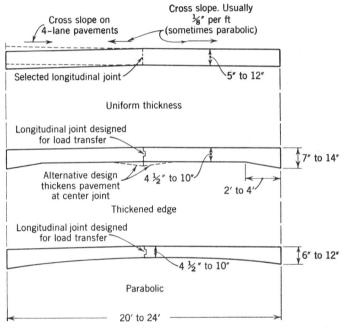

FIG. 4. Typical cross sections of concrete pavements showing extreme dimensions suggested by the Portland Cement Association

the stress near the unsupported edge at a safe level, the remainder of the slab may be overdesigned. In order to make flexural stresses equal over the entire slab, "thickened-edge" pavements were developed which provided extra slab thickness close to all unsupported edges (see Fig. 4). A variety of such designs has been adopted.

Thickened-edge pavements first came into widespread use after road tests at Pittsburg, Calif., and Bates, Ill., in 1921 and 1922 had demonstrated that thickened-edge pavements were less susceptible to cracking at corners and edges. In the 1930 decade, thickened-edge designs predominated. Since that time, however, the trend has been toward pavements of uniform thickness. Lanes on present-day highways are wide, often 12 ft, and most of the vehicles are centrally positioned in them. With this load placement, the need for a thickened-edge design largely disappears. It is argued also that preparing the subgrade for a thickened-edge pavement is more expensive since it calls for more hand labor, and, furthermore, that good compaction cannot be achieved on the sloped section of subgrade.

Slab thicknesses for concrete pavements

The foregoing paragraphs have listed the many variables that must be considered in designing concrete pavement slabs. They have also indicated that many of these variables are not subject to precise evaluation so that design calculations give only approximate answers. Because of this, highway agencies generally have each adopted one or more slab cross sections as standard and use them for all concrete paving projects. Figure 4 shows the three most common types and the extremes in dimensions that might be encountered in practice. Figure 5 is a design chart of the Portland Cement Association for heavy-duty pavements carrying loads on dual tires. This chart applies only if slab corners are protected by load-transfer devices or other means so that at least 20% of the load on a corner is carried by an adjoining section. There is a companion chart for heavy-duty pavements without corner protection. Another pair of diagrams, applying to roads or streets that carry lighter traffic on single tires, is also available. In each case the interrelation is between allowable flexural stress in the concrete, coefficient of subgrade reaction (k), average wheel load, and pavement thickness. Also offered are graphs from which the dimensions of thickened edge or parabolic cross sections of equivalent strength can be selected.

Table 1 shows typical results obtained from the Portland Cement Association method.[10] These presume protected corners, a subgrade modulus of 100 lb per cu in., and a pavement design life of 30 years. Design wheel loads, including a 20% allowance for impact, are weighted on the basis of traffic estimates. Fatigue modulus of rupture is set at 350 lb per sq in., a value found by applying a factor of 2 to a static modulus of rupture of 700 lb per sq in.

[10] For details see *Concrete Pavement Design*, pp. 18–40 (1951).

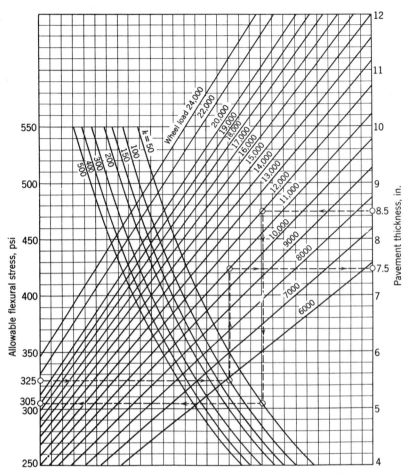

Fig. 5. Design chart for Portland-cement-concrete pavement. Wheel loads on dual tires. Pavement has protected corners (Courtesy Portland Cement Association)

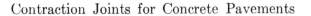
Contraction joints for concrete pavements [11]

On preceding pages it has been established that the tensile stresses in concrete slabs of any great length will exceed the fatigue strength

[11] Intensive study has been given the problem of joints for concrete pavements, and the literature on the subject is extensive: Among other excellent references are Experience in Illinois with Joints in Concrete Pavements, *University of Illinois Engineering Experiment Station Bulletin 365*, December 1947; Van Breemen and Finney, *Journal American Concrete Institute*, June 1950, pp. 789–813, Anderson, Gardner, Woods, Knoerle, and Conwell, *Transactions Ameri-*

TABLE 1. CONCRETE PAVEMENT THICKNESSES, AS DETERMINED BY PORTLAND CEMENT ASSOCIATION METHODS

Based on Average Traffic Distributions

Class of Highway	Indicated Depth, In.	Thick-ness, In.	Type of Section	Width, Ft	Concrete per Mile, Cu Yd
I		9	Uniform thickness	24	3520
Primary route in or near	8.64	10–7½–10	Thickened edge	24	3056
a metropolitan area			with 3-ft slope		
		9–7½–9	Parabolic	24	3129
II		8½	Uniform thickness	24	3324
Primary route in a rural	8.15	10–7–10	Thickened edge	24	2852
area			with 2-ft, 4-in.		
			slope		
		9–7–9	Parabolic	24	3000
III		7½	Uniform thickness	22	2688
Lightly traveled primary	7.47	9–6½–9	Thickened edge	22	2439
route			with 2-ft, 8-in.		
			slope		
		8–6½–8	Parabolic	22	2509
IV		7½	Uniform thickness	20	2444
Secondary or county	7.35	9–6½–9	Thickened edge	20	2200
trunk route			with 2-ft slope		
		8–6½–8	Parabolic	20	2281

of the concrete. It can be expected, therefore, that long, continuous slabs of plain concrete will crack at intervals in a random and unsightly manner. There is now indisputable evidence that such cracking, if uncontrolled, leads to early deterioration of concrete pavements.

The most common method of crack control provides longitudinal joints between adjoining traffic lanes and transverse joints at frequent intervals. The pavement becomes, in effect, several rows of abutting rectangular slabs. An alternative solution requires distributed reinforcing steel in the pavement to control cracking. This permits wider spacing of transverse joints. These two approaches to the problem of crack control encompass practically all methods currently in use.[12]

can Society of Civil Engineers, pp. 1159–1176 (1949); and Progress Reports of Cooperative Research Projects on Joint Spacing, *Highway Research Board Research Report 3-B* (1945).

[12] Several experimental sections of pavement without joints are under observation (see p. 552). Also research is under way in England on paving slabs of prestressed concrete (see *Engineering News-Record*, April 12, 1951 and April 23, 1953).

Transverse contraction joints. Transverse contraction joints are at right angles to the road center line. In unreinforced slabs the intention is that they be closely enough spaced to prevent cracking at intermediate points. Spacings employed by the state highway departments that build unreinforced slabs range from 12.5 to 30 ft, with the majority favoring 15- or 20-ft distances.

All but a few of the states that use transverse contraction joints specify the "weakened plane" or "dummy" type (see Fig. 6). A plane of weakness is made across the slab by cutting or forming a notch into the top of the concrete. When tension develops, a crack occurs at this point rather than at some other location. Engineers disagree regarding the merits of the various methods for forming the weakened plane. One procedure is to insert a thin strip of bituminous impregnated filler close under the pavement surface. This joint is difficult to seal against the penetration of surface water to the subgrade. Under heavy wheel loads the concrete sometimes chips or spalls off for a width and depth of an inch or more so that maintenance forces must then clean and seal the joint. This may create a rough spot, and in addition is unsightly. Another detail provides a groove downward from the surface. This joint is more costly because considerable hand labor is required in its shaping and finishing. On the other hand, the joint can be effectively sealed against surface water with a bituminous or rubber joint filler. Furthermore, there is less spalling under traffic. Several states are currently experimenting with sawed joints, cut in the finished pavement with special saws.

When a weakened-plane joint cracks through, the break in the concrete is irregular and rough. As long as the joint opening is small, the projecting aggregate faces stay tightly keyed, and, when the edge of one slab deflects under load, the adjoining edge is forced down also. Thus a weakened-plane joint furnishes edge or corner support between adjacent slabs. As of 1949, 20 state highway departments rely solely on aggregate interlock for edge support. Nineteen employed special load-transfer devices part or all of the time to supplement aggregate interlock and to provide positive load transfer in case the joint opens and aggregate interlock is spoiled. A generalization from current practice is that, as a rule, load-transfer devices are not employed where contraction joints are closely spaced, except in the vicinity of expansion joints.

Smooth steel bars called dowels are the most common load-transfer device for contraction joints [13] (see Fig. 6). Dowels are greased or

---

[13] Some agencies permit other load-transfer devices than dowels. For more on them see the first two references in the footnote on p. 541.

painted for one-half their length to break the bond with the concrete and permit the dowel to slip within one of the abutting slab ends. Selected dowel diameters vary between ¾ and 1¼ in., with ¾ in. the most common size. Spacing between bars range from 12 to 16½ in. with the 12-in. spacing predominating. Most common dowel length is 24 in. Extreme care must be taken during construction to keep dowels in careful alinement; otherwise they will prevent proper joint action. Almost all highway agencies have special holding devices for this purpose.

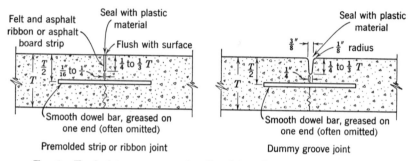

Premolded strip or ribbon joint   Dummy groove joint

Fig. 6. Typical transverse contraction joints for concrete pavements

Formulas for selecting dowel diameters, spacings, and lengths are offered in the pamphlet *Concrete Pavement Design* of the Portland Cement Association (1951). There can be wide variation in results, however, depending on the assumptions used.

Longitudinal joints. Almost all highway agencies place longitudinal joints between adjacent traffic lanes. They are designed as hinges, which means that they provide edge support but permit rotation between the slabs. In this way, flexural stresses are relieved which otherwise might cause irregular and unsightly cracks along the length of the pavement. Generally, longitudinal joints have not been troublesome. Two explanations are: (1) that there are few demands for heavy load transfer across longitudinal joints and (2) that the expansive and contractive movements and forces developed across the width of a pavement are relatively small.

About half of the state highway departments employ weakened-plane longitudinal joints much like those for transverse contraction joints. Principal difference is that deformed reinforcing bars replace the dowels (see Fig. 6). A number of other states have adopted full-depth joints which include some keying arrangement for load transfer. A few use a plain butt joint. Some typical installations are shown in Fig. 7. All but a few agencies call for tie bars across longitudinal joints to hold the slabs tightly together. Deformed reinforcing steel is the most common material, although a few departments use threaded bolts.

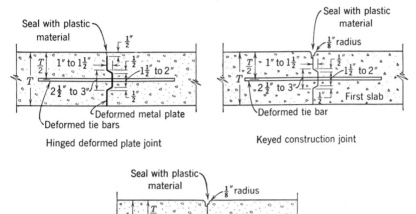

Fig. 7. Typical longitudinal joints for concrete pavements

Sizes of reinforcing steel range from ¼ to ¾ in. Half-inch bars are specified by 26 states. For them the most common spacings are 24 and 30 in. The most common tie bar length [14] is 4 ft.

Reinforcement for concrete pavements

Reinforcing steel in concrete pavement prevents the widening of cracks produced by flexure and holds the fractured faces in intimate contact. In this way, aggregate interlock is preserved, and the intrusion of dirt or water is prevented.. Seldom if ever is reinforcing counted on to resist flexural stresses produced by loads or warping.

Among the 35 state highway departments that in 1949 used re-

[14] An approximate design for tie bars can be made assuming that they must be strong enough to drag one slab to the other over the subgrade. The principal unknown is the average value for the coefficient of subgrade resistance, which for longitudinal joints is about 1.0. Applying these assumptions to current state highway practice gives tensile stresses in the tie bars ranging from 6000 to 36,000 lb per sq in.

inforcing steel in pavements there were wide differences in the kinds and amounts of reinforcing specified. Welded wire fabric was permitted by 32 states and required by 10. Comparable figures for mats of reinforcing bars were 22 and 2, and for expanded metal 7 and 0. The amounts of steel also varied greatly, some states using almost three times as much as others.[15] This is strikingly illustrated by a comparison of the computed stresses: For welded wire fabric, they range from 7800 to 84,000 lb per sq in. For bar mats the limits are 3900 to 57,000 lb per sq in.

Welded wire fabric is made from cold-drawn steel wires.[16] Minimum permitted tensile strength is 70,000 lb per sq in.; the yield point is set at 80% of the tensile strength. Reinforcing bars of billet, rail, or axle steel are permitted by some agencies, whereas others will accept only billet steel.[17] In general, the intermediate and hard grades, with minimum yield points ranging from 40,000 to 50,000 lb per sq in., are specified. A few agencies indicate by their specifications that structural-grade steel (yield point 33,000 lb per sq in.) may sometimes be acceptable.

It is almost universal practice to place the reinforcing steel near the top of the slab.[18] The distance from the surface to the steel varies from 1½ to 3 in., with 2 in. the most common distance.

Design of pavement reinforcement. Reinforcement for concrete pavements is designed to hold the cracks that result from flexural stresses tightly closed. The assumption is made that the reinforcing steel must be strong enough to drag both ends of each individual slab over the subgrade toward its center. This idea expressed as a formula becomes

---

[15] Extremes in wire sizes in welded wire fabric ranged from no. 000 (0.3625 in. diameter) running longitudinally at 6-in. centers and no. 4 (0.2253 in. diameter) running transversely at 12-in. centers to no. 8 (0.1620 in. diameter) at 6-in. centers in both directions. Bar reinforcement usually consisted of ¼- or ⅜-in. sizes. Spacings of longitudinal bars ranged from 6 to 22 in. and averaged 10 in.; spacings of transverse bars ranged from 12 to 27 in. and averaged 17 in. The weights of bar reinforcing per 100 sq ft of pavement ranged from 30 to 86 lb.

[16] Specifications for the wire itself appear as *AASHO Designation M32–42, ASTM Designation A82–34.* Those for the completed fabric are *AASHO Designation M55–37, ASTM Designation A185–37.*

[17] See *AASHO Designations M31–48, M42–48,* and *M53–48.*

[18] Only one state highway department places the steel at mid-depth in the slab. It is uncommon to put reinforcement in both top and bottom although it has been done on a few experimental projects.

$$A_S = \frac{LfW}{2S} \tag{9}$$

where A_S = square inches of steel cross section per foot of slab width.

L = length of the slab between joints, feet.

f = coefficient of friction between the slab and the subgrade: also called the coefficient of subgrade resistance. Assumptions for it usually range from 1 to 2, with 1.5 the most common.

W = weight of the slab per square foot of pavement surface, pounds.

S = working stress in the reinforcing steel, pounds per square inch. This is usually taken as 50% of the yield point stress.

Transverse expansion joints for concrete pavements

Expansion joints provide space into which the ends of pavement slabs can protrude when the slabs lengthen. In early concrete pavings, vertical openings filled with mastic or premolded filler were placed at intervals ranging from 30 to 150 ft along the roadway. When these joints failed to stop cracking at random spacings along the pavement, some engineers decided they were unnecessary and omitted all joints except those placed at the end of each day's run. Many thousands of miles were built without joints, and most of them gave good service. Five or more years after construction, however, some of these pavements suffered blowups, and this was considered conclusive evidence that expansion joints were needed. By 1934, the installation of expansion joints at spacings of 100 ft or less was almost universal practice. Since then the trend has reversed, and several state highway departments now construct pavements without expansion joints, or use them only where pavements join structures or intersect other concrete pavements. Certain other states space the joints at intervals between 300 and 600 ft. However, a majority employ spacings of less than 120 ft. Some place joints closer if construction is done in cold weather. This diversity in practice reflects the wide difference in opinion regarding the function and usefulness of expansion joints.

The principal reason for installing expansion joints is to prevent blowups by relieving direct compressive stresses before they reach dangerous levels. It can be strongly argued that the many miles of satisfactory pavement that have such joints offer strong evidence in favor of their retention.

There is one group of engineers [19] that attributes blowups to the infiltration of dirt and other foreign materials into joints and cracks. Their reasoning is briefly as follows: Under the extreme temperature of 130° F and with the concrete saturated, the unit compressive stress in a paving slab [20] will not exceed 920 lb per sq in. When load stresses are added, the sum is still below the compressive strength of the concrete. Thus blowups cannot be attributed solely to expansion of the concrete. On the other hand, each time the joints and cracks open, dirt enters them which, in effect, increases the slab length. After repeated expansions and contractions, an increase in temperature may result in a blowup. The recommended solution is (1) to space contraction joints closely so that they open less widely and to seal them to prevent dirt infiltration, and (2) to eliminate expansion joints because their presence permits the contraction joints to open more widely.[21]

There are others who assign primary responsibility for blowups to growth of the concrete itself rather than to infiltration of dirt into joints and cracks. On several projects in California alkali-aggregate reaction [22] was blamed. In Indiana growth has been ascribed to swelling of the coarse aggregate under repeated freezing and thawing. In both these instances the highway agencies involved have adopted tests to eliminate unsuitable aggregates, but have eliminated expansion joints from their pavement designs.

Extensive studies of blowups in Indiana have been reported by K. B. Woods.[23] Among the findings are the following:

Although infiltration is, no doubt, an important factor in causing blowups, as are certain combinations of temperature and moisture, it does not follow that infiltration of extraneous material is always the fundamental cause of blowups. Neither does it follow that all old unjointed pavements blow up even though the crack interval may be long and may thus provide many large openings into which extraneous materials can infiltrate. Work done at Purdue University in connection with extensive performance surveys throughout

[19] See A. A. Anderson, *Transactions American Society of Civil Engineers,* pp. 1159–1168 (1949).

[20] In computing this value, allowance is made for shrinkage during setting, but shortening from plastic flow and from drying at this elevated temperature are ignored. When these also are considered, the computations indicate no compression at all in the slab.

[21] For pavements placed in cold weather, expansion joints at intervals of perhaps 600 to 800 ft might be required.

[22] See p. 563 for a discussion of this phenomenon.

[23] See *Transactions American Society of Civil Engineers,* pp. 1169–1172 (1949).

Indiana has shown that blowups should be correlated with the source of coarse aggregate used, at least for conditions prevailing in the State of Indiana.

[Based on a study of 517 blowups:] It was concluded that these blowups occurred predominantly in mid-afternoon at a temperature above 90° F— during a period which was usually preceded by varying amounts of precipitation. . . . The infiltration of dirt into cracks, of course, would accentuate the difficulty by eliminating some of the otherwise available room for expansion.

The Indiana studies also established that "map cracking" of the concrete was associated with blowups. Further, it was found that map cracking and blowups occurred more frequently in pavements over impervious subgrades than in those over free-draining ones.

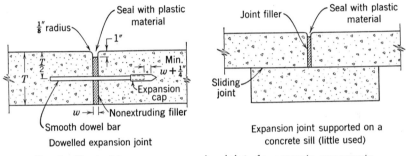

FIG. 8. Typical transverse expansion joints for concrete pavements

It was concluded that blowups are correlated primarily with the type of coarse aggregate. In addition, certain combinations of temperature, moisture, loss of strength due to freezing and thawing, and types of subgrade soil contribute to this action. However, the findings indicate the need to standardize pavement design on a regional rather than a national basis.

Details of transverse expansion joints typical of those currently or formerly employed widely are shown in Fig. 8. It is probably true that no joint satisfactory in every detail has been developed. Faults that occur to some degree in all are infiltration of dirt and other foreign material which decreases the effective width of the joint, penetration of surface water through the joint into the subgrade, and spalling of the pavement surface adjacent to the joint. Further information on the several features of expansion joints appears in the paragraphs that follow.

Joint fillers. The most common expansion joint widths are ¾ in. and 1 in. In order to keep this space open during concrete placing and to prevent the later intrusion of foreign substances, a joint filler is installed for the full width and almost the full depth of the pavement (see Fig. 8). Careful alinement of the completed joint is extremely important, and special holding and supporting devices are almost always employed. After the concrete has hardened, a seal of bituminous or rubberized material is poured.

A bituminous-type preformed filler (*AASHO Designation M33–48*) is the most widely utilized. It consists of felt or a similar material combined with asphalt or tar and a mineral filler like one of those used in asphaltic concrete. Layers of felt at each surface provide strength at high temperatures when the bituminous mixture is soft. The mineral filler reduces brittleness at low temperatures. The specifications require that this joint filler (and all other preformed fillers) compress to 50% of its thickness under a load greater than 100 lb per sq in. and less than 1500 lb per sq in. Samples must also meet certain requirements regarding absorption, distortion at high temperature, and brittleness at low temperature.[24] This type of joint filler has no voids; so, when the concrete expands and the joints close, the filler is extruded upward into the roadway surface, causing a bump that maintenance forces must cut away. When the concrete contracts, the joints remain partially open since the filler has no rebound. These voids often fill with dirt; and after numerous openings and closings the joint filler may be almost completely replaced with foreign matter.

Bituminous, cellular-type preformed joint filler is specified or permitted by some highway agencies. It is made from cane or like fibers of a cellular nature bound together and coated with asphaltic binder (*AASHO Designation M59–49*). It is nonextrusive: The AASHO specifications limit the extrusion at a single free edge to 0.25 in. when a specimen is compressed to one-half its normal thickness. It recovers somewhat when load is removed: as a minimum it must return to 70% of its original thickness after being compressed to half-thickness three times. It also must meet minimum requirements for absorption and sometimes for weathering.

Cork, self-expanding cork, sponge-rubber, and cork-rubber types of preformed filler are accepted or required by some agencies (*AASHO Designation M58–49*). These also are nonextrusive: The extension of the free edge is limited to 0.25 in. Recovery is better than for other types: The specifications require expansion to 90% of original thickness after three compressions to one-half normal thickness. Cork types are tested by boiling in hydrochloric acid. All may be tested for resistance to weathering.

Carefully selected boards of redwood, cypress, long-leaf pine, spruce, or western red cedar are required or permitted as joint filler by some states (*AASHO Designation M90–42* is for redwood). These must be thoroughly soaked before using; otherwise swelling of the wood produced by water from the fresh concrete will disrupt the newly finished surface. Because the wood has considerable strength, less elaborate provisions for retaining and supporting it during pouring will suffice. Some agencies fasten special load-transfer devices to this filler, thus eliminating elaborate and expensive dowel supports.

---

[24] See *AASHO Designation T42–49* for detailed test procedures for all preformed joint fillers. *Highway Research Board Bulletin 78* (1953) gives an excellent and detailed discussion of the behavior of joint fillers and sealers in service.

An advantage claimed for wood fillers is that they offer considerable resistance to compression [25] which results in smaller openings at joints and cracks. It has also been stated that the recovery of wood after compression is good, particularly if it is wet. On the other hand, there have been instances in which certain joint fillers of wood have disintegrated completely and permitted the joint to fill with dirt.

Several agencies have experimented with metal air-chamber expansion joints designed to open and close in accordion fashion. However, the 1949 survey indicated that no state highway agency was using them. Research at the University of Illinois in 1947 found that none of ten joints tested was effective in preventing the flow of water to the subgrade or against the infiltration of foreign material into the expansion space. Principal cause of trouble was failure of the copper seal.[26]

Expansion joint filler is sometimes placed after the concrete has hardened. The usual practice for making the opening is to set a suitable metal header board or installing bar in position before the concrete is poured. Often this header is tapered slightly. Just before the concrete has taken its initial set the bar is loosened and the joint edged. When the concrete will stand the bar is removed. Several different filler materials have served. Cottonseed hulls coated with bitumen (often RC–1 cutback asphalt or RT–3 tar) are used by several southern states. The joint is tamped almost full of the coated hulls after which a poured seal is placed. Sawdust has been employed in a like manner. Another common practice is to fill the joint with air-blown asphalt or tar.

A number of products have been employed to seal expansion and contraction joints. The 1949 survey showed that 29 states specified or accepted bituminous materials. *AASHO Designation M89* is for a combination of about 80% of a harder paving asphalt (selected from products with penetrations between 20 and 70) and 20% mineral filler. Others prefer air-blown asphalts. Rubber compounds under such names as paraplastic and latex are required or permitted by 10 agencies. A mixture of 30% emulsified latex and 70% SC–6 road oil is used by the California Division of Highways.

Load-transfer devices for expansion joints. As with contraction joints, dowel bars are the most widely used load-transfer device for expansion joints. Generally an agency employs the same dowel diameter, spacing, and length as for contraction joints.[27] Methods for alinement

[25] Resistances will be at least 300 to 400 lb per sq in. The AASHO specification M90 sets no minimum, but states that the maximum load required to compress an oven-dry specimen to one-half its original thickness must not exceed 1500 lb per sq in.

[26] See Experience in Illinois with Joints in Concrete Pavements, *University of Illinois Engineering Experiment Station Bulletin 365*, December 1947.

[27] New Jersey experience on roads carrying heavy truck traffic was that ¾-in. dowels, even at 10-in. spacing, were unsatisfactory. Serious faulting at joints was reported. Where pumping was severe, many dowels had broken. Causes of failure were repeated stress reversals beyond the elastic limit and corrosion

and support of dowels are nearly alike also. However, at expansion joints a cap generally is placed over the dowel at its free end to provide space for movement into the concrete (see Fig. 8). A number of states permit special load-transfer devices instead of dowels. These are usually patented, although some are special designs of the particular highway agency. In the past, New Jersey tried 2-in. steel channels rather than round dowels. These were abandoned because corrosion of the steel locked the channel into the concrete at the free end of the joint.

Some earlier designs provided edge support for expansion joints through a concrete sill underneath the joint (see Fig. 8). One slab rests directly on the sill; the other is separated from it by a layer of roofing paper or bituminous paint which permits sliding. This practice has been tried and abandoned by some agencies. In New Jersey, for example, faulting of joints up to $3/8$ in. and cracking of the pavement slabs where they left the sills were prevalent. Another substitute for load-transfer devices is a thickened end to each slab like the thickened edge shown in Fig. 4.

Concrete pavements without joints

It has been proposed that all transverse expansion and contraction joints be eliminated from concrete pavements. Crack control will be by heavy continuous steel reinforcing. Careful measurement of slab movements on experimental pavements laid in Indiana in 1938 have shown that 500 to 1000 ft at the ends of long reinforced pavement slabs move on the subgrade, but that central portions of the slabs do not. In most instances these center sections have given excellent performance.[28] It appears that a heavily reinforced continuous pavement, without joints, should perform like these center sections. Experimental sections to test this theory were constructed in New Jersey in 1947, in Illinois in 1947 and 1948, and in California in 1949. Up until late 1950 the pavements had performed very well.[29] One disadvantage of heavily reinforced pavement is its high cost, which for the New

at the joint. Present practice in that state requires $1\frac{1}{4}$-in. dowels at 12-in. centers. The unbonded end and the center section of the dowel are enclosed in a tightly fitting jacket of Monel metal or stainless steel. See Wm. Van Breemen, *Proceeding Highway Research Board,* pp. 77–91 (1948). For a report on Michigan tests on length and size of dowels see Finney and Freemont, *Proceedings Highway Research Board,* pp. 52–63 (1947).

[28] See H. D. Cashell and S. W. Benham, *Public Roads,* April 1950, pp. 1–24. For an earlier report see *Highway Research Board Research Report 3-B* (1945).

[29] See Stanton, Russell and Lindsay, and Van Breeman, *Proceedings Highway Research Board,* pp. 28–80 (1950).

Jersey project was \$1 to \$1.60 per square yard greater than for pavement of conventional design. According to those conducting the tests, more time must elapse before sound conclusions can be drawn.

Undercourses for concrete pavements

In years past, relatively little attention was paid to the soils on which concrete pavements were laid. They were classed as *rigid* pavements that could spread loads over a considerable area of subgrade by beam action. Trouble developed, however, in pavements laid directly over expansive soils. Sometimes water from the fresh concrete would be drawn into the subgrade, and it would swell and disrupt the newly placed pavement. Again, water percolating through joints and cracks of completed pavements would lead to differential expansion of the subgrade, and the pavement would curl upward at the joints and become exceedingly rough.[30]

Today heavy concrete pavements are laid on carefully prepared undercourses. Accepted practice requires a layer of granular base several inches thick over fine-grained soils. Some agencies further upgrade this undercourse with cement or bituminous treatment in its top few inches.[31] For roads subject to less severe conditions, undercourses are often omitted. The Portland Cement Association states that undercourses should be used only where they will correct or counteract an unsatisfactory or unstable soil condition. It recommends them only where pavement damage from frost action, swell and shrinkage of high-volume-change soils, or pumping of fine-grained soils (see below) are anticipated or known to exist. It also finds that the inclusion of an undercourse for the sole purpose of increasing subgrade support is generally uneconomical.[32]

The widespread inclusion of undercourses in concrete-pavement design has resulted mainly from extensive investigation of the "pumping" of concrete paving slabs.[33] Pumping is the ejection of water and sub-

[30] For an excellent reference and extensive bibliography see K. B. Woods, *Journal American Concrete Institute,* January 1950, pp. 329–346.

[31] The California Division of Highways normally places 16 in. of base or carefully selected soil under an 8-in. paving slab. The top 4 in. of the undercourse is cement-treated and covered with a seal of emulsified asphalt. Pavement for the New York Thruway is a 9-in. reinforced-concrete slab on a 12-in. gravel base. The subgrade under the base is compacted to 95% AASHO standard density for a minimum of 27 in. (See *Civil Engineering,* November 1953, pp. 44–46.)

[32] See *Concrete Pavement Design, Portland Cement Association* (1951).

[33] Much of this research was reported by a Highway Research Board com-

grade soil through joints and cracks and along the edges of concrete pavements. It has been found that repeated depression of pavement joints by heavy axle loads is the primary activating element in pumping. Then, where free water is present and the subgrade is fine grained, churning of the water and soil occurs, forming a slurry which is expelled to the surface. As pumping continues, the supporting soil is flushed from under the pavement at the affected locations. Faulting of the joints and finally transverse cracking or breaking of the corners results. The formation of one crack offers new opportunity for pumping action, so that joint faulting and cracking is progressive.

Pumping is seldom found where the paving slab is underlaid by a granular undercourse containing more than 55% retained on the no. 270 sieve and having a plasticity index less than 7. Furthermore, no sure and effective methods for preventing joint movement or for excluding free water from beneath pavement joints, cracks, and edges has been developed. Thus, the use of dense-graded or open-textured granular undercourses seems the most reliable method for preventing pumping. As yet, however, the minimum safe undercourse thickness is unknown.

Road test One-MD [34]

Much knowledge useful in concrete pavement design has come from Road test One-MD conducted in 1950 in Maryland. This cooperative project was supported by 11 state highway departments, the highway department of the District of Columbia, the U. S. Bureau of Public Roads, various truck manufacturers, the petroleum industry, the Department of Defense, and the Highway Research Board, and was supervised by the Highway Research Board. The test section was a 1.1-mile length of U. S. 301, approximately 9 miles south of La Plata, Md. The pavement, constructed in 1941, was of conventional design and in excellent condition at the start of the tests. The cross section was 24 ft wide, of double-parabolic shape with 9–7–9-in. thickness, and was divided at the center by a butt-type longitudinal joint. Expansion joints were ¾ in. wide spaced at 120-ft intervals. Between expansion joints were two contraction joints of the dummy type. Load transfer was provided at all joints by ¾-in. dowels at 15-in. centers. Welded-wire-fabric reinforcement was of no. 2 wire at 6-in. centers lengthwise and 12-in. centers crosswise.

mittee on maintenance of concrete pavements as related to the pumping action of slabs. The final report of this committee which is authoritative was published in *Proceedings Highway Research Board*, pp. 281–310 (1948). The report contains an extensive bibliography. See also Performance of Concrete Pavement on Granular Subbase, *Highway Research Board Bulletin 52* (1952).

[34] See *Highway Research Board Special Report 4* (1952) for a detailed record. *Special Report 14* (1953) covers a supplemental investigation of the structural effects of a heavy-duty trailer on the same pavement.

Concrete cylinders cored from the 9-year-old pavement showed a compressive strength of 6944 lb per sq in. after being soaked for 28 days. Fifteen per cent of the subgrade was granular; the remainder was of fine-grained plastic soils. These latter compared by group-index ratings with the average types of soils found under "pumping" pavements in Illinois, Indiana, North Carolina, and Tennessee. On a grain-size basis, the average of the soils adjacent to the pavement was slightly better than the average of those in the entire state of Maryland.

The test section was divided lengthwise and crosswise to form four distinct units. One of these was subject to accelerated loading by trucks with rear-

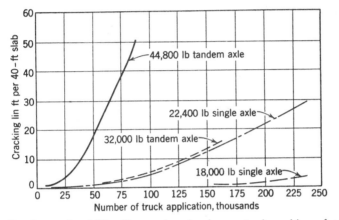

Fig. 9. Road test One-MD. Progressive development of cracking of concrete pavement over A-6 soils

axle loads of 18,000 lb. The section alongside it was loaded with 22,400 lb on single rear axles. The sections at the other end carried 32,000 and 44,800 lb, respectively, on tandem axles. Successive wheel loads were distributed over the lane widths in the manner known to exist on like roads. The trucks operated 24 hr a day, 7 days a week. Elaborate records of crack development, elevation, and deflection at joints and other points on the slabs were kept; and careful determinations of the characteristics of all subgrade soils were made.

Among the findings were the following:

1. There was a definite correlation between soil type and pavement behavior. The higher the granular content and the lower the plasticity of the soil, the better the pavement performed.

2. For these particular test conditions, the destructive effect of increased axle loads is many times greater than the increase in the axle loads themselves. Three evidences of this were:

(a) The 44,800-lb tandem axle loads caused 11 times as much cracking (lineal feet) as the 32,000-lb tandem axle load. Also, the 22,400-lb single-axle load caused approximately six times as much cracking as the 18,000-lb single axle load. The progress of crack development is illustrated in Fig. 9.

(*b*) After 84,000 passes of the tandem trucks, 80% of the joints in the section carrying the 44,800-lb axles were depressed; whereas only 10% of the joints carrying 32,000-lb axles were affected.[35] After 137,000 passes of the single-axle trucks, 22 and 2% of the joints were depressed by heavier and lighter loads, respectively.

(*c*) After 92,000 tandem-truck passes, 96% of the slabs under the heavier truck contained cracks that were analyzed as structural failures. For the lighter tandem truck the percentage was 27. For 238,000 passes of the heavier and lighter single-axle trucks these percentages were 64 and 28, respectively.

3. Variations in joint deflection under load which served as a clue to the stress in the pavement were:

(*a*) Normally much greater at night when the pavement edges were warped upward than in the daytime when the edges were warped downward.

(*b*) Two to three times greater at pumping than nonpumping joints.

(*c*) Larger at pumping expansion joints than at pumping contraction joints.

(*d*) Larger during the period when pumping was receding than at any other time.

MATERIALS FOR CONCRETE PAVEMENTS

The fundamental rules governing the selection of the basic materials—cement, aggregate, and water—must be observed to obtain good concrete for pavements. In addition, the unique properties demanded for pavements as contrasted with those for structures or other engineering works must be recognized. The following paragraphs are devoted to these subjects.[36]

Portland cement

Portland cement is made from combinations of limestone, marl, or other calcareous material and clay, shale, or like agrillaceous substances. These are crushed and pulverized, mixed in carefully determined proportions, and burned to a clinker at 2800° F. Finally the cooled clinker and a small amount of gypsum to control the rate of setting are intimately ground until nearly all passes a no. 200-mesh sieve. The finished product is usually packaged in paper or cloth sacks holding 94 lb, which represents a cubic foot loose measure.[37] How-

---

[35] Depressed joints are those at which marked localized settlement of the pavement has occurred accompanied by cracking of the pavement in the vicinity of the joint.

[36] The fundamentals of concrete-mix design are presented in detail in *Design and Control of Concrete Mixtures,* published by the Portland Cement Association. It has been assumed that students have some acquaintance with this subject, and attention here has been directed mainly to the problems peculiar to concrete for pavements.

[37] Often cement quantities or prices are stated in terms of barrels of 4 sacks each.

ever, cement for large projects frequently is shipped in bulk by rail or ship or in trucks with special bodies.

The AASHO specifications for Portland cement (*AASHO Designations M85–49*) list five types, as follows:

Type I. For general concrete construction when the special properties of the other four types are not required.

Type II. For general concrete construction exposed to moderate sulfate action, or where moderate heat of hydration is required.

Type III. For high early strength.

Type IV. For low heat of hydration.

Type V. For high sulfate resistance.

In addition there are AASHO specifications covering air-entraining and natural cements (*AASHO Designations M134–48* and *M135–49*, respectively). Type I is most commonly specified for pavements, although type II is the choice of a number of agencies. Type III cement is employed by many of the state highway departments when high early strength at particular locations or for earlier opening to traffic is desired. Other agencies gain the same objective by enriching their usual mixes or by adding calcium chloride to the mix. Air-entraining and natural cements are among the means employed for entraining air in concrete. These are discussed further under the topic of air entrainment.

The properties expected in the different types of cements are carefully set out in the specifications of the various highway agencies. Frequently this is done by reference to those prescribed by the AASHO (see *AASHO Designation M85–49*). To meet these specifications, samples must pass a number of chemical and physical tests which can only be conducted in a well-equipped laboratory. The chemical tests constitute, in effect, a chemical analysis to determine whether or not the various strength-giving compounds appear in proper quantity, and if there are excessive amounts of certain undesirable substances. The physical tests include those for fineness,[38] time of set (*AASHO Designation T131–49, ASTM Designation C191–49*), and tensile and compressive strengths of mortars made using Ottawa sand (*AASHO Designations T132–49* and *T106–49, ASTM Designations C190–49* and *C109–49*). Each cement mill operates a complete testing laboratory and maintains close control on its product. Rarely are cements shipped that do not meet specifications.

[38] Formerly fineness of cement was commonly stated in terms of per cent passing the no. 200 sieve (see *AASHO Designation T128–45, ASTM Designation C184–44*). At present the fineness is given as the specific surface in square centimeters per gram, as determined in the Wagner turbidimeter, which measures the rate of settlement through kerosene (*AASHO Designation T98–45, ASTM Designation C115–42*).

Chemically, Portland cement has four principal constituents. These are tricalcium silicate ($3CaO \cdot SiO_2$ abbreviated C_3S), dicalcium silicate ($2CaO \cdot SiO_2$ or C_2S), tricalcium aluminate ($3CaO \cdot Al_2O_3$ or C_3A) and tetracalcium aluminoferrite ($4CaO \cdot Al_2O_3 \cdot Fe_2O_3$ or C_4AF). The proportions of these in typical cements of the five types are shown in Table 2. The rates at which test specimens made with the different cements gain strength also appear in the table. The variations result because the speed of chemical reaction between each compound and water is different. Both tricalcium silicate and tricalcium aluminate hydrate quite rapidly while the others react more slowly. As would be expected, Table 2 shows that high early-strength cement has high per-

TABLE 2. COMPOSITION AND STRENGTH CHARACTERISTICS OF THE VARIOUS TYPES OF PORTLAND CEMENT

Type of Cement	Compound Composition, %				Compressive Strength, % of Strength of Normal Portland-Cement Concrete		
	C_3S	C_2S	C_3A	C_4AF	3 Days	28 Days	3 Months
I—Normal	45	27	11	8	100	100	100
II—Modified	44	31	5	13	80	85	100
III—High early	53	19	10	10	190	130	115
IV—Low heat	28	49	4	12	50	65	90
V—Sulfate resistant	38	43	4	8	65	65	85

centages of the faster-acting compounds. With this rapid gain in strength goes fast liberation of the heat of hydration. An added factor is that the total heat liberated per unit of weight is greater for the faster-acting compounds. Thus, the use of high early-strength cements may under some circumstances produce high temperatures in recently placed concrete.[39] Whether or not this or other properties of high early-strength cements make them unsuitable for pavements is an unsettled question.[40]

Mixing water

Mixing water should be free of acids, alkalies, and oil. Waters containing decayed vegetable matter are to be particularly avoided as they may interfere with the setting of the cement. Generally water that is

[39] In massive structures like large gravity dams, the expansion caused by these high temperatures and the contraction which comes later when the concrete cools cause serious concern. In some cases elaborate cooling systems have been installed to remove this liberated heat. In others a lean mix of low-heat cement has been employed, and the aggregates and mixing water have been precooled to hold temperature rise to a minimum.

[40] See *Journal American Concrete Institute*, May 1951, pp. 729–744, and December 1951, p. 744–4.

suitable for drinking purposes is satisfactory for concrete, with the possible exception of drinking water containing large amounts of sulfates.

Aggregates [41]

Mineral aggregates form about 75% of the volume or roughly 80% of the weight of normal paving concrete. It follows that, if a paving is to be strong, sound, and durable, the aggregates must have like properties. This is of particular importance in areas where winter brings freezing temperatures, snow, and sleet. Under these conditions the concrete is subject to freezing and thawing, the pounding and wear from tire chains, and the action of calcium chloride, salt, or other de-icing or antiskid agents. To make this high quality certain the state highway departments have almost without exception prescribed that aggregates pass appropriate tests for strength, soundness, wear, or combinations of these three. In contrast many of these agencies do not specify like tests for aggregates for bituminous pavements (see p. 468).

Concretes containing granite, limestone, or diabase aggregates have lower coefficients of expansion than those including siliceous aggregates. A problem, still under study, concerns the durability of concretes in which the coefficients of expansion of mortar and aggregates are markedly different.[42]

The maximum permitted size of coarse aggregate for paving concrete is generally 2, 2½, or 3 in. These maximums greatly exceed those for structural concrete, where closely spaced reinforcing steel limits aggregate size. Grading of coarse and fine aggregate is subject to careful control (see below), and the methods for combining them extend this size control to the concrete itself.

Specifications for fine aggregates. The specifications for fine aggregates of most state highway agencies follow fairly closely those proposed by the AASHO (*AASHO Designation M6–48*). A general requirement is that

[41] For an excellent discussion of aggregates and their influence on the properties of concrete see R. F. Blanks, *Transactions American Society of Civil Engineers*, pp. 403–431 (1950). For a summary of the literature on the subject see Bibliography on Mineral Aggregates, *Highway Research Board Bibliography 6* (1949).

[42] The results of one study indicate that there seems to be no relationship between the resistance of concrete to temperature change and the difference in thermal coefficients of aggregate and mortar. However, it was found that concretes with higher coefficients of expansion were less resistant under temperature change. (See Walker, Bloem, and Mullen, *Journal American Concrete Institute*, April 1952, pp. 661–679.

fine aggregates shall consist of natural sand or, subject to approval, other inert materials with similar characteristics, or combinations thereof, having strong, hard durable particles. It is usual to reinforce this requirement by placing maximum limits on the amounts of deleterious substances. Recommended and maximum permissible limits proposed by the AASHO appear in Table 3.

TABLE 3. AMOUNTS OF DELETERIOUS MATERIALS PERMITTED IN FINE AGGREGATES FOR CONCRETE

Substance	Recommended Permissible Limits, % by Wt.	Maximum Permissible Limits, % by Wt.
Clay lumps	0.5	1.0
Coal and lignite	0.25	1.0
Materials passing no. 200 sieve		
In concrete subject to surface abrasion	2	4
In all other classes of concrete	3	5
Other deleterious substances such as shale, alkali, mica, coated grains, soft and flaky particles		To be specified

Based on AASHO specifications for highway materials.

Little uniformity in these requirements appears among the different road-building agencies.

As mentioned, the presence of organic impurities may prevent hardening of cement. The standard test (*AASHO Designation T21–42, ASTM Designation C40–33*) requires that a sample of sand be mixed with a sodium hydroxide solution which turns dark when organic material is present. Approval of sands failing this test rests on satisfactory strength of cement-sand compressive specimens (see below).

Fine-aggregate grading, by weight, as recommended by the AASHO is as follows:

Per cent passing ⅜-in. sieve	100
Per cent passing no. 4 sieve	95–100
Per cent passing no. 16 sieve	45–80
Per cent passing no. 50 sieve	10–30
Per cent passing no. 100 sieve	2–10

Gradings generally like the above are specified by the various highway departments. Some permit a wider variation in the percentages; others have closed these limits somewhat and, in some cases, have interposed additional sieves into the group. Many engineers believe that a "per cent passing" specification alone does not assure uniformity of the fine aggregates, since sands ranging from coarse to fine all will fall within the usual grading limits. To prevent these fluctuations the AASHO specifications and those of about half the states also require that the "fineness modulus" [43] of the sand from a given source

[43] To determine the fineness modulus, add the total percentages by weight retained on the 3-in., 1½-in., ¾-in., ⅜-in., no. 4, no. 8, no. 16, no. 30, no. 50, and no. 100 sieves, and divide this sum by 100.

remain relatively constant. The usual permitted variation is 0.2 either way from the fineness modulus of an original representative sample.

The strength of fine aggregates is measured by compression or tension tests of sand-cement mortars. The AASHO specifications set the minimum compressive strength of specimens containing the aggregate under test at 90% of the strength of those made with the same cement and graded Ottawa sand.[44] Test specimens may be either 2-in. cubes or cylinders of 2-in. diameter and 4-in. height.[45] All states specify tests for fine aggregates but only a few have requirements identical with those set out by the AASHO. Some change the 90% relationship upward or downward by as much as 10%. Others make the control specimens of standard rather than graded Ottawa sand. Another group substitutes a comparative tensile test with the control specimen made of Ottawa sand. Still others employ both compressive and tensile tests.[46]

Soundness of fine aggregates is measured by their resistance to deterioration under the action of solutions of sodium or magnesium sulfate or under freezing and thawing.[47] Specifications of the AASHO and of a number of highway departments favor a 5-cycle sodium sulfate test. Several others substitute magnesium sulfate as the agent or permit the use of either. The Illinois specifications (1952) require that fine aggregates for concrete lose no more than 10% by weight under 5 cycles of sodium sulfate, but will accept materials that fail this test, providing they lose less than 10% under 50 cycles of freezing and thawing. The AASHO specifications are the same, but leave the choice of percentage loss and number of cycles to the discretion of each agency.

Specifications for coarse aggregates. The various state specifications for coarse aggregates follow the pattern proposed by the AASHO (*AASHO Designation M80–49*). The general requirement is that coarse aggregates consist of crushed stone, gravel, blast-furnace slag, or other approved inert materials of similar characteristics, or combinations thereof, having hard, strong, durable pieces free from adherent coatings. Limits to the amounts of deleterious materials, based on AASHO recommendations, appear in Table 4. Few of the individual specifications conform exactly to the limits shown. However, they do outline the pattern of current practice. Some states are forced to accept higher percentages of certain objectionable materials because they are present in all local deposits and it is not economical to import aggregates from distant sources.

Coarse-aggregate gradings for concrete, as recommended by the AASHO, are shown in Table 5. Size numbers 467 (1½ in. to no. 4) and 357 (2 in. to no. 4) are representative of gradings suitable for paving concrete. Gradings often are stated separately for two size ranges, coarse and fine. Aggregates of size no. 3 (2 in. to 1 in.) and no. 57 (1 in. to no. 4) would be combined to produce the desired grading of 2-in. to no. 4 aggregate. Size nos. 4 and 67

[44] Ottawa sand is a natural silica sand of great uniformity from Ottawa, Ill. It is widely used for testing purposes.

[45] See *AASHO Designation T71–48, ASTM Designation C87–47* for details of the test method.

[46] These tensile tests are patterned after that of *AASHO Designation T132–49, ASTM Designation C190–49*.

[47] See pp. 467–468 for descriptions of these tests.

TABLE 4. AMOUNTS OF DELETERIOUS MATERIALS PERMITTED IN COARSE
AGGREGATES FOR CONCRETE

Substance	Recommended Permissible Limits, % by Wt.	Maximum Permissible Limits, % by Wt.
Soft fragments	2	5
Coal and lignite	0.25	1
Clay lumps	0.25	0.25
Material passing no. 200 sieve	0.5	1.0
Thin or elongated pieces (length greater than 5 times average thickness)	....	15
Other local deleterious substances	....	To be specified

Based on AASHO specifications for highway materials.

likewise can be combined, with the separation between them on the ¾-in. sieve. The trend is toward separating coarse aggregates into two sizes, and a majority of the states now follow that practice. The gradings of Table 5 conform generally to present state highway department requirements.

TABLE 5. GRADING OF COARSE AGGREGATES FOR CONCRETE

From *AASHO Designation M80–49*

Range in Size	Size Number *	Percentage by Weight Passing Laboratory Sieves Having Square Openings							
		2½	2	1½	1	¾	½	⅜	No. 4
½ in. to no. 4	7	...	......	......	......	100	90–100	40–70	0–15 †
¾ in. to no. 4	67	...	......	......	100	95–100	......	20–55	0–10 †
1 in. to no. 4	57	...	......	100	95–100	......	25–60	.....	0–10 †
1½ in. to no. 4	467	...	100	95–100	......	35–70	......	10–30	0–5
2 in. to no. 4	357	100	95–100	......	35–70	......	10–30	.....	0–5
1½ in. to ¾ in.	4	...	100	90–100	20–55	0–15	......	0–5	.....
2 in. to 1 in.	3	100	95–100	35–70	0–15	......	0–5	.....	.....

* Based on Standard Sizes of Coarse Aggregate for Highway Construction (*AASHO Designation M43–49*).
† Not more than 5% shall pass a no. 8 sieve.

A test to measure the abrasion resistance of coarse aggregates for pavements is required by every state. The Los Angeles rattler test, prescribed by the AASHO specifications, is most common and represents the procedure of a large majority.[48] The AASHO recommends a maximum percentage of wear of 40, which is typical of current practice. However, one state permits a percentage as high as 65, and several accept a maximum of 50. The Deval test, modified in some instances, is the measure of the remaining states. Percentages of wear of 6 for stone and 15 for gravel are representative. Tests for soundness of coarse aggregates for concrete pavements are required by most of the states.

[48] See p. 467 for brief descriptions of this test, the Deval test, and the soundness tests mentioned below.

Sodium sulfate is the most common test medium. Some use magnesium sulfate as the agent or permit it as a substitute for sodium sulfate. The AASHO specifications, which allow either agent, limit the loss after 5 test cycles to 12% when sodium sulfate is employed. Several states substitute the freezing and thawing test for the sulfate test, or use it as a supplement. A typical limit for the freezing and thawing test is 15% loss after 50 cycles.

Alkali-aggregate reaction. Alkali-aggregate reaction in concrete results when aggregates containing certain silicate or silica minerals are combined with cements containing alkali. As times passes, a gel forms around the affected aggregate particles, and the concrete expands and loses strength. In concrete pavements, surface cracking and blow-ups result.

Alkali-aggregate reaction was first reported by T. E. Stanton, after an investigation of the failure of a year-old section of concrete pavement near Salinas, Calif., in 1938.[49] Since then deterioration of concrete from this cause has been found in numerous localities, including several western and plains states and certain areas in the South.

Intensive research has been done and will continue on all phases of the alkali-aggregate reaction problem.[50] As a practical means of preventing it, agencies employing doubtful aggregates specify that all cement be of low-alkali content. The usual requirement is that the total sodium and potassium oxide [51] (expressed as Na_2O) not exceed 0.6%.

Air entrainment.[52]

Air entrainment is the entrapment of air in concrete in the form of well-distributed, minute bubbles. It was first employed to increase

[49] See *Transactions American Society of Civil Engineers,* pp. 54–126 (1942).

[50] See for example R. F. Blanks, *Transactions American Society of Civil Engineers,* pp. 416–420 (1950). Further references will be found in the bibliography that accompanies this article.

[51] Tests by the Bureau of Public Roads (see D. O. Woolf, *Public Roads,* August 1952, pp. 50–56) indicate that excessive expansion can occur when low-alkali cements are combined with small amounts of reactive material. Little expansion was found when the same cements were combined with highly reactive aggregates. It was concluded that "Tests should be made using the cement, the aggregates, and the admixture, if any, which are considered for use in proposed construction. Only by the preparation and testing of concrete as it will be used can information on stability of the material be obtained."

[52] For a general discussion of air entrainment, see Blanks and Condon, *Journal American Concrete Institute,* February 1949, pp. 469–487. Another excellent publication, which includes specifications for air-entraining Portland cement, descriptions of the tests to determine the percentage of entrained air, and an

the resistance of concrete pavements to alternate freezing and thawing and to the surface scaling caused by de-icing with calcium or
sodium chloride. Other advantages like improved workability and
reduced bleeding in fresh concrete have led to widespread use of air
entrainment in both pavements and structures in nonfrost areas. Air
entrainment also permits surface finishing soon after the concrete is
placed, an important advantage from an efficiency and cost standpoint.

Air may be entrained in concrete with an air-entraining admixture
added to the batch at the time of mixing, or by employing an air-
entraining Portland cement. Numerous commercial air-entraining
admixtures are available. They may be tested for suitability under
ASTM Designation C260–50T. Three types of air-entraining cements
are manufactured under *ASTM Designation C175–51T, AASHO
Designation M134–51*. These are types IA, IIA, and IIIA, corresponding to the comparable types in the specifications for non-air-entraining
cement.[53]

The use of an air-entraining Portland cement avoids the need for an
automatic dispensing device or the services of another workman with
the ever-present chance of error. On the other hand, the practice of
adding the air-entraining admixture at the mixer permits closer control over the air content of the mix. With this procedure the amount
of agent can be varied to recognize the factors that influence air content, which include type and gradation of aggregates, type of mixer,
mixing time, consistency of the concrete, and temperature. Opinion is
divided over which method is better.

A reasonable working range for air content appears to be 3 to 6% by
volume. Four to five per cent seems to give satisfactory improvement
to durability without serious loss of strength.[54]

extensive bibliography is Use of Air Entrained Concrete in Pavements and
Bridges, *Highway Research Board Current Road Problems 13-R*, May 1950.

[53] In specifications for air-entraining cement neither the type nor amount of
agent to be interground is specified. The manufacturer may use any material
that meets *ASTM Designation C226–51T, AASHO Designation M149–51*. However, it is required that the amount of air entrained in a standard mortar equal
$18 \pm 3\%$ (see *ASTM Designation C185–49T* or *AASHO Designation T137–49* for
detailed test procedure).

[54] These data are from *Highway Research Board Current Road Problems 13-R*.
F. H. Jackson of the U. S. Bureau of Public Roads (see *Journal American Concrete Institute*, May 1952, pp. 735–740) recommends an air content of 6% when
frost and salt action are severe. He also suggests protection of the surface by
an application of a light distillate oil. For a theoretical analysis of the air requirements of frost-resistant concrete see paper by T. C. Powers and discussion
by T. F. Willis, *Proceedings Highway Research Board*, pp. 184–211 (1949). For

Many of the states, particularly in the North, specify air-entrained concrete for pavements. Some prefer admixtures; others employ air-entraining cements. A number permit either method.

PROPORTIONING CONCRETE FOR PAVEMENTS

Principles of mix design

Water-cement ratio. For a given combination of materials, the strength and other desirable properties of concrete mixtures vary almost directly with the ratio of cement to mixing water. This idea, developed about 1920 by Duff Abrams, is basic to proper concrete design. It says, in effect, that, for mixes of reasonable proportions and workability, the quality depends on the richness of the cement-water paste. To illustrate, a concrete with a water-cement ratio of 5 gal of water per sack of cement will have a compressive strength in 28 days of about 5000 lb per sq in. Another, with a water-cement ratio of 7 gal per sack but like the first in other respects, will develop a 28-day strength of only 3300 lb per sq in. Durability also is dependent on the water-cement ratio and places a second control on the richness of the paste. In consideration of these factors, the AASHO specifications for concrete pavement construction set the maximum water content at 6 gal per sack of cement. Many state highway departments specify similar maximum water-cement ratios, and the remainder impose like controls by carefully specifying the amounts of cement, aggregate, and water.

Consistency. A concrete mix must be workable enough that it can be placed in the most inaccessible parts of the forms. On the other hand, it must not be so wet that aggregates and mortar will separate. Thus, for each class of concrete work there is a range of consistency that is most suitable. For pavements, where the slab is thin and the concrete can be thoroughly manipulated from the surface, a relatively stiff mix is best. The "slump" usually specified for machine-placed pavements is 2 to 3 in., and that for machine-placed and vibrated pavements [55] 1 to 1½ in.

a report on the performance of pavements of air-entrained concrete see L. E. Andrews in *Highway Research Board Bulletin 70* (1953).

[55] The slump test (*AASHO Designation T119-42, ASTM Designation C143-39*) is most widely used for determining the consistency of concrete. A truncated cone of sheet metal, 12 in. high with base and top diameters 8 and 4 in., respectively, is filled in three layers with fresh concrete. Each layer is rodded 25 times. Then the cone is lifted off vertically, permitting the concrete to subside. The slump is the distance in inches that the top of the specimen falls.

Proportioning aggregates. It is helpful to picture concrete as a mixture of coarse and fine aggregates made workable by the addition of cement-water paste. Economy demands that there be only enough paste to fill the voids in the aggregate and to provide lubrication. Four means for reducing the amount of paste are:

1. Permit the largest-size aggregate that can be accommodated.
2. Make sure the aggregate is properly graded from coarse to fine.
3. Use the smallest percentage of sand consistent with proper workability.
4. Demand the minimum lubrication (lowest slump) consistent with proper placing and finishing.

Methods for mix design

Fixed-cement-factor method. The cement factor is the number of sacks (or barrels) of cement in a cubic yard of concrete. A mix of fixed cement factor, then, must produce a prescribed volume of concrete per sack of cement. Furthermore, the concrete must be workable, and the slump must be within specified limits. Mix design involves finding that combination of cement, aggregates, and water that meets these requirements with the lowest reasonable water-cement ratio. Actual design is usually by the "trial-batch" method. A mixture in proportions that have proved satisfactory on previous work is made in the laboratory. Succeeding batches are of slightly different composition until the mix is found that gives the desired cement content and workability with a minimum of water. Specimens for proving the strength are prepared from the trial batch. It is common practice to permit minor alterations in the proportions during construction if they are necessary to secure proper workability. Table 6 shows trial mixes suggested by the American Concrete Institute.[56] The weight of sand should be adjusted downward and that of coarse aggregate a like amount upward from the tabulated values if the fineness modulus of the sand is less than 2.75. If the fineness modulus of the sand is greater than 2.75 the above procedure should be reversed.

Three-fourths of the state highway departments specify a definite cement factor and slump, with cement contents ranging from 5 to something over 6 sacks per cubic yard. Some do not make trial-mix designs for each project. Rather they prescribe the weights of each

---

[56] Suggested proportions from the AASHO specifications for concrete pavements are almost identical.

component of the mix in the standard specifications, but permit limited job changes to meet particular conditions.

Some engineers argue that the fixed-cement-factor method is wasteful, as generally the strengths obtained are considerably above the usual permitted minimums. Those who favor it declare that it provides a highly desirable factor of safety at small added cost. They further contend that it makes proportioning easier and simplifies payment to contractors.

Calculation of the cement factor for concrete mixes is by the method of "absolute volumes." The space occupied by each ingredient is found by dividing its weight by the product of specific gravity times 62.4, the weight of a cubic foot of water. For the first mix shown in Table 6, the calculations are given in Table 7.

Concrete-mix proportions are given in terms of saturated, surface-dry aggregates, the condition that exists when all the interstices of the individual particles are filled with water but their surfaces are dry. Aggregates, as used, will be wetter or drier than this theoretical state, and job adjustments from the saturated surface-dry proportions are always required. The free water in sands as delivered to the job site normally ranges from 2 to 6% by weight, but may reach 8% or more if the sand is extremely wet. Coarse aggregates seldom contain over 2% of free water by weight. If, on the other hand, the aggregates are air-dry, they will absorb up to 1% of their weight of water before reaching a saturated, surface-dry condition. Dry aggregates that are extremely porous will, of course, absorb several times this amount of water.

Water-cement ratio method. Mix design by the water-cement ratio method starts with requirements for strength and slump. Trial batches and test specimens from them are made with the cement and aggregates that will be employed on the work. The objective is to find the combination that will use a minimum of cement and still provide the prescribed strength and consistency. Previous experience with the same materials offers the best guide for the proportions of the first trial mix. Otherwise a beginning can be made from the suggestions given in Table 6. Secondary controls are the minimum number of sacks of cement per cubic yard and the maximum water-cement ratio for durability requirements.

Tests for flexural strength (modulus of rupture) rather than for compressive strength are the most widely used measures of the quality of paving concrete. They are not standardized among agencies, but that of the AASHO is typical. Specimens are usually 6 in. square in cross section and 21 in. long. Actual span length is set at three times the depth. Symmetrical loading is applied at the third points. Flexural strength is computed by the formula for stress in the extreme fibers of

TABLE 6. PAVING-CONCRETE PROPORTIONS, BASED ON A FIXED CEMENT
CONTENT AND SPECIFIED SLUMP

| | | | | | | Pounds of Aggregates per 94-Lb Bag of Cement ‖ | | |
| Type of Concrete * | Method of Placing | Type of Coarse Aggregate † | Range in Slump, In. | Cement, Bags per Cu Yd ‡ | Water, Gal per Bag | Fine Aggregate § | Coarse Aggregates | |
							Small	Large
Plain	Machine	Gravel	2–3	6.0	5.0	175	140	215
Plain	Machine	Crushed stone	2–3	6.0	5.6	200	130	200
Plain	Machine	Slag	2–3	6.0	5.9	210	110	160
Plain	Vibrated	Gravel	1–1½	5.5	5.0	175	170	255
Plain	Vibrated	Crushed stone	1–1½	5.5	5.6	200	160	240
Plain	Vibrated	Slag	1–1½	5.5	5.9	210	130	200
Air-entrained	Machine	Gravel	2–3	6.0	4.5	155	140	215
Air-entrained	Machine	Crushed stone	2–3	6.0	5.1	180	130	200
Air-entrained	Machine	Slag	2–3	6.0	5.3	190	110	160
Air-entrained	Vibrated	Gravel	1–1½	5.5	4.5	155	170	255
Air-entrained	Vibrated	Crushed stone	1–1½	5.5	5.1	180	160	240
Air-entrained	Vibrated	Slag	1–1½	5.5	5.1	190	130	200

Specification Requirements / Quantities of Materials to Be Used for Proportioning Trial Batches

From *Standard Specifications for Concrete Pavements and Bases*, American Concrete Institute (1951).
Aggregate weights are based on assumed bulk specific gravity of 2.65 for sand, gravel and crushed stone and 2.25 for slag, all in saturated, surface-dry condition. For aggregates having other specific gravities, the desired weights equal tabulated weights of respective materials, divided by the assumed specific gravities multiplied by the actual specific gravities of the materials to be used.

* Air content is assumed as 1% for plain mixes and 4% for air-entraining mixes.

† Coarse aggregates are 1½ in.–no. 4 or 2 in.–no. 4 and graded approximately 40% small and 60% large separated on the ¾ in. or 1 in. sieve, respectively.

‡ Compliance with this requirement shall be determined by means of a yield test made in accordance with ASTM standard method C138. If the cement content calculated from this test varies from the designated cement content by more than 2%, the total weight of aggregate per bag of cement shall be adjusted as necessary to bring the cement content within the specified limits.

§ Fine aggregate proportions are based on the use of well-graded natural sand of 2.75 fineness modulus.

‖ If the aggregates contain more water than required for saturation, the aggregate weights should be increased by the weight of surface water present; if they contain less water than required for saturation, the weights should be decreased by the amount in weight of water necessary to attain saturation of aggregate. Free water on aggregates should be accounted as a part of the mixing water.

TABLE 7. CALCULATION OF CEMENT FACTOR FOR CONCRETE MIXES

Material	Amount Used	Specific Gravity	Absolute Volume, Cu Ft
Cement	1 sack— 94 lb	3.15 *	$\dfrac{94}{3.15 \times 62.4} = 0.48$
Water	5 gal †— 42 lb	1	$\dfrac{42}{1 \times 62.4} = 0.67$
Fine aggregate	175 lb	2.65 ‡	$\dfrac{175}{2.65 \times 62.4} = 1.06$
Coarse aggregate			
Small	140 lb	2.65 ‡	$\dfrac{140}{2.65 \times 62.4} = 0.85$
Large	215 lb	2.65 ‡	$\dfrac{215}{2.65 \times 62.4} = 1.30$
			4.36
Entrained air	1%		$0.01 \times 4.36 = 0.04$
Total weight	666 lb		Absolute volume 4.40

Factors	Air-Free Value	Value Considering Air
Yield, cu ft concrete per sack of cement	4.36	4.40
Weight of concrete, lb per cu ft	$\dfrac{666}{4.36} = 153$	$\dfrac{666}{4.40} = 151$
Cement factor, sacks per cu yd	$\dfrac{27}{4.36} = 6.2$	$\dfrac{27}{4.40} = 6.1$ §

* See *AASHO Designation T133–45, ASTM Designation C188–44*, for laboratory test to determine the specific gravity of cement.

† A gallon of water weighs 8.33 lb.

‡ See *AASHO Designation T84–45, ASTM Designation C128–42*, and *AASHO Designation T85–45, ASTM Designation C127–42*, for tests for specific gravity and absorption of fine and coarse aggregates.

§ The cement factor of 6.1 does not agree exactly with the 6.0 shown in Table 6. However, the difference is no greater than the 2% variation normally permitted.

a rectangular beam. Where failure occurs within the middle third, this becomes

$$R = \frac{Pl}{bd^2}$$

where R is the modulus of rupture in pounds per square inch, P is the total applied load, and l, b, and d are, respectively, span length, beam width, and beam depth, all in inches. The flexural test is particularly well suited for field use, since the testing device is relatively small and light.[57]

The AASHO specifications for concrete pavement construction recommend the water-cement ratio design method. Pertinent statements from them are:

> The proportioning shall be based on laboratory tests and shall be such that they will produce durable concrete of satisfactory plasticity and workability and which will attain at the age of 14 days a modulus of rupture not less than 550 lb per square inch, using a Portland cement which is found to produce the lowest strength concrete of any acceptable cement available for the work. The minimum cement content shall not be less than 5.0 sacks per cubic yard of concrete and the maximum effective water content shall not exceed 6.0 gallons per sack of cement.

Representative of a state highway design method is that for Illinois. It requires that a laboratory trial mix develop a 14-day flexural strength of 650 lb per sq in. and a 14-day compressive strength of 3500 lb per sq in.

Other mix-design methods. Some agencies use the mortar-void ratio method of mix design. This is based on fundamental relationships between the strength of concrete and the *cement-space ratio*. The latter is the ratio between the absolute volume of cement and the space in the mortar occupied by cement, water, and air. Mixtures with constant cement-space ratios have about equal strengths. Using these principles, it is possible to proportion mixes of assigned strengths from a variety of aggregates.[58]

The void content of the coarse aggregate furnishes the starting point for another method of mix design. Enough mortar of required strength is added to the coarse aggregate to fill the voids and to provide lubrication. The practice of the New Jersey Highway Department calls for a mortar volume 10% greater than the loose void content of the coarse aggregates.

Design of air-entrained concrete.[59] For properly designed concrete of fixed cement factor, each per cent increase in the volume of

[57] For details of this test see *AASHO Designation T126–49* and *T97–49*, *ASTM Designations C192–49* and *C78–49*.

[58] For a more detailed discussion of this method and for references see Hewes, *American Highway Practice*, John Wiley & Sons, vol. II, pp. 244–266 (1942).

[59] See *Highway Research Board Current Road Problems 13-R*, for further discussion and an extensive bibliography.

entrained air decreases the flexural strength by 2 to 3% and the compressive strength by 3 to 4%. Thus an air-entrained concrete containing 6% air will develop flexural and compressive strengths, respectively, lower by about 12 and 18%, compared to a plain concrete with 1% entrained air and the same cement factor. These reductions can be expected after all favorable adjustments in the mix have been considered. If the improvements in durability and uniformity brought by air entrainment make the reduced strength acceptable, no change in cement factor will be required. Otherwise, the mix must be enriched, but seldom beyond 7 sacks per cubic yard.

Suggested trial mixes for air-entrained concrete of fixed cement factor appear in Table 6. Changes from plain concrete for most cases are decreases of 0.5 gal of water and 20 lb of sand per sack of cement. The entrained air, in minute particles, takes the space formerly occupied by the water and sand and provides about the same lubrication.

Several factors other than the air-entraining agent influence the percentage of entrained air and must be recognized in mix design and in subsequent field control. Each of the factors and its influence appears in Table 8.

TABLE 8. FACTORS, OTHER THAN AIR-ENTRAINING AGENT, THAT INFLUENCE AIR ENTRAINMENT

Factor	Usual Effect on Air Entrainment
Amount of sand	Increasing the amount of sand will increase the amount of air.
Richness of mix	Rich mixes entrain less air than lean mixes.
Consistency of mix	Wet mixes entrain more air than dry, stiff mixes. Air content increases with slump up to about 7 in., but with further increases in slump it decreases rapidly.
Type of mixing	Machine 'mixing will entrain more air than hand mixing. Different mixers may entrain different amount of air.
Length of mixing time	During initial mixing period, entrained air increases. Extending mixing beyond a point producing the maximum air content causes a reduction in entrained air.
Temperature of concrete	Amount of air entrained decreases as temperature of concrete increases.

The gravimetric method for determining yield, cement factor, and air content of the trial mix is specified by the AASHO (see *AASHO Designation T121–45, ASTM Designation C138–44*). First the actual density of the concrete in pounds per cubic foot is determined by filling and weighing a calibrated measure of ½ or 1 cu ft capacity. Also the absolute volume of a one-sack air-free batch and the air-free weight per cubic foot are computed, as shown in Table 7. The desired factors are determined as follows:

$$\text{Yield in cubic feet per sack} = \frac{\text{total weight of all ingredients per sack of cement}}{\text{weight of concrete per cubic foot, as measured}}$$

$$\left\{\begin{array}{l}\text{Cement factor in sacks per} \\ \text{cubic yard}\end{array}\right\} = \frac{27}{\text{yield}}$$

$$\text{Per cent air by volume} = \frac{\left\{\begin{array}{l}(\text{weight per cubic foot, air-free}) - (\text{weight} \\ \text{per cubic foot, as measured})\end{array}\right\}}{\text{weight per cubic foot, air-free}}$$

Other laboratory or field procedures for determining the air content of freshly mixed concrete are as follows:

> Pressure method—*ASTM Designation C231–49T.*
> Volumetric method—*ASTM Designation C173–42T.*
> Rolling method.
> Hook-gage method.

Each of these is used by one or more state highway departments, the pressure method being by far the most common. Details of all five are presented in *Current Road Problems 13-R,* pages 40–62.

CONCRETE PAVEMENT CONSTRUCTION

Concrete pavement is constructed with highly specialized mechanical equipment operated by skilled workmen. Some parts of the procedure must be done with hand tools, but their number is steadily decreasing. The entire operation is carefully organized, with each workman assigned definite tasks and responsibilities. Inspection by the field engineer and his assistants is exacting. The result of these efforts is a finished pavement of uniform high quality and excellent smoothness. An over-all view of concrete-pavement construction on a prepared subgrade is shown as Fig. 10 . In this one photograph are shown almost all of the equipment and most of the workmen needed to place more than 2000 ft of pavement 12 ft wide per shift.

Methods and standards for the proper construction of subgrades and undercourses have already been presented. The discussion that follows deals with placing, finishing, and curing the paving slab.

Fɪɢ. 10. Over-all view of concrete pavement construction on western extension of the Pennsylvania Turnpike (Courtesy *Constructioneer*)

Side forms

Almost universally, concrete-paving slabs are constructed between side forms, sometimes called headers [60] (see Fig. 11). Heavy wooden planks were used first. With the advent of finishing machines that travel on the side forms there was need for greater strength and durability, and steel forms were developed. Today, with but few exceptions, metal forms are specified except where sharp curvature of other special conditions make them impractical.[61] Steel forms have a "channel" cross section with a broad flange at the base. The outer edge of the top flange has been turned down to provide added rigidity. In addition, the section is stiffened at intervals. Provision is made for steel stakes to pass through the form into the subgrade, and stake and header are fastened tightly together by steel wedges that can be tightened or loosened with a few blows with a hammer. Individual sections are

[60] Techniques and machinery that eliminate the need of side forms in widening existing concrete pavements have been developed in Illinois. See *Engineering News-Record*, April 17, 1952, pp. 59–61.

[61] A few states, mainly those where lumbering is a major industry, permit contractors the option between steel and wooden side forms. The remainder require that side forms be of metal.

commonly 10 ft long and are keyed together by a sliding steel tongue.

Side forms are set carefully to line and grade on a prepared base, the steel stakes are driven, and forms and stakes locked together. The AASHO specifications require that "the earth under the base of the form shall be thoroughly tamped, both inside and outside, either by

FIG. 11.   Installation of side forms for concrete pavement (Courtesy Portland Cement Association)

hand or mechanically." They also suggest that "in exceptional cases the engineer may require that suitable stakes be driven to the grade of the bottom of the forms to afford additional firmness."

Some agencies place two lanes of pavement at once; others place them one at a time. In the latter case, the distance between side forms is only 11 or 12 ft. After one lane is poured, the edge of the completed section serves as a form for the adjacent slab. Pouring the second or subsequent strips must wait until the concrete develops strength enough to support subgrading and finishing equipment. Often a flat steel bar is laid on the concrete as a track. This distributes the heavy wheel loads of the machines, thus permitting earlier placing of adjacent lanes.

Final subgrade preparation

After the side forms are set, the subgrade between them is dressed to close tolerances. Originally this was done by hand-labor methods. Today the operation is largely mechanized. One of several available machines is shown in Fig. 12. Here the subgrader is self-propelled by

Fig. 12. Self-propelling subgrading machine in operation in Indiana (Courtesy Portland Cement Association)

cables fastened to the forms. The machine shapes the subgrade and by a conveyor system deposits the excess material outside the forms.[62] The subgrader is followed by a roller which recompacts the surface. Finally a "subgrade planer," a steel template shaped to the exact cross section, is dragged along to knock off any remaining high spots. Some agencies make this final check with a "scratch template" which has teeth projecting to the subgrade level.

At times, job conditions require that the concrete mixer and the trucks that serve it travel within the strip being paved. In this case,

[62] The AASHO specifications for concrete pavement construction require that this machine shall weigh not less than 1800 lb for a 20-ft width of pavement and shall have such strength and rigidity that under test made by changing the support from the wheels to the center it will not develop a deflection of more than ⅛ in.

some agencies require that final trimming of the subgrade follow the passage of the concrete mixer.

Where the design calls for assembled joints and dowels or other load-transfer devices, a crew placing them follows the subgrading operation. Extreme care in placing and alining them is a must. A typical joint assembly, ready for concreting, appears as Fig. 13.

Fig. 13. A typical expansion joint assembly ready for concreting (Courtesy Portland Cement Association)

Before concrete is placed, the subgrade should be carefully moistened to prevent absorption of water from the concrete. Regarding this operation, the AASHO specifications state that:

The subgrade shall be moist but not muddy at the time of placing concrete. If required by the engineer, it shall be saturated with water the previous night or not less than six hours previous to the placing of concrete. If it subsequently becomes too dry, the subgrade shall be sprinkled, but the method of sprinkling shall not be such as to form mud or pools of water.

A few highway agencies specify that subgrade paper (*AASHO Designation M74–49*) separate subgrade and concrete. Its principal function is to prevent the passage of water from the concrete into highly absorptive soils.

Proportioning paving concrete

Materials for paving concrete are carefully proportioned at a "batching plant" set up at the aggregate source, a convenient railroad siding, or some other carefully selected location. Figure 14 shows a typical

(a) Aggregate storage bins and twin weighing batcher

(b) Bulk cement bin and twin cement batcher

Fig. 14. Portable plant for batching aggregates and cement for concrete pavement construction (Courtesy Blaw-Knox Co.)

installation. Batching plants usually consist of a group of elevated aggregate bins equipped with a weigh box and multiple-beam scales for weighing the aggregates. Commonly the installation includes a separate silo and scales for storing and weighing bulk cement. Dump trucks with beds divided into units holding a single batch haul the proportioned materials from plant to mixer.

Most specifications have exacting requirements for batching plants. For example, the AASHO specifications for concrete pavements read in part as follows:

Unless otherwise permitted by the engineer, the batching plant shall include batcher bins, either of the stationary or mobile type, with adequate separate compartments for fine aggregate and for each required "separate size" of coarse aggregate, each compartment designed to discharge efficiently and freely into the weighing hopper or hoppers. Means of control shall be provided in each case so that, when the quantity desired in the weighing hopper is being approached, the material may be added slowly in small quantities and shut off with precision. Means of removing an overload of any one of the several materials shall be provided. . . . . Hoppers shall be constructed so as to eliminate accumulations of tare materials and to fully discharge without jarring the scales. Partitions between bins and hoppers shall be ample to prevent spilling under any working conditions.

The scales for weighing aggregates and cement may be either the horizontal beam or the springless dial type, designed as an integral unit of the batching plant, of rugged construction to withstand hard usage due to working conditions, with a maximum allowable error of one-half of one per cent of net load and with significant graduation down to two pounds.

Careful handling of coarse aggregates at the batching plant is essential if uniform grading is to be maintained. If, for example, aggregates are heaped into a single large cone-shaped pile, the larger and smaller sizes will separate. Many of the states avoid this by requiring that stockpiles of coarse aggregate be placed in lifts (ranging from 2 to 4 ft in height). Likewise, a uniform moisture content in the aggregates, particularly in the sand, is highly desirable as it makes for closer control over the consistency of the concrete. All but a few states specify a definite procedure to accomplish this end. The most common is to stockpile the aggregates for a period, usually 12 to 24 hr, which permits free water to drain out. Others require that materials brought by railroad drain in the cars for a period before use.

Care must be exercised not to lose bulk cement from the batch trucks. The usual operation places the cement in the truck between layers of aggregate. If the cement is placed on top of the load, it must be covered with a tarpaulin. Batches combining cement with moist aggregate must be used within a few hours; otherwise the cement will harden in the truck.

Mixing and placing paving concrete

Generally paving concrete is mixed in large crawler-mounted machines that produce a cubic yard or more of concrete per batch [63] (see Fig. 10). Many of these are of the "single-drum" type, with all mixing accomplished in a single horizontal cylinder. More recently, dual mixers with two drums end to end have been developed. Partial

[63] Paving mixers are rated by the cubic feet of mixed concrete they will produce. For example, a 27E single-drum paver is designed to mix a cubic yard of concrete at a time, although the AASHO specifications permit overloads up to 10%. The 34E is a common model of dual-drum mixer. The symbol "E" designates end discharge, as contrasted with "S" for side discharge.

mixing in one drum is followed by transfer to and final mixing in the second. In this manner, the one mixer handles two batches at a time. A mixer is loaded by backing a batch truck into the large "skip" at its forward end. If the cement is in sacks distributed along the mixer path, laborers dump it into the skip while the truck is unloading. After the truck has discharged a batch and pulled away, the skip is raised, and the material slides into the mixer. At the same time, a

Fig. 15. Mechanical spreader on a Missouri project. Two pavement lanes, separated by a full-depth longitudinal joint, are being placed simultaneously. Note bottom-dump bucket of mixer discharging in left center of photograph (Courtesy Portland Cement Association)

measured quantity of water flows into the drum. After the concrete is mixed for the prescribed time, it is discharged into a bottom dump bucket that travels out a horizontal boom and spreads its load uniformly over the subgrade (see Fig. 15).

Within reasonable limits, the strength of concrete increases with mixing time, but as a diminishing rate. Each agency has established a minimum mixing time by weighing this strength increase against the added cost of longer mixing. Among the state highway departments, this minimum mixing period for paving machines varies from 50 to 90 sec, with 60 sec the most common requirement. Measurement of this time interval begins after all ingredients (except the last of the water) are in the mixer and ends before the discharge of any mixed concrete.[64] Some agencies also specify minimum and maximum drum speed, often 14 and 20 revolutions per minute, respectively. Observation of minimum mixing periods is stringently enforced by automatic timing devices that lock the discharge lever during the mixing period and ring a bell to indicate its end. Most specifications bar mixers with defective timing mechanisms.

Water for the mixer is supplied either by a flexible hose connected to a pipeline that extends along the project or by a truck or trailer moving along with the mixer. All specifications require accurate devices for metering mixing water. Generally measurement is by volume in a calibrated tank that can be set to supply any desired amount. However, a few states require that the water be weighed, and several others permit measurement by either method.

The specifications of most highway departments permit contractors the option of furnishing concrete ready-mixed rather than site-mixed, as described above. Specifications for concrete pavement construction of the AASHO define ready mix as "any concrete which is proportioned and mixed in a central plant and hauled to the site of the work in agitator trucks of approved type; or, concrete which is proportioned and partially mixed in a central plant and transported to the site of the work in approved transit-mix trucks, the mixing being completed en route (called shrink mixing); or, concrete which is proportioned in a central plant and mixed in approved transit-mix trucks en route to the site of the work." A few agencies do not insist on agitation of the concrete after central mixing but will accept concrete mixed at a central plant and hauled in open trucks of special design that permit easy discharge of the concrete. Transit-mix trucks are manufactured in various sizes, but few of them will accommodate unmixed materials for more than 5 cu yd of concrete. However, if central mixing precedes hauling, the capacity of a given transit mixer will be increased by as much as 40%.

The same principles of proportioning and mixing apply to ready-mixed concrete as to that mixed on the site, but certain added precautions may be necessary. For example, ready-mix trucks are loaded some time before the concrete is needed. If pouring is interrupted for a period, several truck loads of mixed concrete may be on hand. It is common to specify that the concrete be placed within a stated period after the mixer is charged. For the state highway departments this interval ranges from 30 to 90 min. Again, with transit mix, it is very difficult for inspectors to check on mixing time, drum speed, and amount of water in the concrete. Some agencies which permit transit mixers require that water be added and full mixing accomplished after the trucks reach the point of discharge. Finally, where transit mixers are unloaded by chutes, segregation may become a problem. Some agencies require that the transit-mixed concrete be passed into a hopper before being placed or that a special spreading device be used.

---

[64] Some specifications increase the mixing time somewhat for tandem mixers.

Finishing concrete pavements

Originally, finishing operations on concrete pavements were per-formed entirely by hand-labor methods. However, increasing labor costs and demands for uniform high quality have resulted in a gradual introduction of finishing machines. Today almost all the state highway departments require machine finishing on projects of any size, although hand-labor methods may be substituted on transitions or other sections with variable widths or warped surfaces. Many combinations of equip-ment and methods will produce excellent surface finishes, and only the most common can be mentioned briefly in this presentation.

Machine finishing. The three machines in most widespread use are the mechanical spreader, the transverse finishing machine, and the longitudinal finisher. All are self-powered and travel on the side forms. The three appear in the foreground of Fig. 10.

The mechanical spreader distributes the concrete deposited by the mixer uniformly and without segregation. Figure 15 shows a front view of one such machine and the left foreground of Fig. 16 shows the appearance of the concrete after the machine has passed. Only a few state highway departments insist on their use, but contractors usually employ them because the spreader replaces several workmen. Spread-ers are particularly helpful where mats of bar or mesh reinforcing steel must be placed in the slab. On its first trip, the machine levels the concrete to the plane of the reinforcing. After the mats are laid in place the remainder of the concrete is deposited and is leveled by a second trip of the spreader.

Figure 16 shows a transverse finishing machine. In this instance, vibrating devices are attached to its front. At the forward edge of the machine proper is a strike-off screed that moves back and forth transversely and slices the concrete surface flush with the tops of the side forms. Notice that some concrete remains piled up ahead of the screed. At the rear is a tamping bar that works the coarse aggregate down from the surface in order to make subsequent finishing operations easier. Among the features of most transverse finishers are adjust-ments for placing a slight arch in the screeds if a parabolic or other curved surface is desired. Particular care in operating the transverse finishing machine must be exercised when crossing previously embedded transverse joints.

The vibrator shown in Fig. 16 consists of a cylindrical bar submerged in the concrete, plus auxiliary units operating along the side forms and on each side of the center joint. Certain other machines provide vibration to the surface of the concrete either on the front screed of the finishing machine or with a vibrating pan mounted independently. Many state highway departments specify vibration, but of these several limit their requirement to treatment with hand-operated machines along the forms and at the joints. On many projects where vibrators are not required, contractors supply them voluntarily to facilitate concrete placing and to eliminate hand spudding along side forms and joints.

FIG. 16.   Transverse finishing machine on a Missouri project.   Mechanical vibrators are attached ahead of the front screed (Courtesy Portland Cement Association)

Figure 17 pictures a longitudinal finisher, often called a longitudinal float. The strike-off bar is set parallel to the roadway center line and moves across the roadway in a sawing motion. This action cuts off high spots and fills in low ones along the direction of vehicular travel. After a transverse pass is completed the machine moves ahead approximately half a float length to its next position. The overlap in succeeding passes eliminates abrupt changes in the surface in the direction of traffic. All but a few of the state highway departments specify longitudinal floating. Two, California and Washington, require diagonal floating.[65]

[65] This operation is performed with the Johnson finisher, a device having a series of diagonally placed wooden floats mounted on a rigid steel frame. The entire unit is self-powered, and rolls on the side forms on widely spaced pairs of wheels. For details see L. I. Hewes, *American Highway Practice*, John Wiley

The steps in machine-finishing air-entrained concrete are like those already outlined. However, air-entrained concrete is more plastic, cohesive, and sticky than plain concrete. There is sometimes a tendency for the surface to tear or become pockmarked under the screeds of the finishing machine. For these reasons some details of the procedures and the timing of operations may be different from those with plain concrete. Practices among states are not standardized, however.[66]

Fig. 17. Longitudinal finisher on a Missouri project. Workman in center of picture stands on the strike-off bar (Courtesy Portland Cement Association)

Installing weakened-plane or dummy joints. As shown in Fig. 6, page 544, a weakened-plane joint is merely a strip of wood, metal, or impregnated fiber embedded close under the pavement surface. After the transverse finisher has passed, a groove of the proper depth is formed in the fresh concrete. A common grooving tool consists of a steel tee section with its stem facing down. Plow handles at each end provide convenient handling. The joint material, held rigid in a removable metal sleeve, is inserted in the formed groove, and the concrete is tamped around it. Subsequent finishing operations proceed

& Sons, vol. II, pp. 173 and 463–466 (1942), or *Western Construction News*, June 1938, pp. 213–214.

[66] For further discussion see C. W. Allen, *Journal American Concrete Institute*, January 1951, pp. 373–376, and J. H. Swanberg, *Proceedings Highway Research Board*, pp. 170–178 (1947).

as though the strips were not there. Installation of the dummy joint (see Fig. 6) also begins with opening a groove in the concrete, as outlined above. In this case a greased steel bar of proper dimension is inserted. After the longitudinal float has passed but before the concrete has set, the bar is loosened. When the concrete has set somewhat, the joint is edged and the steel bar removed for re-use.

Belting and brooming. Almost all the state highway departments specify belting as the means for producing a gritty, nonskid surface (see Fig. 18). Workmen draw a narrow strip of canvas or burlap back

Fig. 18. Belting concrete pavement to obtain a nonskid surface (Courtesy Portland Cement Association)

and forth across the surface. A few inches forward progress is made with each short cross stroke. Final belting is done after the water sheen has disappeared but before the concrete sets. In about half the states, transverse brooming is substituted for final belting. A coarse fiber broom on a long handle is pulled lightly from the center outward, which leaves the marks of the individual fibers in the concrete. Scorings should not be over $\frac{1}{16}$ in. in depth.

Edging. Pavement details of almost all the state highway departments require that all exposed corners be rounded with a metal hand tool. This operation is called edging. Preliminary edging to force coarse aggregate back from the surface usually follows close behind the finishing machines. Final edging normally succeeds final belting or brooming. Edging of transverse expansion and contraction joints must be done with extreme care; otherwise the pavement adjacent to the joint will be left higher or lower than adjacent surfaces. Some agencies insist that the pavement surface be reshaped across the joints after edging. The tool employed for this purpose is commonly a hand-operated "bull float" consisting of a straight blade several feet in length on a long handle.

Straight-edging the surface pavement. Surfaces are checked for smoothness by means of long straightedges placed in successive positions parallel to the roadway center line. Advance along the roadway is in increments measuring half a straightedge length. Most agencies use a straightedge 10 ft long and limit variations under it to ⅛ in. Tolerances more and less severe than these are specified by some. Straightedges are swung from handles which permit easy inspection of soft concrete. The first check is made after longitudinal floating while the concrete is still plastic (see left foreground, Fig. 10). Low spots are filled with fresh concrete, and high ones are cut down, after which the surface is refinished. A second check is conducted after the concrete has set, usually on the succeeding day. Only minor corrections are permitted at that time. More serious irregularities are cause for removal and replacement of the affected sections. In this regard, the specifications for concrete pavement construction of the AASHO state that

> After the concrete has hardened, but not sooner than 12 hours after the concrete was placed, the inspector shall test the surface of the pavement with a 10-foot straight edge, and shall clearly mark all high spots. Any high spot which shows variation or departure from the testing edge of more than ⅛ inch and not over ¼ inch shall be at once ground down by the contractor at his expense. Where the departure from correct cross section exceeds ¼ inch, the pavement shall be removed and replaced by and at the expense of the contractor. Any area or section so removed shall be not less than 10 feet in length and not less than the full width of the lane involved.

Some of the state highway departments check the roughness of concrete and other pavements by means of road-roughness indicators. These devices when towed or pushed along the highway summarize the irregularities in the road surface. Results are stated in inches of roughness per mile.[67]

Curing concrete pavements

Concrete gains strength as the chemical action between cement and water (hydration) proceeds. If the concrete dries out, hydration and

[67] See, for example, *Public Roads*, February 1941, pp. 227–234; *Proceedings Highway Research Board*, pp. 621–638 (1940), pp. 13–52 (1942), and pp. 137–153 (1948); and R. A. Moyer and J. W. Shupe, *Highway Research Board Bulletin 37* (1951).

strength gain stop. When water again becomes available, strength gain is resumed. Thus, even with sporadic wetting, concrete will eventually gain considerable strength. With pavements, however, rapid drying of the fresh concrete results in crazing or cracking of the surface. Where these conditions are extremely unfavorable, severe cracking occurs. Although hydration will resume with rewetting, the fine hair cracks caused by drying of the surface will not heal. From these facts it is clear that any curing method that prevents drying of the newly finished surface and that keeps the concrete continuously moist is satisfactory.

Curing procedures employed in the United States and the number of state highway departments permitting each procedure [68] are shown in Table 9. All state highway departments permit selection by contractors from two or more of the methods shown. Three-fourths of these

TABLE 9. METHODS FOR CURING CONCRETE PAVEMENTS AND THEIR PREVALENCE AMONG STATE HIGHWAY DEPARTMENTS

Method	Number of State Highway Departments Permitting Method	Preliminary Curing with Burlap Preceding Method Named
Ponding or earth cover, kept wet	34	31
Hay or straw cover, kept wet	27	25
Cover of felt mats, kept wet	17	2
Cover of cotton mats, kept wet	35	6
Cover of burlap (usually 2 layers), kept wet	26	26
Sawdust cover, kept wet	1	
Continuous sprinkling	1	
Cover of waterproof paper	32	7
Impervious membrane, sprayed on	30	2
Surface application of calcium chloride	3	
Surface application of sodium silicate	2	

Based on data presented by D. L. Robinson in *Journal American Concrete Institute*, April 1952.

[68] For a more detailed description of these methods see D. L. Robinson, *Journal American Concrete Institute*, April 1952, pp. 705–711. Also see J. H. Swanberg, *Proceedings Highway Research Board*, pp. 335–342 (1953). See *Highway Research Board Current Road Problems 1-R* (1952), for collected specifications for curing materials. For evaluations of the effectiveness of certain common curing methods and extensive bibliographies see papers by P. L. Melville and R. W. Czaban and by R. L. Peyton, *Proceedings Highway Research Board*, pp. 148–176 (1952).

agencies allow choices among four or more. Most states include among their options locally produced materials like cotton mats in the South, straw or hay in farm states, and sawdust in Oregon.

The six curing methods listed first in Table 9 apply a surface cover of water-absorbent material that must be rewet from time to time. How often rewetting is required depends on such factors as moisture-holding properties of the cover, temperature, and relative humidity. With any of these methods the cover material must be removed after curing is completed. The remaining methods, except continuous sprinkling and surface applications of calcium chloride,[69] prevent evaporation of the water already in the fresh concrete. This is sufficient for curing as long as moisture loss is prevented, since water requirements for hydration are less than those for workability. It is to be observed that curing by spraying or surface-application methods is completed in a single operation, whereas other procedures call for two or more steps.

Waterproof paper for curing consists of two sheets of plain kraft paper cemented together with a bituminous material. Added strength is gained by embedding fibers in both directions (see *AASHO Designation M139–48, ASTM Designation C171–42 T*).

Impervious membranes are supplied as liquids but, when sprayed on, form a watertight seal on the surface of the concrete. "Clear" curing compounds are most widely employed. With them, uniform coverage is assured by addition of a fugitive dye that disappears after spreading. Pigmented compounds that leave a white or light-gray surface are gaining increasing favor and are permitted in several states. An advantage is that they reflect the radiant heat of the sun and thus reduce temperature rise in the slab in hot, clear weather.[70] Only a few of the states permit black curing membranes. In some of these, moreover, immediate covering with whitewash is specified to gain light-reflecting properties.

Many states require that preliminary curing with wet burlap precede final curing by the selected method (see Table 9). The burlap will not mar the surface even though it is placed immediately after finishing, and it offers a means for maintaining surface moisture dur-

[69] See p. 413 for a discussion of the properties of calcium chloride.

[70] See *AASHO Designation M148–49* for specifications for clear and pigmented curing compounds. For a detailed and careful study of membrane curing see C. C. Rhodes and J. R. Evans, *Michigan Engineering Experiment Station Bulletin 108*. This report is abstracted in *Journal American Concrete Institute, December 1950, pp. 277–295.*

ing the critical early curing period. A few states require early curing with fog sprays. Some agencies will not permit construction on extremely hot days when rapid evaporation makes early curing even more difficult.

Most of the states set the minimum permissible curing period between 3 and 7 days, but a few agencies specify intervals greater than a week. Others set certain minimum strengths of test specimens as the control over curing time.

Traffic must be kept from concrete pavements until they can carry the superimposed loads without suffering damage. This is assured by specifications that defer use for a stated number of days after pouring or until test specimens develop a stated flexural or compressive strength. Among the state highway departments, the shortest period is 5 days, and the lowest acceptable flexural stress is 500 lb per sq in. If the design includes exposed joints, they must be cleaned and sealed before the pavement is opened to traffic.

Cold-weather concreting

Concrete hydrates and gains strength very slowly at temperatures near the freezing point. Further, severe damage results if fresh concrete freezes. For these reasons, many agencies prohibit paving when the air temperature is below some minimum [71] such as 40° F. Where pouring is permitted during cold weather, heating of the aggregates, mixing water, or both is usually required. The AASHO specifications state that "the temperature of the mixed concrete shall not be less than 60° F nor more than 100° F at the time of placing in the forms." After placing, heat generated by. hydration helps to keep the slab warm so that strength will develop. Some agencies employ the added precaution of insulating the finished slab to prevent heat loss.

Payment for concrete pavements

Payment for concrete pavements is usually on a unit price basis, most commonly stated as square yards of completed pavement surface. A few agencies use measured or computed concrete volume in cubic yards. Compensation for subgrade preparation and watering, furnishing and placing side forms, curing, and other work are included in this price. In most instances, pay for joint materials, dowels, and like items is also included in the unit price of the pavement, but some

[71] Sometimes two minimum temperatures are used, for example, 35° F when the air temperature is rising and 45° F when it is falling.

agencies treat them as separate items. Compensation for reinforcing bars or welded wire fabric is sometimes included in the price of the pavement and sometimes made separately at a price per pound or per square yard of pavement.

Many agencies check the thickness of completed pavements by taking cores at intervals along the roadway. Payment may be reduced or denied when these tests show the slab to be thinner than specified. For example, the Indiana Highway Commission (1) requires removal and replacement without extra compensation when the pavement is too thin by more than 1 in., (2) denies payment if the deficiency falls between ½ and 1 in. unless the faulty section is removed and replaced, and (3) reduces payment for sections too thin by less than ½ in.

MAINTENANCE OF CONCRETE PAVEMENTS [72]

Routine maintenance of concrete pavements consists largely of treating cracks and transverse and longitudinal contraction and expansion joints. It often is necessary to free expansion joints of dirt and other extraneous matter and to refill them with a hot sealing compound such as 50–70 penetration asphalt cement or rubber-asphalt mixtures. If expansion joints contain extrusive fillers, they will project upward into the roadway with the advent of warm weather and must be trimmed flush with the pavement surface. Wide cracks or spalled joints must first be blown out with compressed air or cleaned in some other manner and then be sealed to prevent the intrusion of extraneous material and to block the downward penetration of surface water. There is serious question, however, whether sealing narrow cracks is effective, and many maintenance engineers recommend against it. Surface scaling from frost or salt action is corrected by applying a bituminous surface treatment.[73]

Where concrete pavement is in good condition except for small, scattered areas that have broken or spalled badly, patching with concrete is economical. At affected locations, the old concrete should be removed by vertical straight-line cuts parallel and perpendicular to the roadway center line. For corner repairs, the angle from the roadway

---

[72] For a more detailed discussion of concrete-pavement maintenance see *Policy on Maintenance of Roadway Surfaces*, AASHO (1948). See also *Concrete Resurfacing of Concrete Pavements, Highway Research Board Bulletin 87* (1954).

[73] For a detailed report on joint and crack cleaning and resealing procedures of the Minnesota Department of Highways, see *Highway Research Board Bulletin 63* (1952).

center line should be greater than 30 degrees and less than 60 degrees. Sections removed should have minimum areas of 20 sq. ft. The new slab should always be as thick as the original pavement, and, if the subgrade is questionable, it should be replaced with suitable material, properly compacted. It is excellent practice to provide extra thickness adjoining the old concrete and to extend the patch under the old pavement to a width and depth of at least 4 in. High early-strength concrete produced with extra cement, high early-strength cement, or an accelerator-like calcium chloride is commonly employed for patching in order to gain early use of the pavement.

A maintenance technique known as "mud jacking" is widely employed to restore subgrade support under pumping pavements and to level uneven slabs. A liquid filler is forced under the slab through previously drilled holes. This "mud" or "slurry" fills all vacant spaces and, if injection continues, applies hydrostatic pressure which forces the slab upward. Subsided pavements have been raised several inches without damage to the concrete. Slurrys for mud jacking usually consist of mixtures of fine-grained soil, Portland cement, and water; or of these three ingredients plus a small amount of cutback asphalt. The final mixture must pass through the pump without gumming and flow readily under the pavement and into small voids. It should harden quite rapidly without excessive shrinkage and without becoming hard and brittle. Spacing of holes through the concrete should be carefully planned. Where slabs are to be lifted by pumping slurry into several holes, the nozzle should be moved frequently so that lifting is in small increments.

An alternative to mud jacking is "undersealing." Here a heated asphalt, often an air-blown product, is substituted for the slurry. An advantage of undersealing is that the asphalt forms an effective seal against the penetration of surface water into the subgrade.

Many highway agencies have developed special equipment combinations solely for mud-jacking or undersealing purposes. These are truck-mounted and proceed down the highway as a train.[74]

[74] *Highway Research Board Current Road Problems 4-R* (1947), titled Maintenance Methods for Preventing and Correcting the Pumping Action of Concrete Pavement Slabs, offers an excellent and complete description of the mud-jacking and undersealing practices of the various states. It also contains an extensive bibliography. See also articles by Goetz and Green, *Proceedings Highway Research Board*, pp. 232–257 (1947), and W. E. Chastain and J. E. Burke, *Proceedings Highway Research Board*, pp. 343–354 (1953).

TWO-COURSE PAVEMENTS WITH CONCRETE BASES

Brick wearing surfaces supported on concrete bases have been widely employed in the United States in past years.[75] Today, however, there are few new installations except on isolated city streets or in special situations like the Brooklyn–Battery tunnel. Only 2400 miles of brick and other block surfaces remained on state-administered roads and streets in 1951. However, much additional mileage has been covered with bituminous material and so is actually still in service.

Probably the biggest single factor restricting present-day use of brick pavements is the high initial cost occasioned by two-course con-

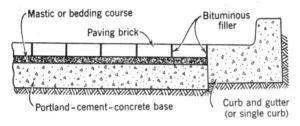

FIG. 19. Partial cross section through a typical brick pavement

struction and relatively large amounts of hand labor. Particular advantages are excellent resistance to wear and easy and quick repair without large and cumbersome equipment. A typical cross section of a brick pavement of recent design is shown in Fig. 19.

In the earliest pavements, the mastic or bedding course was of sand, and later of cement grout. Current practice employs a mastic composed of sand and 5 to 8% of fluid bituminous binder, usually RC–2 or MC–2 cutback asphalt or a cutback tar.

Paving brick is hard burned and extremely tough. It also differs from conventional brick in that special lugs are formed on one side and one end to hold the placed brick slightly apart to leave room for the filler.

Clean sand was originally employed as filler between the bricks. In later installations, cement grout was used, but it produced such rigidity that the pavement was subject to severe cracking. Bituminous filler is now standard, and generally is a hard-grade petroleum asphalt, often of 23–32 or 30–45 penetration. Before the heated filler is poured

[75] See p. 498 for a discussion of sheet asphalts, which also often have a concrete base.

over the laid brick the exposed surface is treated with a separating agent in order that the excess asphalt can be stripped away easily.[76]

A limited mileage of highways and streets surfaced with asphalt and stone blocks has also been constructed in the United States. These pavement types are no longer employed.

[76] For a detailed description of materials and construction practices for brick pavements see L. I. Hewes, *American Highway Practice*, John Wiley & Sons, vol. II, pp. 337–374 (1942). Specifications and tests for paving brick and for filler appear in the current edition of *Highway Materials*, published by the AASHO.

19 ———————— Highway Maintenance

INTRODUCTION

Highway maintenance has been defined as "the preserving and keeping of each type of roadway, roadside, structure, and facility as nearly as possible in its original condition as constructed or as subsequently improved, and the operation of highway facilities and services to provide satisfactory and safe transportation." Roughly one-third of all highway funds go to maintenance: For example, in 1950, $1.4 billion from the $4.3 billion of highway expenditures went to this purpose. In that year, the average annual expenditure per mile of road or street was $400. Average maintenance expenditures per mile for rural roads, by systems were: interstate $2000, other primary Federal-aid $700, Federal-aid secondary $400, and local access $200. On the other hand, maintenance costs per vehicle-mile for these systems were roughly $0.002, $0.002, $0.003, and $0.011, respectively. For city streets the average maintenance expenditure was about $1200 per mile or $0.001 per vehicle-mile.[1] From the early 1930's to 1950, maintenance costs tripled. Principal reasons were inflation and the added demands created by increases in numbers and weights of vehicles.

Maintenance is performed for the most part by the various highway agencies themselves. This is in direct contrast to construction, where 95% of the work, exclusive of engineering, is done by contract. The principal explanation is that maintenance work is so diverse, so subject to variation from the expected, and on occasion so hurried that it does not lend itself to competitive bidding. Sometimes maintenance forces also perform "betterment" work that might also be done by contract. Common betterment projects include grading and paving for small

[1] Maintenance costs per vehicle-mile on the interstate system are actually somewhat less than on the primary Federal-aid system, although that fact is not indicated by the approximate figures given above.

line changes, resurfacing, and mulching, planting, or other erosion-control work.

Maintenance by most of the state highway departments and many local rural and urban agencies is a well-organized, efficient operation. Without question, however, there are still many instances where maintenance positions are used to discharge political obligations. Among the state highway departments there is an encouraging trend toward making maintenance a well-paid and profitable career. By 1951, the employees of 17 states were under civil service, and in 20 pay increases were automatic or automatic on recommendation. In 47 states workers were protected by workman's compensation and in 44 by retirement plans.[2]

There is a close relationship between design and construction practices and maintenance costs. For example, insufficient pavement or base thickness or improper construction of these elements soon results in expensive patching or surface repair. Shoulder care becomes a serious problem where narrow lanes force heavy vehicles to travel with one set of wheels off the pavement. Improperly designed drainage facilities mean erosion or deposition of materials and costly cleaning operations or other corrective measures. Sharp ditches and steep slopes require hand maintenance whereas flatter ditches and slopes permit machines to do the work more cheaply. In snow country, improper location, extremely low fills, and narrow cuts that leave no room for snow storage can create extremely difficult snow-removal problems. In many instances, high maintenance costs resulting from poor design or construction practices offer the most compelling reason for reconstruction.

Maintenance problems are much different among highway agencies. With many state highway departments, principal attention goes to caring for limited mileages of high-type pavements and their appurtenances. Some rural road agencies are mainly concerned with large mileages of lightly traveled roads having gravel or low-type surfaces. In cities, street sweeping and cleaning becomes a major task. Also the northern states have serious snow- and ice-control problems whereas many southern and southwestern states do not. Table 1, which shows the distribution of state highway funds by operation and class of ex-

---

[2] This information is from the Progress Report of Joint Committee on Maintenance Personnel, published in *Highway Research Abstracts,* January 1953. This survey also includes definitions of maintenance positions, further data on personnel policies, and a tabulation of salaries paid to all classifications of maintenance workers by each state highway department.

TABLE 1. DISTRIBUTION OF THE STATE HIGHWAY MAINTENANCE DOLLAR BY
OPERATION AND USE (1948)

% of Total Expenditure

Operation	Labor	Equipment	Material	Total
Surface maintenance	22	16	12	50
Roadside and drainage	12	5	1	18
Shoulders and approaches	6	3	1	10
Snow, ice, and sand control	5	4	1	10
Bridges	4	2	1	7
Traffic service	2	1	2	5
Totals	51	31	18	100

penditure, offers a general idea of the relative cost of the various maintenance functions.

Highway maintenance forces have the responsibility for keeping roads open and traffic moving under all conditions. Often they are called on in time of flood, heavy snow, or other disasters to rescue stranded motorists or residents of afflicted areas. In carrying out these duties, maintenance workers have performed many difficult and sometimes heroic feats.

The courts have in many instances held highway agencies legally responsible for injury or property damage resulting from improper highway maintenance. Rough pavements, inadequately marked obstructions and equipment, and negligent acts of maintenance employees are among the causes of large damage suits.

SURFACE MAINTENANCE [3]

Over half the state highway maintenance dollar goes for care of the roadway surface. With other road agencies also, surface maintenance is a major expense. For gravel roads, this involves blading and occasional resurfacing. For surface treatments and low-type bituminous surfaces, patching, seal coating, or possibly loosening, oiling, remixing, and re-laying are involved. For high-type surfaces like bituminous concrete and Portland-cement concrete, removal and replacement of failed areas and resurfacing are appropriate treatments. Mud-jacking or undersealing Portland-cement-concrete pavements is a common

[3] See particularly *A Policy on Maintenance of Roadway Surfaces,* AASHO (1948).

operation. These subjects are treated at some length in the discussions of the various surface types.

In general, the same materials and methods are employed for surface construction as for surface maintenance. However, construction machinery and methods are designed for quantity production whereas maintenance operations involve small output at widely separated locations. Furthermore, maintenance operations must be planned for rapid performance and to cause the least possible disruption or hazard to traffic. As an illustration, patching of bituminous surfaces is often done with premixed aggregate and binder that have been stockpiled along the road ready for immediate use. The mix is hauled from the stockpile by truck and placed with hand shovels. Another method utilizes a tank trailer for bituminous binder towed by a dump truck loaded with aggregate. A pump, mounted on the trailer, forces the fluid binder through a hose to a hand spray.

ROADSIDE AND DRAINAGE MAINTENANCE [4]

The character of the roadside determines what maintenance is required. Where the roadside is grass, this must be mowed, fertilized, and sometimes treated with lime. Reseeding or resodding may be necessary in some instances. If weeds are troublesome, cutting, plowing, or spraying with weed killer may be required. If dry grass along the roadside and on adjacent lands constitutes a fire hazard, burning or plowing may be in order. Where back-slopes are covered with brush, trimming to maintain clearance and sight distance is needed occasionally. Control of slope erosion by mulching, seeding or other means often becomes a maintenance operation. Where there are shrubs and trees, spraying and mulching and occasional tree surgery will be required. Picking up litter thrown or blown along the roadside or into wayside areas is another annoying but necessary chore.

Many ingenious machines have been developed to reduce the cost of roadside development and maintenance. Included are mechanical sod cutters, combined seed and fertilizer spreaders, sprayers for distributing seed and fertilizer in suspension in water, power mowers, motor-driven but portable grass cutters for use in close quarters, brush mowers for cutting heavy bushes along the roadside and brush choppers that reduce the stalks to chips suitable for mulch.[5] For roadside cleanup, the Cali-

[4] See *Policy on Maintenance of Shoulders, Road Approaches, and Sidewalks* and *Policy on Maintenance of Roadsides* (in one booklet), AASHO, 1949.

[5] For pictures and brief descriptions of these and other machines see *Report*

fornia Division of Highways has machines that pick up papers, cans, bottles and other roadside trash and sort them for disposal.[6]

Drainage maintenance involves keeping ditches, culverts, structures, and appurtenances like drop inlets and catch basins clean and ready to carry the next flow of water. Sediments deposited during periods of heavy flow must be removed. Brush, branches, and other debris that collect in trash racks or at culvert and structure entrances must be disposed of. Badly eroded channels and dikes must be repaired, and paving, seeding, sodding, riprap, bank protection, or other means must be adopted to prevent recurrence. After extreme storm damage, maintenance forces may be called upon to reconstruct much of the drainage system.

SHOULDER AND APPROACH MAINTENANCE

Shoulder and approach maintenance procedures depend on the surface character of these areas. Sod shoulders must be mowed and occasionally bladed down to the level of the roadway so that water is not trapped in the traveled way. The grass must be fertilized, reseeded, and otherwise treated to keep it in good condition. Care of shoulders protected by bituminous blankets or surface treatments is the same as for roadways with like surfaces. Gravels and earth shoulders are maintained by blading under proper weather conditions.

Rutting or settling of the shoulders that leaves a dropoff at the pavement edge creates a serious accident hazard: if this condition develops, it should be corrected as soon as possible by reconstruction, resurfacing, or other appropriate means.

SNOW AND ICE CONTROL [7]

Snow removal is the major winter maintenance problem in affected areas. To solve it properly requires careful organization and advance

of Committee.on Roadside Development, Highway Research Board, pp. 113–118 (1949); pp. 94–104 (1950); pp. 45–56 (1951); and pp. 55–64 (1952). See also Mechanization of Roadside Operations, *Highway Research Board Special Report 16* (1953). For a report on chemical mowing techniques see *American Highways,* April 1950.

[6] See *California Highways and Public Works,* November, December 1951, pp. 46–48.

[7] See Recommended Practice for Snow Removal and Treatment of Icy Pavements, *Highway Research Board Current Road Problems 9–3R,* 3d revision (1954). Also see Report of Committee on Treatment of Icy Pavements and

training. Often "dry runs" are held in the fall to discover and correct deficiencies in equipment or plans that would cause serious trouble during a storm. Quick communication by means of two-way radio equipment has been a major forward step in co-ordinating snow-removal operations.

Measures to minimize the formation of snowdrifts across the roadway should be taken before the coming of winter. *Snow fences* offer an effective and economical means of reducing wind velocity and thus causing snowdrifts to form adjacent to rather than on the traveled way. Snow fences are placed before the ground freezes and are removed in the spring. Proper location is on the windward side at right angles to the prevailing wind and about 15 fence heights from the road. The most common fence consists of wooden slats or pickets 4 ft long woven together with galvanized wire. Sections can be rolled up for handling and storage. Support is furnished by posts or angle irons driven into the ground. Trees, particularly of the coniferous variety, or other vegetation at a sufficient distance from the roadway are also effective in controlling drift formation. However, guard rails, fences, or planting close to the road aggravate the drift problem and should be avoided whenever possible.

In rural areas, snow that falls on the roadway is bladed or thrown to the roadside. Removal operations should start soon after snow begins to fall. Where annual snowfall is less than about 30 in., regular maintenance trucks of 1½- to 2-ton size equipped with blade plows are effective. Larger trucks, usually four-wheel drive and equipped with wing plows or hydraulically operated blade or V plows, are widely employed in areas of heavier snowfall. In mountain passes and other locations where heavy snowfall and drift formation create extreme snowdrifts, rotary plows that throw the snow a considerable distance are most effective.

In the downtown areas of cities, snow from heavy falls is generally loaded into trucks and hauled away. There are a few instances where short stretches of pavement or sidewalk have been heated to melt the snow as it falls.

Ice forming on the roadways after rains or snow reduces the coefficient of friction between tires and surface to 0.05 or less and makes proper vehicle control almost impossible. To minimize the danger thus created, most highway agencies apply abrasives to heavily traveled roads and streets. Suitable materials are clean, sharp sand, cinders,

Snow Removal, *American Road Builders Association Technical Bulletin 153* (1948).

and washed stone screenings. Normally the abrasives are treated with calcium or sodium chloride in solid or brine form before storage. As salt solutions have a lower freezing point than water, these additives prevent freezing in the stockpile or bin and insure penetration of the particles into the icy surface. Experience has shown that untreated aggregates, even if heated before application, whip or blow off the roadway. Flake calcium chloride will lower the freezing point of abrasives in storage or stockpile somewhat further than an equal quantity of rocksalt.[8] Materials are hauled by truck and distributed with hand shovel or spreader box.

BRIDGE MAINTENANCE

Most bridge maintenance is of a specialized nature. On structures having exposed steelwork, cleaning by sandblasting, flame, or other means followed by repainting represents the biggest maintenance item.[9] At times cleaning, freeing, and painting bridge seats and rollers may be required. Deck joints may extrude or become filled with dirt so that their cleaning and resealing is necessary. On occasion vehicles out of control strike handrails or other appurtenances, and these must be repaired and straightened. If bridge decks become rough, resurfacing is in order. Remedial measures are sometimes required to correct serious scour around and under piers and abutments. It is common practice among highway agencies to have traveling crews exclusively for bridge work. Often painting and other specialty work is carried out under contract.

TRAFFIC SERVICE

Traffic service includes such continuing functions as striping, sign repair, and maintenance of street and highway lights. Generally these are performed by special crews of the highway agency, although street-light maintenance may be turned over to the local utility company. Regular maintenance forces perform many emergency services, particularly during stormy weather.

[8] See references at beginning of this section for amounts of calcium or sodium to be added to insure proper results at different temperatures and aggregate moisture contents.

[9] In the fiscal year 1951–52, expenditures for painting the 146,000 tons of exposed structural steel in the 3.9-mile steel portions of the San Francisco–Oakland Bay Bridge totaled $367,000. Approximately 57 men were employed full time at the task.

MAINTENANCE COST RECORDS

Carefully segregated maintenance costs are a "must" for scientific highway planning and management. For example, high costs of surface maintenance on a particular stretch of road may point up the need for early resurfacing or reconstruction. Again, wide differences in cost when different crews do similar work suggest a comparison of methods and work habits. All other maintenance expenditure likewise can be subject to critical study and evaluation.

Maintenance reports should assign expenditures to the specific stretch of road on which the work is done. By 1951, 17 state highway departments had subdivided their systems into *control sections*. These are chosen to (1) have reasonably uniform traffic volume over their lengths, (2) demand the same type and standard of development, (3) be a practical unit for reporting maintenance costs, and (4) be a convenient unit for compilation of statistical and research data. In the eastern states average section lengths range from 5 to 8 miles; in the western states they vary between 15 and 18 miles. Designation of sections is by 4 to 6 digit numbers, with the first 2 or 3 digits representing counties and the remainder indicating the particular stretch of road. Materials, labor, and equipment charges against each control section are segregated among a standard list of maintenance tasks. By punching maintenance charges onto tabulating machine cards, any desired combination of maintenance-cost data can be quickly obtained.

Capital expenditures for construction and betterment also should be segregated by control section and work classification. These records, combined with those on maintenance costs, will provide the means for determining the true cost of providing highways.[10]

[10] For added data and references on control sections and maintenance and construction cost records see G. D. Gronberg, *Public Roads*, August 1951, pp. 180–185, and Fred B. Farrell, *Highway Research Board Special Report 13* (1953). R. W. Gamble, *Proceedings Highway Research Board*, pp. 1–13 (1946), presents the Milwaukee method for setting control sections in cities. For a discussion of procedures for determining annual highway costs from such records see H. W. Hansen, *Public Roads*, April 1951, pp. 141–147.

Problems

Chapter 1

1-1. Secure data on national motor-vehicle registrations, motor-fuel consumption, highway expenditures, and highway-user imposts for the last year of record. Plot this information on Fig. 1, page 6, in your textbook. (Suggested sources are *Highway Statistics,* published annually by the U. S. Bureau of Public Roads, and *Automobile Facts and Figures,* released annually by the Automobile Manufacturers Association.)

Chapter 2

2-1. Locate and copy the organization chart of the state highway department of the state in which your college is located. (Suggested sources are the reports of the State Highway Departments, prepared annually or biennially, or Highway Research Board Special Report 20, 1954.)

2-2. Investigate the local road or street organization in the area where your college is located. In particular, what agency administers the roads or streets, and how is it organized; if an engineer is in charge, what limitations are there on his authority to establish standards and priorities for improvement; are the employees under civil service; is the majority of the construction work done by contract?

Chapter 3

3-1. Assume that you are representing the highway department of your state at a public hearing to explain why a bypass is to be constructed around a small town. Prepare a brief written statement outlining the advantages of the bypass to motorists and to the town. (References: pp. 27–29, 118, and footnote 11, p. 129)

3-2. Assume that representatives of a large city, concerned about the congestion in the downtown areas, are demanding that the state highway department construct bypasses around their city to relieve this congestion. Would you agree with them, or would you propose another solution? Prepare a brief written statement supporting your conclusion. (References: pp. 27–30, 113–118)

3-3. Prepare a brief written statement favoring the adoption of the freeway principle for major highways in your state. (References: pp. 36–37 and appropriate topics listed under freeways in the index)

Chapter 4

· **4-1.** A very impatient driver attempts to maintain a speed of 60 miles per hour on a "normal" two-lane highway.

a. If his vehicle performs like the average vehicle described in the text, what will be his fuel consumption, stated in miles per gallon?

b. What running speed will the driver be able to attain?

(References: pp. 43 and 46)

4-2. * By regrading and repaving a section of road crossing a divide through a range of hills, the up and down grades can be reduced from 8% to 4%. The length of the road remains approximately the same, a total of 2 miles.

a. What is the saving in fuel cost expressed in cents per vehicle mile on the uphill sections? Gasoline costs 30 cents per gallon; operation is normal at 40 mph on both old and new locations. (Reference: p. 44)

b. If the average daily traffic is 2000 passenger cars, what is the annual saving? (Note: Savings apply only on the uphill one mile.)

c. If the economic life of the improved road is taken as 30 years and 4% is considered an appropriate interest rate, what expenditure for the new road is justified? (Use *CRF* from Table 5, page 60.)

4-3. Vehicles are now operating on an unsurfaced, two-lane, farm-to-market road at 28 mph. It has been proposed that the road either be gravel-surfaced or that it be paved. In either case, vehicles will operate at 40 mph. Surfacing will cost $6000 per mile and last 5 years; base course and road-mix bituminous pavement will cost $14,000 per mile and last 15 years.

a. What saving in operating cost per vehicle-mile for passenger cars results from each of these improvements? Assume free operation for the paved road. (Reference: p. 45)

b. What average daily passenger car traffic is required to justify each of these improvements, based solely on savings in operating costs? Assume that maintenance costs are equal in all cases. This road agency has many demands against its very limited funds, so that 8% interest seems appropriate. (Take values for the *CRF* from Table 5, page 60.)

4-4. Work problem 4-3, including time-savings valued at $1.35 per vehicle-hour in your analysis. (Reference: pp. 50–51)

4-5. Assuming that time-saving (see pp. 50–51) is properly valued at $1.35 per vehicle-hour, extend the portion of Table 1, page 45, that applies to divided highways and free operation to include time-saving. What is the most economical operating speed for these conditions?

4-6. Work problem 4-5 for two-lane pavements, free operation.

4-7. What is the difference in tire costs in cents per vehicle-mile between operation at 30 mph and at 55 mph? Assume that the data in Fig. 3, page 48, apply, and that a set of four tires costs $130.

4-8. Two major highways now intersect at grade, and traffic is controlled by fixed-time signals that operate 24 hours a day. Average daily traffic on highway A is 9000 passenger vehicles and that on highway B is 4000. There is relatively little left-turn traffic and a simple undercrossing like that shown in Fig. 34a, page 207, offers a satisfactory plan for grade separation.

Observations taken over a typical 24-hour period show that 60% of the vehicles on highway A and 40% of those on highway B pass through the intersection without stopping or making an appreciable change from their usual speed of 40 mph. The remaining cars are stopped by the signal. Average standing delay to those stopped on highway A is 20 seconds and on highway B 30 seconds.

a. What are the additional operating costs, without time costs, for each vehicle stopped (*1*) on highway A? (*2*) on highway B? (Reference: pp. 52–54)

b. What are the additional operating costs, including time costs at $1.35 per vehicle-hour, for each vehicle stopped (*1*) on highway A? (*2*) on highway B?

c. What are the annual stopping costs at the intersection (*1*) without time costs? (*2*) with time costs?

d. What investment in a grade separation structure is justified (*1*) without considering time costs? (*2*) considering time costs? Four percent is an appropriate interest rate and 25 years a reasonable useful life. Assume that improved operating conditions for turning vehicles offset any added distances that they must travel and also offset the cost of rise and fall through the grade-separation structure. (Take values for the *CRF* from Table 5, page 60.)

4-9. A section of heavily traveled rural highway carrying 30,000 vehicles per day is now four-lane, undivided. Its accident record over the last few years (with accidents stated in terms of occurrences per million vehicle miles) is as follows: Fatalities, 0.07; personal injury, 2.1; property damage over $25, 8.0. Based on experience with comparable facilities, a freeway on the same route would have only one-fourth as many accidents in each category.

a. Using the accident cost data of the National Safety Council (Reference: pp. 56–58) compute the annual savings in accident costs per mile of road if the highway is reconstructed to freeway standards.

b. Based on 5% interest and a 30-year life, what capital expenditure per mile is justified by these savings?

4-10. Work through the sample economy study in the text (pp. 69–72) by the annual-cost and benefit-cost methods using an interest rate of 5%.[1]

4-11. Revise the sample economy study in the text (pp. 69–72) on the assumption that the average daily traffic, now 800 vehicles per day, will increase at the rate of 20 vehicles each year for the 60-year life of the road. The percentage and character of truck traffic will remain the same. Employ the formula for equivalent annual traffic volume on page 66.

a. Solve by the annual-cost and benefit-cost methods with interest at 4%.

b. Solve by the rate-of-return method.

4-12. Revise the sample economy study in the text (pp. 69–72) on the assumption that the road's accident experience will be as follows:

Alternative *A*. 7.0 fatalities per 100 million vehicle-miles.
Alternative *B*. 4.0   "   "   "   "   "   "   .
Alternative *C*. 2.0   "   "   "   "   "   "   .

Determine accident costs on the basis that the fractional number of fatalities can be multiplied by $95,000 to set the cost of all accidents. (Reference: p. 57)

a. Solve by the annual-cost and benefit-cost methods using interest at 4%.

b. Solve by the rate-of-return method.

4-13.* Change the basic data for the sample economy study in the text (pp. 69–72) to read as follows:

Element	Estimated Useful Life, Years	Cost Alternative *A*	Alternative *B*	Alternative *C*
Right of way	60	$ 0	$ 14,000	$ 12,000
Grading	30	42,000	200,000	380,000
Structures	40	40,000	250,000	475,000
Surfaces	20	6,000	160,000	140,000

Solve this problem by the method or methods and at the interest rate designated by the instructor, assuming:

a. That traffic volume remains constant.

b. That the average daily traffic increases as indicated in problem 4-11.

c. That the accident experience of the different alternatives will be different as indicated in problem 4-12.

d. That the average daily traffic increases and that the accident experience differs between alternatives as indicated in problems 4-11 and 4-12.

4-14.[1] Two six-lane metropolitan traffic arteries controlled by traffic lights now carry a total average daily traffic of 50,000 vehicles, of which 15% are trucks. Attempted speed of travel is 32 mph, but average attained speed is 20 mph, since drivers average 2½ stops per mile. Average standing time at each stop is 20 seconds.

An eight-lane freeway costing $4,500,000 per mile, including interchanges and connections, is planned to take through traffic from these streets. Half the cost is for rights of way having a 60-year assumed life; the remainder is for grading, structures, and pavement with an assumed life of 30 years. The freeway will divert 75% of the traffic from the present arteries. Average speed on the freeway will be 44 mph and delays will be negligible. Maintenance and administrative costs for the freeway and streets will be $6000 per mile per year more than for the streets alone.

a. Compute, for passenger cars, the average saving in operating costs per vehicle-mile. Use data from pp. 45–54. Assume restricted operation (divided roadway) at 32 mph for street conditions and free operation at 44 mph for the freeway.

(1) Omit time costs from your answer.

(2) Include time costs at $1.35 per hour in your answer.

b. Compute the average saving per vehicle-mile for trucks, including time costs. Assume that operating costs for trucks are three times those for passenger cars. Time costs are 5 cents per minute.

---

[1] Data for this problem have been adapted and simplified from three reports on the economy of freeways made between 1951 and 1954 by the City of Los Angeles. These studies found that the "minimum benefits" to motorists traveling on freeways in densely built-up areas (as contrasted to travel on surface streets) was 2.00 cents per vehicle-mile. This total included 0.33 cents per vehicle-mile gasoline savings, counting those from eliminated stops; 0.24 cents per vehicle-mile reduction in maintenance costs from elimination of stop-and-go travel; 0.56 cents per vehicle-mile in accident reduction; and 0.87 cents per vehicle-mile time saving. (The figure for time saving is an average for all vehicles but counts only the savings to commercial vehicles.) It was found, for four typical freeway sections, that first costs would be equaled by cumulated benefits in periods ranging from 3.4 to 9.5 years.

c. Compute the total annual savings in operating costs per mile of freeway.

(*1*) Include time saving for trucks only.

(*2*) Include time savings for all vehicles.

d. Compute the difference in annual costs, including road-user costs, between continued operation on the streets and operation if the freeway is constructed. Employ the sample economy study on pp. 69–72 as a guide. Interest is at 4%.

(*1*) Include time saving for trucks only in your study.

(*2*) Include time saving for all vehicles.

e. Compute benefit-cost ratios based on the costs and benefits found in part *d.*

f. Compute the rate of return on the investment in the freeway.

(*1*) Include time savings for trucks only.

(*2*) Include time saving for all vehicles.

(Note: Capital recovery factors for interest rates greater than 10% may be found in the references cited in footnote 16, page 61.)

4-15. Solve problem 4-14 assuming that the average daily traffic of 50,000 vehicles traveling streets and freeway will increase at the rate of 1000 vehicles per year for the 60-year life of the facility. Employ the formula on page 66 to find the equivalent annual traffic volume.

4-16. Solve problem 4-14 including the expected reduction in accident costs in your analysis. Assume that accident experience will be as follows:

Street operation, with or without freeway, 4.2 fatalities per 100 million vehicle miles.

Freeway operation, 1.5 fatalities per 100 million vehicle miles.

Determine accident costs on the basis that the fractional number of fatalities can be multiplied by $95,000 to set the cost of all accidents. (Reference: p. 57)

4-17. Solve problem 4-14 considering the traffic increase described in problem 4-15 and the reduction in accident costs outlined by problem 4-16.

4-18. Investigate the sufficiency rating plan of the state in which your college is located or of a nearby state designated by the instructor. Reference 27 on page 72 should be helpful.

4-19.* The average vehicle in a given state travels 9000 miles per year and consumes gasoline at a rate of 14 miles per gallon. State gasoline taxes are currently $0.055 per gallon; license fees average $20 annually and are all employed for highway purposes.

a. Compute the average annual tax payment per vehicle-mile.

b. Compute the yearly revenue per mile of highway for traffic volumes of 250, 500, 1000, 3000, 5000, and 10,000 vehicles per day.

c. The estimated cost of a stretch of new four-lane divided highway with Portland-cement-concrete pavement is $275,000 per mile. Of this, $75,000 is for rights of way, $100,000 for grading, and $100,000 for paving, for which the estimated useful lives are respectively 60, 40, and 25 years. Estimated annual maintenance cost will be $3100 and the average annual cost of periodic major repairs $2000 per mile. Administrative overhead is assigned at $200 per mile per year. At 3% interest, calculate the average daily traffic at which the annual payments in taxes equal the annual cost of highway construction and operation.

d. If 40% of the initial investment for the road described in part *c* is to come from Federal-aid funds, what then is the average daily traffic at which the annual payments in taxes equal the State's portion of the annual cost of construction and operation?

e. What is the "solvency quotient" for the road described in part *c*, if the average daily traffic is 20,000 vehicles? (Reference: p. 74)

Chapter 5

5-1. Prepare a brief summary of highway financing requirements in the United States, based on data released since September 1954. Use the statement on pages 75–76 as a guide. *Engineering News-Record*, available in the college library, is a valuable source of information. Articles on financing can be found quickly by reference to the topical index prepared each six months. *American Highways*, published by the AASHO, also carries numerous 'articles on the subject. For example, the April 1955 issue, page 18, reports estimated construction needs by states, by systems, and as rural and urban for the period 1955–1964. (The total for the continental United States is $100 billion, segregated as follows: Interstate, 23 billions; other Federal-aid primary, 30 billions; Federal-aid secondary, 15 billions; other state highways, 5 billions; other roads and streets, 27 billions. For all systems, rural needs total 64 billions and urban needs 36 billions.)

5-2. List the subjects that brought particular controversy when President Eisenhower's highway program was presented to Congress early in 1955. References listed for problem 5-1 should be helpful.

5-3. What sums of money, by sources, are available annually for highway purposes in the state in which your college is located? How, by amounts, is this money distributed among state highways, local rural roads, and city streets? Data will be found in *Highway Statistics*, published annually by the U. S. Bureau of Public Roads.

5-4. For the state in which your college is located, compare the actual responsibilities for highway financing with those outlined in the textbook on pages 77 and 78.

a. Direct your study particularly at the state highway system.

b. Direct your study particularly at local road agencies.

5-5. Extend Fig. 1, page 83, and Fig. 2, page 90, through the last year of record. Data will be found in *Highway Statistics*, published annually by the U. S. Bureau of Public Roads.

5-6. How much, if any, user-tax revenue is diverted to non-highway purposes in the state in which your college is located? (Same reference as for problem 5-5.)

Chapter 6

6-1. On a map of your college campus or of a nearby community (as designated by the instructor), determine the approximate location of a suitable route for either a bypass or a circumferential road system to remove through traffic from the congested central area. Reconnaissance in the field or a study of aerial photographs is highly desirable if time and facilities permit. Defend your selection with a brief written statement. (References: pp. 27–30 and 113–118)

6-2. Submit a freehand sketch showing a plan view of a badly located or otherwise inadequate bridge or culvert in the area near your college campus. On the same sketch, show the realignment that you propose. Defend your proposal with a brief written statement. (Reference: pp. 110–113)

Chapter 7

7-1. Determine, from the most recent budget of the highway department in the state where your college is located, or from *Highway Statistics*, published by the U. S. Bureau of Public Roads:

a. The amounts budgeted for rights of way, construction, maintenance, administration, and other major items.

b. The percentages of the total budget devoted to each of these items.

7-2. Define, in your own words: police power, weight of authority, eminent domain, market value, severance damage, special benefit, general benefit, excess condemnation.

7-3. In general terms, for what losses is a property owner compensated in the following situations? What losses go uncompensated? Explain each answer briefly.

a. A new highway diverts 75% of the traffic from the road in front of his service station so that his business declines very substantially.

b. The property occupied by a grocery store is taken for highway purposes. The store is moved to a nearby site, but business is interrupted for a month during the move and a large number of customers begin trading with other stores.

c. An entire house and lot are taken for highway purposes.

d. A storage yard for raw materials adjacent to a manufacturing plant is taken. The factory building itself is not disturbed.

7-4. *a.* What is control of access?

b. In general, must property owners be compensated when access rights to an existing road or street are taken? Are there exceptions to the general rule?

c. What have the courts ruled as to compensation for access rights to controlled access highways on entirely new locations?

7-5. In general, can property owners collect damages when a highway improvement lengthens the route of access to or egress from their property? Explain briefly.

Chapter 8

8-1. Compare the limitations on truck dimensions, axle loads, and weights in the state where your college is located with those recommended by the AASHO. (References: Table 1, page 139, and the Motor Vehicle Code of your state)

8-2. Based on Fig. 1, page 140, determine the ratio between maximum flow in vehicles per hour in one direction (as indicated by the upper diagrams) and the average annual daily traffic. Assume that, at peak hours, truck and bus traffic is equally divided between eastbound and westbound.

8-3.* The average daily traffic volume, as measured, on a given rural highway is 8000 vehicles.

a. What is the estimated 30th-hour volume for an average traffic distribution?

b. Within what range would you reasonably expect the 30th-hour volume to fall? (Reference: p. 141)

8-4. Convert minimum vehicle spacing, as shown in Fig. 3, page 144, into maximum capacity of a traffic lane as shown in Fig. 4 on the same page. Specifically, make the computation for a two-lane highway in daytime and for speeds of 10, 30, and 50 mph.

8-5.* For a two-lane highway with 12-foot lanes and for speeds in the 50–55 mph range, find practical capacities in the following situations: (Reference: pp. 148–155) *a.* If the roadway has no features that limit capacity.

b. If 40% of the roadway has sight distances less than 1500 feet.

c. If obstructions are located within 4 feet of the pavement edge on both sides.

d. If the terrain is rolling and 10% of the traffic is commercial vehicles.

e. If the road is straight, on a 5% grade one mile long, and carries 10% truck traffic. Give separately the number of passenger vehicles and the number of trucks.

8-6. What is the practical capacity of a two-lane highway designed for 45–50 mph? Trucks make up 10% of the total traffic. Other characteristics are: lane width 10 feet, with obstructions on both sides within 2 feet of the roadway; rolling terrain; and sight distances less than 1500 feet for 60% of the road's length. (Reference: pp. 150–154)

8-7. Based on the 30th-hour principle and average fluctuation in traffic flow, what average daily traffic can the road described in problem 8-6 accommodate? (Reference: p. 141)

8-8. What is the practical capacity per hour in one direction for a four-lane urban freeway in the following situations? (Reference: pp. 148–151)

a. If the roadway has no features that limit capacity.

b. If the terrain is rolling and the traffic is 20% trucks.

c. If, during construction of an overcrossing, the roadway width is limited to two 9-foot lanes by piers supporting formwork for the overcrossing.

8-9.* What increase in capacity per clock-hour results when the curb to curb width of a two-way downtown street is increased from 36 to 44 feet? Give your answer for one direction of travel. Assume that parking is prohibited, and that 50% of the total traffic signal cycle time is given to the street in question. (Reference: p. 157)

8-10.* What percentage increase in capacity of a two-way downtown street 40 feet wide (curb to curb) can be gained by prohibiting parking during peak hours? (Reference: p. 157)

8-11. Congestion is serious at peak hours in the downtown area of a city. At present, much of the traffic is carried on two parallel streets each 36 feet wide, curb to curb. Traffic moves two ways on each street and parking is permitted. What percentage increase over present capacity can be gained if: (Reference: p. 157)

a. Parking is prohibited during peak hours?

b. Parking is prohibited during peak hours and the streets are converted to one-way operation?

8-12. A rural section of two-lane highway is to be built to interstate standards and for a design speed of 70 mph. For this situation, determine: (a) advisable lane width, (b) advisable shoulder width, (c) steepest side slopes in earth cuts, (d) steepest side slopes on low fills, (e) pavement cross-slope, (f) desirable right-of-way width, (g) nonpassing sight distance, (h) passing sight distance,[1] (i) maximum desirable grade, (j) degree of curve of sharpest horizontal curve, (k) minimum length of easement curve for sharpest horizontal curve. (Reference: pp. 160–191)

8-13. Change the design speed for problem 8-12 to 60 mph and obtain the answers called for in that problem.

8-14. A cement-rubble wall 15 feet high from base to top is to retain the side slopes of a fill on a parkway project. Based on Fig. 16, page 168, draw a cross section of the wall. Show all dimensions.

8-15.* a. A vehicle is traveling at 50 mph. Assuming that driver perception time is 1.5 sec and reaction time is 0.5 sec, what will be his stopping distance on dry concrete pavement for which f is 0.56? (Reference: pp. 171–173)

b. Assume conditions as in part a, except that the driver's attention is off the road and his perception time becomes 3.0 sec.

c. Assume conditions as in part a, except that the vehicle is traveling down a 3% grade.

8-16. Work problem 8-15 for a speed of 20 mph.

8-17. A driver is traveling at 35 mph on a wet pavement made slick by oil droppings ($f = 0.20$). He is alert for danger, so that his perception plus reaction time is one second. What is the safe nonpassing sight distance for these conditions? (Reference: pp. 171–172)

8-18. The driver of a vehicle traveling 45 mph requires 125 feet to stop after he has applied the brakes. What coefficient of friction f was developed between tires and pavement? (Reference: p. 171)

8-19. Determine minimum vertical curve lengths to provide (a) nonpassing and (b) passing sight distances in each of the following situations. Use passing sight distances from the footnote to problem

---

[1] *A Policy on Geometric Design of Rural Highways*, published by the AASHO in late 1954, supersedes the individual policy pamphlets referred to in the textbook (see footnote 2, page 137). In the new publication, nonpassing sight distances remain unchanged, but minimum safe passing sight distances for 2-lane roads were changed as follows:

Design speed, mph	30	40	50	60	70
Minimum safe passing sight distance for 2-lane highways, feet	800	1300	1700	2000	2300

8-12 rather than from the textbook. (References: pp. 170–172, 176–179)

Percent Grade of Grade Lines

Case	Design Speed, mph	Approaching Intersection Point (+ grades are uphill)	Leaving Intersection Point (+ grades are uphill)
1	30	+6	−5
2	40	+5	−2
3	50	+2	−3
4	60	+5	+1
5	70	+2	−0
6	70	+4	−3

8-20.* Vehicle performance is being tested on a large flat paved area. For this situation: (Reference: pp. 181–182)

a. What coefficient of side friction must be developed to hold a car going 60 mph on a 6-degree circular curve?

b. What is the sharpest curve (stated in degree of curve) that a vehicle traveling 60 mph can travel if the coefficient of side friction is 0.40?

8-21. For a maximum superelevation of 0.10 feet per foot, compute the maximum permissible degree of curve for design speeds of 30, 40, 50, 60, and 70 mph. Use the revised values for coefficients of side friction as recommended by the AASHO.[1] (Reference: pp. 184–185)

8-22.* Work problem 8-21, using the maximum permissible superelevation where snow and ice conditions prevail.

8-23. In an effort to discourage drivers from exceeding the design speed of a road, superelevations are set at values that develop the maximum permissible coefficient of side friction. (See the footnote to problem 8-21.) Determine the superelevations to employ in the following situations: (Reference: p. 184)

a. Design speed 70 mph, (*1*) 2½-degree curve, (*2*) 3-degree curve.

b. Design speed 50 mph, (*1*) 5-degree curve, (*2*) 7-degree curve.

8-24. For each of the combinations indicated below, develop profiles like Fig. 26a, page 192. The pavement is two-lane; each lane is 12 feet wide. Show stationing along the roadway by assuming that normal crown ends at station 19 + 00 and that the *TS* is at station 20 + 00. For vertical dimensions, show differences in elevation between centerline grade and each edge of pavement at each point where

[1] *A Policy on Geometric Design of Rural Highways*, AASHO, 1954, recommends side friction factors as follows:

Design speed, mph	30	40	50	60	70
Maximum safe side friction factors	.16	.15	.14	.13	.12

the profile breaks. Determine superelevation for the circular curves from Fig. 23, page 186. Select easement curve lengths from Table 13, page 191.

a. Design speed 40 mph, 8-degree circular curve.

b. Design speed 50 mph, 6-degree circular curve.

c. Design speed 70 mph, 3-degree circular curve.

8-25. Work problem 8-24, assuming the inside edge of the pavement remains on a uniform grade as shown in Fig. 26b, page 192.

8-26. A corner of an existing building is 25 feet from centerline on a curved portion of a two-lane highway. Considering horizontal sight distance, what is the safe operating speed if the curve is (a) 12-degree? (b) 5-degree? (Reference: pp. 194–195)

8-27. Cuts on the backslopes of a highway lie on a 2 (horizontal) to 1 (vertical) slope. The grade line is straight. Superelevation is constant across pavement, shoulder, and to the toe of the cut slope. For a two-lane highway and 70 mph design speed, what distance is required between the centerline and the toe of the cut slope to satisfy horizontal sight distance requirements: (a) for a 2½-degree circular curve (e = 0.08)? (b) for a 4-degree circular curve (e = 0.12)? (Reference: pp. 194–196)

8-28. Work problem 8-27 for a 50 mph design speed. For part a, use a 6-degree circular curve (e = 0.10), and for part b, an 8-degree circular curve (e = 0.12).

8-29. As a class project, plan the channelization for a troublesome intersection in the vicinity of your campus. This problem may involve field measurements and peak-hour traffic counts. (References: pp. 197–201; publication on *Channelization*, see footnote 51, page 198; and chapters VII and VIII of *A Policy on Geometric Design for Rural Highways*, AASHO, 1954)

Chapter 9

9-1. For a location in southern Ohio (or some other place designated by the instructor), and for each of the cases given below, find peak rates of runoff by means of Fig. 1, page 219:

Case 1. Twenty-five-year frequency, row crops, 5 acres area, flat slopes.

Case 2. Case 1, but for 900 acres.

Case 3. Fifty-year frequency, mixed cover, 10 acres, steep slopes.

Case 4. Case 3, but with 5-year frequency.

9-2.* What runoff would be expected for a 5-year flood frequency from 200 acres of mixed-cover land in a rural area near Chicago, Illinois? Land slope is 0.2%. (Reference: p. 219)

9-3. For a small drainage area in the vicinity of your college, as designated by the instructor:

a. Measure the area, the developed length of channel, the fall of the basin, and the average cross-slope from a U. S. Geological Survey or other topographic map. Select a coefficient of runoff based on field examination of the area.

b. Determine the peak runoff for the area by the rational method. Assume that the coefficients in Table 1, the formula for time of concentration, and the rainfall intensity chart given in the textbook (see pp. 220–221) apply unless otherwise directed by the instructor.

c. If your location is in the east, south, or middle-west, compare the peak runoff obtained in part *b* with that obtained from Fig. 1, page 219.

9-4. A channel of roughly graded clay and gravel ($n = 0.03$), with a 2-foot flat bottom and 2 to 1 side slopes (see Fig. 5, page 231) is laid out on a 6% grade. Design flow is 100 cfs.

a. How deep must the channel be to provide 6 inches vertical freeboard against overtopping?

b. Would erosion be a serious problem? Explain.

9-5. Assume that, at a downstream point, the grade of the channel described in problem 9-4 flattens to 0.2%:

a. How deep must the channel then be to provide 6 inches of freeboard?

b. Would you expect a hydraulic jump near the transition point? Explain.

c. Would the flatter channel require lining for erosion-control purposes?

9-6. Design flow for a channel with dimensions as shown in Fig. 5, page 231, lies on a 3% grade and is lined with heavy grass. Design flow is 20 cfs.

a. How deep is the water in the channel?

b. Does the grass offer suitable protection against erosion? Explain.

c. Is the flow in the channel rapid or tranquil?

9-7.* A 48-inch pipe on a 1.5% grade flows part full at a discharge of 125 cfs. (Case IIa of Fig. 8, page 242.)

a. What is the headwater elevation if the invert elevation is 100.0 ft? (Reference: p. 243)

b. Is some arrangement for energy dissipation necessary to prevent erosion if the downstream channel is lined with well-established grass? Note: For a given rate of flow, velocity in a part-full pipe must always be greater than in a full pipe. (References: pp. 230, 239, 243)

9-8. A 36-inch concrete pipe ($n = 0.015$) 150 feet long is on a 4%

grade. Design flow is 100 cfs. How high, in feet, will the headwater rise above the invert in each of the following situations:

a. The pipe entrance is square-edged so that the culvert will not flow full. (References: Case IIa, Fig. 8, and Fig. 9; pp. 242–243)

b. The pipe entrance is rounded so that the culvert flows full at the outlet, which is not submerged. (Reference: pp. 246–249)

9-9. A 24-inch pipe 150 feet long has a uniform fall of 2 feet in its full length. It will flow full, but the outlet will not be submerged. (Case IIb, Fig. 8, page 242.) What flow will the pipe carry when the inlet is submerged 2 feet above the crown of the pipe: (Reference: pp. 245–247)

a. For concrete pipe $(n = 0.015)$?

b. For corrugated metal pipe $(n = 0.024)$?

9-10. A concrete box culvert is 8 feet by 8 feet in cross section and 500 feet long $(n = 0.015)$. It lies on a 0.1% grade and will flow full with the outlet unsubmerged at the design discharge of 500 cfs. (Case IIb, Fig. 8, page 242.) How high will the headwater rise above the crown of the culvert if:

a. The entrance is square-edged $(K_e = 0.4)$? (Reference: page 246)

b. The entrance is rounded $(K_e = 0.1)$?

9-11. Work problem 9-10 assuming that the culvert is rectangular in cross section and is 10 feet wide and 6 feet high.

9-12. A culvert under a high fill is 300 feet long and is laid out on a 3% grade. Design flow is 250 cfs. Headwater can rise 9 feet above the flow line at the inlet without causing serious damage. The channel is rocky, so that erosion upstream or downstream is not a problem. Tailwater elevation is below the culvert crown. Select a concrete box culvert of square cross section and standard size (4 x 4, 5 x 5, 6 x 6, etc.) for these conditions assuming:

a. That the culvert entrance is square-edged and the culvert will not flow full. (Solve by trial and error in Fig. 10, page 244.)

b. That the culvert entrance is rounded $(K = 0.1)$ and the culvert flows full. (Use Fig. 11, page 246.)

9-13. Work problem 9-12 for a circular concrete pipe culvert using $n = 0.015$. Use Fig. 9, page 243, in place of Fig. 10 for solving part *a.* Culvert sizes are in 6-inch increments.

Chapter 10

10-1. For an existing highway in the vicinity of your college which, at present, is unattractive or subject to unsightly erosion: Prepare a brief statement outlining improvements that you would recommend. Be sure to justify your recommendations on economic and aesthetic grounds.

Chapter 11

11-1. Compare the pavement marking practices of your state or local road agency with those recommended by the *Manual of Uniform Traffic Control Devices* and its 1954 supplement of 19 pages. (References: pp. 267–269, the *Manual,* and appropriate standard drawings of the local highway agency)

11-2. Study a troublesome intersection in the vicinity of your college campus and determine whether it can best be regulated by (*a*) making one street an arterial, (*b*) installing 4-way stop signs, or (*c*) installing fixed-time or traffic-actuated signals. (References: pp. 269–280, 294 and appropriate references listed on those pages)

11-3. Traffic signals with a master controller for flexible progressive operation have been installed at eight intersections on the main street of a small town. Intersection spacing is uniformly 300 feet center to center. For this situation, develop progressive timing for the signals. Proceed step by step as follows: (Reference: pp. 275–278)

a. On a full-size sheet of drafting paper, plot street spacing as the ordinate *vs.* time in seconds as the abscissa (see Fig. 2). It will be more convenient to plot street spacing as 0.682 times the distance in feet, for then slopes of lines on the graph are in miles per hour.

b. Mark out signal timing for each intersection on separate narrow strips of paper. For this simplified problem, assume that total cycle time is 60 seconds, divided at all intersections into 30 seconds green, 6 seconds yellow, and 24 seconds red. Also procure black string or thread for laying out the through bands.

c. Determine signal offsets to give equal width through bands in both directions (see Fig. 2*b*). Assume that floating-car observations indicate that 14 miles per hour is the prevailing vehicle speed. Use a trial and error procedure, shifting the signal-interval strips and thread as required.

d. How wide are the through bands? Also determine the number of cars that can go through uninterrupted on each band. (Reference: p. 156)

e. Determine signal offsets to give the maximum width through band to vehicles traveling in one direction.

11-4. Using the chart and strips developed for parts *a* and *b* of problem 11-3, determine answers for parts *c, d,* and *e* of that problem for a prevailing vehicle speed of 18 mph.

11-5. Using the instructions of problem 11-3 as a guide, review the timing of a system of progressive signals located near your college.

11-6. Outline a plan for a system of one-way streets for a town or city near your college. (Reference: pp. 280–282)

11-7. From the latest edition of *Accident Facts,* published annually by the National Safety Council:

a. Determine the number of deaths, the mileage death rate, and the population death rate for the state in which your college is located. Compare the record of your state with that of the United States as a whole.

b. Compare the accident experience of the city or town where your college is located to the weighted average of all cities and towns in the United States.

11-8. *a.* Based on accident reports in the file of your local police department, plot a collision diagram for the accidents in the last calendar year at one of the more dangerous intersections.

b. Prepare recommendations to improve conditions at the intersection. (Reference: pp. 292–295)

Chapter 12

12-1.* Specimens of two soils were compacted in the laboratory employing the AASHO standard (Proctor) test method. Unit weights for varying moisture contents were as follows:

Soil A		*Soil B*	
Moisture Content, % by wt. of dry soil	Wet Weight of Soil, lbs/cu. ft.	Moisture Content, % by wt. of dry soil	Wet Weight of Soil, lbs/cu. ft.
4.43	134.1	12.6	122.6
6.77	144.0	14.2	125.0
7.37	145.2	16.3	128.8
8.36	145.2	17.0	128.8
8.95	144.0	19.7	127.5

On a single graph, plot the wet weight and dry weight curves for these soils and determine the optimum moisture content for each. If one of these soils is a well-graded sandy soil and the other is a clay type, which soil is the clay type and why? (Reference: pp. 325–326)

12-2. On the graph prepared for problem 12-1, plot the zero air-voids curve for the soils, assuming that the soil particles have a specific gravity of 2.68. (Reference: page 325)

12-3. Compute the energy in ft-lb per cubic foot of compacted soil that is applied to laboratory samples in conducting: (Reference: page 328) *a.* The AASHO standard impact compaction test.

b. The modified AASHO impact compaction test.

c. The California impact test. (Use 11-inch sample height.)

12-4. A soil identical with sample number 3 of Fig. 8, page 326, has been compacted in an embankment. A test hole measuring 6 inches in diameter and 8 inches deep is dug in the fill. The material, as taken from the hole, weighs 16.7 pounds and has a moisture percentage of 10, based on dry weight. What is the dry weight per cubic foot and the relative compaction of the soil in the fill? (Reference: pp. 329–330)

12-5. Find the textural classification for each soil listed in Table A. (Reference: pp. 331–333)

12-6. Find the AASHO classification for each soil listed in Table A. (Reference: pp. 333–336)

12-7. Find the Group Index for soils numbered 1 through 6 inclusive of Table A. (Reference: pp. 337–338)

12-8. A new two-lane rural highway is to traverse an area for which the native soil corresponds to No. 2 of Table A. This soil will be the subgrade or basement soil in cuts and will be used for embankments. A select material like soil No. 4, Table A, is available in a nearby borrow pit, and a granular base course comparable to soil No. 11, Table A, can be produced from a streambed within an economical haul distance of the project. Pavement is to be bituminous road mix 2 inches thick. Traffic is light and totals 500 vehicles per day for both directions. Ten percent of the vehicles are trucks; and, of these, 50% are two-axle, 30% are three-axle, 10% are four-axle, and 10% are five-axle.

For the situation outlined in the preceding paragraph, develop typical roadway cross sections like Fig. 1, page 309. Show the depth of each individual layer to the nearest one-half inch.

a. Base your design on the Group Index method. (References: pp. 337–338, 344–345)

b. Base your design on the *CBR* method and the Wyoming design chart. Assume that curve 5 applies. (Reference: pp. 346–349)

c. Base your design on the Hveem stabilometer method.[1] Traffic

---

[1] *The Laboratory Manual of California Standard Test Procedures,* California Division of Highways, November 1954, recommends that determination of Equivalent 5000-lb Wheel Loads for the Hveem stabilometer method be based on estimated truck traffic, subdivided in terms of axles per truck. Annual equivalent 5000-lb wheel loads for each class of truck are found by multiplying the daily one-directional count for each truck class by the constants given below. Pickups are excluded from the count.

(Footnote continued on p. 22.)

TABLE A. TABULATION OF TEST RESULTS ON ELEVEN SOILS *

Test	Soil Number										
	1	2	3	4	5	6	7	8	9	10	11
Sieve analysis											
Total % passing											
1½ in. sieve									100		
1 in. "									98		
¾ in. "	100			100	100		100		96	100	100
⅜ in. "	99		100	96	96		81	100	83	73	80
No. 4 "	98		99	92	89	100	68	99	62	60	64
No. 8 "	98		96	87	83	96	59	84	50	53	53
No. 10 "	97	100	95	86	81	94	57	80	47	50	50
No. 16 "	97	99	91	81	72	87	48	64	38	41	40
No. 30 "	96	98	86	77	66	82	38	50	29	25	26
No. 40 "	94	95	82	70	61	70	34	44	24	21	18
No. 50 "	93	92	78	65	52	57	30	38	18	16	12
No. 100 "	90	81	68	55	40	42	25	26	12	10	7
No. 200 "	86	67	58	47	29	31	21	16	10	8	4
No. 270 "	85	64	52	45	25	28	21	14	9	7	1
0.005 mm	48	24	21	15	10	8	10	4	4	0	0
0.001 mm	32	11	13	4	5	3	5	2	2		
Atterberg limits											
Liquid limit	30	25	48	30	20	41	24	—	22	—	—
Plastic limit	21	14	36	22	17	36	20	—	17	—	—
Plasticity index	9	11	12	8	3	5	4	NP	5	NP	NP
Sand equivalent	4	4	6	13	18	31	21	38	31	31	66
CBR at 0.1 in. penetration, %	3	4	5	23	102	32	151	96	113	152	116
% Swell, CBR method	8.8	4.7	10.9	2.6	0.9	2.2	0.4	1.0	0.6	0.1	0.1
R value by stabilometer	5	17	27	38	45	55	60	64	71	78	81

* Courtesy F. N. Hveem, Materials and Research Engineer, California Division of Highways. (Data slightly modified.)

Number of axles on truck	2	3	4	5	6
EWL constant	300	700	1400	2100	1600

Cohesiometer values are as given on Fig. 18, page 352, of the textbook. Minimum value is 100, which applies to granular base courses and thin bituminous surfaces. For two-layer construction, as with a cement-treated base overlaid by a bituminous plant-mix surfacing, an equivalent cohesiometer value C_m is employed. C_m is given by the formula:

$$C_m = C_1 + \left(\frac{t_2}{t_1 + t_2}\right)^2 (C_2 - C_1)$$

(Footnote continued on facing page.)

is equally divided between directions. Pavement life is 10 years. Cohesiometer value for the road-mix surfacing, before correction for depth, is 150. (Reference: pp. 350–352)

d. Extend the design of part c (Hveem stabilometer method) to recognize expansive forces in the basement soil. Select material, base, and pavement weigh 130 lbs per cu ft. Expansion test results on soil No. 2 are as follows: (Reference: pp. 351–353)

Moisture, % of dry weight	12.3	14.0	16.3
Resistance value, Hveem stabilometer	17	13	10
Expansion pressure, psi	1.5	1.1	0.8

12-9. Work part c of problem 12-8, assuming that the 2-inch road-mix surface (cohesiometer value 150) is underlain by a 5-inch cement-treated base (cohesiometer value 2000).

12-10. Work problem 12-8, changed as follows:

The native soil, which is the basement soil in cuts and is used for embankments, is like soil No. 1 of Table A. Select material underlying the base course is like soil No. 5 of Table A.

Expansion tests for soil No. 1 give the following results:

Moisture, % of dry weight	18.0	20.4	22.7
Resistance value, Hveem stabilometer	5	4	3
Expansion pressure, psi	2	1	0.7

12-11. A new four-lane divided highway traverses an area for which the native soil corresponds to soil No. 2 of Table A. This soil will be the subgrade or basement soil in cuts and will be used for embankments. A select material like soil No. 4, Table A, is available in a nearby borrow pit. Granular base course comparable to soil No. 11 of Table A can be purchased from a nearby commercial plant. Pavement is to be 4 inches of bituminous plant mix. Traffic totals 8000 vehicles per day for both directions, and is 15% trucks. Of these, 40% are two-axle, 30% are three-axle, 15% are four-axle, and 15% are five-axle.

For the situation outlined in the preceding paragraph, develop typical roadway cross sections for each roadway like Fig. 1, page 309. Show the depth of each individual layer to the nearest one-half inch. Since almost all trucks will travel in the right-hand lane, traffic volume determinations for roadway design are the same as if the road were two-lane.

where t_1 and t_2 represent thicknesses of top and bottom layers respectively, and C_1 and C_2 are cohesiometer readings for top and bottom layers. For a three-layer system, the equivalent cohesiometer value is first obtained for the top two layers, then the procedure is repeated treating the top two courses as a single layer.

a. Base your design on the Group Index method. Assume that thicknesses do not change after the daily volume of trucks and buses exceeds 1000. (References: pp. 337–338, 344–345)

b. Base your design on the *CBR* method and the Wyoming design chart. Assume that curve 15 applies. (Reference: pp. 346–349)

c. Base your design on the Hveem stabilometer method. Traffic is equally divided between directions. Cohesiometer value for the plant-mix surfacing, before correction for thickness, is 300. Pavement life is 20 years. (References: pp. 350–352 and the footnote to problem 12-8)

d. Extend the design of part *c* (Hveem stabilometer method) to recognize expansive forces in the basement soil. Select material, base, and pavement weigh 130 lb per cu ft. Expansion test results for soil No. 2 appear in part *d* of problem 12-8.

12-12. Work part *c* of problem 12-11, assuming that the 4-inch plant-mix surfacing (cohesiometer value 300) is underlain by 6 inches of cement-treated base (cohesiometer value 2000).

12-13. Work problem 12-11, changed as follows:

The native soil, which is the basement soil in cuts and is used for embankments, is like soil No. 1 of Table A. Select material underlying the base course is like soil No. 5 of Table A. Expansion tests results for soil No. 1 appear in problem 12-10.

Chapter 13

13-1. Obtain a set of specifications and contract documents for a particular project of the state highway department of your state. From them, determine the basis of payment for the grading items of clearing and grubbing, excavation, overbreak, overhaul, watering, and compaction. If possible, determine unit prices for these items for one or more typical projects. (Reference: pp. 367–390)

13-2. By a study of the standard specifications of the state highway department of your state, determine its practices for embankment construction. Consider each of the topics discussed in the textbook on pages 381 to 390.

Chapter 14

14-1. *a.* Which of the soils listed in Table A of this problem set meet the AASHO grading requirements for an untreated road surface? In which grading classification do they fall? (Reference: p. 398)

b. Of the soils that meet the grading requirements for untreated road surface (part *a*) which also meet the plasticity requirements of the AASHO specifications? (Reference: p. 399)

Chapter 15

15-1. *a.* Which of the soils listed in Table A of this problem set meet the AASHO grading requirements for granular base courses? In which classification do they fall? (References: pp. 398, 418–419)

b. Of the soils that meet the grading requirements for granular base courses (part *a*) which also meet the strength and/or plasticity requirements of (*1*) the AASHO, (*2*) the *CBR* specification, and (*3*) the California Division of Highways? (Reference: p. 419)

Chapter 16

16-1. Compare the specifications of your state highway department for waterbound macadam base course with those of the AASHO. In your comparison consider requirements for aggregate grading and toughness, the use of a blanket of screenings and its thickness, and construction and compaction methods and requirements. (Reference: pp. 439–442)

Chapter 17

17-1. A crushed gravel (specific gravity 2.65) having the same grading as soil No. 10 of Table A of this problem set is employed as aggregate for a road-mix pavement. How many pounds of SC-2 oil are required per pound of aggregate, based on:

a. The McKesson-Frickstad formula? (Reference: p. 477)

b. The California formula? (Reference: pp. 477–478)

c. The surface-area method? The aggregate is of average absorption and roughness (curve 5, Fig. 5). (Reference: pp. 478–481)

d. The surface-area method? Aggregate is slick and nonabsorptive (curve 1 of Fig. 5).

17-2. Work problem 17-1, using soil No. 9 of Table A as the aggregate. Specific gravity is 2.61.

17-3.* Aggregate for a dense-graded asphaltic mixture is blended from gravel, sand, and limestone to give the grading of soil No. 11 of Table A of this problem set. The average specific gravity of the blended aggregate is 2.67. The aggregate is relatively nonabsorptive. The paving asphalt has a normal penetration of 150.

a. How many pounds of paving asphalt are required per pound of aggregate? Base your answer on the surface-area method, pp. 478–481. Use the surface-area constants of Table 8.

b. What percentage of the total weight of the paving mixture is asphalt?

17-4.* Answer question 17-3, if SC-5 liquid asphalt is substituted for paving asphalt.

17-5.* The maximum theoretical specific gravity (density) D for bituminous paving mixtures is determined by the formula:

$$D = \frac{100}{\dfrac{W_1}{G_1} + \dfrac{W_2}{G_2} + \dfrac{W_3}{G_3} \cdots \dfrac{W_n}{G_n}} \tag{1}$$

where W_1 is the percent by weight of bitumen,

   G_1 is the specific gravity of the bitumen,

   W_2, $W_3 \cdots W_n$ are percents by weight of the different aggregate fractions, and

   G_2, $G_3 \cdots G_n$ are specific gravities of the respective aggregate fractions.

The percent voids, V, in an actual paving mixture is determined by the formula:

$$V = \frac{(D - d) \times 100}{D} \tag{2}$$

where d is the measured bulk specific gravity of the compacted mixture.[1]

Data on a particular asphaltic concrete paving mixture are as follows:

Material	Specific Gravity	Percent by Weight
Asphalt cement	1.02	6.3
Limestone dust	2.82	13.7
Sand	2.65	30.4
Gravel	2.65	49.6

For this mixture determine:

a. The maximum theoretical specific gravity.

b. The percent voids, if the measured specific gravity is 2.34.

17-6.* The formula for determining d, the bulk specific gravity of a compacted specimen, is:

[1] A more detailed discussion of methods for computing specific gravities and void ratios of mixes and of aggregates will be found in *Highway Research Board Bulletin 105* (1955) titled *Bituminous Paving Mixtures, Fundamentals for Design.* This excellent publication also gives detailed descriptions of the common methods for proportioning bituminous mixtures and of the test procedures that underlie the methods.

$$d = \frac{A}{B - C} \tag{3}$$

where A = weight of the dry specimen in air, in grams.

B = weight of saturated surface-dry specimen in air, in grams.

C = weight of saturated specimen in water, in grams.

The proportions by weight and the specific gravities of each of the constituents of a particular sheet asphalt paving mixture are as follows:

Material	Specific Gravity	Percent by Weight
Asphalt cement	1.04	10.0
Limestone dust	2.82	16.5
South River sand (New Jersey)	2.66	73.5

A cylindrical specimen of the mixture was molded in the laboratory and weighed in air and in water with the following results:

Weight of dry specimen in air, grams	111.95
Weight of saturated surface-dry specimen in air, grams	112.09
Weight of saturated specimen in water, grams	61.20

a. Calculate the bulk specific gravity of the compacted specimen.

b. Compute the maximum theoretical specific gravity of the sheet asphalt paving mixture. (See formula 1, problem 17-5.)

c. Determine the percentage of voids in the laboratory molded specimen. (See formula 2, problem 17-5.)

d. When this mixture was placed and rolled on the street, a core of compacted pavement was removed and its specific gravity was found to be 2.13. The specifications require a minimum density in completed pavements equaling or exceeding 95% of that obtained in a standard laboratory specimen. Does the core meet this requirement? Show calculations.

e. Calculate the weight of a square yard of 1½-inch wearing surface composed of this sheet asphalt mixture.

17-7.* The formula for determining d, the bulk specific gravity of an asphaltic mixture, when the specimen is coated with paraffin, is as follows: (See ASTM Designation D1188-53.)

$$d = \frac{A}{D - E - \dfrac{(D - A)}{F}} \tag{4}$$

where A = weight of the dry specimen in air, in grams.

D = weight of the specimen plus paraffin coating in air, in grams.

E = weight of the specimen plus paraffin coating in water, in grams.

F = bulk specific gravity of the paraffin.

A core of compacted asphaltic concrete pavement was tested for specific gravity. The following weights were obtained:

Weight of the dry specimen in air, grams	2007.5
Weight of the specimen plus paraffin coating in air, grams	2036.5
Weight of the specimen plus paraffin coating in water, grams	1135.0
Bulk specific gravity of the paraffin	0.903

Calculate the bulk specific gravity of the core.

17-8.* During a working day of 9 hours, it is possible for a particular hot plant to produce enough asphaltic concrete to lay 4800 sq yd of wearing course 2 in. thick. Specific gravity of the compacted pavement is 2.37. Mix proportions, by weight, the specific gravities of each of the materials, and the unit weights of sand and stone are as follows:

	Proportions, % by weight	Specific Gravity	Weight per cu ft
Asphaltic cement (100% bitumen)	6	1.02	—
Limestone dust	8	2.75	—
Sand	41	2.66	106
Crushed stone	45	2.77	106

The capacity of the mixer, counting all ingredients, is 4000 lb per batch. The sand and crushed stone are run through the drier, but the limestone dust is not. For this situation:

a. What is the weight, in pounds, of a square yard of this 2-inch asphaltic concrete wearing course?

b. Calculate the required daily capacity of the drier in cubic yards of loose material.

c. Calculate the required daily capacity of the melting tanks for asphaltic cement, in gallons. (Note: There are 7.48 gallons in a cubic foot.)

d. Determine the number of batches that must be run to produce the 4800 sq yd of surfacing.

e. If 60 seconds is required to mix each batch, calculate the time that remains to charge each batch to the mixer, assuming no delays.

f. What would be the percentage of voids in the mixture as compacted on the street?

17-9.* A hard asphalt has a normal penetration of 20 points. It is desired to flux it so that the asphaltic cement produced will have a normal penetration of 70 points. If the addition of 1 pound of flux oil to 100 pounds of hard asphalt increases the penetration of the asphalt 2.5 points, how many pounds of flux should be added to a 1200-pound batch of hard asphalt?

17-10. Secure a sheet of 4 cycle semi-log x 10 to the inch graph paper. Mark the sheet horizontally on the logarithmic scale with sieve openings and sieve numbers. Mark it vertically on the natural scale with per cent passing. (See Fig. 7, page 485, as an example and for the required data.) On the ruled sheet plot, in different colors:

a. The grading limits of the Asphalt Institute specification for asphaltic concrete surface course of ¾-inch maximum size (see Table 9, page 486).

b. The grading limits of the Pennsylvania Dept. of Highways for asphaltic concrete wearing course (see Table 9).

c. The grading of soil No. 11, Table A, of this problem set. Determine which, if either, of the specifications soil No. 11 passes. Also determine which of the two grading specifications is more likely to introduce stability problems. Explain.

17-11.* A sheet asphalt wearing course is being constructed under specifications that require 10.0% bitumen, 16.5% passing the No. 200 sieve and 73.5% retained on the No. 200 sieve, by weight. The asphalt cement is practically 100% bitumen. The oyster shell dust has 23% retained on the No. 200 sieve and the commercial sand from a local source has 4.1% passing the No. 200 sieve and 100% passing the No. 10 sieve. Calculate the percentages of shell dust and of sand for this paving mixture.

17-12.* Sands *A* and *B* are available for a sheet asphalt wearing course. Select a mixing ratio for the two sands which will produce a grading meeting the requirements of the specification given below. (Reference: p. 499)

Passing	Retained	Specification in percent	Sand *A*	Sand *B*
—	No. 10	98–100	1	0
No. 10	No. 40	14–50	47	0
No. 40	No. 80	30–60	46	15
No. 80	No. 200	15–40	6	77
No. 200	—	0–5	0	8

17-13. A bituminous road-mix wearing course is 2½ inches thick when compacted and 22 feet wide. The aggregate is graded gravel and sand. The binder is SC-2 road oil; its weight is 4% of the weight of the aggregate. The compacted mixture weighs 140 lb per cu ft.

The road oil has a specific gravity of 0.94 and the aggregate weighs 105 lb per cu ft, loose.

a. How many cubic yards of loose aggregate are required (*1*) per square yard of pavement and (*2*) per mile of road?

b. How many gallons of road oil are required (*1*) per square yard of pavement and (*2*) per mile of road? (There are 7.48 gallons in a cubic foot.)

c. The loose aggregate costs $4 per cubic yard, delivered; the road oil costs 12 cents per gallon, delivered; and the charge for mixing and laying is $1000 per mile. What, then, is the cost of a mile of completed surface?

17-14. Compute the cost of a mile of three-application bituminous macadam pavement 24 feet wide. Costs of base, shoulders, etc. are not included. Quantities of materials are as shown in Table 12, page 514. Prices are as follows: Bituminous material, 15 cents per gallon; coarse stone, $2 per ton; key stone, $4 per ton; and chips $5 per ton; all prices complete in place.

17-15.* A tack coat is to be applied on top of an old concrete pavement 22 feet wide that is to be resurfaced with a bituminous plant-mix pavement.

a. Select a bituminous material for the tack coat and estimate the quantity needed for a project that is 1.3 miles long.

b. What application temperature would be suitable for the selected bituminous material? (References: pp. 521, 449)

17-16.* A thin bituminous surface treatment is to be constructed on top of a gravel road 24 feet wide which has a tight surface. A prime coat is to be applied using MC-0 liquid asphaltic material. RC-2 liquid asphaltic material has been selected for the surface treatment to be covered with clean stone screenings of grading ranging between the ⅜-inch and No. 10 sieve sizes. Estimate the approximate quantities of materials needed for a mile of road. (Reference: pp. 521–522)

17-17.* A tar of grade RT-4 was loaded into a transport tank at a temperature of 280° F (t_2). The amount loaded was 8490 gallons. The coefficient of expansion per degree F at 60° F (K) for this tar is 0.00035.

a. Calculate the invoice volume at 60° F (t_1) for this shipment.

b. Compute the cost of this shipment if the purchase price is $0.145 per gallon based upon the volume of the tar at 60° F. Hint:

$$V_{60° \text{ F}} = \frac{V_{280° \text{ F}}}{1 + K(t_2 - t_1)}$$

(Reference: p. 526)

Chapter 18

18-1. For a concrete paving slab 10 inches thick, and with conditions and properties as given in Fig. 2, pages 532–533, find the maximum combined flexural stress at any location in the slab:

a. When the slab is 30 feet long.

b. When the slab is 15 feet long.

c. When the slab is 10 feet long.

Compare these stresses with the safe flexural stress in plain paving concrete (see page 530).

18-2.* In an attempt to reduce flexural stresses in a concrete pavement, the thickness was increased from 10 to 11 inches. What would be the reduction in combined stresses in the daytime for edge loading:

a. If the slab were 30 feet long? (Reference: Fig. 2, p. 532)

b. If the slab were 15 feet long?

18-3.* The current practice of a certain highway agency is to space transverse joints in concrete pavements at 40-foot centers. The suggestion has been made that warping stresses along the edge of the slab can be substantially reduced by reducing the joint spacing. If $E = 5 \times 10^6$, $\mu = 0.15$, $h = 8$ in., $k = 100$, $e = 0.000005$, and $t = 3$, find the warping stress along the edge of the slab for: (Reference: pp. 534–535)

a. The present 40-foot joint spacing.

b. A 30-foot joint spacing.

c. A 15-foot joint spacing.

Where possible check your answers against the plotted values on Fig. 2, page 532.

18-4.* Work problem 18-3 for a 10-inch slab thickness.

18-5. If the allowable flexural stress in paving concrete is 350 psi, the pavement is designed for 12,000-lb wheel loads on dual tires, and the corners are protected by load transfer devices:

a. What pavement thickness is called for by Fig. 5, page 541, if the subgrade is poor so that k, the coefficient of subgrade reaction, equals 50? (Reference: p. 541)

b. What pavement thickness is called for if the subgrade is excellent so that k equals 500?

c. If a base course 12 inches thick is required to bring this improvement in k value, is it justified from a cost standpoint? Assume that paving concrete costs $18 per cu yd and that base course costs $3 per cu yd, both prices complete in place.

d. What problems other than possible added cost of base course may affect the decision indicated by part c? (Reference: pp. 553–554)

18-6.* What total cross-sectional area of longitudinal reinforcing steel is required for a slab 12 feet wide, 30 feet long, and 8 inches thick? The concrete weighs 150 lb per cu ft; the steel is intermediate grade with a yield point of 40,000 psi. Employ the usual assumptions given on pages 546–547.

18-7. Based on data offered in Table 6, page 568, determine the weight of cement, sand, small and large coarse aggregates, and water to fill a 34-E (34 cubic foot) mixer for paving concrete to capacity, under the following conditions:

a. Plain, vibrated concrete, crushed-stone aggregate, 5½ bags cement per cu yd concrete, all aggregates saturated surface dry.

b. Air-entrained, machine-finished concrete, slag aggregate, 6 bags cement per cu yd concrete, all aggregates saturated surface dry.

c. Plain, vibrated concrete, crushed stone aggregate, 6 bags cement per cu yd, free water in sand 6%, based on saturated, surface-dry weight, coarse aggregates, 1% free water based on saturated, surface-dry weight.

18-8. Materials and their conditions as used in a batch of paving concrete are as follows:

Material	Batch Quantities	Specific Gravity (Aggregates on Saturated, Surface-dry Basis)	Moisture Content, Based on Oven-dry Weights	
			For Saturated, Surface-dry Condition	As Used
Cement	7.5 bags	3.15	—	—
Sand	1420 lb	2.70	1.2	5.0
Crushed stone	2470 lb	2.66	0.8	1.4
Water	30.0 gal	1.00	—	—

For the mix shown above, (Reference: pp. 566–569)

a. Calculate the cement factor on an air-free basis.

b. Calculate the water-cement ratio in gallons per sack, on the basis of saturated, surface-dry aggregates.

c. If the actual weight of a cubic foot of wet concrete is 147.0 lb, what is the percentage of entrained air?

d. What is the cement factor, including the entrained air?

Index